D1486888

Campbell Biology in Focus

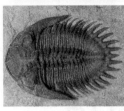

PEARSON ALWAYS LEARNING

Lisa A. Urry • Michael L. Cain • Steven A. Wasserman
Peter V. Minorsky • Robert B. Jackson • Jane B. Reece

Campbell Biology in Focus

Custom Edition for Drexel University
Bio 124

Taken from:
Campbell Biology in Focus
by Lisa A. Urry, Michael L. Cain, Steven A. Wasserman,
Peter V. Minorsky, Robert B. Jackson, and Jane B. Reece

ISBN 10: 1-323-30913-6
ISBN 13: 978-1-323-30913-1

Preface

The short-toed snake eagle (*Circaetus gallicus*) that gazes from the cover of this book has an eye much like our own, yet evolutionary forces have honed its ability to spot a snake from a quarter mile up in the air. The eagle's keen eye is a metaphor for our goal in writing this text: to focus with high intensity on the core concepts that biology majors need to master in the introductory biology course. The current explosion of biological information, while exhilarating in its scope, poses a significant challenge—how best to teach a subject that is constantly expanding its own boundaries. In particular, instructors have become increasingly concerned that their students are overwhelmed by a growing volume of detail and are losing sight of the important ideas in biology.

In response to this challenge, groups of biologists have initiated efforts to refine and in some cases redesign the introductory biology course, summarizing their findings in reports that include *Bio 2010: Transforming Undergraduate Education for Future Research Biologists*[1] and *Vision and Change in Undergraduate Biology Education.*[2] Clear recommendations emerging from these initiatives are to focus course material and instruction on key ideas while transforming the classroom through active learning and scientific inquiry. Many instructors have embraced such approaches and changed how they teach. Cutting back on the amount of detail they present, they focus on core biological concepts, explore select examples, and engage in a rich variety of active learning exercises. We were inspired by the ongoing changes in biology education to develop this text, *CAMPBELL BIOLOGY IN FOCUS*. Based on the best-selling *CAMPBELL BIOLOGY*, this new, shorter textbook provides undergraduate biology majors and their instructors with a more focused exploration of the key questions, approaches, and ideas of modern biology.

Our Guiding Principles

Our objective in creating *CAMPBELL BIOLOGY IN FOCUS* was to produce a shorter text by streamlining selected material, while emphasizing conceptual understanding and maintaining clarity, proper pacing, and rigor. Here, briefly, are the four guiding principles for our approach.

Focus on Core Concepts and Skills

We developed this text to help students master the fundamental content and scientific skills they need as college biology majors. In structuring the text, we were guided by discussions with many biology professors, analysis of hundreds of syllabi, study of the debates in the literature of scientific pedagogy, and our experience as instructors at a range of institutions. The result is a **briefer book for biology majors** that is designed to inform, engage, and inspire.

Evolution as the Foundation of Biology

Evolution is the central theme of all biology, and it is the core theme of this text, as exemplified by the various ways that evolution is integrated into the text:

- Every chapter explicitly addresses the topic of evolution through an **Evolution section** that leads students to consider the material in the context of natural selection and adaptation.
- Each Chapter Review includes a **Focus on Evolution Question** that asks students to think critically about how an aspect of the chapter relates to evolution.
- Evolution is the unifying idea of **Chapter 1**, *Introduction: Evolution and the Foundations of Biology*, which outlines five key themes that students will encounter throughout the text and introduces the process of scientific inquiry.
- Following the in-depth coverage of evolutionary mechanisms in Unit 3, evolution also provides the storyline for the **novel approach to presenting biological diversity** in Unit 4, The Evolutionary History of Life. Focusing on landmark events in the history of life, the text highlights how

---

[1] The National Research Council of the National Academies, 2003

[2] The American Association for the Advancement of Science, supported by the National Science Foundation, the National Institutes of Health, and Howard Hughes Medical Institute, 2009

key adaptations arose within groups of organisms and how evolutionary events led to the diversity of life on Earth today.

Engaging Students in Scientific Thinking

Helping students learn to "think like a scientist" is a nearly universal goal of introductory biology courses. Students need to understand how to formulate and test hypotheses, design experiments, and interpret data. Scientific thinking and data interpretation skills top lists of learning outcomes and foundational skills desired for students entering higher-level courses. CAMPBELL BIOLOGY IN FOCUS meets this need in several ways:

- **Scientific Skills Exercises** in every chapter use real data to build skills in graphing, interpreting data, designing experiments, and working with math—skills essential for students to succeed in biology. These exercises can also be assigned and automatically graded in MasteringBiology.
- **Scientific Inquiry Questions** in the end-of-chapter material give students further practice in scientific thinking.
- **Inquiry Figures** and **Research Method Figures** reveal *how* we know *what* we know and model the process of scientific inquiry.

Outstanding Pedagogy

Since the publication of the first edition in 1987, CAMPBELL BIOLOGY has been praised for its clear and engaging narrative, superior pedagogy, and innovative use of art to promote student learning. These hallmark values are also at the core of CAMPBELL BIOLOGY IN FOCUS:

- In each chapter, a framework of carefully selected **Key Concepts** helps students distinguish the "forest" from the "trees."
- Questions throughout the text catalyze learning by encouraging students to **actively engage with and synthesize key material**:
  - To counter students' tendencies to compartmentalize information, **Make Connections Questions** ask students to connect what they are learning in a particular chapter to material covered in other chapters or units.
  - **Figure Legend Questions** foster student interaction with the figures.
  - Tiered **Concept Check Questions** test comprehension, require application, and prompt synthesis.
  - **Draw It Exercises** encourage students to test their understanding of biology through drawing.
  - **Summary of Key Concepts Questions** make reading the summary an active learning experience.

Our overall aim is to help students see biology as a whole, with each chapter adding to the network of knowledge they are building. To support this goal further, each unit in CAMPBELL

BIOLOGY IN FOCUS opens with a **visual preview** that tells the story of the chapters' contents, showing how the material in the unit fits into a larger context.

Organization of the Text

CAMPBELL BIOLOGY IN FOCUS is organized into an introductory chapter and seven units that cover thoughtfully paced core concepts. In the course of streamlining this material, we have worked diligently to maintain the finely tuned coverage of fundamental concepts found in CAMPBELL BIOLOGY. As we developed this alternative text, we carefully considered each chapter of CAMPBELL BIOLOGY. Based on surveys and discussions with instructors and analyses of hundreds of syllabi and reviews, we made informed choices about how to design each chapter of CAMPBELL BIOLOGY IN FOCUS to meet the needs of instructors and students. In some chapters, we retained most of the material; in other chapters, we pruned material; and in still others, we completely reconfigured the material. We summarize the highlights here.

Chapter 1: Introduction: Evolution and the Foundations of Biology

Chapter 1 introduces the **five biological themes** woven throughout this text: the core theme of **Evolution**, together with **Organization**, **Information**, **Energy and Matter**, and **Interactions**. Chapter 1 also explores the process of scientific inquiry through a case study describing experiments on the evolution of coat color in the beach mouse. The chapter concludes with a discussion of the importance of diversity within the scientific community.

Unit 1: Chemistry and Cells

A succinct, two-chapter treatment of basic chemistry provides the foundation for this unit focused on cell structure and function. The related topics of cell membranes and cell signaling are consolidated into one chapter. Due to the importance of the fundamental concepts in Units 1 and 2, much of the material in the rest of these two units has been retained from CAMPBELL BIOLOGY.

Unit 2: Genetics

Topics in this unit include meiosis and classical genetics as well as the chromosomal and molecular basis for genetics and gene expression. We also include a chapter on the regulation of gene expression and one on the role of gene regulation in development, stem cells, and cancer. Methods in biotechnology are integrated into appropriate chapters. The stand-alone chapter on viruses can be taught at any point in the course. The final chapter in the unit, on genome evolution, provides both a capstone for the study of genetics and a bridge to the evolution unit.

Unit 3: Evolution

This unit provides in-depth coverage of essential evolutionary topics, such as mechanisms of natural selection, population genetics, and speciation. Early in the unit, Chapter 20 introduces "tree thinking" to support students in interpreting phylogenetic trees and thinking about the big picture of evolution. Chapter 23 focuses on mechanisms that have influenced long-term patterns of evolutionary change. Throughout the unit, new discoveries in fields ranging from paleontology to phylogenomics highlight the interdisciplinary nature of modern biology.

Unit 4: The Evolutionary History of Life

This unit employs a novel approach to studying the evolutionary history of biodiversity. Each chapter focuses on one or more major steps in the history of life, such as the origin of cells or the colonization of land. Likewise, the coverage of natural history and biological diversity emphasizes the evolutionary process—how factors such as the origin of key adaptations have influenced the rise and fall of different groups of organisms over time.

Unit 5: Plant Form and Function

The form and function of higher plants are often treated as separate topics, thereby making it difficult for students to make connections between the two. In Unit 5, plant anatomy (Chapter 28) and the acquisition and transport of resources (Chapter 29) are bridged by a discussion of how plant architecture influences resource acquisition. Chapter 30 provides a solid introduction to plant reproduction. It also explores crop domestication, examining controversies surrounding the genetic engineering of crop plants. The final chapter explores how environmental sensing and the integration of information by plant hormones influence plant growth and reproduction.

Unit 6: Animal Form and Function

A focused exploration of animal physiology and anatomy applies a comparative approach to a limited set of examples to bring out fundamental principles and conserved mechanisms. Students are first introduced to the closely related topics of homeostasis and endocrine signaling in an integrative introductory chapter. Additional melding of interconnected material is reflected in chapters that combine treatment of circulation and gas exchange, reproduction and development, neurons and nervous systems, and motor mechanisms and behavior.

Unit 7: Ecology

This unit applies the key themes of the text, including evolution, interactions, and energy and matter, to help students learn ecological principles. Chapter 40 integrates material on population growth and Earth's environment, highlighting the importance of both biological and physical processes in determining where species are found. Chapter 43 ends the book with a focus on global ecology and conservation biology. This chapter illustrates the threats to all species from increased human population growth and resource use. It begins with local factors that threaten individual species and ends with global factors that alter ecosystems, landscapes, and biomes.

MasteringBiology®

MasteringBiology is the most widely used online assessment and tutorial program for biology, providing an extensive library of homework assignments that are graded automatically. Self-paced tutorials provide individualized coaching with specific hints and feedback on the most difficult topics in the course. For example:

- The **Scientific Skills Exercises** from the text can be assigned and automatically graded in MasteringBiology.
- **Make Connections Tutorials** help students connect what they are learning in one chapter with material they have learned in another chapter.
- **Data Analysis Tutorials** allow students to analyze real data from online databases.
- **BioFlix® Tutorials** use 3-D movie-quality animations to help students master tough topics.

In addition, Reading Quiz questions, Student Misconception questions, and approximately 3,000 Test Bank questions are available for assignment.

MasteringBiology and the text work together to provide an unparalleled learning experience.

* * *

Our overall goal in developing this text was to assist instructors and students in their exploration of biology by emphasizing essential content and skills while maintaining rigor. Although this first edition is now completed, we recognize that CAMPBELL BIOLOGY IN FOCUS, like its subject, will evolve. As its authors, we are eager to hear your thoughts, questions, comments, and suggestions for improvement. We are counting on you—our teaching colleagues and all students using this book—to provide us with this feedback, and we encourage you to contact us directly by e-mail:

Lisa Urry (Chapter 1, Units 1 and 2): lurry@mills.edu

Michael Cain (Chapter 1, Units 3 and 4): mcain@bowdoin.edu

Peter Minorsky (Unit 5): pminorsky@mercy.edu

Steven Wasserman (Chapter 1, Unit 6): stevenw@ucsd.edu

Rob Jackson (Unit 7): jackson@duke.edu

Jane Reece: janereece@cal.berkeley.edu

The author team's contributions reflect their biological expertise as researchers and their teaching sensibilities gained from years of experience as instructors at diverse institutions. They are also experienced textbook authors, having written CAMPBELL *BIOLOGY* in addition to CAMPBELL *BIOLOGY IN FOCUS*.

Lisa A. Urry

Lisa Urry (Chapter 1 and Units 1 and 2) is Professor of Biology and Chair of the Biology Department at Mills College in Oakland, California, and a Visiting Scholar at the University of California, Berkeley. After graduating from Tufts University with a double major in biology and French, Lisa completed her Ph.D. in molecular and developmental biology at Massachusetts Institute of Technology (MIT) in the MIT/Woods Hole Oceanographic Institution Joint Program. She has published a number of research papers, most of them focused on gene expression during embryonic and larval development in sea urchins. Lisa has taught a variety of courses, from introductory biology to developmental biology and senior seminar. As a part of her mission to increase understanding of evolution, Lisa also teaches a nonmajors course called Evolution for Future Presidents and is on the Teacher Advisory Board for the Understanding Evolution website developed by the University of California Museum of Paleontology. Lisa is also deeply committed to promoting opportunities for women and underrepresented minorities in science.

Michael L. Cain

Michael Cain (Chapter 1 and Units 3 and 4) is an ecologist and evolutionary biologist who is now writing full-time. Michael earned a joint degree in biology and math at Bowdoin College, an M.Sc. from Brown University, and a Ph.D. in ecology and evolutionary biology from Cornell University. As a faculty member at New Mexico State University and Rose-Hulman Institute of Technology, he taught a wide range of courses, including introductory biology, ecology, evolution, botany, and conservation biology. Michael is the author of dozens of scientific papers on topics that include foraging behavior in insects and plants, long-distance seed dispersal, and speciation in crickets. In addition to his work on CAMPBELL *BIOLOGY IN FOCUS*, Michael is also the lead author of an ecology textbook.

Steven A. Wasserman

Steve Wasserman (Chapter 1 and Unit 6) is Professor of Biology at the University of California, San Diego (UCSD). He earned his A.B. in biology from Harvard University and his Ph.D. in biological sciences from MIT. Through his research on regulatory pathway mechanisms in the fruit fly *Drosophila*, Steve has contributed to the fields of developmental biology, reproduction, and immunity. As a faculty member at the University of Texas Southwestern Medical Center and UCSD, he has taught genetics, development, and physiology to undergraduate, graduate, and medical students. He currently focuses on teaching introductory biology. He has also served as the research mentor for more than a dozen doctoral students and more than 50 aspiring scientists at the undergraduate and high school levels. Steve has been the recipient of distinguished scholar awards from both the Markey Charitable Trust and the David and Lucille Packard Foundation. In 2007, he received UCSD's Distinguished Teaching Award for undergraduate teaching.

Peter V. Minorsky

Peter Minorsky (Unit 5) is Professor of Biology at Mercy College in New York, where he teaches introductory biology, evolution, ecology, and botany. He received his A.B. in biology from Vassar College and his Ph.D. in plant physiology from Cornell University. He is also the science writer for the journal *Plant Physiology*. After a postdoctoral fellowship at the University of Wisconsin at Madison, Peter taught at Kenyon College, Union College, Western Connecticut State University, and Vassar College. His research interests concern how plants sense environmental change. Peter received the 2008 Award for Teaching Excellence at Mercy College.

Robert B. Jackson

Rob Jackson (Unit 7) is Professor of Biology and Nicholas Chair of Environmental Sciences at Duke University. Rob holds a B.S. in chemical engineering from Rice University, as well as M.S. degrees in ecology and statistics and a Ph.D. in ecology from Utah State University. Rob directed Duke's Program in Ecology for many years and just finished a term as the Vice President of Science for the Ecological Society of America. Rob has received numerous awards, including a Presidential Early Career Award in Science and Engineering from the National Science Foundation. He also enjoys popular writing, having published a trade book about the environment, *The Earth Remains Forever*, and two books of poetry for children, *Animal Mischief* and *Weekend Mischief*.

Jane B. Reece

The head of the author team for recent editions of *CAMPBELL BIOLOGY*, Jane Reece was Neil Campbell's longtime collaborator. Earlier, Jane taught biology at Middlesex County College and Queensborough Community College. She holds an A.B. in biology from Harvard University, an M.S. in microbiology from Rutgers University, and a Ph.D. in bacteriology from the University of California, Berkeley. Jane's research as a doctoral student and postdoctoral fellow focused on genetic recombination in bacteria. Besides her work on the Campbell textbooks for biology majors, she has been an author of *Campbell Biology: Concepts & Connections*, *Campbell Essential Biology*, and *The World of the Cell*.

Neil A. Campbell

Neil Campbell (1946–2004) combined the investigative nature of a research scientist with the soul of an experienced and caring teacher. He earned his M.A. in zoology from the University of California, Los Angeles, and his Ph.D. in plant biology from the University of California, Riverside, where he received the Distinguished Alumnus Award in 2001. Neil published numerous research articles on desert and coastal plants and how the sensitive plant (*Mimosa*) and other legumes move their leaves. His 30 years of teaching in diverse environments included introductory biology courses at Cornell University, Pomona College, and San Bernardino Valley College, where he received the college's first Outstanding Professor Award in 1986. Neil was a visiting scholar in the Department of Botany and Plant Sciences at the University of California, Riverside.

See the Story of the Unit

Each unit begins with a **visual preview** of the chapters' contents, showing how the material in the unit fits into a larger context.

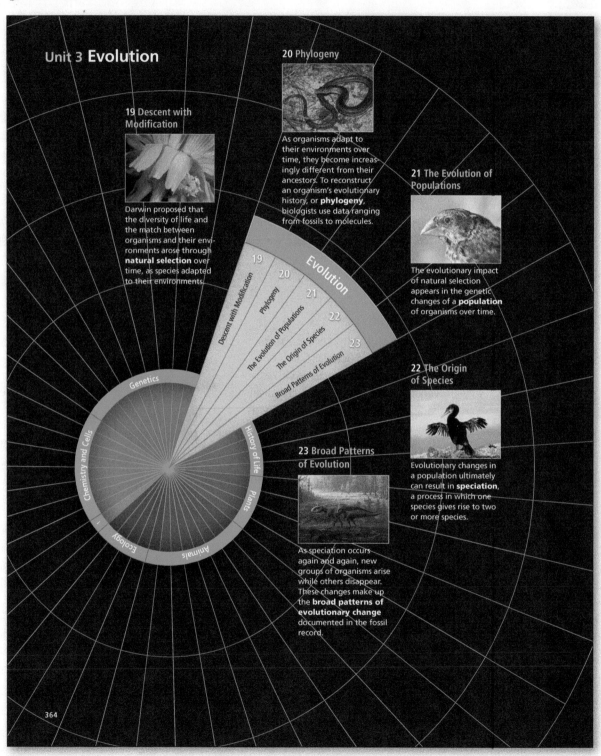

Unit 3 Evolution

19 Descent with Modification

Darwin proposed that the diversity of life and the match between organisms and their environments arose through **natural selection** over time, as species adapted to their environments.

20 Phylogeny

As organisms adapt to their environments over time, they become increasingly different from their ancestors. To reconstruct an organism's evolutionary history, or **phylogeny**, biologists use data ranging from fossils to molecules.

21 The Evolution of Populations

The evolutionary impact of natural selection appears in the genetic changes of a **population** of organisms over time.

22 The Origin of Species

Evolutionary changes in a population ultimately can result in **speciation**, a process in which one species gives rise to two or more species.

23 Broad Patterns of Evolution

As speciation occurs again and again, new groups of organisms arise while others disappear. These changes make up the **broad patterns of evolutionary change** documented in the fossil record.

364

Focus on the Key Concepts

Each chapter is organized around a framework of 3 to 6 **Key Concepts** that focus on the big picture and provide a context for the supporting details.

Students can get oriented by reading the **list of Key Concepts,** which introduces the big ideas covered in the chapter.

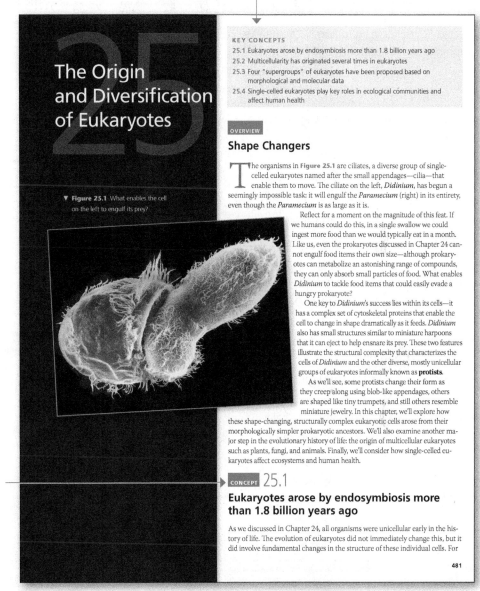

The Origin and Diversification of Eukaryotes

KEY CONCEPTS

25.1 Eukaryotes arose by endosymbiosis more than 1.8 billion years ago
25.2 Multicellularity has originated several times in eukaryotes
25.3 Four "supergroups" of eukaryotes have been proposed based on morphological and molecular data
25.4 Single-celled eukaryotes play key roles in ecological communities and affect human health

OVERVIEW

Shape Changers

The organisms in **Figure 25.1** are ciliates, a diverse group of single-celled eukaryotes named after the small appendages—cilia—that enable them to move. The ciliate on the left, *Didinium*, has begun a seemingly impossible task: it will engulf the *Paramecium* (right) in its entirety, even though the *Paramecium* is as large as it is.

Reflect for a moment on the magnitude of this feat. If we humans could do this, in a single swallow we could ingest more food than we would typically eat in a month. Like us, even the prokaryotes discussed in Chapter 24 cannot engulf food items their own size—although prokaryotes can metabolize an astonishing range of compounds, they can only absorb small particles of food. What enables *Didinium* to tackle food items that could easily evade a hungry prokaryote?

One key to *Didinium*'s success lies within its cells—it has a complex set of cytoskeletal proteins that enable the cell to change in shape dramatically as it feeds. *Didinium* also has small structures similar to miniature harpoons that it can eject to help ensnare its prey. These two features illustrate the structural complexity that characterizes the cells of *Didinium* and the other diverse, mostly unicellular groups of eukaryotes informally known as **protists**.

As we'll see, some protists change their form as they creep along using blob-like appendages, others are shaped like tiny trumpets, and still others resemble miniature jewelry. In this chapter, we'll explore how these shape-changing, structurally complex eukaryotic cells arose from their morphologically simpler prokaryotic ancestors. We'll also examine another major step in the evolutionary history of life: the origin of multicellular eukaryotes such as plants, fungi, and animals. Finally, we'll consider how single-celled eukaryotes affect ecosystems and human health.

▼ **Figure 25.1** What enables the cell on the left to engulf its prey?

CONCEPT 25.1

Eukaryotes arose by endosymbiosis more than 1.8 billion years ago

As we discussed in Chapter 24, all organisms were unicellular early in the history of life. The evolution of eukaryotes did not immediately change this, but it did involve fundamental changes in the structure of these individual cells. For

481

Each **Key Concept** serves as the heading for a major section of the chapter.

After reading a concept section, students can check their understanding using the **Concept Check questions** on their own or in a study group.

Make Connections questions ask students to relate content in the chapter to a concept presented earlier in the course.

What If? questions ask students to apply what they've learned.

CONCEPT CHECK 25.2

1. Summarize the evidence that choanoflagellates are the sister group of animals.
2. **MAKE CONNECTIONS** Describe how the origin of multicellularity in animals illustrates Darwin's concept of descent with modification (see Concept 19.2).
3. **WHAT IF?** Cells in *Volvox*, plants, and fungi are similar in being enclosed by a cell wall. Predict whether the cell-to-cell attachments of these organisms form using similar or different molecules. Explain.

For suggested answers, see Appendix A.

Practice Scientific Skills

Scientific Skills Exercises in every chapter use real data to build key skills needed for biology, including data analysis, graphing, experimental design, and math skills.

Selected Scientific Skills Exercises include:

- Making a Line Graph and Calculating a Slope
- Interpreting Histograms
- Using the Chi-Square (χ^2) Test
- Analyzing DNA Deletion Experiments
- Making and Testing Predictions
- Interpreting Data in a Phylogenetic Tree
- Using the Hardy-Weinberg Equation to Interpret Data and Make Predictions
- Understanding Experimental Design and Interpreting Data
- Interpreting Data Values Expressed in Scientific Notation
- Designing an Experiment Using Genetic Mutants
- Interpreting a Graph with Log Scales
- Using the Logistic Equation to Model Population Growth

Scientific Skills Exercise

Interpreting a Scatter Plot with a Regression Line

How Does the Carbonate Ion Concentration of Seawater Affect the Calcification Rate of a Coral Reef? Scientists predict that acidification of the ocean due to higher levels of atmospheric CO_2 will lower the concentration of dissolved carbonate ions, which living corals use to build calcium carbonate reef structures. In this exercise, you will analyze data from a controlled experiment that examined the effect of carbonate ion concentration ($[CO_3^{2-}]$) on calcium carbonate deposition, a process called calcification.

How the Experiment Was Done The Biosphere 2 aquarium in Arizona contains a large coral reef system that behaves like a natural reef. For several years, a group of researchers measured the rate of calcification by the reef organisms and examined how the calcification rate changed with differing amounts of dissolved carbonate ions in the seawater.

Data from the Experiment The black data points in the graph below form a scatter plot. The red line, known as a linear regression line, is the best-fitting straight line for these points. These data are from one set of experiments, in which the pH, temperature, and calcium ion concentration of the seawater were held constant.

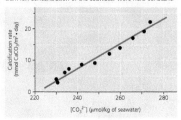

Interpret the Data
1. When presented with a graph of experimental data, the first step in analysis is to determine what each axis represents. (a) In words, explain what is being shown on the x-axis. Be sure to include the units. (b) What is being shown on the y-axis (including units)? (c) Which variable is the independent variable—the variable that was *manipulated* by the researchers? (d) Which variable is the dependent variable—the variable that responded to or depended on the treatment, which was *measured* by the researchers? (For additional information about graphs, see the Scientific Skills Review in Appendix F and in the Study Area in MasteringBiology.)

2. Based on the data shown in the graph, describe in words the relationship between carbonate ion concentration and calcification rate.

3. (a) If the seawater carbonate ion concentration is 270 µmol/kg, what is the approximate rate of calcification, and approximately how many days would it take 1 square meter of reef to accumulate 30 mmol of calcium carbonate ($CaCO_3$)? To determine the rate of calcification, draw a vertical line up from the x-axis at the value of 270 µmol/kg until it intersects the red line. Then draw a horizontal line from the intersection over to the y-axis to see what the calcification rate is at that carbonate ion concentration. (b) If the seawater carbonate ion concentration is 250 µmol/kg, what is the approximate rate of calcification, and approximately how many days would it take 1 square meter of reef to accumulate 30 mmol of calcium carbonate? (c) If carbonate ion concentration decreases, how does the calcification rate change, and how does that affect the time it takes coral to grow?

4. (a) Referring to the equations in Figure 2.24, determine which step of the process is measured in this experiment. (b) Do the results of this experiment support the hypothesis that increased atmospheric $[CO_2]$ will slow the growth of coral reefs? Why or why not?

Data from C. Langdon et al., Effect of calcium carbonate saturation state on the calcification rate of an experimental coral reef, *Global Biogeochemical Cycles* 14:639–654 (2000).

A version of this Scientific Skills Exercise can be assigned in MasteringBiology.

MasteringBiology®
www.masteringbiology.com

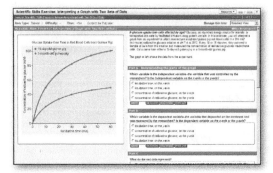

Scientific Skills Exercises from the text have assignable versions in MasteringBiology.

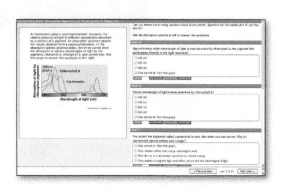

Interpreting Data Tutorials coach students on how to read and interpret data and graphs.

Engage in Scientific Thinking

Scientific Skills Exercise

Analyzing Polypeptide Sequence Data

Are Rhesus Monkeys or Gibbons More Closely Related to Humans? As discussed in Concept 3.6, DNA and polypeptide sequences from closely related species are more similar to each other than are sequences from more distantly related species. In this exercise, you will look at amino acid sequence data for the β polypeptide chain of hemoglobin, often called β-globin. You will then interpret the data to hypothesize whether the monkey or the gibbon is more closely related to humans.

How Such Experiments Are Done Researchers can isolate the polypeptide of interest from an organism and then determine the amino acid sequence. More frequently, the DNA of the relevant gene is sequenced, and the amino acid sequence of the polypeptide is deduced from the DNA sequence of its gene.

Data from the Experiments In the data below, the letters give the sequence of the 146 amino acids in β-globin from humans, rhesus monkeys, and gibbons. Because a complete sequence would not fit on one line here, the sequences are broken into three segments. Note that the sequences for the three different species are aligned so that you can compare them easily. For example, you can see that for all three species, the first amino acid is V (valine; see Figure 3.17) and the 146th amino acid is H (histidine).

Interpret the Data

1. Scan along the monkey and gibbon sequences, letter by letter, circling any amino acids that do not match the human sequence. (a) How many amino acids differ between the monkey and the human sequences? (b) Between the gibbon and human?

2. For each nonhuman species, what percent of its amino acids are identical to the human sequence of β-globin?

3. Based on these data alone, state a hypothesis for which of these two species is more closely related to humans. What is your reasoning?

4. What other evidence could you use to support your hypothesis?

Data from Human: http://www.ncbi.nlm.nih.gov/protein/AAA21113.1; rhesus monkey: http://www.ncbi.nlm.nih.gov/protein/122634; gibbon: http://www.ncbi.nlm.nih.gov/protein/122616

A version of this Scientific Skills Exercise can be assigned in MasteringBiology.

Species	Alignment of Amino Acid Sequences of β-globin
Human	1 VHLTPEEKSA VTALWGKVNV DEVGGEALGR LLVVYPWTQR FFESFGDLST PDAVMGNPKV
Monkey	1 VHLTPEEKNA VTTLWGKVNV DEVGGEALGR LLLVYPWTQR FFESFGDLSS PDAVMGNPKV
Gibbon	1 VHLTPEEKSA VTALWGKVNV DEVGGEALGR LLVVYPWTQR FFESFGDLST PDAVMGNPKV
Human	61 KAHGKKVLGA FSDGLAHLDN LKGTFATLSE LHCDKLHVDP ENFRLLGNVL VCVLAHHFGK
Monkey	61 KAHGKKVLGA FSDGLNHLDN LKGTFAQLSE LHCDKLHVDP ENFKLLGNVL VCVLAHHFGK
Gibbon	61 KAHGKKVLGA FSDGLAHLDN LKGTFAQLSE LHCDKLHVDP ENFRLLGNVL VCVLAHHFGK
Human	121 EFTPPVQAAY QKVVAGVANA LAHKYH
Monkey	121 EFTPQVQAAY QKVVAGVANA LAHKYH
Gibbon	121 EFTPQVQAAY QKVVAGVANA LAHKYH

▼ **Inquiry Figures** reveal "how we know what we know" by highlighting how researchers designed an experiment, interpreted their results, and drew conclusions.

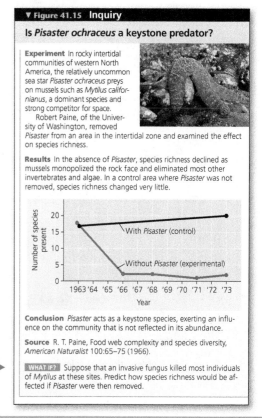

▼ Figure 41.15 **Inquiry**

Is *Pisaster ochraceus* a keystone predator?

Experiment In rocky intertidal communities of western North America, the relatively uncommon sea star *Pisaster ochraceus* preys on mussels such as *Mytilus californianus*, a dominant species and strong competitor for space.
   Robert Paine, of the University of Washington, removed *Pisaster* from an area in the intertidal zone and examined the effect on species richness.

Results In the absence of *Pisaster*, species richness declined as mussels monopolized the rock face and eliminated most other invertebrates and algae. In a control area where *Pisaster* was not removed, species richness changed very little.

Conclusion *Pisaster* acts as a keystone species, exerting an influence on the community that is not reflected in its abundance.

Source R. T. Paine, Food web complexity and species diversity, *American Naturalist* 100:65–75 (1966).

WHAT IF? Suppose that an invasive fungus killed most individuals of *Mytilus* at these sites. Predict how species richness would be affected if *Pisaster* were then removed.

After exploring the featured experiment, ▶ students test their analytical skills by answering the **What If? question**.

Experimental Inquiry Tutorials, based on some of biology's most influential experiments, give students practice analyzing experimental design and data and help students understand how to reach conclusions based on collected data. Topics include:

- What Can You Learn About the Process of Science from Investigating a Cricket's Chirp?

- Which Wavelengths of Light Drive Photosynthesis?

- Does DNA Replication Follow the Conservative, Semiconservative, or Dispersive Model?

- Did Natural Selection of Ground Finches Occur When the Environment Changed?

- What Factors Influence the Loss of Nutrients from a Forest Ecosystem?

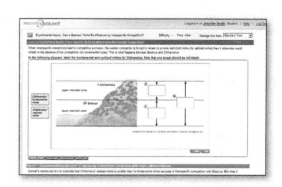

Make Connections Across Biology

By relating the content of a chapter to material presented earlier in the course, Make Connections questions help students develop a deeper understanding of biological principles.

MAKE CONNECTIONS *Review the idea of energy coupling (see Concept 6.3). Then use that idea to explain why heat is produced in the absorption of nutrients, in cellular respiration, and in the synthesis of large biological molecules.*

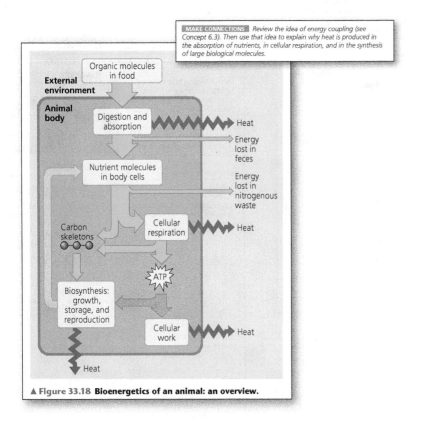

▲ Figure 33.18 **Bioenergetics of an animal: an overview.**

CONCEPT CHECK 28.3
1. Contrast primary growth in roots and shoots.
2. WHAT IF? If a plant species has vertically oriented leaves, would you expect its mesophyll to be divided into spongy and palisade layers? Explain.
3. MAKE CONNECTIONS How are root hairs and microvilli analogous structures? (See Figure 4.7 and the discussion of analogy in Concept 20.2.)

▼ Figure 4.7 **Exploring Eukaryotic Cells**

Animal Cell (cutaway view of generalized cell)

MasteringBiology®
www.masteringbiology.com

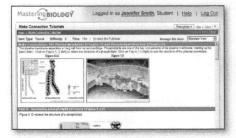

Make Connections Tutorials help students connect biological concepts across chapters in an interactive way.

Focus on Evolution

Every chapter has a section explicitly relating the chapter content to **evolution**, the fundamental theme of biology. Each section is highlighted by an Evolution banner.

The Evolutionary Origins of Mitochondria and Chloroplasts

EVOLUTION Mitochondria and chloroplasts display similarities with bacteria that led to the **endosymbiont theory**, illustrated in Figure 4.16. This theory states that an early ancestor of eukaryotic cells engulfed an oxygen-using non-photosynthetic prokaryotic cell. Eventually, the engulfed cell formed a relationship with the host cell in which it was enclosed, becoming an *endosymbiont* (a cell living within another cell). Indeed, over the course of evolution, the host cell and its endosymbiont...

Review and Test Understanding

Chapter Reviews help students master the chapter content by focusing on the main points and offering opportunities to practice for exams.

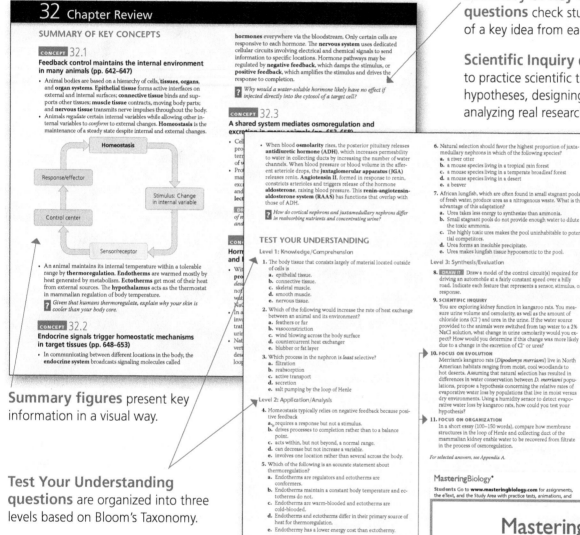

Summary of Key Concepts questions check students' understanding of a key idea from each concept.

Scientific Inquiry questions ask students to practice scientific thinking by developing hypotheses, designing experiments, and analyzing real research data.

Summary figures present key information in a visual way.

Test Your Understanding questions are organized into three levels based on Bloom's Taxonomy.

Focus on a Theme questions give students practice writing a short essay that connects the chapter's content to the five bookwide themes introduced in Chapter 1: **Evolution, Organization, Information, Energy and Matter,** and **Interactions.**

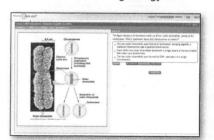

MasteringBiology®

www.masteringbiology.com

Student Misconception Questions provide assignable quizzes for each chapter to assess and remediate common student misconceptions.

Visualize Biology

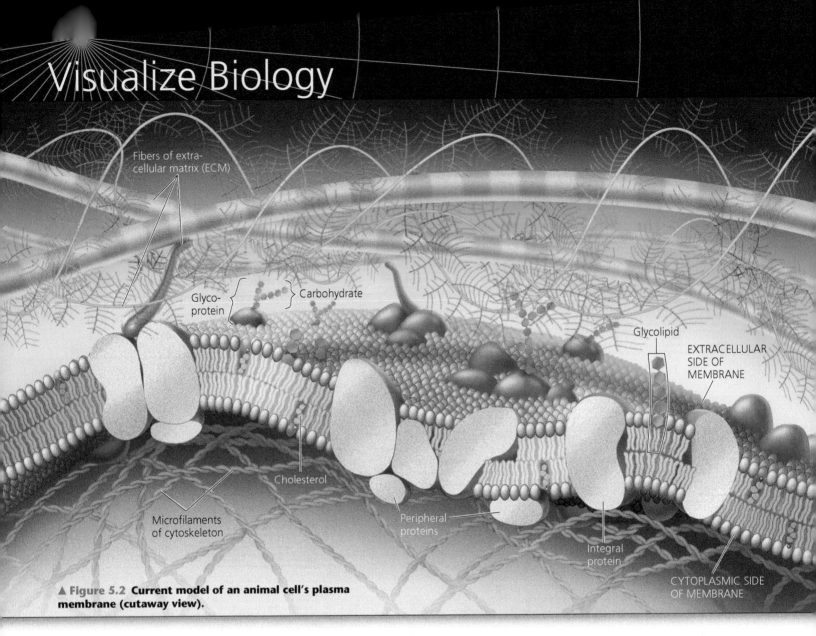

Fibers of extra-cellular matrix (ECM)

Glyco-protein

Carbohydrate

Glycolipid

EXTRACELLULAR SIDE OF MEMBRANE

Cholesterol

Microfilaments of cytoskeleton

Peripheral proteins

Integral protein

CYTOPLASMIC SIDE OF MEMBRANE

▲ **Figure 5.2 Current model of an animal cell's plasma membrane (cutaway view).**

▲ Selected figures are rendered in a **3-D style** to help students visualize biological structures.

MasteringBiology®
www.masteringbiology.com

Many **Tutorials** and **Activities** integrate art from the textbook, providing a unified learning experience.

▼ Figure 33.14 **Dentition and diet.**

Carnivore

Carnivores, such as members of the dog and cat families, generally have large, pointed incisors and canines that can be used to kill prey and rip or cut away pieces of flesh. The jagged premolars and molars crush and shred food.

Herbivore

Herbivores, such as horses and deer, usually have premolars and molars with broad, ridged surfaces that grind tough plant material. The incisors and canines are generally modified for biting off pieces of vegetation. In some herbivores, canines are absent.

Omnivore

As omnivores, humans are adapted to eating both plants and meat. Adults have 32 teeth. From front to back along either side of the mouth are four bladelike incisors for biting, a pair of pointed canines for tearing, four premolars for grinding, and six molars for crushing (see inset, top view).

Key Incisors   Canines   Premolars   Molars

◀ **Visual Organizers** highlight the main parts of a figure, helping students see the key categories at a glance.

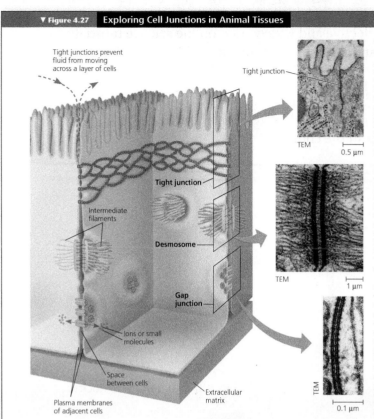

▼ Figure 4.27 Exploring Cell Junctions in Animal Tissues

Tight junctions prevent fluid from moving across a layer of cells

Tight junction

Tight junction

Intermediate filaments

Desmosome

Gap junction

Ions or small molecules

Space between cells

Plasma membranes of adjacent cells

Extracellular matrix

Tight Junctions

At **tight junctions**, the plasma membranes of neighboring cells are very tightly pressed against each other, bound together by specific proteins (purple). Forming continuous seals around the cells, tight junctions prevent leakage of extracellular fluid across a layer of epithelial cells. For example, tight junctions between skin cells make us watertight by preventing leakage between cells in our sweat glands.

TEM $0.5\ \mu m$

Desmosomes

Desmosomes (also called anchoring junctions) function like rivets, fastening cells together into strong sheets. Intermediate filaments made of sturdy keratin proteins anchor desmosomes in the cytoplasm. Desmosomes attach muscle cells to each other in a muscle. Some "muscle tears" involve the rupture of desmosomes.

TEM $1\ \mu m$

Gap Junctions

Gap junctions (also called communicating junctions) provide cytoplasmic channels from one cell to an adjacent cell and in this way are similar in their function to the plasmodesmata in plants. Gap junctions consist of membrane proteins that surround a pore through which ions, sugars, amino acids, and other small molecules may pass. Gap junctions are necessary for communication between cells in many types of tissues, such as heart muscle, and in animal embryos.

TEM $0.1\ \mu m$

◄ By integrating text, art, and photos, **Exploring Figures** help students access information efficiently.

MasteringBiology®
www.masteringbiology.com

BioFlix

BioFlix® 3-D Animations help students visualize biology with movie-quality animations that can be presented in class, reviewed by students on their own in the Study Area, and assigned in MasteringBiology. **BioFlix Tutorials** use the animations as a jumping-off point for coaching exercises on tough topics in MasteringBiology. Tutorials and animations include:

- A Tour of the Animal Cell
- A Tour of the Plant Cell
- Membrane Transport
- Cellular Respiration
- Photosynthesis
- Mitosis
- Meiosis
- DNA Replication
- Protein Synthesis
- Mechanisms of Evolution

- Water Transport in Plants
- Homeostasis: Regulating Blood Sugar
- Gas Exchange
- How Neurons Work
- How Synapses Work
- Muscle Contraction
- Population Ecology
- The Carbon Cycle

MasteringBiology®

www.masteringbiology.com

is the most effective and widely used online science tutorial, homework, and assessment system available.

Personalized Coaching and Feedback

Assign self-paced MasteringBiology tutorials that provide individualized coaching with specific hints and feedback on the toughest topics in the course.

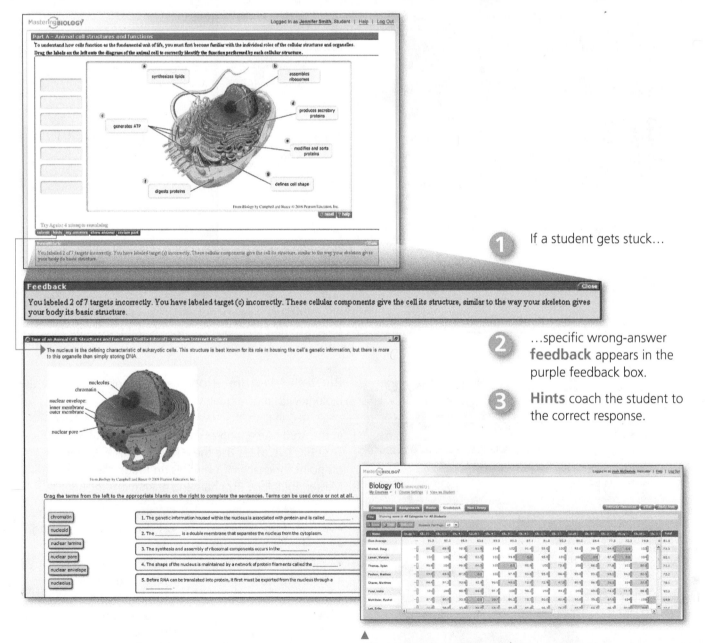

1 If a student gets stuck…

2 …specific wrong-answer **feedback** appears in the purple feedback box.

3 **Hints** coach the student to the correct response.

▲

The MasteringBiology **gradebook** provides instructors with quick results and easy-to-interpret insights into student performance. Every assignment is **automatically graded** and shades of red highlight vulnerable students and challenging assignments.

Students can use the Study Area on their own or in a study group.

BioFlix

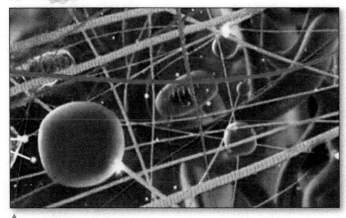

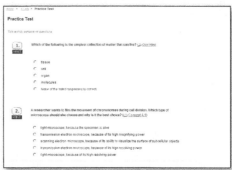

▲ **Practice Tests** help students assess their understanding of each chapter, providing feedback for right and wrong answers.

▲ **BioFlix 3-D Animations** explore the most difficult biology topics, reinforced with tutorials, quizzes, and more.

The **Study Area** also includes:
- Scientific Skills Review
- Cumulative Test
- MP3 Tutor Sessions
- Videos
- Activities
- Investigations
- Lab Media
- Audio Glossary
- Word Roots
- Key Terms
- Flashcards
- Art

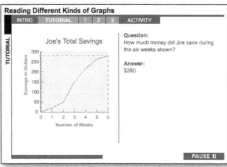

▲ **Get Ready for Biology** helps students get up to speed for their course by covering study skills, basic math review, terminology, biology basics, chemistry, and cell biology.

Access *Campbell BIOLOGY IN FOCUS* Online

◄ The Pearson **eText** gives students access to the text whenever and wherever they can access the Internet. The eText can be viewed on PCs, Macs, and tablets, including iPad and Android. The eText includes powerful interactive and customization functions:

- Write notes
- Highlight text
- Bookmark pages
- Zoom
- Click hyperlinked words to view definitions
- Search
- Link to media activities and quizzes

Instructors can even write notes for the class and highlight important material using a tool that works like an electronic pen on a whiteboard.

Supplements

For Instructors

Instructor's Resource DVD Package
978-0-321-83322-8 • 0-321-83322-8

Assets for each chapter include:

- Editable figures (art and photos) and tables from the text in PowerPoint®
- Prepared PowerPoint Lecture Presentations for each chapter, with lecture notes, editable figures, tables, and links to animations and videos
- JPEG Images, including labeled and unlabeled art, photos from the text, and extra photos
- Clicker Questions in PowerPoint
- 250+ Instructor Animations and Videos, including BioFlix® 3-D Animations and *ABC News* Videos
- Test Bank questions in TestGen® software and Microsoft® Word
- Digital Transparencies
- Quick Reference Guide

BioFlix® Animations invigorate classroom lectures with 3-minute "movie-quality" 3-D graphics.
▼

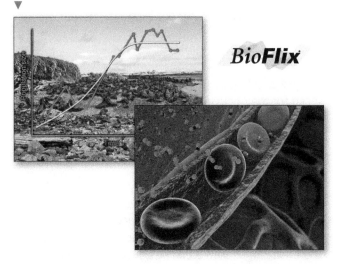

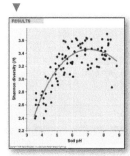

Customizable PowerPoints provide a jumpstart for each lecture.
▼

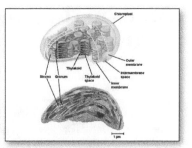

Clicker Questions can be used to stimulate effective classroom discussions (for use with or without clickers).
▼

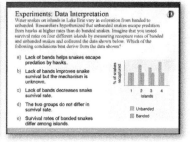

All of the art and photos from the book are provided with customizable labels.

Test Bank
978-0-321-83153-8 • 0-321-83153-5

The Test Bank is available as part of the Instructor's Resource DVD Package or separately.

Course Management Systems

Content is available in Blackboard. Also, **MasteringBiology New Design** offers the usual Mastering features plus:

- Blackboard integration with single sign-on
- Temporary access (grace period)
- Discussion boards
- Email
- Chat and class live (synchronous whiteboard presentation)
- Submissions (dropbox)

Instructor Resources Area in MasteringBiology

This area includes:

- Figures and Tables in PowerPoint®
- PowerPoint Lecture Presentations
- JPEG Images
- Clicker Questions
- Animations
- Videos
- Test Bank Files
- Digital Transparencies
- Quick Reference Guide
- Instructor Guides for Supplements
- Rubric and Tips for Grading Short-Answer Essays
- Suggested Answers for Essay Questions
- Lab Media

For Students

Study Guide
by Martha R. Taylor, Cornell University
978-0-321-86499-4 • 0-321-86499-9

This study guide helps students extract key ideas from the textbook and organize their knowledge of biology. Exercises include concept maps, chapter summaries, word roots, chapter tests, and a variety of interactive questions in various formats.

Inquiry in Action: Interpreting Scientific Papers, Second Edition*
by Ruth Buskirk, University of Texas at Austin, and Christopher M. Gillen, Kenyon College
978-0-321-68336-6 • 0-321-68336-6

Nine research papers are summarized in Inquiry Figures. Each complete original research paper is also reprinted and accompanied by questions that help students analyze the paper.

Practicing Biology: A Student Workbook, Fourth Edition*
by Jean Heitz and Cynthia Giffen, University of Wisconsin, Madison
978-0-321-68328-1 • 0-321-68328-5

This workbook offers a variety of activities to suit different learning styles. Activities such as modeling and mapping allow students to visualize and understand biological processes. Other activities focus on basic skills, such as reading and drawing graphs.

Biological Inquiry: A Workbook of Investigative Cases, Third Edition*
by Margaret Waterman, Southeast Missouri State University, and Ethel Stanley, BioQUEST Curriculum Consortium and Beloit College
978-0-321-68320-5 • 0-321-68320-X

This workbook offers ten investigative cases. A link to a student website is in the Study Area in MasteringBiology.

Study Card
978-0-321-68322-9 • 0-321-68322-6

This quick-reference card provides an overview of the entire field of biology and helps students see the connections between topics.

Spanish Glossary
by Laura P. Zanello, University of California, Riverside
978-0-321-68321-2 • 0-321-68321-8

This resource provides definitions in Spanish for all the glossary terms.

Into the Jungle: Great Adventures in the Search for Evolution
by Sean B. Carroll, University of Wisconsin, Madison
978-0-321-55671-4 • 0-321-55671-2

These nine short tales vividly depict key discoveries in evolutionary biology and the excitement of the scientific process. Online resources available at www.aw-bc.com/carroll.

* An Instructor Guide is available for download in the Instructor Resources Area at www.masteringbiology.com.

Get Ready for Biology
by Lori K. Garrett, Parkland College
978-0-321-50057-1 • 0-321-50057-1

This engaging workbook helps students brush up on important math and study skills and get up to speed on biological terminology and the basics of chemistry and cell biology. Also available online through MasteringBiology.

A Short Guide to Writing About Biology, Seventh Edition
by Jan A. Pechenik, Tufts University
978-0-321-66838-7 • 0-321-66838-3

This best-selling writing guide teaches students to think as biologists and to express ideas clearly and concisely through their writing.

An Introduction to Chemistry for Biology Students, Ninth Edition
by George I. Sackheim, University of Illinois, Chicago
978-0-8053-9571-6 • 0-8053-9571-7

This text/workbook helps students review and master all the basic facts, concepts, and terminology of chemistry that they need for their life science course.

For Lab

Investigating Biology Laboratory Manual, Seventh Edition
by Judith Giles Morgan, Emory University, and M. Eloise Brown Carter, Oxford College of Emory University
978-0-321-66821-9 • 0-321-66821-9

The Seventh Edition emphasizes connections to recurring themes in biology, including structure and function, unity and diversity, and the overarching theme of evolution.

Annotated Instructor Edition for Investigating Biology Laboratory Manual, Seventh Edition
by Judith Giles Morgan, Emory University, and M. Eloise Brown Carter, Oxford College of Emory University
978-0-321-67668-9 • 0-321-67668-8

Preparation Guide for Investigating Biology Laboratory Manual, Seventh Edition
by Judith Giles Morgan, Emory University, and M. Eloise Brown Carter, Oxford College of Emory University
978-0-321-67669-6 • 0-321-67669-6

Symbiosis: The Pearson Custom Library for the Biological Sciences
www.pearsonlearningsolutions.com/custom-library/symbiosis
Professors can create a custom lab manual.

MasteringBiology® Virtual Biology Labs
www.masteringbiology.com

This online environment promotes critical thinking skills using virtual experiments and explorations that may be difficult to perform in a wet lab environment due to time, cost, or safety concerns. Designed to supplement or substitute for existing wet labs, this product offers students unique learning experiences and critical thinking exercises in the areas of microscopy, molecular biology, genetics, ecology, and systematics.

Featured Figures

Exploring Figures

Inquiry Figures

Research Method Figures

*The Inquiry Figure, original research paper, and a worksheet to guide you through the paper are provided in *Inquiry in Action: Interpreting Scientific Papers*, Second Edition.

†A related Experimental Inquiry Tutorial can be assigned in MasteringBiology.

(MB) Each Scientific Skills Exercise is also available as an automatically graded Tutorial in MasteringBiology.

The authors wish to express their gratitude to the global community of instructors, researchers, students, and publishing professionals who have contributed to the first edition of *CAMPBELL BIOLOGY IN FOCUS*.

As authors of this text, we are mindful of the daunting challenge of keeping up to date in all areas of our rapidly expanding subject. We are grateful to the many scientists who helped shape this text by discussing their research fields with us, answering specific questions in their areas of expertise, and sharing their ideas about biology education. We are especially grateful to the following, listed alphabetically: Monika Abedin, John Archibald, Daniel Boyce, Nick Butterfield, Jean DeSaix, Eileen Gregory, Hopi Hoekstra, Fred Holtzclaw, Theresa Holtzclaw, Azarias Karamanlidis, Patrick Keeling, David Lamb, Teri Liegler, Thomas Montavon, Joe Montoya, Kevin Peterson, Michael Pollock, Susannah Porter, Andrew Roger, Andrew Schaffner, Tom Schneider, Alastair Simpson, Doug Soltis, Pamela Soltis, and George Watts. In addition, the biologists listed on pages xxiii–xxiv provided detailed reviews, helping us ensure the text's scientific accuracy and improve its pedagogical effectiveness. We thank Marty Taylor, author of the Study Guide, for her many contributions to the accuracy, clarity, and consistency of the text; and we thank Carolyn Wetzel, Ruth Buskirk, Joan Sharp, Jennifer Yeh, and Charlene D'Avanzo for their contributions to the Scientific Skills Exercises.

Thanks also to the other professors and students, from all over the world, who contacted the authors directly with useful suggestions. We alone bear the responsibility for any errors that remain, but the dedication of our consultants, reviewers, and other correspondents makes us confident in the accuracy and effectiveness of this text.

The value of *CAMPBELL BIOLOGY IN FOCUS* as a learning tool is greatly enhanced by the supplementary materials that have been created for instructors and students. We recognize that the dedicated authors of these materials are essentially writing mini (and not so mini) books. We appreciate the hard work and creativity of all the authors listed, with their creations, on page xix. We are also grateful to Kathleen Fitzpatrick and Nicole Tunbridge (PowerPoint® Lecture Presentations) and Fleur Ferro, Brad Stith, and Loraine Washburn (Clicker Questions).

MasteringBiology® and the electronic media for this text are invaluable teaching and learning aids. We thank the hardworking, industrious instructors who worked on the revised and new media: Willy Cushwa, Tom Kennedy, Michael Pollock, and Heather Wilson-Ashworth. We are also grateful to the many other people—biology instructors, editors, and production experts—who are listed in the credits for these and other elements of the electronic media that accompany the text.

CAMPBELL BIOLOGY IN FOCUS results from an unusually strong synergy between a team of scientists and a team of publishing professionals. Our editorial team at Pearson Science again demonstrated unmatched talents, commitment, and pedagogical insights. Our Senior Acquisitions Editor, Josh Frost, brought publishing savvy, intelligence, and a much appreciated level head to leading the whole team. The clarity and effectiveness of every page owe much to our extraordinary Supervising Editors Pat Burner and Beth Winickoff, who worked with a top-notch team of Developmental Editors in Matt Lee and Mary Ann Murray. Our unsurpassed Senior Editorial Manager Ginnie Simione Jutson, Executive Director of Development Deborah Gale, Assistant Editor Katherine Harrison-Adcock, and Editor-in-Chief Beth Wilbur were indispensable in moving the project in the right direction. We also want to thank Robin Heyden for organizing the annual Biology Leadership Conferences and keeping us in touch with the world of AP Biology.

You would not have this beautiful text if not for the work of the production team: Director of Production Erin Gregg; Managing Editor Michael Early; Assistant Managing Editor Shannon Tozier; Senior Photo Editor Donna Kalal; Photo Researcher Maureen Spuhler; Copy Editor Janet Greenblatt; Proofreader Joanna Dinsmore; Permissions Editor Sue Ewing; Permissions Project Manager Joe Croscup; Permissions Manager Tim Nicholls; Senior Project Editor Emily Bush, Paging Specialists Jodi Gaherty and Donna Healy, and the rest of the staff at S4Carlisle; Art Production Manager Kristina Seymour, Developmental Artist Andrew Recher, and the rest of the staff at Precision Graphics; Design Manager Marilyn Perry; Text Designer Gary Hespenheide; Cover Designer Yvo Riezebos; and Manufacturing Buyer Michael Penne. We also thank those who worked on the text's supplements: Susan Berge, Brady Golden, Jane Brundage, David Chavez, Kris Langan, Pete Shanks, and John Hammett. And for creating the wonderful package of electronic media that accompanies the text, we are grateful to Tania Mlawer (Director of Content Development for MasteringBiology), Sarah Jensen, Jonathan Ballard, Brienn Buchanan, Katie Foley, and Caroline Ross, as well as Director of Media Development Lauren Fogel and Director of Media Strategy Stacy Treco.

For their important roles in marketing the text and media, we thank Christy Lesko, Lauren Harp, Scott Dustan, Chris Hess, Lillian Carr, Jane Campbell, and Jessica Perry. For their market development support, we thank Brooke Suchomel, Michelle Cadden, and Cassandra Cummings. We are grateful to Paul Corey, President of Pearson Science, for his enthusiasm, encouragement, and support.

The Pearson sales team, which represents *CAMPBELL BIOLOGY IN FOCUS* on campus, is an essential link to the users of the text. They tell us what you like and don't like about the text, communicate the features of the text, and provide prompt service. We thank them for their hard work and professionalism. For representing our text to our international audience, we thank our sales and marketing partners throughout the world. They are all strong allies in biology education.

Finally, we wish to thank our families and friends for their encouragement and patience throughout this long project. Our special thanks to Lily, Ross, Lily-too, and Alex (L.A.U.); Debra and Hannah (M.L.C.); Harry, Elga, Aaron, Sophie, Noah, and Gabriele (S.A.W.); Natalie (P.V.M.); Sally, Robert, David, and Will (R.B.J.); and Paul, Dan, Maria, Armelle, and Sean (J.B.R.). And, as always, thanks to Rochelle, Allison, Jason, McKay, and Gus.

Lisa A. Urry, Michael L. Cain, Steve A. Wasserman,
Peter V. Minorsky, Robert B. Jackson, and Jane B. Reece

Ann Aguanno, *Marymount Manhattan College*
Marc Albrecht, *University of Nebraska*
John Alcock, *Arizona State University*
Eric Alcorn, *Acadia University*
Rodney Allrich, *Purdue University*
John Archibald, *Dalhousie University*
Terry Austin, *Temple College*
Brian Bagatto, *University of Akron*
Virginia Baker, *Chipola College*
Teri Balser, *University of Wisconsin, Madison*
Bonnie Baxter, *Westminster College*
Marilee Benore, *University of Michigan, Dearborn*
Catherine Black, *Idaho State University*
William Blaker, *Furman University*
Edward Blumenthal, *Marquette University*
David Bos, *Purdue University*
Scott Bowling, *Auburn University*
Beverly Brown, *Nazareth College*
Beth Burch, *Huntington University*
Warren Burggren, *University of North Texas*
Dale Burnside, *Lenoir-Rhyne University*
Ragan Callaway, *The University of Montana*
Kenneth M. Cameron, *University of Wisconsin, Madison*
Patrick Canary, *Northland Pioneer College*
Cheryl Keller Capone, *Pennsylvania State University*
Mickael Cariveau, *Mount Olive College*
Karen I. Champ, *Central Florida Community College*
David Champlin, *University of Southern Maine*
Brad Chandler, *Palo Alto College*
Wei-Jen Chang, *Hamilton College*
Jung Choi, *Georgia Institute of Technology*
Steve Christenson, *Brigham Young University, Idaho*
Reggie Cobb, *Nashville Community College*
James T. Colbert, *Iowa State University*
Sean Coleman, *University of the Ozarks*
William Cushwa, *Clark College*
Deborah Dardis, *Southeastern Louisiana University*
Shannon Datwyler, *California State University, Sacramento*
Melissa Deadmond, *Truckee Meadows Community College*
Eugene Delay, *University of Vermont*
Daniel DerVartanian, *University of Georgia*
Jean DeSaix, *University of North Carolina, Chapel Hill*
Janet De Souza-Hart, *Massachusetts College of Pharmacy & Health Sciences*
Jason Douglas, *Angelina College*
Kathryn A. Durham, *Lorain Community College*
Anna Edlund, *Lafayette College*
Curt Elderkin, *College of New Jersey*
Mary Ellard-Ivey, *Pacific Lutheran University*
Kurt Elliott, *Northwest Vista College*
George Ellmore, *Tufts University*
Rob Erdman, *Florida Gulf Coast College*
Dale Erskine, *Lebanon Valley College*
Robert C. Evans, *Rutgers University, Camden*
Sam Fan, *Bradley University*
Paul Farnsworth, *University of New Mexico*
Myriam Alhadeff Feldman, *Cascadia Community College*
Teresa Fischer, *Indian River Community College*
David Fitch, *New York University*
T. Fleming, *Bradley University*
Robert Fowler, *San Jose State University*
Robert Franklin, *College of Charleston*
Art Fredeen, *University of Northern British Columbia*
Kim Fredericks, *Viterbo University*
Matt Friedman, *University of Chicago*
Cynthia M. Galloway, *Texas A&M University, Kingsville*

Kristen Genet, *Anoka Ramsey Community College*
Phil Gibson, *University of Oklahoma*
Eric Gillock, *Fort Hayes State University*
Simon Gilroy, *University of Wisconsin, Madison*
Edwin Ginés-Candelaria, *Miami Dade College*
Jim Goetze, *Laredo Community College*
Lynda Goff, *University of California, Santa Cruz*
Roy Golsteyn, *University of Lethbridge*
Barbara E. Goodman, *University of South Dakota*
Eileen Gregory, *Rollins College*
Bradley Griggs, *Piedmont Technical College*
David Grise, *Texas A&M University, Corpus Christi*
Edward Gruberg, *Temple University*
Karen Guzman, *Campbell University*
Carla Haas, *Pennsylvania State University*
Pryce "Pete" Haddix, *Auburn University*
Heather Hallen-Adams, *University of Nebraska, Lincoln*
Monica Hall-Woods, *St. Charles Community College*
Bill Hamilton, *Washington & Lee University*
Devney Hamilton, *Stanford University (student)*
Matthew B. Hamilton, *Georgetown University*
Dennis Haney, *Furman University*
Jean Hardwick, *Ithaca College*
Luke Harmon, *University of Idaho*
Jeanne M. Harris, *University of Vermont*
Stephanie Harvey, *Georgia Southwestern State University*
Bernard Hauser, *University of Florida*
Chris Haynes, *Shelton State Community College*
Andreas Hejnol, *Sars International Centre for Marine Molecular Biology*
Albert Herrera, *University of Southern California*
Chris Hess, *Butler University*
Kendra Hill, *San Diego State University*
Jason Hodin, *Stanford University*
Laura Houston, *Northeast Lakeview College*
Sara Huang, *Los Angeles Valley College*
Catherine Hurlbut, *Florida State College, Jacksonville*
Diane Husic, *Moravian College*
Thomas Jacobs, *University of Illinois*
Kathy Jacobson, *Grinnell College*
Mark Jaffe, *Nova Southeastern University*
Emmanuelle Javaux, *University of Liege, Belgium*
Douglas Jensen, *Converse College*
Lance Johnson, *Midland Lutheran College*
Roishene Johnson, *Bossier Parish Community College*
Cheryl Jorcyk, *Boise State University*
Caroline Kane, *University of California, Berkeley*
The-Hui Kao, *Pennsylvania State University*
Nicholas Kapp, *Skyline College*
Jennifer Katcher, *Pima Community College*
Judy Kaufman, *Monroe Community College*
Eric G. Keeling, *Cary Institute of Ecosystem Studies*
Chris Kennedy, *Simon Fraser University*
Hillar Klandorf, *West Virginia University*
Mark Knauss, *Georgia Highlands College*
Charles Knight, *California Polytechnic State University*
Roger Koeppe, *University of Arkansas*
Peter Kourtev, *Central Michigan University*
Jacob Krans, *Western New England University*
Eliot Krause, *Seton Hall University*
Steven Kristoff, *Ivy Tech Community College*
William Kroll, *Loyola University*
Barb Kuemerle, *Case Western Reserve University*
Rukmani Kuppuswami, *Laredo Community College*
Lee Kurtz, *Georgia Gwinnett College*
Michael P. Labare, *United States Military Academy, West Point*
Ellen Lamb, *University of North Carolina, Greensboro*

(Continued)

William Lamberts, *College of St. Benedict and St. John's University*
Tali D. Lee, *University of Wisconsin, Eau Claire*
Hugh Lefcort, *Gonzaga University*
Alcinda Lewis, *University of Colorado, Boulder*
Jani Lewis, *State University of New York*
Graeme Lindbeck, *Valencia Community College*
Hannah Lui, *University of California, Irvine*
Nancy Magill, *Indiana University*
Cindy Malone, *California State University, Northridge*
Mark Maloney, *University of South Mississippi*
Julia Marrs, *Barnard College (student)*
Kathleen Marrs, *Indiana University-Purdue University, Indianapolis*
Mike Mayfield, *Ball State University*
Kamau Mbuthia, *Bowling Green State University*
Tanya McGhee, *Craven Community College*
Darcy Medica, *Pennsylvania State University*
Susan Meiers, *Western Illinois University*
Mike Meighan, *University of California, Berkeley*
Jan Mikesell, *Gettysburg College*
Alex Mills, *University of Windsor*
Sarah Milton, *Florida Atlantic University*
Eli Minkoff, *Bates College*
Subhash Minocha, *University of New Hampshire*
Ivona Mladenovic, *Simon Fraser University*
Linda Moore, *Georgia Military College*
Courtney Murren, *College of Charleston*
Karen Neal, *Reynolds University*
Ross Nehm, *Ohio State University*
Kimberlyn Nelson, *Pennsylvania State University*
Jacalyn Newman, *University of Pittsburgh*
Kathleen Nolta, *University of Michigan*
Gretchen North, *Occidental College*
Margaret Olney, *St. Martin's University*
Aharon Oren, *The Hebrew University*
Rebecca Orr, *Spring Creek College*
Henry R. Owen, *Eastern Illinois University*
Matt Palmtag, *Florida Gulf Coast University*
Stephanie Pandolfi, *Michigan State University*
Nathalie Pardigon, *Institut Pasteur*
Cindy Paszkowski, *University of Alberta*
Andrew Pease, *Stevenson University*
Nancy Pelaez, *Purdue University*
Irene Perry, *University of Texas of the Permian Basin*
Roger Persell, *Hunter College*
Eric Peters, *Chicago State University*
Larry Peterson, *University of Guelph*
Mark Pilgrim, *College of Coastal Georgia*
Vera M. Piper, *Shenandoah University*
Deb Pires, *University of California, Los Angeles*
Crima Pogge, *City College of San Francisco*
Michael Pollock, *Mount Royal University*
Roberta Pollock, *Occidental College*
Therese M. Poole, *Georgia State University*
Angela R. Porta, *Kean University*
Jason Porter, *University of the Sciences, Philadelphia*
Robert Powell, *Avila University*
Elena Pravosudova, *University of Nevada, Reno*
Eileen Preston, *Tarrant Community College Northwest*
Terrell Pritts, *University of Arkansas, Little Rock*
Pushpa Ramakrishna, *Chandler-Gilbert Community College*
David Randall, *City University Hong Kong*
Monica Ranes-Goldberg, *University of California, Berkeley*
Robert S. Rawding, *Gannon University*
Robert Reavis, *Glendale Community College*
Sarah Richart, *Azusa Pacific University*

Todd Rimkus, *Marymount University*
John Rinehart, *Eastern Oregon University*
Kenneth Robinson, *Purdue University*
Deb Roess, *Colorado State University*
Heather Roffey, *Marianopolis College*
Suzanne Rogers, *Seton Hill University*
Patricia Rugaber, *College of Coastal Georgia*
Scott Russell, *University of Oklahoma*
Glenn-Peter Saetre, *University of Oslo*
Sanga Saha, *Harold Washington College*
Kathleen Sandman, *Ohio State University*
Louis Santiago, *University of California, Riverside*
Tom Sawicki, *Spartanburg Community College*
Andrew Schaffner, *California Polytechnic State University, San Luis Obispo*
Thomas W. Schoener, *University of California, Davis*
Patricia Schulte, *University of British Columbia*
Brenda Schumpert, *Valencia Community College*
David Schwartz, *Houston Community College*
Duane Sears, *University of California, Santa Barbara*
Brent Selinger, *University of Lethbridge*
Alison M. Shakarian, *Salve Regina University*
Joan Sharp, *Simon Fraser University*
Robin L. Sherman, *Nova Southeastern University*
Eric Shows, *Jones County Junior College*
Sedonia Sipes, *Southern Illinois University, Carbondale*
John Skillman, *California State University, San Bernardino*
Doug Soltis, *University of Florida, Gainesville*
Joel Stafstrom, *Northern Illinois University*
Alam Stam, *Capital University*
Judy Stone, *Colby College*
Cynthia Surmacz, *Bloomsburg University*
David Tam, *University of North Texas*
Yves Tan, *Cabrillo College*
Emily Taylor, *California Polytechnic State University*
Marty Taylor, *Cornell University*
Franklyn Tan Te, *Miami Dade College*
Kent Thomas, *Wichita State University*
Mike Toliver, *Eureka College*
Saba Valadkhan, *Center for RNA Molecular Biology*
Sarah VanVickle-Chavez, *Washington University, St. Louis*
William Velhagen, *New York University*
Amy Volmer, *Swarthmore College*
Janice Voltzow, *University of Scranton*
Margaret Voss, *Penn State Erie*
Charles Wade, *C.S. Mott Community College*
Claire Walczak, *Indiana University*
Jerry Waldvogel, *Clemson University*
Robert Lee Wallace, *Ripon College*
James Wandersee, *Louisiana State University*
Fred Wasserman, *Boston University*
James Wee, *Loyola University*
John Weishampel, *University of Central Florida*
Susan Whittemore, *Keene State College*
Murray Wiegand, *University of Winnipeg*
Kimberly Williams, *Kansas State University*
Janet Wolkenstein, *Hudson Valley Community College*
Grace Wyngaard, *James Madison University*
Shuhai Xiao, *Virginia Polytechnic Institute*
Paul Yancey, *Whitman College*
Anne D. Yoder, *Duke University*
Ed Zalisko, *Blackburn College*
Nina Zanetti, *Siena College*
Sam Zeveloff, *Weber State University*
Theresa Zucchero, *Methodist University*

23 Broad Patterns of Evolution 436

OVERVIEW Lost Worlds 436

CONCEPT 23.1 The fossil record documents life's history 436
The Fossil Record 438
How Rocks and Fossils Are Dated 438
The Geologic Record 438
The Origin of New Groups of Organisms 440

CONCEPT 23.2 The rise and fall of groups of organisms reflect differences in speciation and extinction rates 440
Plate Tectonics 442
Mass Extinctions 444
Adaptive Radiations 447

CONCEPT 23.3 Major changes in body form can result from changes in the sequences and regulation of developmental genes 449
Effects of Developmental Genes 449
The Evolution of Development 450

CONCEPT 23.4 Evolution is not goal oriented 452
Evolutionary Novelties 453
Evolutionary Trends 454

UNIT 4 The Evolutionary History of Life 457

24 Early Life and the Diversification of Prokaryotes 458

OVERVIEW The First Cells 458

CONCEPT 24.1 Conditions on early Earth made the origin of life possible 459
Synthesis of Organic Compounds on Early Earth 459
Abiotic Synthesis of Macromolecules 460
Protocells 460
Self-Replicating RNA 460
Fossil Evidence of Early Life 461

CONCEPT 24.2 Diverse structural and metabolic adaptations have evolved in prokaryotes 462
Cell-Surface Structures 462
Motility 464

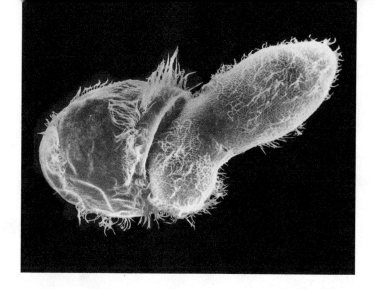

Internal Organization and DNA 464
Nutritional and Metabolic Adaptations 465
Reproduction 466
Adaptations of Prokaryotes: *A Summary* 466

CONCEPT 24.3 Rapid reproduction, mutation, and genetic recombination promote genetic diversity in prokaryotes 467
Rapid Reproduction and Mutation 467
Genetic Recombination 468

CONCEPT 24.4 Prokaryotes have radiated into a diverse set of lineages 470
An Overview of Prokaryotic Diversity 470
Bacteria 471
Archaea 471

CONCEPT 24.5 Prokaryotes play crucial roles in the biosphere 474
Chemical Recycling 474
Ecological Interactions 475
Impact on Humans 475

25 The Origin and Diversification of Eukaryotes 481

OVERVIEW Shape Changers 481

CONCEPT 25.1 Eukaryotes arose by endosymbiosis more than 1.8 billion years ago 481
The Fossil Record of Early Eukaryotes 483
Endosymbiosis in Eukaryotic Evolution 484

CONCEPT 25.2 Multicellularity has originated several times in eukaryotes 487
Multicellular Colonies 487
Independent Origins of Complex Multicellularity 487
Steps in the Origin of Multicellular Animals 488

CONCEPT 25.3 Four "supergroups" of eukaryotes have been proposed based on morphological and molecular data 489
Four Supergroups of Eukaryotes 489
Excavates 492
The "SAR" Clade 493
Archaeplastids 495
Unikonts 496

CONCEPT 25.4 Single-celled eukaryotes play key roles in ecological communities and affect human health 499
Structural and Functional Diversity in Protists 499
Photosynthetic Protists 499
Symbiotic Protists 500
Effects on Human Health 500

Unit 2 Genetics

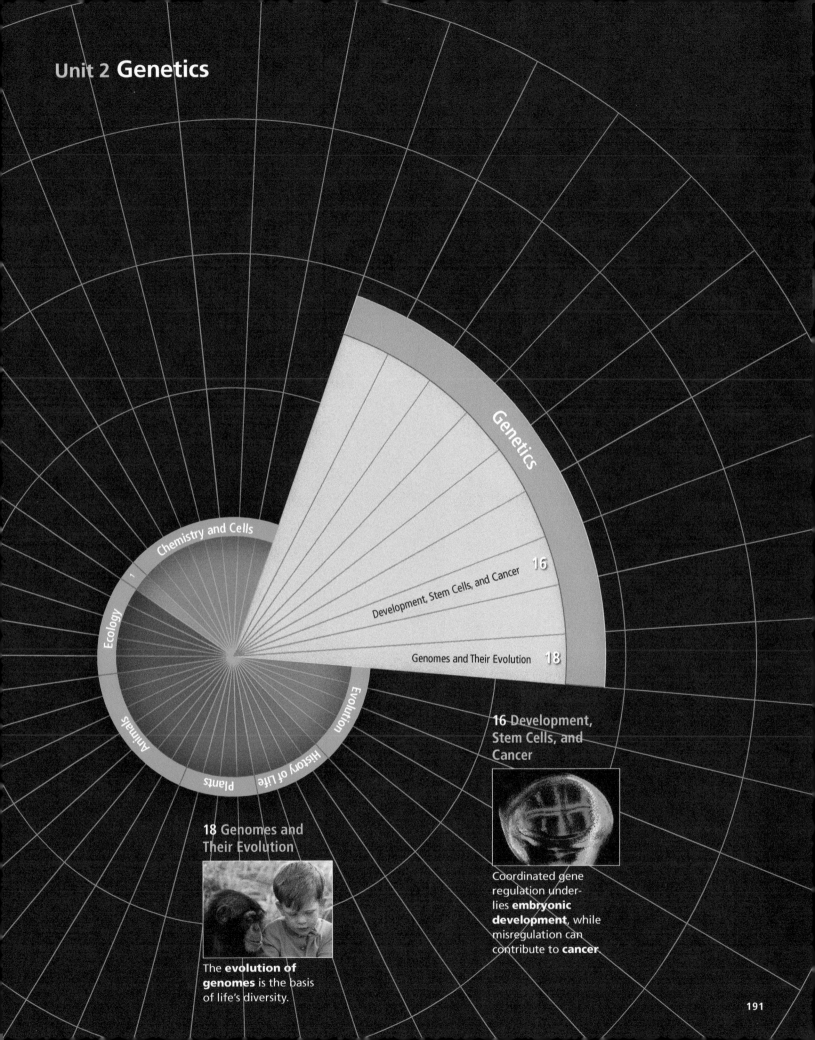

Genetics

Chemistry and Cells

Ecology

Animals

Plants

History of Life

Evolution

Development, Stem Cells, and Cancer 16

Genomes and Their Evolution 18

16 Development, Stem Cells, and Cancer

Coordinated gene regulation underlies **embryonic development**, while misregulation can contribute to **cancer**.

18 Genomes and Their Evolution

The **evolution of genomes** is the basis of life's diversity.

191

16

Development, Stem Cells, and Cancer

KEY CONCEPTS

16.1 A program of differential gene expression leads to the different cell types in a multicellular organism

16.2 Cloning of organisms showed that differentiated cells could be "reprogrammed" and ultimately led to the production of stem cells

16.3 Abnormal regulation of genes that affect the cell cycle can lead to cancer

OVERVIEW

Orchestrating Life's Processes

The development of the fertilized egg, a single cell, into an embryo and later an adult is an astounding transformation that requires a precisely regulated program of gene expression. All of the levels of eukaryotic gene regulation you learned about in the previous chapter come into play during embryonic development. The elaborate sequence of genes being turned on and off in different cells is the ultimate example of regulation of gene expression.

Understanding the genetic underpinnings of development has progressed mainly by studying the process in **model organisms**, species that are easy to raise in the lab and use in experiments. A prime example is the fruit fly *Drosophila melanogaster*. An adult fruit fly develops from a fertilized egg, passing through a wormlike stage called a larva. At every stage, gene expression is carefully regulated, ensuring that the right genes are expressed only at the correct time and place. In the larva, the adult wing forms in a disk-shaped pocket of several thousand cells, shown in **Figure 16.1**. The tissue in this image has been analyzed by *in situ* hybridization (see Figure 15.14) to reveal the mRNA for three genes—labeled red, blue, and green. (Red and green together appear yellow.) The intricate pattern of expression for each gene is the same from larva to larva at this stage, and it provides a graphic display of the precision of gene regulation. But what is the molecular basis for this pattern? Why is one particular gene expressed only in the few hundred cells that appear blue in this image and not in the other cells?

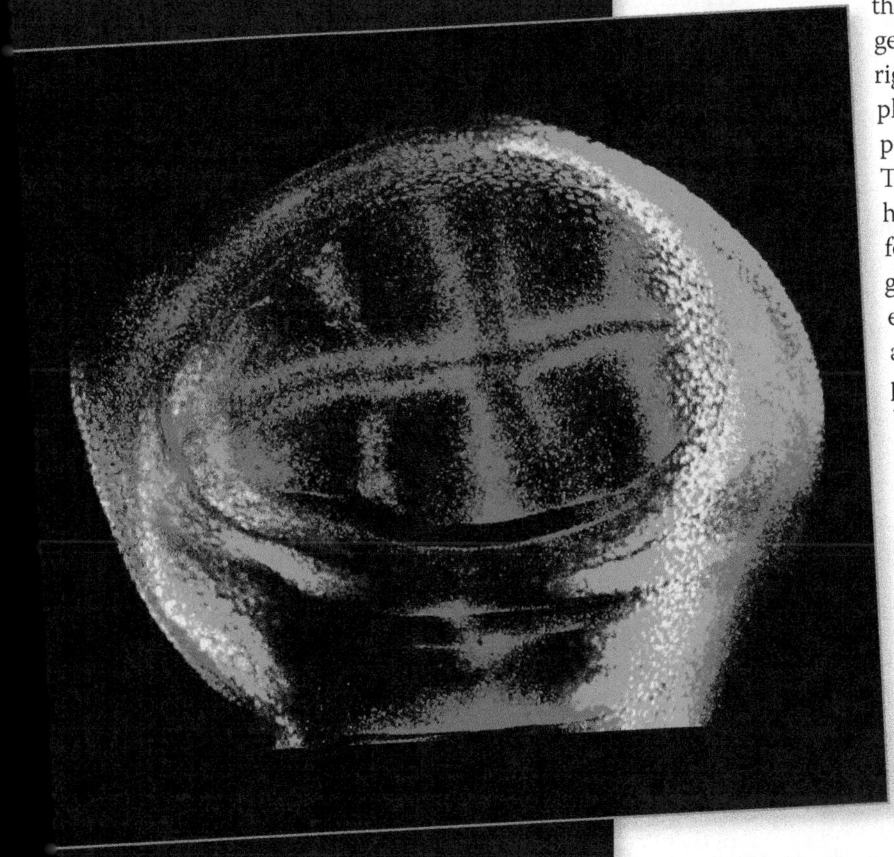

Part of the answer involves the transcription factors and other regulatory molecules you learned about in the previous chapter. But how do they come to be different in distinct cell types? In this chapter, we'll first explain the mechanisms that send cells down diverging genetic pathways to adopt different fates. Then we'll take a closer look at *Drosophila* development. Next, we'll describe the discovery of stem cells, a powerful cell type that is key to the developmental process. These cells offer hope for medical treatments as well. Finally, after having explored embryonic development and stem cells, we will underscore the crucial role played by regulation of gene expression by investigating how cancer can result when this regulation goes awry. Orchestrating proper gene expression by all cells is crucial to the functions of life.

▼ **Figure 16.1** What regulates the precise pattern of gene expression in the developing wing of a fly embryo?

A program of differential gene expression leads to the different cell types in a multicellular organism

In the embryonic development of multicellular organisms, a fertilized egg (a zygote) gives rise to cells of many different types, each with a different structure and corresponding function. Typically, cells are organized into tissues, tissues into organs, organs into organ systems, and organ systems into the whole organism. Thus, any developmental program must produce cells of different types that form higher-level structures arranged in a particular way in three dimensions. Here, we'll focus on the program of regulation of gene expression that orchestrates development using a few animal species as examples.

A Genetic Program for Embryonic Development

The photos in **Figure 16.2** illustrate the dramatic difference between a zygote and the organism it becomes. This remarkable transformation results from three interrelated processes: cell division, cell differentiation, and morphogenesis. Through a succession of mitotic cell divisions, the zygote gives rise to a large number of cells. Cell division alone, however, would merely produce a great ball of identical cells, nothing like a tadpole. During embryonic development, cells not only increase in number, but also undergo cell **differentiation**, the process by which cells become specialized in structure and function. Moreover, the different kinds of cells are not randomly distributed but are organized into tissues and organs in a particular three-dimensional arrangement. The physical processes that give an organism its shape constitute **morphogenesis**, the development of the form of an organism and its structures.

All three processes have their basis in cellular behavior. Even morphogenesis, the shaping of the organism, can be

traced back to changes in the motility, shape, and other characteristics of the cells that make up various regions of the embryo. As you have seen, the activities of a cell depend on the genes it expresses and the proteins it produces. Almost all cells in an organism have the same genome; therefore, differential gene expression results from the genes being regulated differently in each cell type.

In Figure 15.11, you saw a simplified view of how differential gene expression occurs in two cell types, a liver cell and a lens cell. Each of these fully differentiated cells has a particular mix of specific activators that turn on the collection of genes whose products are required in the cell. The fact that both cells arose through a series of mitoses from a common fertilized egg inevitably leads to a question: How do different sets of activators come to be present in the two cells?

It turns out that materials placed into the egg by the mother set up a sequential program of gene regulation that is carried out as cells divide, and this program makes the cells become different from each other in a coordinated fashion. To understand how this works, we'll consider two basic developmental processes: First, we'll explore how cells that arise from early embryonic mitoses develop the differences that start each cell along its own differentiation pathway. Second, we'll see how cellular differentiation leads to one particular cell type, using muscle development as an example.

Cytoplasmic Determinants and Inductive Signals

What generates the first differences among cells in an early embryo? And what controls the differentiation of all the various cell types as development proceeds? You can probably deduce the answer: The specific genes expressed in any particular cell of a developing organism determine its path. Two sources of information, used to varying extents in different species, "tell" a cell which genes to express at any given time during embryonic development.

One important source of information early in development is the egg's cytoplasm, which contains both RNA and proteins encoded by the mother's DNA. The cytoplasm of an unfertilized egg is not homogeneous. Messenger RNA, proteins, other substances, and organelles are distributed unevenly in the unfertilized egg, and this unevenness has a profound impact on the development of the future embryo in many species. Maternal substances in the egg that influence the course of early development are called **cytoplasmic determinants** **(Figure 16.3a)**. After fertilization, early mitotic divisions distribute the zygote's cytoplasm into separate cells. The nuclei of these cells may thus be exposed to different cytoplasmic determinants, depending on which portions of the zygotic cytoplasm a cell received. The combination of cytoplasmic determinants in a cell helps determine its developmental fate by regulating expression of the cell's genes during the course of cell differentiation.

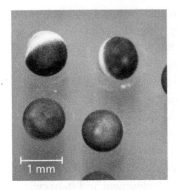
1 mm

(a) Fertilized eggs of a frog

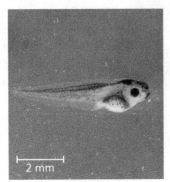
2 mm

(b) Newly hatched tadpole

▲ **Figure 16.2 From fertilized egg to animal: What a difference four days makes.** It takes just four days for cell division, differentiation, and morphogenesis to transform each of the fertilized frog eggs shown in (a) into a tadpole like the one in (b).

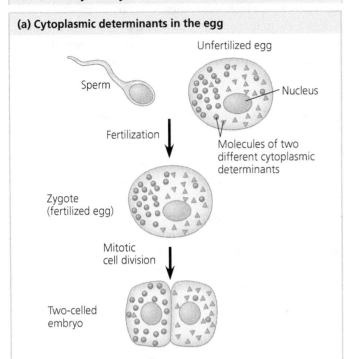

▼ **Figure 16.3 Sources of developmental information for the early embryo.**

(a) Cytoplasmic determinants in the egg

The unfertilized egg has molecules in its cytoplasm, encoded by the mother's genes, that influence development. Many of these cytoplasmic determinants, like the two shown here, are unevenly distributed in the egg. After fertilization and mitotic division, the cell nuclei of the embryo are exposed to different sets of cytoplasmic determinants and, as a result, express different genes.

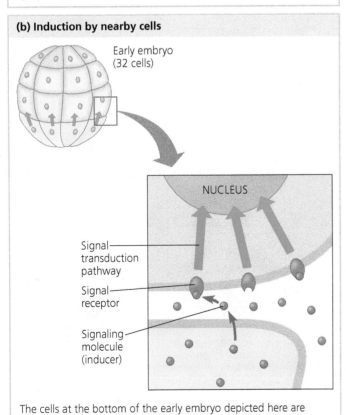

(b) Induction by nearby cells

The cells at the bottom of the early embryo depicted here are releasing chemicals that signal nearby cells to change their gene expression.

The other major source of developmental information, which becomes increasingly important as the number of embryonic cells increases, is the environment around a particular cell. Most influential are the signals communicated to an embryonic cell from other embryonic cells in the vicinity, including contact with cell-surface molecules on neighboring cells and the binding of growth factors secreted by neighboring cells (see Concept 5.6). Such signals cause changes in the target cells, a process called **induction** (Figure 16.3b). The molecules conveying these signals within the target cell are cell-surface receptors and other proteins expressed by the embryo's own genes. In general, the signaling molecules send a cell down a specific developmental path by causing changes in its gene expression that eventually result in observable cellular changes. Thus, interactions between embryonic cells help induce differentiation of the many specialized cell types making up a new organism.

Sequential Regulation of Gene Expression during Cellular Differentiation

As the tissues and organs of an embryo develop and their cells differentiate, the cells become noticeably different in structure and function. These observable changes are actually the outcome of a cell's developmental history, which begins at the first mitotic division of the zygote, as we have just seen. The earliest changes that set a cell on a path to specialization are subtle ones, showing up only at the molecular level. Before biologists knew much about the molecular changes occurring in embryos, they coined the term **determination** to refer to the unseen events that lead to the observable differentiation of a cell. Once it has undergone determination, an embryonic cell is irreversibly committed to its final fate. If a committed cell is experimentally placed in another location in the embryo, it will still differentiate into the cell type that is its normal fate.

Differentiation of Cell Types

Today we understand determination in terms of molecular changes. The outcome of determination, observable cell differentiation, is marked by the expression of genes for *tissue-specific proteins*. These proteins are found only in a specific cell type and give the cell its characteristic structure and function. The first evidence of differentiation is the appearance of mRNAs for these proteins. Eventually, differentiation is observable with a microscope as changes in cellular structure. On the molecular level, different sets of genes are sequentially expressed in a regulated manner as new cells arise from division of their precursors. A number of the steps in gene expression may be regulated during differentiation, with transcription among the most important. At the end of the process, in the fully differentiated cell, transcription remains the principal regulatory point for maintaining appropriate gene expression.

Differentiated cells are specialists at making tissue-specific proteins. For example, as a result of transcriptional regulation, liver cells specialize in making albumin, and lens cells specialize in making crystallin (see Figure 15.11). Skeletal muscle cells in vertebrates are another instructive example. Each of these cells is a long fiber containing many nuclei within a single plasma membrane. Skeletal muscle cells have high concentrations of muscle-specific versions of the contractile proteins myosin and actin, as well as membrane receptor proteins that detect signals from nerve cells.

Muscle cells develop from embryonic precursor cells that have the potential to develop into a number of cell types, including cartilage cells and fat cells, but particular conditions commit them to becoming muscle cells. Although the committed cells appear unchanged under the microscope, determination has occurred, and they are now *myoblasts*. Eventually, myoblasts start to churn out large amounts of muscle-specific proteins and fuse to form mature, elongated, multinucleate skeletal muscle cells.

Researchers have worked out what happens at the molecular level during muscle cell determination **(Figure 16.4)**. To do so, they grew embryonic precursor cells in culture and analyzed them using molecular biological techniques like those described in Chapters 13 and 15. They isolated different genes one by one, caused each to be expressed in a separate precursor cell, and then looked for differentiation into myoblasts and muscle cells. In this way, they identified several so-called "master regulatory genes" whose protein products commit the cells to becoming skeletal muscle. Thus, in the case of muscle cells, the molecular basis of determination is the expression of one or more of these master regulatory genes.

To understand more about how commitment occurs in muscle cell differentiation, let's focus on the master regulatory gene called *myoD* (see Figure 16.4). This gene encodes MyoD protein, a transcription factor that binds to specific control elements in the enhancers of various target genes and stimulates their expression (see Figure 15.9). Some target genes for MyoD encode still other muscle-specific transcription factors. MyoD also stimulates expression of the *myoD* gene itself, thus perpetuating its effect in maintaining the cell's differentiated state. Since all the genes activated by MyoD have enhancer control elements recognized by MyoD, they are coordinately controlled. Finally, the secondary transcription factors activate the genes

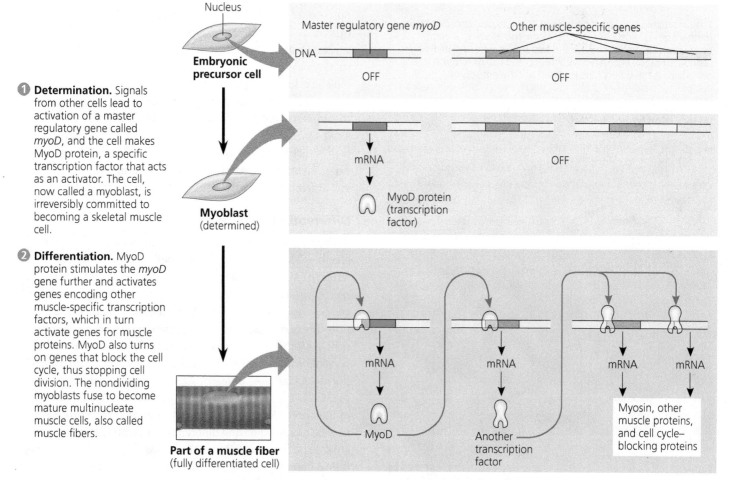

▲ **Figure 16.4 Determination and differentiation of muscle cells.** Skeletal muscle cells arise from embryonic cells as a result of changes in gene expression. (In this depiction, the process of gene activation is greatly simplified.)

WHAT IF? *What would happen if a mutation in the* myoD *gene resulted in a MyoD protein that could not activate the* myoD *gene?*

for proteins such as myosin and actin that confer the unique properties of skeletal muscle cells. The MyoD protein deserves its designation as a master regulatory gene.

The regulation of genes that play important roles in development of embryonic tissues and structures is often complex. In the **Scientific Skills Exercise**, you'll work with data from an experiment that tested how different regulatory regions in the DNA affect expression of a gene that helps establish the pattern of the different digits in a mouse's paw.

Apoptosis: A Type of Programmed Cell Death

During the time when most cells are differentiating, some cells in the developing organism are genetically programmed to die. The best-understood type of "programmed cell death" is **apoptosis** (from the Greek, meaning "falling off," and used in a classic Greek poem to refer to leaves falling from a tree). Apoptosis also occurs in cells of the mature organism that are infected, damaged, or have reached the end of their functional life span. During this process, cellular agents chop up the DNA and fragment the organelles and other cytoplasmic components. The cell becomes multilobed, a change called "blebbing" **(Figure 16.5)**, and the cell's parts are packaged up in vesicles. These "blebs" are then engulfed by scavenger cells, leaving no trace. Apoptosis protects neighboring cells from damage that they would otherwise suffer if a dying cell merely leaked out all its contents, including its many digestive enzymes.

Apoptosis plays a crucial role in the developing embryo. The molecular mechanisms underlying apoptosis were worked out in detail by researchers studying embryonic development of a small soil worm, a nematode called *Caenorhabditis elegans* that has now become a popular model organism for genetic studies. Because the adult worm has only about a thousand cells, the researchers were able to work out the complete ancestry of each cell. The timely suicide of cells occurs exactly 131 times during normal development of *C. elegans*, at precisely the same points in the cell lineage of each worm. In worms and other species, apoptosis is triggered by signal transduction pathways (see Figure 5.20). These activate a cascade of apoptotic "suicide"

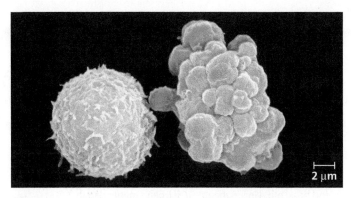

▲ **Figure 16.5 Apoptosis of a human white blood cell.** We can compare a normal white blood cell (left) with a white blood cell undergoing apoptosis (right). The apoptotic cell is shrinking and forming lobes ("blebs"), which eventually are shed as membrane-enclosed cell fragments (colorized SEMs).

proteins in the cells destined to die, including the enzymes that break down and package cellular molecules in the "blebs."

Apoptosis is essential to development and maintenance in all animals. There are similarities in genes encoding apoptotic proteins in nematodes and mammals, and apoptosis is known to occur as well in multicellular fungi and single-celled yeasts, evidence that the basic mechanism evolved early among eukaryotes. In vertebrates, apoptosis is essential for normal development of the nervous system and for normal morphogenesis of hands and feet in humans and paws in other mammals **(Figure 16.6)**. The level of apoptosis between the developing digits is lower in the webbed feet of ducks and other water birds than in the nonwebbed feet of land birds, such as chickens. In the case of humans, the failure of appropriate apoptosis can result in webbed fingers and toes.

We have seen how different programs of gene expression that are activated in the fertilized egg can result in differentiated cells and tissues as well as the death of some cells. But for tissues to function properly in the organism as a whole, the organism's *body plan*—its overall three-dimensional arrangement—must be established and superimposed on the differentiation process. Next we'll look at the molecular basis for establishing the body plan, using the well-studied *Drosophila* as an example.

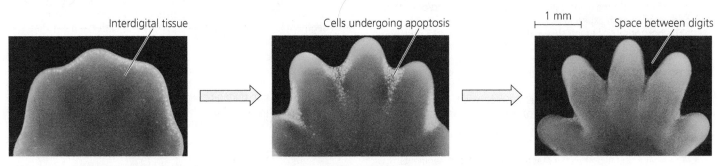

▲ **Figure 16.6 Effect of apoptosis during paw development in the mouse.** In mice, humans, other mammals, and land birds, the embryonic region that develops into feet or hands initially has a solid, platelike structure. Apoptosis eliminates the cells in the interdigital regions, thus forming the digits. The embryonic mouse paws shown in these fluorescence light micrographs are stained so that cells undergoing apoptosis appear a bright yellowish green. Apoptosis of cells begins at the margin of each interdigital region (left), peaks as the tissue in these regions is reduced (middle), and is no longer visible when the interdigital tissue has been eliminated (right). (Note that the Scientific Skills Exercise shows a different genetic process involved in mouse paw development.)

Analyzing Quantitative and Spatial Gene Expression Data

How Is a Particular *Hox* Gene Regulated During Paw Development? *Hox* genes code for transcription factor proteins, which in turn control sets of genes important for animal development (see Concept 18.6 for more information on *Hox* genes). One group of *Hox* genes, the *Hoxd* genes, plays a role in establishing the pattern of the different digits (fingers and toes) at the end of a limb. Unlike the *mPGES-1* gene mentioned in the last chapter, *Hox* genes have very large, complicated regulatory regions, including control elements that may be hundreds of kilobases (kb; thousands of nucleotides) away from the gene.

In cases like this, how do biologists narrow down the segments that contain important elements? They begin by removing (deleting) large segments of DNA and studying the effect on gene expression. In this exercise, you'll compare data from two different but complementary approaches that look at the expression of a specific *Hoxd* gene (*Hoxd13*). One approach quantifies overall expression; the other approach is less quantitative but gives important spatial localization information.

How the Experiment Was Done Researchers interested in the regulation of *Hoxd13* gene expression genetically engineered a set of mice (*transgenic* mice) that had different segments of DNA deleted upstream of the gene. They then compared levels and patterns of *Hoxd13* gene expression in the developing paws of 12.5-day-old transgenic mouse embryos with those seen in wild-type mouse embryos of the same age.

They used two different approaches: In some mice, they extracted the mRNA from the embryonic paws and quantified the overall level of *Hoxd13* mRNA in the whole paw. In another set of the same transgenic mice, they used *in situ* hybridization (see Concept 15.4) to pinpoint exactly where in the paws the *Hoxd13* gene was expressed as mRNA. The particular technique that was used causes the *Hoxd13* mRNA to appear blue.

Data from the Experiment The top diagram (upper right) depicts the very large regulatory region upstream of the *Hoxd13* gene. The area between the slashes represents the DNA located between the promoter and the regulatory region.

The diagrams to the left of the bar graph show, first, the intact DNA (830 kb) and, next, the three altered DNA sequences. (Each is called a "deletion," since a particular section of DNA has been deleted from it.) A red X indicates the segment (A, B, and/or C) that was deleted in each experimental treatment.

The horizontal bar graph shows the amount of *Hoxd13* mRNA that was present in the digit-formation zone of each mutant 12.5-day-old embryo paw relative to the amount that was in the digit-formation zone of the mouse that had the intact regulatory region (top bar = 100%).

The images on the right are the embryo paws showing the location of the *Hoxd13* mRNA (blue stain). The white triangles show the location where the thumb will form.

Interpret the Data

1. The researchers hypothesized that all three regulatory segments (A, B, and C) were required for full expression of the *Hoxd13* gene. By measuring the amount of *Hoxd13* mRNA in the embryo paw

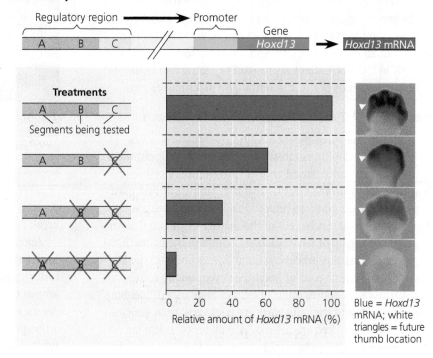

Blue = *Hoxd13* mRNA; white triangles = future thumb location

zones where digits will develop, they could measure the effect of the regulatory segments singly and in combination. Refer to the graph to answer these questions, noting that the segments being tested are shown on the vertical axis and the relative amount of *Hoxd13* mRNA is shown on the horizontal axis. (a) Which of the four treatments was used as a control for the experiment? (b) Their hypothesis is that all three segments are required for highest expression of the *Hoxd13* gene. Is this supported by their results? Explain your answer.

2. (a) What is the effect on the amount of *Hoxd13* mRNA when segments B and C are both deleted, compared with the control? (b) Is this effect visible in the blue-stained regions of the *in situ* hybridizations? How would you describe the spatial pattern of gene expression in the embryo paws that lack segments B and C?

3. (a) What is the effect on the amount of *Hoxd13* mRNA when just segment C is deleted, compared with the control? (b) Is this effect visible in the *in situ* hybridizations? How would you describe the spatial pattern of gene expression in embryo paws that lack just segment C, compared with the control and with the paws that lack segments B and C?

4. If the researchers had only measured the amount of *Hoxd13* mRNA and not done the *in situ* hybridizations, what important information about the role of the regulatory segments in *Hoxd13* gene expression during paw development would have been missed? Conversely, if the researchers had only done the *in situ* hybridizations, what information would have been inaccessible?

Data from T. Montavon et al., A regulatory archipelago controls *Hox* genes transcription in digits, *Cell* 147:1132–1145 (2011). doi 10.1016/j.cell.2011.10.023

(MB) A version of this Scientific Skills Exercise can be assigned in MasteringBiology.

Pattern Formation: Setting Up the Body Plan

Cytoplasmic determinants and inductive signals both contribute to the development of a spatial organization in which the tissues and organs of an organism are all in their characteristic places. This process is called **pattern formation**.

Just as the locations of the front, back, and sides of a new building are determined before construction begins, pattern formation in animals begins in the early embryo, when the major axes of an animal are established. In a bilaterally symmetric animal, the relative positions of head and tail, right and left sides, and back and front—the three major body axes—are set up before the tissues and organs appear. The molecular cues that control pattern formation, collectively called **positional information**, are provided by cytoplasmic determinants and inductive signals (see Figure 16.3). These cues tell a cell its location relative to the body axes and to neighboring cells and determine how the cell and its progeny will respond to future molecular signals.

During the first half of the 20th century, classical embryologists made detailed anatomical observations of embryonic development in a number of species and performed experiments in which they manipulated embryonic tissues. This research laid the groundwork for understanding the mechanisms of development, but it did not reveal the specific molecules that guide development or determine how patterns are established.

In the 1940s, scientists began using the genetic approach—the study of mutants—to investigate *Drosophila* development. That approach has had spectacular success and continues today. Genetic studies have established that genes control development and have led to an understanding of the key roles that specific molecules play in defining position and directing differentiation. By combining anatomical, genetic, and biochemical approaches to the study of *Drosophila* development, researchers have discovered developmental principles common to many other species, including humans.

The Life Cycle of Drosophila

Fruit flies and other arthropods have a modular construction, an ordered series of segments. These segments make up the body's three major parts: the head, the thorax (the midbody, from which the wings and legs extend), and the abdomen **(Figure 16.7a)**. Like other bilaterally symmetric animals, *Drosophila* has an anterior-posterior (head-to-tail) axis, a dorsal-ventral (back-to-belly) axis, and a right-left axis. In *Drosophila*, cytoplasmic determinants that are localized in the unfertilized egg provide positional information for the placement of anterior-posterior and dorsal-ventral axes even before fertilization. We'll focus here on the molecules involved in establishing the anterior-posterior axis as a case in point.

The *Drosophila* egg develops in the female's ovary, surrounded by ovarian cells called nurse cells and follicle cells **(Figure 16.7b**, top). These support cells supply the egg with

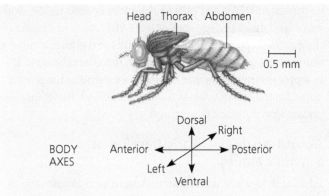

(a) Adult. The adult fly is segmented, and multiple segments make up each of the three main body parts—head, thorax, and abdomen. The body axes are shown by arrows.

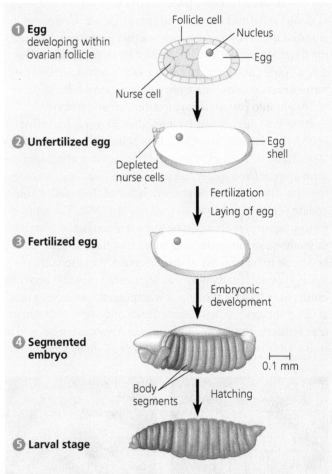

(b) Development from egg to larva. ❶ The egg (yellow) is surrounded by other cells that form a structure called the follicle within one of the mother's ovaries. ❷ The nurse cells shrink as they supply nutrients and mRNAs to the developing egg, which grows larger. Eventually, the mature egg fills the egg shell that is secreted by the follicle cells. ❸ The egg is fertilized within the mother and then laid. ❹ Embryonic development forms ❺ a larva, which goes through three stages. The third stage forms a cocoon (not shown), within which the larva metamorphoses into the adult shown in (a).

▲ **Figure 16.7 Key developmental events in the life cycle of *Drosophila*.**

nutrients, mRNAs, and other substances needed for development, and make the egg shell. After fertilization and laying of the egg, embryonic development results in the formation of a segmented larva, which goes through three larval stages. Then, in a process much like that by which a caterpillar becomes a butterfly, the fly larva forms a cocoon in which it metamorphoses into the adult fly pictured in Figure 16.7a.

Genetic Analysis of Early Development: *Scientific Inquiry*

Edward B. Lewis was a visionary American biologist who, in the 1940s, first showed the value of the genetic approach to studying embryonic development in *Drosophila*. Lewis studied bizarre mutant flies with developmental defects that led to extra wings or legs in the wrong place **(Figure 16.8)**. He located the mutations on the fly's genetic map, thus connecting the developmental abnormalities to specific genes. This research supplied the first concrete evidence that genes somehow direct the developmental processes studied by embryologists. The genes Lewis discovered, called **homeotic genes**, control pattern formation in the late embryo, larva, and adult.

Insight into pattern formation during early embryonic development did not come for another 30 years, when two researchers in Germany, Christiane Nüsslein-Volhard and Eric Wieschaus, set out to identify *all* the genes that affect segment formation in *Drosophila*. The project was daunting for three reasons. The first was the sheer number of *Drosophila* protein-coding genes, now known to total about 13,900. The genes affecting segmentation might be just a few needles in a haystack or might be so numerous and varied that the scientists would be unable to make sense of them. Second, mutations affecting a process as fundamental as segmentation would surely be **embryonic lethals**, mutations with phenotypes causing death at the embryonic or larval stage. Since organisms with embryonic lethal mutations never reproduce, they cannot be bred for study. The researchers dealt with this problem by looking for

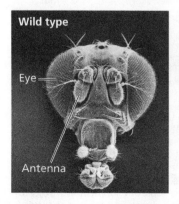

▲ **Figure 16.8 Abnormal pattern formation in *Drosophila*.** Mutations in certain regulatory genes, called homeotic genes, cause a misplacement of structures in an animal. These scanning electron micrographs contrast the head of a wild-type fly, bearing a pair of small antennae, with that of a homeotic mutant (a fly with a mutation in a single gene), bearing a pair of legs in place of antennae.

recessive mutations, which can be propagated in heterozygous flies that act as genetic carriers. Third, cytoplasmic determinants in the egg were known to play a role in axis formation, so the researchers knew they would have to study the mother's genes as well as those of the embryo. It is the mother's genes that we will discuss further as we focus on how the anterior-posterior body axis is set up in the developing egg.

Nüsslein-Volhard and Wieschaus began their search for segmentation genes by exposing flies to a mutagenic chemical that affected the flies' gametes. They mated the mutagenized flies and then scanned their descendants for dead embryos or larvae with abnormal segmentation or other defects. For example, to find genes that might set up the anterior-posterior axis, they looked for embryos or larvae with abnormal ends, such as two heads or two tails, predicting that such abnormalities would arise from mutations in maternal genes required for correctly setting up the offspring's head or tail end.

Using this approach, Nüsslein-Volhard and Wieschaus eventually identified about 1,200 genes essential for pattern formation during embryonic development. Of these, about 120 were essential for normal segmentation. Over several years, the researchers were able to group these segmentation genes by general function, to map them, and to clone many of them for further study in the lab. The result was a detailed molecular understanding of the early steps in pattern formation in *Drosophila*.

When the results of Nüsslein-Volhard and Wieschaus were combined with Lewis's earlier work, a coherent picture of *Drosophila* development emerged. In recognition of their discoveries, the three researchers were awarded a Nobel Prize in 1995.

Let's consider further the genes that Nüsslein-Volhard, Wieschaus, and co-workers found for cytoplasmic determinants deposited in the egg by the mother. These genes set up the initial pattern of the embryo by regulating gene expression in broad regions of the early embryo.

Axis Establishment

As we mentioned earlier, cytoplasmic determinants in the egg are the substances that initially establish the axes of the *Drosophila* body. These substances are encoded by genes of the mother, fittingly called maternal effect genes. A **maternal effect gene** is a gene that, when mutant in the mother, results in a mutant phenotype in the offspring, regardless of the offspring's own genotype. In fruit fly development, the mRNA or protein products of maternal effect genes are placed in the egg while it is still in the mother's ovary. When the mother has a mutation in such a gene, she makes a defective gene product (or none at all), and her eggs are defective; when these eggs are fertilized, they fail to develop properly.

Because they control the orientation (polarity) of the egg and consequently of the fly, maternal effect genes are also called **egg-polarity genes**. One group of these genes sets up the anterior-posterior axis of the embryo, while a second group establishes the dorsal-ventral axis. Like mutations in segmentation genes, mutations in maternal effect genes are generally embryonic lethals.

Bicoid: A Morphogen Determining Head Structures To see how maternal effect genes determine the body axes of the offspring, we'll focus on one such gene, called *bicoid*, a term meaning "two-tailed." An embryo whose mother has two mutant alleles of the *bicoid* gene lacks the front half of its body and has posterior structures at both ends **(Figure 16.9)**. This phenotype suggested to Nüsslein-Volhard and her colleagues that the product of the mother's *bicoid* gene is essential for setting up the anterior end of the fly and might be concentrated at the future anterior end of the embryo. This hypothesis is an example of the *morphogen gradient hypothesis* first proposed by embryologists a century ago; in this hypothesis, gradients of substances called **morphogens** establish an embryo's axes and other features of its form.

DNA technology and other modern biochemical methods enabled the researchers to test whether the *bicoid* product, a protein called Bicoid, is in fact a morphogen that determines the anterior end of the fly. The first question they asked was whether the mRNA and protein products of these genes are located in the egg in a position consistent with the hypothesis. They found that *bicoid* mRNA is highly concentrated at the extreme anterior end of the mature egg, as predicted by the hypothesis **(Figure 16.10)**. After the egg is fertilized, the mRNA is translated into protein. The Bicoid protein then diffuses from the anterior end toward the posterior, resulting in a gradient of protein within the early embryo, with the highest concentration at the anterior end. These results are consistent with the hypothesis that Bicoid protein specifies the fly's anterior end. To test the hypothesis more specifically, scientists injected

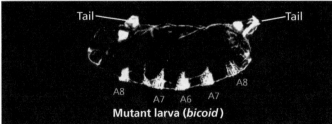
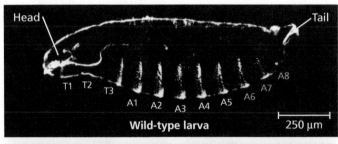

▲ **Figure 16.9 Effect of the *bicoid* gene on *Drosophila* development.** A wild-type fruit fly larva has a head, three thoracic (T) segments, eight abdominal (A) segments, and a tail. A larva whose mother has two mutant alleles of the *bicoid* gene has two tails and lacks all anterior structures (LMs).

▼ **Figure 16.10 Inquiry**

Could Bicoid be a morphogen that determines the anterior end of a fruit fly?

Experiment Using a genetic approach to study *Drosophila* development, Christiane Nüsslein-Volhard and colleagues at the European Molecular Biology Laboratory in Heidelberg, Germany, analyzed expression of the *bicoid* gene. The researchers hypothesized that *bicoid* normally codes for a morphogen that specifies the head (anterior) end of the embryo. To begin to test this hypothesis, they used molecular techniques to determine whether the mRNA and protein encoded by this gene were found in the anterior end of the fertilized egg and early embryo of wild-type flies.

Results *Bicoid* mRNA (dark blue) was confined to the anterior end of the unfertilized egg. Later in development, Bicoid protein (dark orange) was seen to be concentrated in cells at the anterior end of the embryo.

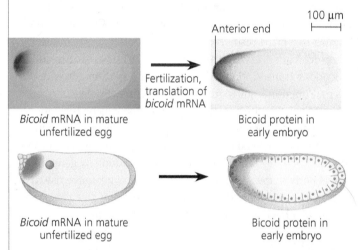

Conclusion The location of *bicoid* mRNA and the diffuse gradient of Bicoid protein seen later are consistent with the hypothesis that Bicoid protein is a morphogen specifying formation of head-specific structures.

Source C. Nüsslein-Volhard et al., Determination of anteroposterior polarity in *Drosophila*, *Science* 238:1675–1681 (1987); W. Driever and C. Nüsslein-Volhard, A gradient of *bicoid* protein in *Drosophila* embryos, *Cell* 54:83–93 (1988); T. Berleth et al., The role of localization of *bicoid* RNA in organizing the anterior pattern of the *Drosophila* embryo, *EMBO Journal* 7:1749–1756 (1988).

WHAT IF? *The researchers needed further evidence, so they injected* bicoid *mRNA into the anterior end of an egg from a female with a mutation disabling the* bicoid *gene. Given that the hypothesis was supported, predict what happened.*

pure *bicoid* mRNA into various regions of early embryos. The protein that resulted from its translation caused anterior structures to form at the injection sites.

The *bicoid* research was groundbreaking for several reasons. First, it led to the identification of a specific protein required for some of the earliest steps in pattern formation. It thus helped us understand how different regions of the egg can give rise to cells that go down different developmental pathways. Second, it increased our understanding of the mother's critical role in the initial phases of embryonic development. Finally, the principle that a gradient of morphogens can determine polarity and position has proved to be a key developmental concept for a number of species, just as early embryologists had hypothesized.

Maternal mRNAs are crucial during development of many species. In *Drosophila*, gradients of specific proteins encoded by maternal mRNAs determine the posterior and anterior ends and establish the dorsal-ventral axis. As the fly embryo grows, it reaches a point when the embryonic program of gene expression takes over, and the maternal mRNAs must be destroyed. (This process involves miRNAs in *Drosophila* and other species.) Later, positional information encoded by the embryo's genes, operating on an ever finer scale, establishes a specific number of correctly oriented segments and triggers the formation of each segment's characteristic structures. When the genes operating in this final step are abnormal, the pattern of the adult is abnormal, as you saw in Figure 16.8.

EVOLUTION The fly with legs emerging from its head in Figure 16.8 is the result of a single mutation in one gene. The gene does not encode an antenna protein, however. Instead, it encodes a transcription factor that regulates other genes, and its malfunction leads to misplaced structures like legs instead of antennae. The observation that a change in gene regulation during development could lead to such a fantastic change in body form prompted some scientists to consider whether these types of mutations could contribute to evolution by generating novel body shapes. Ultimately this line of inquiry gave rise to the field of evolutionary developmental biology, so-called "evo-devo," which will be discussed further in Chapter 18.

CONCEPT CHECK 16.1

1. **MAKE CONNECTIONS** As you learned in Chapter 9, mitosis gives rise to two daughter cells that are genetically identical to the parent cell. Yet you, the product of many mitotic divisions, are not composed of identical cells. Why?

2. **MAKE CONNECTIONS** Explain how the signaling molecules released by an embryonic cell can induce changes in a neighboring cell without entering the cell. (See Figure 5.26.)

3. Why are fruit fly maternal effect genes also called egg-polarity genes?

For suggested answers, see Appendix A.

CONCEPT 16.2

Cloning of organisms showed that differentiated cells could be "reprogrammed" and ultimately led to the production of stem cells

When the field of developmental biology (then called embryology) was first taking shape at the beginning of the 20th century, a major question was whether all the cells of an organism have the same genes (a concept called *genomic equivalence*) or whether cells lose genes during the process of differentiation.

Today, we know that genes are not lost—but the question that remains is whether each cell is able to express all of its genes.

One way to answer this question is to see whether a differentiated cell has the potential to generate a whole organism. Because the organism develops from a single cell without either meiosis or fertilization, this is called "cloning." In this context, cloning produces one or more organisms genetically identical to the "parent" that donated the single cell. This is often called *organismal cloning* to differentiate it from gene cloning and, more significantly, from cell cloning—the division of an asexually reproducing cell into a collection of genetically identical cells. (The common theme for all types of cloning is that the product is genetically identical to the parent. In fact, the word *clone* comes from the Greek *klon*, meaning "twig.")

The current interest in organismal cloning arises primarily from its potential to generate stem cells, which can in turn generate many different tissues. Conceptually, though, the series of experiments discussed here provides a context for thinking about how regulation of gene expression genetically programs the overall potential of a cell—what genes it can express. Let's discuss early organismal cloning experiments before we consider more recent progress in cloning and procedures for producing stem cells.

Cloning Plants and Animals

The successful cloning of whole plants from single differentiated cells was accomplished during the 1950s by F. C. Steward and his students at Cornell University, who worked with carrot plants. They found that single differentiated cells taken from the root (the carrot) and incubated in culture medium could grow into normal adult plants, each genetically identical to the parent plant. These results showed that differentiation does not necessarily involve irreversible changes in the DNA. In plants, at least, mature cells can "dedifferentiate" and then give rise to all the specialized cell types of the organism. Any cell with this potential is said to be **totipotent**.

Differentiated cells from animals generally do not divide in culture, much less develop into the multiple cell types of a new organism. Therefore, early researchers had to use a different approach to the question of whether differentiated animal cells can be totipotent. Their approach was to remove the nucleus of an unfertilized or fertilized egg and replace it with the nucleus of a differentiated cell, a procedure called *nuclear transplantation*. If the nucleus from the differentiated donor cell retains its full genetic capability, then it should be able to direct development of the recipient cell into all the tissues and organs of an organism.

Such experiments were conducted on one species of frog (*Rana pipiens*) by Robert Briggs and Thomas King in the 1950s and on another (*Xenopus laevis*) by John Gurdon in the 1970s. These researchers transplanted a nucleus from an embryonic or tadpole cell into an enucleated (nucleus-lacking) egg of the same species. In Gurdon's experiments, the transplanted nucleus was often able to support normal development of the egg into a tadpole (Figure 16.11). However, he found that the potential of a transplanted nucleus to direct normal development was inversely related to the age of the donor: the older the donor nucleus, the lower the percentage of normally developing tadpoles.

From these results, Gurdon concluded that something in the nucleus *does* change as animal cells differentiate. In frogs and most other animals, nuclear potential tends to be restricted more and more as embryonic development and cell differentiation progress.

Reproductive Cloning of Mammals

In addition to cloning frogs, researchers have long been able to clone mammals by transplanting nuclei or cells from a variety of early embryos. But until about 15 years ago, it was not known whether a nucleus from a fully differentiated cell could be reprogrammed to successfully act as a donor nucleus. In 1997, however, researchers at the Roslin Institute in Scotland captured newspaper headlines when they announced the birth of Dolly, a lamb cloned from an adult sheep by nuclear transplantation from a differentiated cell (Figure 16.12). These researchers achieved

▼ Figure 16.11 **Inquiry**

Can the nucleus from a differentiated animal cell direct development of an organism?

Experiment John Gurdon and colleagues at Oxford University, in England, destroyed the nuclei of frog (*Xenopus laevis*) eggs by exposing the eggs to ultraviolet light. They then transplanted nuclei from cells of frog embryos and tadpoles into the enucleated eggs.

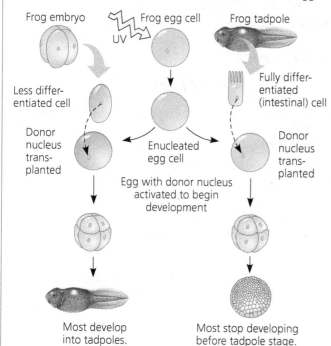

Results When the transplanted nuclei came from an early embryo, whose cells are relatively undifferentiated, most of the recipient eggs developed into tadpoles. But when the nuclei came from the fully differentiated intestinal cells of a tadpole, fewer than 2% of the eggs developed into normal tadpoles, and most of the embryos stopped developing at a much earlier stage.

Conclusion The nucleus from a differentiated frog cell can direct development of a tadpole. However, its ability to do so decreases as the donor cell becomes more differentiated, presumably because of changes in the nucleus.

Source J. B. Gurdon et al., The developmental capacity of nuclei transplanted from keratinized cells of adult frogs, *Journal of Embryology and Experimental Morphology* 34:93–112 (1975).

WHAT IF? *If each cell in a four-cell embryo was already so specialized that it was not totipotent, what results would you predict for the experiment on the left side of the figure?*

▼ Figure 16.12 **Research Method**

Reproductive Cloning of a Mammal by Nuclear Transplantation

Application This method produces cloned animals with nuclear genes identical to those of the animal supplying the nucleus.

Technique The procedure below produced Dolly, the first case of a mammal cloned using the nucleus of a differentiated cell.

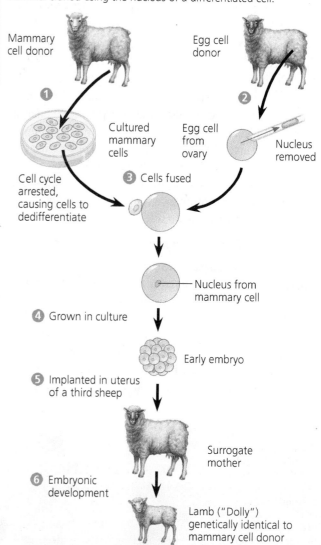

Results The cloned animal is genetically identical to the animal supplying the nucleus but differs from the egg donor and surrogate mother. (The latter two are "Scottish blackface" sheep.)

the necessary dedifferentiation of donor nuclei by culturing mammary cells in nutrient-poor medium. They then fused these cells with enucleated sheep eggs. The resulting diploid cells divided to form early embryos, which were implanted into surrogate mothers. Out of several hundred embryos, one successfully completed normal development, and Dolly was born.

Later analyses showed that Dolly's chromosomal DNA was indeed identical to that of the nucleus donor. (Her mitochondrial DNA came from the egg donor, as expected.) At the age of 6, Dolly suffered complications from a lung disease usually seen only in much older sheep and was euthanized. Dolly's premature death, as well as an arthritic condition, led to speculation that her cells were in some way not quite as healthy as those of a normal sheep, possibly reflecting incomplete reprogramming of the original transplanted nucleus.

Since that time, researchers have cloned numerous other mammals, including mice, cats, cows, horses, pigs, dogs, and monkeys. In most cases, their goal has been the production of new individuals; this is known as *reproductive cloning*. We have already learned a lot from such experiments. For example, cloned animals of the same species do *not* always look or behave identically. In a herd of cows cloned from the same line of cultured cells, certain cows are dominant in behavior and others are more submissive. Another example of nonidentity in clones is the first cloned cat, named CC for Carbon Copy (**Figure 16.13**). She has a calico coat, like her single female parent, but the color and pattern are different because of random X chromosome inactivation, which is a normal occurrence during embryonic development (see Figure 12.8). And identical human twins, which are naturally occurring "clones," are always slightly different. Clearly, environmental influences and random phenomena can play a significant role during development.

Faulty Gene Regulation in Cloned Animals

In most nuclear transplantation studies thus far, only a small percentage of cloned embryos develop normally to birth. And like Dolly, many cloned animals exhibit defects. Cloned mice, for instance, are prone to obesity, pneumonia, liver failure, and premature death. Scientists assert that even cloned animals that appear normal are likely to have subtle defects.

In recent years, we have begun to uncover some reasons for the low efficiency of cloning and the high incidence of abnormalities. In the nuclei of fully differentiated cells, a small subset of genes is turned on and expression of the rest is repressed. This regulation often is the result of epigenetic changes in chromatin, such as acetylation of histones or methylation of DNA (see Figure 15.7). During the nuclear transfer procedure, many of these changes must be reversed in the later-stage nucleus from a donor animal for genes to be expressed or repressed appropriately in early stages of development. Researchers have found that the DNA in cells from cloned embryos, like that of differentiated cells, often has more methyl groups than does the DNA in equivalent cells from normal embryos of the same species. This finding suggests that the reprogramming of donor nuclei requires more accurate and complete chromatin restructuring than occurs during cloning procedures. Because DNA methylation helps regulate gene expression, misplaced or extra methyl groups in the DNA of donor nuclei may interfere with the pattern of gene expression necessary for normal embryonic development. In fact, the success of a cloning attempt may depend in large part on whether or not the chromatin in the donor nucleus can be artificially "rejuvenated" to resemble that of a newly fertilized egg.

Stem Cells of Animals

The successful cloning of many mammals, including primates, has heightened speculation about the cloning of humans, which has not yet been achieved. The main reason researchers are trying to clone human embryos is not for reproduction, but for the production of stem cells to treat human diseases. A **stem cell** is a relatively unspecialized cell that can both reproduce itself indefinitely and, under appropriate conditions, differentiate into specialized cells of one or more types (**Figure 16.14**). Thus, stem cells can both replenish their own undifferentiated population and generate cells that travel down specific differentiation pathways.

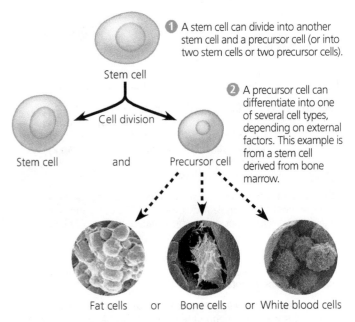

1 A stem cell can divide into another stem cell and a precursor cell (or into two stem cells or two precursor cells).

Stem cell

Cell division

Stem cell   and   Precursor cell

2 A precursor cell can differentiate into one of several cell types, depending on external factors. This example is from a stem cell derived from bone marrow.

Fat cells   or   Bone cells   or   White blood cells

▲ **Figure 16.14 How stem cells maintain their own population and generate differentiated cells.**

► **Figure 16.13 CC, the first cloned cat (right), and her single parent.** Rainbow (left) donated the nucleus in a cloning procedure that resulted in CC. However, the two cats are not identical: Rainbow has orange patches on her fur, but CC does not.

Many early animal embryos contain stem cells capable of giving rise to differentiated embryonic cells of any type. Stem cells can be isolated from early embryos at a stage called the blastula stage or its human equivalent, the blastocyst stage (Figure 16.15). In culture, these *embryonic stem (ES) cells* reproduce indefinitely; and depending on culture conditions, they can be made to differentiate into a wide variety of specialized cells, including even eggs and sperm.

The adult body also has stem cells, which serve to replace nonreproducing specialized cells as needed. In contrast to ES cells, *adult stem cells* are not able to give rise to all cell types in the organism, though in many cases they can generate multiple types. For example, one of the several types of stem cells in bone marrow can generate all the different kinds of blood cells (see Figure 16.15), and another can differentiate into bone, cartilage, fat, muscle, and the linings of blood vessels. To the surprise of many, the adult brain has been found to contain

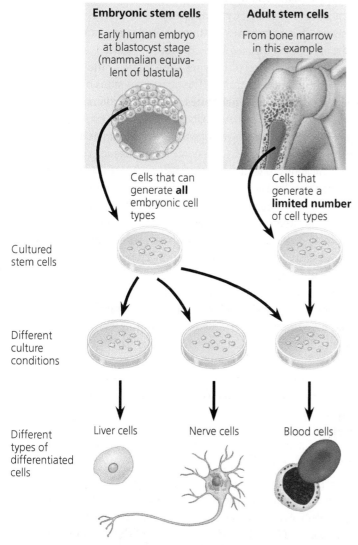

Embryonic stem cells
Early human embryo at blastocyst stage (mammalian equivalent of blastula)

Adult stem cells
From bone marrow in this example

Cells that can generate **all** embryonic cell types

Cells that generate a **limited number** of cell types

Cultured stem cells

Different culture conditions

Different types of differentiated cells

Liver cells

Nerve cells

Blood cells

▲ **Figure 16.15 Working with stem cells.** Animal stem cells, which can be isolated from early embryos or adult tissues and grown in culture, are self-perpetuating, relatively undifferentiated cells. Embryonic stem cells are easier to grow than adult stem cells and can theoretically give rise to *all* types of cells in an organism. The range of cell types that can arise from adult stem cells is not yet fully understood.

stem cells that continue to produce certain kinds of nerve cells there. Researchers have also reported finding stem cells in skin, hair, eyes, and dental pulp. Although adult animals have only tiny numbers of stem cells, scientists are learning to identify and isolate these cells from various tissues and, in some cases, to grow them in culture. With the right culture conditions (often including the addition of specific growth factors), cultured stem cells from adult animals have been made to differentiate into multiple types of specialized cells, although none are as versatile as ES cells.

Research with embryonic or adult stem cells is a source of valuable data about differentiation and has enormous potential for medical applications. The ultimate aim is to supply cells for the repair of damaged or diseased organs: for example, insulin-producing pancreatic cells for people with type 1 diabetes or certain kinds of brain cells for people with Parkinson's disease or Huntington's disease. Adult stem cells from bone marrow have long been used as a source of immune system cells in patients whose own immune systems are nonfunctional because of genetic disorders or radiation treatments for cancer.

The developmental potential of adult stem cells is limited to certain tissues. ES cells hold more promise than adult stem cells for most medical applications because ES cells are **pluripotent**, capable of differentiating into many different cell types. The only way to obtain ES cells thus far, however, has been to harvest them from human embryos, which raises ethical and political issues.

ES cells are currently obtained from embryos donated (with informed consent) by patients undergoing infertility treatment or from long-term cell cultures originally established with cells isolated from donated embryos. If scientists were able to clone human embryos to the blastocyst stage, they might be able to use such clones as the source of ES cells in the future. Furthermore, with a donor nucleus from a person with a particular disease, they might be able to produce ES cells for treatment that match the patient and are thus not rejected by his or her immune system. When the main aim of cloning is to produce ES cells to treat disease, the process is called *therapeutic cloning*. Although most people believe that reproductive cloning of humans is unethical, opinions vary about the morality of therapeutic cloning.

Resolving the debate now seems less imperative because researchers have been able to turn back the clock in fully differentiated cells, reprogramming them to act like ES cells. The accomplishment of this feat, which posed formidable obstacles, was announced in 2007, first by labs using mouse skin cells and then by additional groups using cells from human skin and other organs or tissues. In all these cases, researchers transformed the differentiated cells into ES cells by using types of viruses called retroviruses to introduce extra cloned copies of four "stem cell" master regulatory genes. All the tests that were carried out at the time indicated that the transformed cells, known as *induced pluripotent stem (iPS) cells*, could do everything ES cells can do. More recently, however, several research groups have uncovered differences between iPS and ES cells in gene expression and other cellular functions, such as cell division. At least until these differences are fully understood, the study of ES cells will continue to make important contributions to the development of stem cell therapies. (In fact, ES cells will likely always be a focus of basic research as well.) In the meantime, work is proceeding using the iPS cells in hand.

There are two major potential uses for human iPS cells. First, cells from patients suffering from diseases can be reprogrammed to become iPS cells, which can act as model cells for studying the disease and potential treatments. Human iPS cell lines have already been developed from individuals with type 1 diabetes, Parkinson's disease, and at least a dozen other diseases. Second, in the field of regenerative medicine, a patient's own cells could be reprogrammed into iPS cells and then used to replace nonfunctional tissues. Developing techniques that direct iPS cells to become specific cell types for this purpose is an area of intense research, one that has already seen some success. The iPS cells created in this way could eventually provide tailor-made replacement cells for patients without using any human eggs or embryos, thus circumventing most ethical objections.

The research described in this and the preceding section on stem cells and cell differentiation has underscored the key role of gene regulation in embryonic development. The genetic program is carefully balanced between turning on the genes for differentiation in the right place and turning off other genes. Even when an organism is fully developed, gene expression is regulated in a similarly fine-tuned manner. In the final section of the chapter, we'll consider how fine this tuning is by looking at how specific changes in expression of one or a few genes can lead to the development of cancer.

CONCEPT CHECK 16.2

1. Based on current knowledge, how would you explain the difference in the percentage of tadpoles that developed from the two kinds of donor nuclei in Figure 16.11?

2. If you were to clone a sheep using the technique shown in Figure 16.12, would all the progeny sheep ("clones") look identical? Why or why not?

3. **WHAT IF?** If you were a doctor who wanted to use iPS cells to treat a patient with severe type 1 diabetes, what new technique would have to be developed?

For suggested answers, see Appendix A.

CONCEPT 16.3

Abnormal regulation of genes that affect the cell cycle can lead to cancer

In Chapter 9, we considered cancer as a set of diseases in which cells escape from the control mechanisms that normally limit their growth. Now that we have discussed the molecular basis of gene expression and its regulation, we are ready to look at

cancer more closely. The gene regulation systems that go wrong during cancer turn out to be the very same systems that play important roles in embryonic development, the maintenance of stem cell populations, and many other biological processes. Thus, research into the molecular basis of cancer has both benefited from and informed many other fields of biology.

Types of Genes Associated with Cancer

The genes that normally regulate cell growth and division during the cell cycle include genes for growth factors, their receptors, and the intracellular molecules of signaling pathways. (To review the cell cycle, see Chapter 9; for cell signaling, see Concept 5.6.) Mutations that alter any of these genes in somatic cells can lead to cancer. The agent of such change can be random spontaneous mutation. However, it is likely that many cancer-causing mutations result from environmental influences, such as chemical carcinogens, X-rays and other high-energy radiation, and some viruses.

Cancer research led to the discovery of cancer-causing genes called **oncogenes** (from the Greek *onco*, tumor) in certain types of viruses (see Chapter 17). Subsequently, close counterparts of viral oncogenes were found in the genomes of humans and other animals. The normal versions of the cellular genes, called **proto-oncogenes**, code for proteins that stimulate normal cell growth and division.

How might a proto-oncogene—a gene that has an essential function in normal cells—become an oncogene, a cancer-causing gene? In general, an oncogene arises from a genetic change that leads to an increase either in the amount of the proto-oncogene's protein product or in the intrinsic activity of each protein molecule. The genetic changes that convert proto-oncogenes to oncogenes fall into three main categories: movement of DNA within the genome, amplification of a proto-oncogene, and point mutations in a control element or in the proto-oncogene itself **(Figure 16.16)**.

Cancer cells are frequently found to contain chromosomes that have broken and rejoined incorrectly, translocating fragments from one chromosome to another (see Figure 12.14). Now that you have learned how gene expression is regulated, you can understand the possible consequences of such translocations. If a translocated proto-oncogene ends up near an especially active promoter (or other control element), its transcription may increase, making it an oncogene. The second main type of genetic change, amplification, increases the number of copies of the proto-oncogene in the cell through repeated gene duplication (discussed in Chapter 18). The third possibility is a point mutation either (1) in the promoter or an enhancer that controls a proto-oncogene, causing an increase in its expression, or (2) in the coding sequence of the proto-oncogene, changing the gene's product to a protein that is more active or more resistant to degradation than the normal protein. All these mechanisms can lead to abnormal stimulation of the cell cycle and put the cell on the path to becoming malignant.

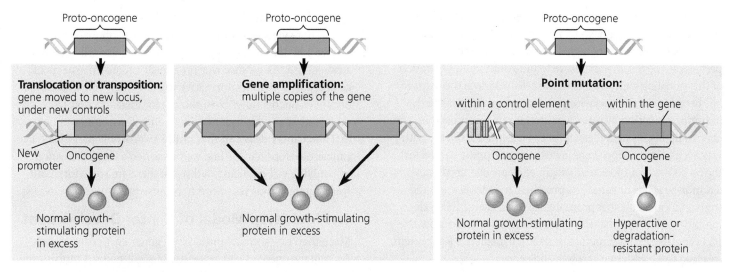

▲ **Figure 16.16 Genetic changes that can turn proto-oncogenes into oncogenes.**

In addition to genes whose products normally promote cell division, cells contain genes whose normal products *inhibit* cell division. Such **tumor-suppressor genes** encode proteins that help prevent uncontrolled cell growth. Any mutation that decreases the normal activity of a tumor-suppressor protein may contribute to the onset of cancer, in effect stimulating growth through the absence of suppression.

Tumor-suppressor gene products have various functions. Some tumor-suppressor proteins repair damaged DNA, a function that prevents the cell from accumulating cancer-causing mutations. Other tumor-suppressor proteins control the adhesion of cells to each other or to the extracellular matrix; proper cell anchorage is crucial in normal tissues—and is often absent in cancers. Still other tumor-suppressor proteins are components of cell-signaling pathways that inhibit the cell cycle.

Interference with Cell-Signaling Pathways

The proteins encoded by many proto-oncogenes and tumor-suppressor genes are components of cell-signaling pathways.

Let's take a closer look at how such proteins function in normal cells and what goes wrong with their function in cancer cells. We'll focus on the products of two key genes, the *ras* proto-oncogene and the *p53* tumor-suppressor gene. Mutations in *ras* occur in about 30% of human cancers, and mutations in *p53* in more than 50%.

The Ras protein, encoded by the ***ras* gene** (named for r̲a̲t sarcoma, a connective tissue cancer), is a G protein that relays a signal from a growth factor receptor on the plasma membrane to a cascade of protein kinases (see Figure 5.21). The cellular response at the end of the pathway is the synthesis of a protein that stimulates the cell cycle **(Figure 16.17)**. Normally, such a pathway will not operate unless triggered by the appropriate growth factor. But certain mutations in the *ras* gene can lead to production of a hyperactive Ras protein that triggers the kinase cascade even in the absence of growth factor, resulting in increased cell division. In fact, hyperactive versions or excess amounts of any of the pathway's components can have the same outcome: excessive cell division.

▶ **Figure 16.17 Normal and mutant cell cycle–stimulating pathway. (a)** The normal pathway is triggered by ❶ a growth factor that binds to ❷ its receptor in the plasma membrane. The signal is relayed to ❸ a G protein called Ras. Like all G proteins, Ras is active when GTP is bound to it. Ras passes the signal to ❹ a series of protein kinases. The last kinase activates ❺ a transcription factor (activator) that turns on one or more genes for ❻ a protein that stimulates the cell cycle. **(b)** If a mutation makes Ras or any other pathway component abnormally active, excessive cell division and cancer may result.

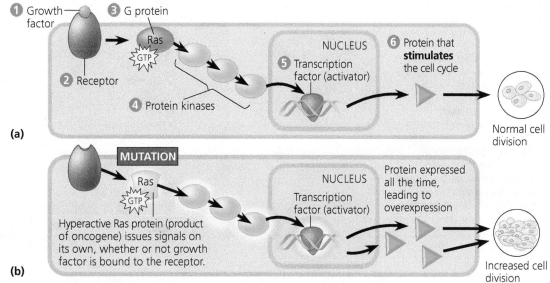

Figure 16.18 shows a pathway in which an intracellular signal leads to the synthesis of a protein that suppresses the cell cycle. In this case, the signal is damage to the cell's DNA, perhaps as the result of exposure to ultraviolet light. Operation of this signaling pathway blocks the cell cycle until the damage has been repaired. Otherwise, the damage might contribute to tumor formation by causing mutations or chromosomal abnormalities. Thus, the genes for the components of the pathway act as tumor-suppressor genes. The **p53 gene**, named for the 53,000-dalton molecular weight of its protein product, is a tumor-suppressor gene. The protein it encodes is a specific transcription factor that promotes the synthesis of cell cycle–inhibiting proteins. That is why a mutation that knocks out the *p53* gene, like a mutation that leads to a hyperactive Ras protein, can lead to excessive cell growth and cancer.

The *p53* gene has been called the "guardian angel of the genome." Once the gene is activated—for example, by DNA damage—the p53 protein functions as an activator for several other genes. Often it activates a gene called *p21*, whose product halts the cell cycle by binding to cyclin-dependent kinases, allowing time for the cell to repair the DNA. Researchers recently showed that p53 also activates expression of a group of miRNAs, which in turn inhibit the cell cycle. In addition, the p53 protein can turn on genes directly involved in DNA repair. Finally, when DNA damage is irreparable, p53 activates "suicide" genes, whose protein products bring about apoptosis, as described in the first section of this chapter. Thus, p53 acts in several ways to prevent a cell from passing on mutations due to DNA damage. If mutations do accumulate and the cell survives through many divisions—as is more likely if the *p53* tumor-suppressor gene is defective or missing—cancer may ensue.The many functions of p53 suggest a complex picture of regulation in normal cells, one that we do not yet fully understand.

For the present, the diagrams in Figures 16.17 and 16.18 are an accurate view of how mutations can contribute to cancer, but we still don't know exactly how a particular cell becomes a cancer cell. As we discover previously unknown aspects of gene regulation, it is informative to study their role in the onset of cancer. Such studies have shown, for instance, that DNA methylation and histone modification patterns differ in normal and cancer cells and that miRNAs probably participate in cancer development. While we've learned a lot about cancer by studying cell-signaling pathways, there are still a lot of outstanding questions that need to be answered.

The Multistep Model of Cancer Development

More than one somatic mutation is generally needed to produce all the changes characteristic of a full-fledged cancer cell. This may help explain why the incidence of cancer increases greatly with age. If cancer results from an accumulation of mutations and if mutations occur throughout life, then the longer we live, the more likely we are to develop cancer.

The model of a multistep path to cancer is well supported by studies of one of the best-understood types of human cancer, colorectal cancer. About 140,000 new cases of colorectal cancer are diagnosed each year in the United States, and the disease causes 50,000 deaths each year. Like most cancers, colorectal cancer develops gradually **(Figure 16.19)**. The first sign is often a polyp, a small, benign growth in the colon lining. The cells of the polyp look normal, although they divide unusually frequently. The tumor grows and may eventually become malignant, invading other tissues. The development of a malignant tumor is paralleled by a gradual accumulation of mutations that convert proto-oncogenes to oncogenes and knock out tumor-suppressor genes. A *ras* oncogene and a mutated *p53* tumor-suppressor gene are often involved.

▶ **Figure 16.18 Normal and mutant cell cycle–inhibiting pathway. (a)** In the normal pathway, ❶ DNA damage is an intracellular signal that is passed via ❷ protein kinases and leads to activation of ❸ p53. Activated p53 promotes transcription of the gene for a protein that inhibits the cell cycle. The resulting suppression of cell division ensures that the damaged DNA is not replicated. If the DNA damage is irreparable, the p53 signal leads to programmed cell death (apoptosis). **(b)** Mutations causing deficiencies in any pathway component can contribute to the development of cancer.

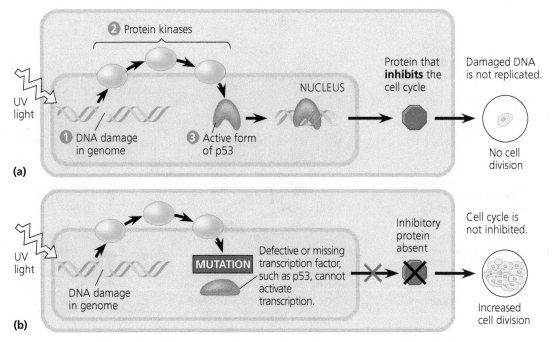

About half a dozen changes must occur at the DNA level for a cell to become fully cancerous. These changes usually include the appearance of at least one active oncogene and the mutation or loss of several tumor-suppressor genes. Furthermore, since mutant tumor-suppressor alleles are usually recessive, in most cases mutations must knock out *both* alleles in a cell's genome to block tumor suppression. (Most oncogenes, on the other hand, behave as dominant alleles.) The order in which these changes must occur is still under investigation, as is the relative importance of different mutations.

Since we understand the progression of this type of cancer, routine screenings are recommended to identify and remove any suspicious polyps. The colorectal cancer rate has been declining for the past 20 years, due in part to increased screening and in part to improved treatments. Treatments for other cancers have improved as well. Technical advances in the sequencing of DNA and mRNA have allowed medical researchers to compare the genes expressed by different types of tumors and by the same type in different individuals. These comparisons have led to personalized cancer treatments based on the molecular characteristics of an individual's tumor.

Inherited Predisposition and Other Factors Contributing to Cancer

The fact that multiple genetic changes are required to produce a cancer cell helps explain the observation that cancers can run in families. An individual inheriting an oncogene or a mutant allele of a tumor-suppressor gene is one step closer to accumulating the necessary mutations for cancer to develop than is an individual without any such mutations.

Geneticists are devoting much effort to identifying inherited cancer alleles so that predisposition to certain cancers can

be detected early in life. About 15% of colorectal cancers, for example, involve inherited mutations. Many of these affect the tumor-suppressor gene called *adenomatous polyposis coli*, or *APC* (see Figure 16.19). This gene has multiple functions in the cell, including regulation of cell migration and adhesion. Even in patients with no family history of the disease, the *APC* gene is mutated in 60% of colorectal cancers. In these individuals, new mutations must occur in both *APC* alleles before the gene's function is lost. Since only 15% of colorectal cancers are associated with known inherited mutations, researchers continue in their efforts to identify "markers" that could predict the risk of developing this type of cancer.

There is evidence of a strong inherited predisposition in 5–10% of patients with breast cancer. This is the second most common type of cancer in the United States, striking over 230,000 women (and some men) annually and killing 40,000 each year. In 1990, after 16 years of research, geneticist Mary-Claire King convincingly demonstrated that mutations in one gene—*BRCA1*—were associated with increased susceptibility to breast cancer, a finding that flew in the face of medical opinion at the time. (*BRCA* stands for <u>br</u>east <u>ca</u>ncer.) Mutations in that gene or the related *BRCA2* gene are found in at least half of inherited breast cancers, and tests using DNA sequencing can detect these mutations. A woman who inherits one mutant *BRCA1* allele has a 60% probability of developing breast cancer before the age of 50, compared with only a 2% probability for an individual homozygous for the normal allele. Both *BRCA1* and *BRCA2* are considered tumor-suppressor genes because their wild-type alleles protect against breast cancer and their mutant alleles are recessive. Apparently, the BRCA1 and BRCA2 proteins both function in the cell's DNA damage repair pathway. More is known about BRCA2, which, in association with another protein, helps repair breaks that occur in both strands of DNA; it is crucial for maintaining undamaged DNA in a cell's nucleus.

Because DNA breakage can contribute to cancer, it makes sense that the risk of cancer can be lowered by minimizing exposure to DNA-damaging agents, such as the ultraviolet radiation in sunlight and chemicals found in cigarette smoke. Novel methods for early diagnosis and treatment of specific cancers

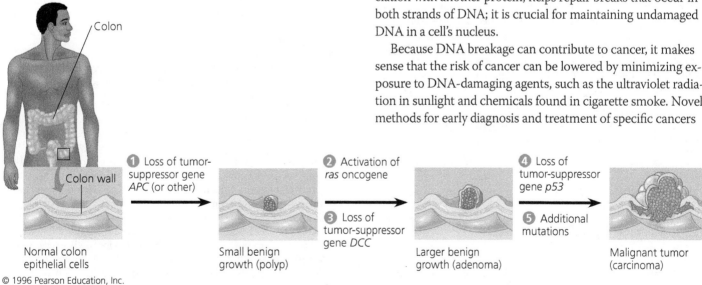

© 1996 Pearson Education, Inc.

▲ **Figure 16.19 A multistep model for the development of colorectal cancer.** Affecting the colon and/or rectum, this type of cancer is one of the best understood. Changes in a tumor parallel a series of genetic changes, including mutations affecting several tumor-suppressor genes (such as *p53*) and the *ras* proto-oncogene. Mutations of tumor-suppressor genes often entail loss (deletion) of the gene. *APC* stands for "adenomatous polyposis coli," and *DCC* stands for "deleted in colorectal cancer." Other mutation sequences can also lead to colorectal cancer.

are being developed that rely on new techniques for analyzing, and perhaps interfering with, gene expression in tumors. Ultimately, such approaches may lower the death rate from cancer.

The study of genes associated with cancer, inherited or not, increases our basic understanding of how disruption of normal gene regulation can result in this disease. In addition to the mutations and other genetic alterations described in this section, a number of *tumor viruses* can cause cancer in various animals, including humans. In fact, one of the earliest breakthroughs in understanding cancer came in 1911, when Peyton Rous, an American pathologist, discovered a virus that causes cancer in chickens. The Epstein-Barr virus, which causes infectious mononucleosis, has been linked to several types of cancer in humans, notably Burkitt's lymphoma. Papillomaviruses are associated with cancer of the cervix, and a virus called HTLV-1 causes a type of adult leukemia. Worldwide, viruses seem to play a role in about 15% of the cases of human cancer.

Viruses may at first seem very different from mutations as a cause of cancer. However, we now know that viruses can interfere with gene regulation in several ways if they integrate their

genetic material into the DNA of a cell. Viral integration may donate an oncogene to the cell, disrupt a tumor-suppressor gene, or convert a proto-oncogene to an oncogene. In addition, some viruses produce proteins that inactivate p53 and other tumor-suppressor proteins, making the cell more prone to becoming cancerous. Viruses are powerful biological agents, and you'll learn more about their function in Chapter 17.

CONCEPT CHECK 16.3

1. The p53 protein can activate genes involved in apoptosis, or programmed cell death. Review Concept 16.1 and discuss how mutations in genes coding for proteins that function in apoptosis could contribute to cancer.
2. Under what circumstances is cancer considered to have a hereditary component?
3. **WHAT IF?** Explain how the types of mutations that lead to cancer are different for a proto-oncogene and a tumor-suppressor gene in terms of the effect of the mutation on the activity of the gene product.

For suggested answers, see Appendix A.

16 Chapter Review

SUMMARY OF KEY CONCEPTS

CONCEPT 16.1

A program of differential gene expression leads to the different cell types in a multicellular organism (pp. 312–320)

- Embryonic cells undergo **differentiation**, becoming specialized in structure and function. **Morphogenesis** encompasses the processes that give shape to the organism and its various structures. Cells differ in structure and function not because they contain different genes but because they express different portions of a common genome.
- Localized **cytoplasmic determinants** in the unfertilized egg are distributed differentially to daughter cells, where they regulate the expression of genes that affect those cells' developmental fates. In the process called **induction**, signaling molecules from embryonic cells cause transcriptional changes in nearby target cells.

Cytoplasmic determinants 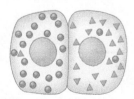 Induction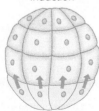

- Differentiation is heralded by the appearance of tissue-specific proteins, which enable differentiated cells to carry out their specialized roles.
- **Apoptosis** is a type of programmed cell death in which cell components are disposed of in an orderly fashion, without damage to neighboring cells. Studies of the soil worm *Caenorhabditis elegans* showed that apoptosis occurs at defined times during

embryonic development. Related apoptotic signaling pathways exist in the cells of humans and other mammals, as well as yeasts.
- In animals, **pattern formation**, the development of a spatial organization of tissues and organs, begins in the early embryo. **Positional information**, the molecular cues that control pattern formation, tells a cell its location relative to the body's axes and to other cells. In *Drosophila*, gradients of **morphogens** encoded by **maternal effect genes** determine the body axes. For example, the gradient of **Bicoid** protein determines the anterior-posterior axis.

> **?** *Describe the two main processes that cause embryonic cells to head down different pathways to their final fates.*

CONCEPT 16.2

Cloning of organisms showed that differentiated cells could be "reprogrammed" and ultimately led to the production of stem cells (pp. 320–324)

- Studies showing genomic equivalence (that an organism's cells all have the same genome) provided the first examples of organismal cloning.
- Single differentiated cells from plants are often **totipotent**: capable of generating all the tissues of a complete new plant.
- Transplantation of the nucleus from a differentiated animal cell into an enucleated egg can sometimes give rise to a new animal.
- Certain embryonic **stem cells** (ES cells) from animal embryos or adult stem cells from adult tissues can reproduce and differentiate *in vitro* as well as *in vivo*, offering the potential for medical use. ES cells are **pluripotent** but difficult to acquire. Induced pluripotent stem (iPS) cells resemble ES cells in their capacity to differentiate; they can be generated by reprogramming differentiated cells. iPS cells hold promise for medical research and regenerative medicine.

> **?** *Describe how a researcher could carry out organismal cloning, production of ES cells, and generation of iPS cells, focusing on how the cells are reprogrammed and using mice as an example. (The procedures are basically the same in humans and mice.)*

Abnormal regulation of genes that affect the cell cycle can lead to cancer (pp. 324–328)

- The products of **proto-oncogenes** and **tumor-suppressor genes** control cell division. A DNA change that makes a proto-oncogene excessively active converts it to an **oncogene**, which may promote excessive cell division and cancer. A tumor-suppressor gene encodes a protein that inhibits abnormal cell division. A mutation in such a gene that reduces the activity of its protein product may also lead to excessive cell division and possibly to cancer.
- Many proto-oncogenes and tumor-suppressor genes encode components of growth-stimulating and growth-inhibiting signaling pathways, respectively, and mutations in these genes can interfere with normal cell-signaling pathways. A hyperactive version of a protein in a stimulatory pathway, such as **Ras** (a G protein), functions as an oncogene protein. A defective version of a protein in an inhibitory pathway, such as **p53** (a transcription activator), fails to function as a tumor suppressor.

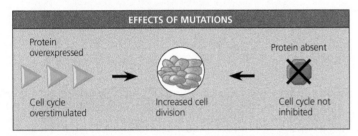

- In the multistep model of cancer development, normal cells are converted to cancer cells by the accumulation of mutations affecting proto-oncogenes and tumor-suppressor genes. Technical advances in DNA and mRNA sequencing are enabling cancer treatments that are more individually based.
- Individuals who inherit a mutant oncogene or tumor-suppressor allele have a predisposition to develop a particular cancer. Certain viruses promote cancer by integration of viral DNA into a cell's genome.

> ? *Compare the usual functions of proteins encoded by proto-oncogenes with the functions of proteins encoded by tumor-suppressor genes.*

TEST YOUR UNDERSTANDING

Level 1: Knowledge/Comprehension

1. Muscle cells differ from nerve cells mainly because they
   a. express different genes.
   b. contain different genes.
   c. use different genetic codes.
   d. have unique ribosomes.
   e. have different chromosomes.

2. Cell differentiation always involves
   a. the production of tissue-specific proteins, such as muscle actin.
   b. the movement of cells.
   c. the transcription of the *myoD* gene.
   d. the selective loss of certain genes from the genome.
   e. the cell's sensitivity to environmental cues, such as light or heat.

Level 2: Application/Analysis

3. Apoptosis involves all but which of the following?
   a. fragmentation of the DNA
   b. cell-signaling pathways
   c. activation of cellular enzymes
   d. lysis of the cell
   e. digestion of cellular contents by scavenger cells

4. Absence of *bicoid* mRNA from a *Drosophila* egg leads to the absence of anterior larval body parts and mirror-image duplication of posterior parts. This is evidence that the product of the *bicoid* gene
   a. is transcribed in the early embryo.
   b. normally leads to formation of tail structures.
   c. normally leads to formation of head structures.
   d. is a protein present in all head structures.
   e. leads to programmed cell death.

5. Proto-oncogenes can change into oncogenes that cause cancer. Which of the following best explains the presence of these potential time bombs in eukaryotic cells?
   a. Proto-oncogenes first arose from viral infections.
   b. Proto-oncogenes normally help regulate cell division.
   c. Proto-oncogenes are genetic "junk."
   d. Proto-oncogenes are mutant versions of normal genes.
   e. Cells produce proto-oncogenes as they age.

Level 3: Synthesis/Evaluation

6. **SCIENTIFIC INQUIRY**
   Prostate cells usually require testosterone and other androgens to survive. But some prostate cancer cells thrive despite treatments that eliminate androgens. One hypothesis is that estrogen, often considered a female hormone, may be activating genes normally controlled by an androgen in these cancer cells. Describe one or more experiments to test this hypothesis. (See Figure 5.23 to review the action of these steroid hormones.)

7. **FOCUS ON EVOLUTION**
   Cancer cells can be considered a population that undergoes evolutionary processes such as random mutation and natural selection. Apply what you learned about evolution in Chapter 1 and about cancer in this chapter to discuss this concept.

8. **FOCUS ON ORGANIZATION**
   The property of life emerges at the biological level of the cell. The highly regulated process of apoptosis is not simply the destruction of a cell; it is also an emergent property. In a short essay (about 100–150 words), briefly explain the role of apoptosis in the development and proper functioning of an animal and describe how this form of programmed cell death is a process that emerges from the orderly integration of signaling pathways.

For selected answers, see Appendix A.

MasteringBiology®

Students Go to **MasteringBiology** for assignments, the eText, and the Study Area with practice tests, animations, and activities.

Instructors Go to **MasteringBiology** for automatically graded tutorials and questions that you can assign to your students, plus Instructor Resources.

18 Genomes and Their Evolution

OVERVIEW

Reading the Leaves from the Tree of Life

The chimpanzee (*Pan troglodytes*) is our closest living relative on the evolutionary tree of life. The boy in **Figure 18.1** and his chimpanzee companion are intently studying the same leaf, but only one of them is able to talk about what he sees. What accounts for this difference between two primates that share so much of their evolutionary history? With the advent of recent techniques for rapidly sequencing complete genomes, we can now start to address the genetic basis of intriguing questions like this.

The chimpanzee genome was sequenced two years after sequencing of the human genome was largely completed. Now that we can compare our genome, base by base, with that of the chimpanzee, we can tackle the more general issue of what differences in genetic information account for the distinct characteristics of these two species of primates.

In addition to determining the sequences of the human and chimpanzee genomes, researchers have obtained complete genome sequences for *E. coli* and numerous other prokaryotes, as well as many eukaryotes, including *Zea mays* (corn), *Drosophila melanogaster* (fruit fly), *Mus musculus* (house mouse), and *Pongo pigmaeus* (orangutan). In 2010, a draft sequence was announced for the genome of *Homo neanderthalensis*, an extinct species closely related to present-day humans. These whole and partial genomes are of great interest in their own right and are also providing important insights into evolution and other biological processes. Broadening the human-chimpanzee comparison to the genomes of other primates and more distantly related animals should reveal the sets of genes that control group-defining characteristics. Beyond that, comparisons with the genomes of bacteria, archaea, fungi, protists, and plants will enlighten us about the long evolutionary history of shared ancient genes and their products.

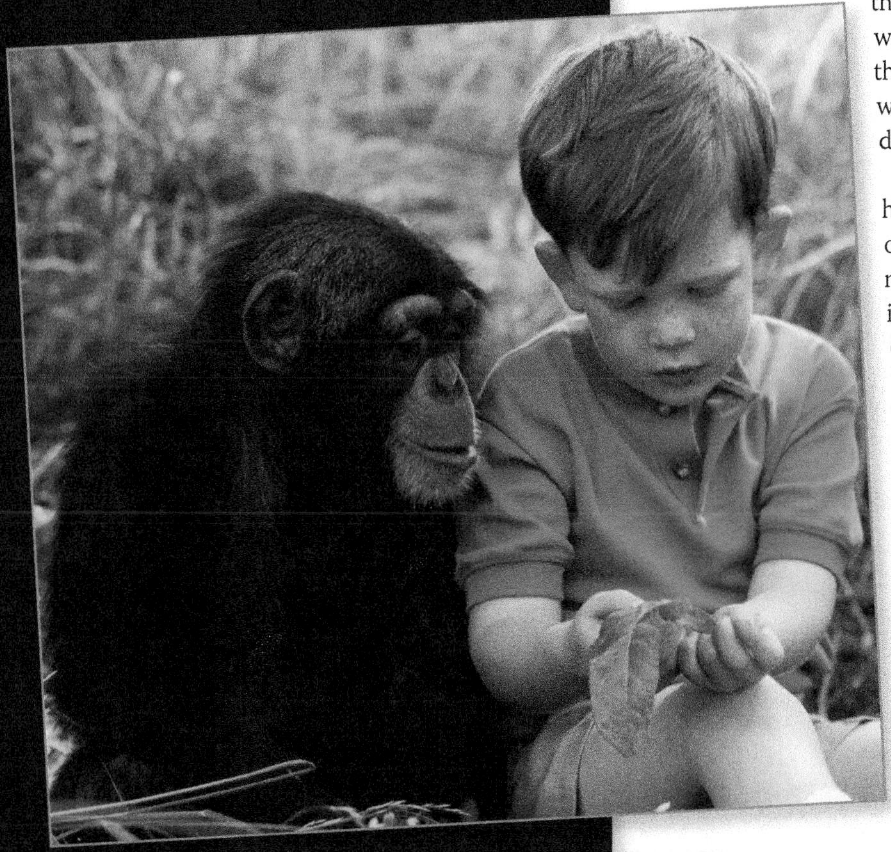

With the genomes of many species fully sequenced, scientists can study whole sets of genes and their interactions, an approach called **genomics**. The sequencing efforts that feed this approach have generated, and continue to generate, enormous volumes of data. The need to deal with this

▼ **Figure 18.1** What genomic information distinguishes a human from a chimpanzee?

ever-increasing flood of information has spawned the field of **bioinformatics**, the application of computational methods to the storage and analysis of biological data.

We'll begin this chapter by discussing genome sequencing and some of the advances in bioinformatics and its applications. We'll then summarize what has been learned from the genomes that have been sequenced thus far. Next, we'll describe the composition of the human genome as a representative genome of a complex multicellular eukaryote. Finally, we'll explore current ideas about how genomes evolve and about how the evolution of developmental mechanisms could have generated the great diversity of life on Earth today.

CONCEPT 18.1

The Human Genome Project fostered development of faster, less expensive sequencing techniques

Sequencing of the human genome, an ambitious undertaking, officially began as the **Human Genome Project** in 1990. Organized by an international, publicly funded consortium of scientists at universities and research institutes, the project involved 20 large sequencing centers in six countries plus a host of other labs working on small projects.

After sequencing of the human genome was reported in 2003, the sequence of each chromosome was analyzed and described in a series of papers, the last of which covered chromosome 1 and was published in 2006. With this refinement, researchers termed the sequencing "virtually complete."

The ultimate goal in mapping any genome is to determine the complete nucleotide sequence of each chromosome. For the human genome, this was accomplished by sequencing machines. Even with automation, the sequencing of all 3 billion base pairs in a haploid set of human chromosomes presented a formidable challenge. In fact, a major thrust of the Human Genome Project was the development of technology for faster sequencing. Improvements over the years chipped away at each time-consuming step, enabling the rate of sequencing to accelerate impressively: Whereas a productive lab could typically sequence 1,000 base pairs a day in the 1980s, by the year 2000 each research center working on the Human Genome Project was sequencing 1,000 base pairs *per second*, 24 hours a day, seven days a week. Methods that can analyze biological materials very rapidly and produce enormous volumes of data are said to be "high-throughput." Sequencing machines are an example of high-throughput devices.

Two approaches complemented each other in obtaining the complete sequence. The initial approach was a methodical one that built on an earlier storehouse of human genetic information. In 1998, however, molecular biologist J. Craig Venter set up a company (Celera Genomics) and declared his intention to

① Cut the DNA from many copies of an entire chromosome into overlapping fragments short enough for sequencing.

② Clone the fragments in plasmid or other vectors.

③ Sequence each fragment.

CGCCATCAGT AGTCCGCTATACGA ACGATACTGGT

④ Order the sequences into one overall sequence with computer software.

CGCCATCAGT ACGATACTGGT

AGTCCGCTATACGA

···CGCCATCAGTCCGCTATACGATACTGGT···

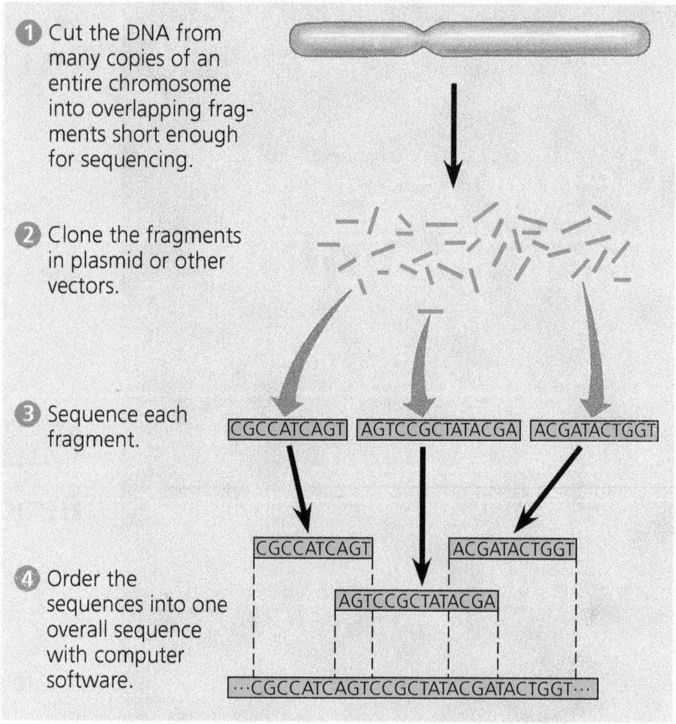

▲ **Figure 18.2 Whole-genome shotgun approach to sequencing.** In this approach, developed by J. Craig Venter and colleagues at the company he founded, Celera Genomics, random DNA fragments are sequenced and then ordered relative to each other.

? *The fragments in stage 2 of this figure are depicted as scattered, rather than being in an ordered array. How does this depiction accurately reflect the approach?*

sequence the entire human genome using an alternative strategy. The **whole-genome shotgun approach** starts with the cloning and sequencing of DNA fragments from randomly cut DNA. Powerful computer programs then assemble the resulting very large number of overlapping short sequences into a single continuous sequence **(Figure 18.2)**.

Today, the whole-genome shotgun approach is widely used. Also, the development of newer sequencing techniques, generally called *sequencing by synthesis* (see Chapter 13), has resulted in massive increases in speed and decreases in the cost of sequencing entire genomes. In these new techniques, many very small fragments (fewer than 100 base pairs) are sequenced at the same time, and computer software rapidly assembles the complete sequence. Because of the sensitivity of these techniques, the fragments can be sequenced directly; the cloning step (stage ② in Figure 18.2) is unnecessary. By 2010, the worldwide output was astronomical: close to 100 *billion* bases per day, with the rate estimated to double every 9 months. Whereas sequencing the first human genome took 13 years and cost $100 million, biologist James Watson's genome was sequenced during 4 months in 2007 for about $1 million, and we are rapidly approaching the day when an individual's genome can be sequenced in a matter of hours for less than $1,000!

These technological advances have also facilitated an approach called **metagenomics** (from the Greek *meta*, beyond), in which DNA from a group of species (a *metagenome*) is collected from an environmental sample and sequenced. Again, computer software accomplishes the task of sorting out the partial sequences and assembling them into specific genomes. So far, this approach has been applied to microbial communities found in environments as diverse as the Sargasso Sea and the human intestine. The ability to sequence the DNA of mixed populations eliminates the need to culture each species separately in the lab, a difficulty that has limited the study of many microbial species.

At first glance, genome sequences of humans and other organisms are simply dry lists of nucleotide bases—millions of A's, T's, C's, and G's in mind-numbing succession. Crucial to making sense of this massive amount of data have been new analytical approaches, which we discuss next.

CONCEPT CHECK 18.1

1. Describe the whole-genome shotgun approach to genome sequencing.

   For suggested answers, see Appendix A.

CONCEPT 18.2

Scientists use bioinformatics to analyze genomes and their functions

Each of the 20 or so sequencing centers around the world working on the Human Genome Project in the 1990s churned out voluminous amounts of DNA sequence day after day. As the data began to accumulate, the need to coordinate efforts to keep track of all the sequences became clear. Thanks to the foresight of research scientists and government officials involved in the Human Genome Project, its goals included the establishment of banks of data, or databases, and the refining of analytical software. These databases and software programs would then be centralized and made readily accessible on the Internet. Accomplishing this aim has accelerated progress in DNA sequence analysis by making bioinformatics resources available to researchers worldwide and by speeding up the dissemination of information.

Centralized Resources for Analyzing Genome Sequences

Government-funded agencies carried out their mandate to establish databases and provide software with which scientists could analyze the sequence data. For example, in the United States, a joint endeavor between the National Library of Medicine and the National Institutes of Health (NIH) created the National Center for Biotechnology Information (NCBI), which maintains a website (www.ncbi.nlm.nih.gov) with extensive bioinformatics resources. On this site are links to databases,

software, and a wealth of information about genomics and related topics. Similar websites have also been established by the European Molecular Biology Laboratory, the DNA Data Bank of Japan, and BGI (formerly known as the Beijing Genome Institute) in Shenzhen, China, three genome centers with which NCBI collaborates. These large, comprehensive websites are complemented by others maintained by individual or small groups of laboratories. Smaller websites often provide databases and software designed for a narrower purpose, such as studying genetic and genomic changes in one particular type of cancer.

The NCBI database of sequences is called GenBank. As of August 2012, it included the sequences of 156 million fragments of genomic DNA, totaling 143 billion base pairs! GenBank is constantly updated, and the amount of data it contains is estimated to double approximately every 18 months. Any sequence in the database can be retrieved and analyzed using software from the NCBI website or elsewhere.

One software program available on the NCBI website, called BLAST, allows the visitor to compare a DNA sequence with every sequence in GenBank, base by base, to look for similar regions. Another program allows comparison of predicted protein sequences. Yet a third can search any protein sequence for common stretches of amino acids (domains) for which a function is known or suspected, and it can show a three-dimensional model of the domain alongside other relevant information (**Figure 18.3**). There is even a software program that can compare a collection of sequences, either nucleic acids or polypeptides, and diagram them in the form of an evolutionary tree based on the sequence relationships. (One such diagram is shown in Figure 18.15.)

Two research institutions, Rutgers University and the University of California, San Diego, also maintain a worldwide Protein Data Bank, a database of all three-dimensional protein structures that have been determined. (The database is accessible at www.wwpdb.org.) These structures can be rotated by the viewer to show all sides of the protein.

There is a vast array of resources available for researchers anywhere in the world to use. Now let's consider the types of questions scientists can address using these resources.

Understanding the Functions of Protein-Coding Genes

The identities of about half of the human genes were known before the Human Genome Project began. But what about the others, the previously unknown genes revealed by analysis of DNA sequences? Clues about their identities and functions come from comparing sequences that might be genes with known genes from other organisms, using the software described previously. Due to redundancy in the genetic code, the DNA sequence itself may vary more than the protein sequence does. Thus, scientists interested in proteins often compare the predicted amino acid sequence of a protein with that of other proteins.

Sometimes a newly identified sequence will match, at least partially, the sequence of a gene or protein whose function

In this window, a partial amino acid sequence from an unknown muskmelon protein ("Query") is aligned with sequences from other proteins that the computer program found to be similar. Each sequence represents a domain called WD40.

Four hallmarks of the WD40 domain are highlighted in yellow. (Sequence similarity is based on chemical aspects of the amino acids, so the amino acids in each hallmark region are not always identical.)

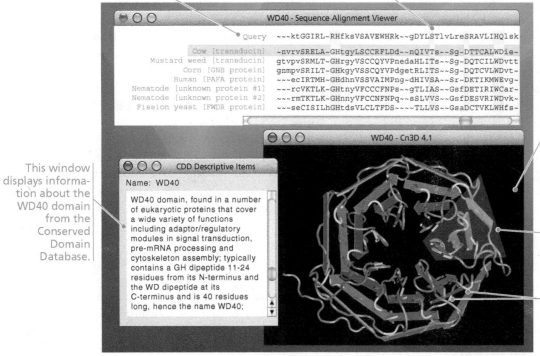

WD40 - Sequence Alignment Viewer

Query	~~~ktGGIRL~RHfksVSAVEWHRk~~gDYLSTlvLreSRAVLIHQlsk
Cow [transducin]	~nrvvSRELA~GHtgyLSCCRFLDd~~nQIVTs~~Sg~DTTCALWDie~
Mustard weed [transducin]	gtvpvSRMLT~GHrgyVSCCQYVPnedaHLITs~~Sg~DQTCILWDvtt
Corn [GNB protein]	gnmpvSRILT~GHkgyVSSCQYVPdgetRLITs~~Sg~DQTCVLWDvt~
Human [PAFA protein]	~~~ecIRTMH~GHdhnVSSVAIMPng~dHIVSA~~Sr~DKTIKMWEvg~
Nematode [unknown protein #1]	~~~rcVKTLK~GHtnyVFCCCFNPs~~gTLIAS~~GsfDETIRIWCar~
Nematode [unknown protein #2]	~~~rmTKTLK~GHnnyVFCCNFNPq~~sSLVVS~~GsfDESVRIWDvk~
Fission yeast [FWDR protein]	~~~seCISILhGHtdsVLCLTFDS~~~~TLLVS~~GsaDCTVKLWHfs~

WD40 - Cn3D 4.1

CDD Descriptive Items

Name: WD40

WD40 domain, found in a number of eukaryotic proteins that cover a wide variety of functions including adaptor/regulatory modules in signal transduction, pre-mRNA processing and cytoskeleton assembly; typically contains a GH dipeptide 11-24 residues from its N-terminus and the WD dipeptide at its C-terminus and is 40 residues long, hence the name WD40;

This window displays information about the WD40 domain from the Conserved Domain Database.

The Cn3D program displays a three-dimensional ribbon model of cow transducin (the protein highlighted in purple in the Sequence Alignment Viewer). This protein is the only one of those shown for which a structure has been determined. The sequence similarity of the other proteins to cow transducin suggests that their structures are likely to be similar.

Cow transducin contains seven WD40 domains, one of which is highlighted here in gray.

The yellow segments correspond to the WD40 hallmarks highlighted in yellow in the window above.

▲ **Figure 18.3 Bioinformatics tools available on the Internet.** A website maintained by the National Center for Biotechnology Information allows scientists and the public to access DNA and protein sequences and other stored data. The site includes a link to a protein structure database (Conserved Domain Database, CDD) that can find and describe similar domains in related proteins, as well as software (Cn3D, "See in 3D") that displays three-dimensional models of domains for which the structure has been determined. Some results are shown from a search for regions of proteins similar to an amino acid sequence in a muskmelon protein.

is well known. For example, part of a new gene may match a known gene that encodes an important signaling pathway protein such as a protein kinase (see Chapter 5), suggesting that the new gene does, too. Alternatively, the new gene sequence may be similar to a previously encountered sequence whose function is still unknown. Another possibility is that the sequence is entirely unlike anything ever seen before. This was true for about a third of the genes of *E. coli* when its genome was sequenced. In the last case, protein function is usually deduced through a combination of biochemical and functional studies. The biochemical approach aims to determine the three-dimensional structure of the protein as well as other attributes, such as potential binding sites for other molecules. Functional studies usually involve blocking or disabling the gene to see how the phenotype is affected.

Understanding Genes and Gene Expression at the Systems Level

The impressive computational power provided by the tools of bioinformatics allows the study of whole sets of genes and their interactions, as well as the comparison of genomes from different species. Genomics is a rich source of new insights into

fundamental questions about genome organization, regulation of gene expression, growth and development, and evolution.

One informative approach has been taken by a research project called ENCODE (Encyclopedia of DNA Elements). First, researchers focused intensively on 1% of the human genome and attempted to learn all they could about the functionally important elements in that sequence. They looked for protein-coding genes and genes for noncoding RNAs as well as sequences that regulate DNA replication, gene expression (such as enhancers and promoters), and chromatin modifications. This pilot project, completed in 2007, yielded a wealth of information. One big surprise, discussed in Concept 18.3, was that over 90% of the region was transcribed into RNA, even though less than 2% codes for proteins. The success of this approach led to two follow-up studies, one extending the analysis to the entire human genome and the other analyzing in a similar fashion the genomes of two model organisms, the soil nematode *Caenorhabditis elegans* and the fruit fly *Drosophila melanogaster*. Because genetic and molecular biological experiments can be performed on these species, testing the activities of potentially functional DNA elements in their genomes is expected to reveal much about how the human genome works.

Systems Biology

The success in sequencing genomes and studying entire sets of genes has encouraged scientists to attempt similar systematic study of the full protein sets (*proteomes*) encoded by genomes, an approach called **proteomics**. Proteins, not the genes that encode them, actually carry out most of the activities of the cell. Therefore, we must study when and where proteins are produced in an organism if we are to understand the functioning of cells and organisms.

Genomics and proteomics are enabling molecular biologists to approach the study of life from an increasingly global perspective. Using the tools we have described, biologists have begun to compile catalogs of genes and proteins—listings of all the "parts" that contribute to the operation of cells, tissues, and organisms. With such catalogs in hand, researchers have shifted their attention from the individual parts to their functional integration in biological systems. This is called the **systems biology** approach, which aims to model the dynamic behavior of whole biological systems based on the study of the interactions among the system's parts. Because of the vast amounts of data generated in these types of studies, the systems biology approach has really been made possible by advances in computer technology and bioinformatics.

Application of Systems Biology to Medicine

The Cancer Genome Atlas is an example of systems biology in which a large group of interacting genes and gene products are analyzed together. This project, under the joint leadership of the National Cancer Institute and NIH, aims to determine how changes in biological systems lead to cancer. A three-year pilot project that ended in 2010 set out to find all the common mutations in three types of cancer—lung cancer, ovarian cancer, and glioblastoma of the brain—by comparing gene sequences and patterns of gene expression in cancer cells with those in normal cells. Work on glioblastoma has confirmed the role of several suspected genes and identified a few unknown ones, suggesting possible new targets for therapies. The approach has proved so fruitful for these three types of cancer that it has been extended to ten other types, chosen because they are common and often lethal in humans.

Systems biology has tremendous potential in human medicine that is just starting to be explored. Silicon and glass "chips" have been developed that hold a microarray of most of the known human genes (**Figure 18.4**). Such chips are being used to analyze gene expression patterns in patients suffering from various cancers and other diseases, with the eventual aim of tailoring their treatment to their unique genetic makeup and the specifics of their cancers. This approach has had modest success in characterizing subsets of several cancers.

Ultimately, people may carry with their medical records a catalog of their DNA sequence, a sort of genetic bar code, with regions highlighted that predispose them to specific diseases. The use of such sequences for personalized medicine—disease prevention and treatment—has great potential.

◀ **Figure 18.4 A human gene microarray chip.** Tiny spots of DNA arranged in a grid on this silicon wafer represent almost all of the genes in the human genome. Using this chip, researchers can analyze expression patterns for all these genes at the same time.

Systems biology is a very efficient way to study emergent properties at the molecular level. Novel properties emerge at each successive level of biological complexity as a result of the arrangement of building blocks at the underlying level (see Chapter 1). The more we can learn about the arrangement and interactions of the components of genetic systems, the deeper will be our understanding of whole organisms. The rest of this chapter will survey what we've learned from genomic studies thus far.

CONCEPT CHECK 18.2

1. What role does the Internet play in current genomics and proteomics research?
2. Explain the advantage of the systems biology approach to studying cancer versus the approach of studying a single gene at a time.
3. **MAKE CONNECTIONS** The ENCODE pilot project found that more than 90% of the genomic region being studied was transcribed into RNAs, far more than could be accounted for by protein-coding genes. Suggest some roles that these RNAs might play. (Review Concept 15.3.)

For suggested answers, see Appendix A.

CONCEPT 18.3

Genomes vary in size, number of genes, and gene density

By August 2012, the sequencing of about 3,700 genomes had been completed and that of over 7,500 genomes and about 340 metagenomes was in progress. In the completely sequenced group, about 3,300 are genomes of bacteria, and 160 are archaeal genomes. Among the 183 eukaryotic species in the group are vertebrates, invertebrates, protists, fungi, and plants. The accumulated genome sequences contain a wealth of information that we are now beginning to mine. What have we learned so far by comparing the genomes that have been sequenced? In this section, we'll examine the characteristics of genome size, number of genes, and gene density. Because these characteristics are so broad, we'll focus on general trends, for which there are often exceptions.

Genome Size

Comparing the three domains (Bacteria, Archaea, and Eukarya), we find a general difference in genome size between prokaryotes and eukaryotes (Table 18.1). While there are some exceptions, most bacterial genomes have between 1 and 6 million base pairs (Mb); the genome of *E. coli*, for instance, has 4.6 Mb. Genomes of archaea are, for the most part, within the size range of bacterial genomes. (Keep in mind, however, that many fewer archaeal genomes have been completely sequenced, so this picture may change.) Eukaryotic genomes tend to be larger: The genome of the single-celled yeast *Saccharomyces cerevisiae* (a fungus) has about 12 Mb, while most animals and plants, which are multicellular, have genomes of at least 100 Mb. There are 165 Mb in the fruit fly genome, while humans have 3,000 Mb, about 500 to 3,000 times as many as a typical bacterium.

Aside from this general difference between prokaryotes and eukaryotes, a comparison of genome sizes among eukaryotes fails to reveal any systematic relationship between genome size and the organism's phenotype. For instance, the genome of *Fritillaria assyriaca*, a flowering plant in the lily family, contains 124 billion base pairs (124,000 Mb), about 40 times the size of the human genome. On a finer scale, comparing two insect species, the cricket (*Anabrus simplex*) genome turns out to have 11 times as many base pairs as the *Drosophila melanogaster* genome. There is a wide range of genome sizes within the groups of protists, insects, amphibians, and plants and less of a range within mammals and reptiles.

Number of Genes

The number of genes also varies between prokaryotes and eukaryotes: Bacteria and archaea, in general, have fewer genes than eukaryotes. Free-living bacteria and archaea have from 1,500 to 7,500 genes, while the number of genes in eukaryotes ranges from about 5,000 for unicellular fungi to at least 40,000 for some multicellular eukaryotes (see Table 18.1).

Within the eukaryotes, the number of genes in a species is often lower than expected from simply considering the size of its genome. Looking at Table 18.1, you can see that the genome of the nematode *C. elegans* is 100 Mb in size and contains 20,100 genes. The *Drosophila* genome, in comparison, is much bigger (165 Mb) but has about two-thirds the number of genes—only 13,900 genes.

Considering an example closer to home, we noted that the human genome contains 3,000 Mb, well over ten times the size of either the *Drosophila* or *C. elegans* genome. At the outset of the Human Genome Project, biologists expected somewhere between 50,000 and 100,000 genes to be identified in the completed sequence, based on the number of known human proteins. As the project progressed, the estimate was revised downward several times, and currently, the most reliable count

Table 18.1 Genome Sizes and Estimated Numbers of Genes*

Organism	Haploid Genome Size (Mb)	Number of Genes	Genes per Mb
Bacteria			
Haemophilus influenzae	1.8	1,700	940
Escherichia coli	4.6	4,400	950
Archaea			
Archaeoglobus fulgidus	2.2	2,500	1,130
Methanosarcina barkeri	4.8	3,600	750
Eukaryotes			
Saccharomyces cerevisiae (yeast, a fungus)	12	6,300	525
Caenorhabditis elegans (nematode)	100	22,000	200
Arabidopsis thaliana (mustard family plant)	120	27,400	228
Drosophila melanogaster (fruit fly)	165	17,000	84
Oryza sativa (rice)	430	40,600	95
Zea mays (corn)	2,300	32,000	14
Mus musculus (house mouse)	2,600	22,000	11
Ailuropoda melanoleuca (giant panda)	2,400	21,000	9
Homo sapiens (human)	3,000	<21,000	7
Fritillaria assyriaca (lily family plant)	124,000	ND	ND

*Some values given here are likely to be revised as genome analysis continues. Mb = million base pairs. ND = not determined.

has placed the number at fewer than 21,000. This relatively low number, similar to the number of genes in the nematode *C. elegans*, has surprised biologists, who had clearly expected many more human genes.

What genetic attributes allow humans (and other vertebrates) to get by with no more genes than nematodes? An important factor is that vertebrate genomes "get more bang for the buck" from their coding sequences because of extensive alternative splicing of RNA transcripts. Recall that this process generates more than one functional protein from a single gene (see Figure 15.12). A typical human gene contains about ten exons, and an estimated 90% or more of these multi-exon genes are spliced in at least two different ways. Some genes are expressed in hundreds of alternatively spliced forms, others in just two. It is not yet possible to catalog all of the different forms, but it is clear that the number of different proteins encoded in the human genome far exceeds the proposed number of genes.

Additional polypeptide diversity could result from post-translational modifications such as cleavage or the addition of carbohydrate groups in different cell types or at different developmental stages. Finally, the discovery of miRNAs and other small RNAs that play regulatory roles have added a new variable to the mix (see Concept 15.3). Some scientists think that this added level of regulation, when present, may contribute to greater organismal complexity for a given number of genes.

Gene Density and Noncoding DNA

In addition to genome size and number of genes, we can compare gene density in different species—in other words, how many genes there are in a given length of DNA. When we compare the genomes of bacteria, archaea, and eukaryotes, we see that eukaryotes generally have larger genomes but fewer genes in a given number of base pairs. Humans have hundreds or thousands of times as many base pairs in their genome as most bacteria, as we already noted, but only 5 to 15 times as many genes; thus, gene density is lower in humans (see Table 18.1). Even unicellular eukaryotes, such as yeasts, have fewer genes per million base pairs than bacteria and archaea. Among the genomes that have been sequenced completely thus far, humans and other mammals have the lowest gene density.

In all bacterial genomes studied so far, most of the DNA consists of genes for protein, tRNA, or rRNA; the small amount remaining consists mainly of nontranscribed regulatory sequences, such as promoters. The sequence of nucleotides along a bacterial protein-coding gene proceeds from start to finish without interruption by noncoding sequences (introns). In eukaryotic genomes, by contrast, most of the DNA neither encodes protein nor is transcribed into RNA molecules of known function, and the DNA includes more complex regulatory sequences. In fact, humans have 10,000 times as much noncoding DNA as bacteria. Some of this DNA in multicellular eukaryotes is present as introns within genes. Indeed, introns account for most of the difference in average length between human genes (27,000 base pairs) and bacterial genes (1,000 base pairs).

In addition to introns, multicellular eukaryotes have a vast amount of non-protein-coding DNA between genes. In the next section, we'll explore the composition and arrangement of these great stretches of DNA in the human genome.

CONCEPT CHECK 18.3

1. According to the best current estimate, the human genome contains fewer than 21,000 genes. However, there is evidence that human cells produce many more than 21,000 different polypeptides. What processes might account for this discrepancy?

2. The number of sequenced genomes is constantly being updated. Go to www.genomesonline.org to find the current number of completed genomes for each domain as well as the number of genomes whose sequencing is in progress. (*Hint*: Click on "Complete Projects" for extra information.)

3. **WHAT IF?** What evolutionary processes might account for prokaryotes having smaller genomes than eukaryotes?

For suggested answers, see Appendix A.

Multicellular eukaryotes have much noncoding DNA and many multigene families

We have spent most of this chapter, and indeed this unit, focusing on genes that code for proteins. Yet the coding regions of these genes and the genes for RNA products such as rRNA, tRNA, and miRNA make up only a small portion of the genomes of most multicellular eukaryotes. For example, once the sequencing of the human genome was completed, it became clear that only a tiny part—1.5%—codes for proteins or is transcribed into rRNAs or tRNAs. **Figure 18.5** shows what is known about the makeup of the remaining 98.5% of the genome.

Gene-related regulatory sequences and introns account, respectively, for 5% and about 20% of the human genome. The rest, located between functional genes, includes some unique noncoding DNA, such as gene fragments and **pseudogenes**, former genes that have accumulated mutations over a long time

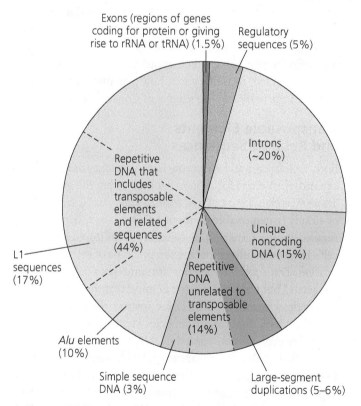

▲ **Figure 18.5 Types of DNA sequences in the human genome.** The gene sequences that code for proteins or are transcribed into rRNA or tRNA molecules make up only about 1.5% of the human genome (dark purple in the pie chart), while introns and regulatory sequences associated with genes (lighter purple) make up about a quarter. The vast majority of the human genome does not code for proteins or give rise to known RNAs, and much of it is repetitive DNA (dark and light green and teal). Because repetitive DNA is the most difficult to sequence and analyze, classification of some portions is tentative, and the percentages given here may shift slightly as genome analysis proceeds.

and no longer produce functional proteins. (The genes that produce small noncoding RNAs are a tiny percentage of the genome, distributed between the 20% introns and the 15% unique noncoding DNA.) Most intergenic DNA, however, is **repetitive DNA**, which consists of sequences that are present in multiple copies in the genome. Somewhat surprisingly, about 75% of this repetitive DNA (44% of the entire human genome) is made up of units called transposable elements and sequences related to them.

The bulk of many eukaryotic genomes likewise consists of DNA sequences that neither code for proteins nor are transcribed to produce RNAs with known functions; this noncoding DNA was often described in the past as "junk DNA." However, much evidence is accumulating that this DNA plays important roles in the cell. One measure of its importance is the high degree of sequence conservation between species that diverged many hundreds of generations ago. For example, comparison of the genomes of humans, rats, and mice has revealed the presence of almost 500 regions of noncoding DNA that are *identical* in sequence in all three species. This is a higher level of sequence conservation than is seen for protein-coding regions in these species, strongly suggesting that the noncoding regions have important functions. In this section, we'll examine how genes and noncoding DNA sequences are currently organized within genomes of multicellular eukaryotes, using the human genome as our main example. Genome organization tells us much about how genomes have evolved and continue to evolve, the subject of Concept 18.5.

Transposable Elements and Related Sequences

Both prokaryotes and eukaryotes have stretches of DNA that can move from one location to another within the genome. These stretches are known as *transposable genetic elements*, or simply **transposable elements**. During the process called *transposition*, a transposable element moves from one site in a cell's DNA to a different target site by a type of recombination process. Transposable elements are sometimes called "jumping genes," but it should be kept in mind that they never completely detach from the cell's DNA. Instead, the original and new DNA sites are brought very close together by enzymes and other proteins that bend the DNA.

The first evidence for wandering DNA segments came from American geneticist Barbara McClintock's breeding experiments with Indian corn (maize) in the 1940s and 1950s **(Figure 18.6)**. As she tracked corn plants through multiple generations, McClintock identified changes in the color of corn kernels that made sense only if she postulated the existence of genetic elements capable of moving from other locations in the genome into the genes for kernel color, disrupting the genes so that the kernel color was changed. McClintock's discovery was met with great skepticism and virtually discounted at the time. Her careful work and insightful ideas

▲ **Figure 18.6 The effect of transposable elements on corn kernel color.** Barbara McClintock first proposed the idea of mobile genetic elements after observing variegations in corn kernel color (right). She received the Nobel Prize in 1983.

were finally validated many years later when transposable elements were found in bacteria. In 1983, at the age of 81, McClintock received the Nobel Prize for her pioneering research.

Movement of Transposons and Retrotransposons

Eukaryotic transposable elements are of two types. The first type, **transposons**, can move within a genome by means of a DNA intermediate. Transposons can move by a "cut-and-paste" mechanism, which removes the element from the original site, or by a "copy-and-paste" mechanism, which leaves a copy behind **(Figure 18.7)**. Both mechanisms require an enzyme called *transposase*, which is generally encoded by the transposon.

Most transposable elements in eukaryotic genomes are of the second type, **retrotransposons**, which move by means of an RNA intermediate that is a transcript of the retrotransposon DNA. Retrotransposons always leave a copy at the original site during transposition, since they are initially transcribed

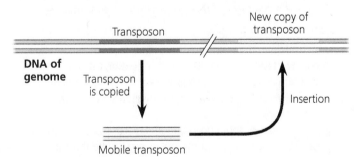

© 1996 Pearson Education, Inc.

▲ **Figure 18.7 Transposon movement.** Movement of transposons by either the copy-and-paste mechanism (shown here) or the cut-and-paste mechanism involves a double-stranded DNA intermediate that is inserted into the genome.

? *How would this figure differ if it showed the cut-and-paste mechanism?*

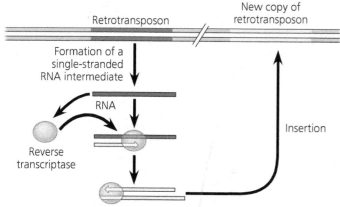

Retrotransposon

New copy of retrotransposon

Formation of a single-stranded RNA intermediate

RNA

Reverse transcriptase

Insertion

© 1996 Pearson Education, Inc.

▲ **Figure 18.8 Retrotransposon movement.** Movement begins with formation of a single-stranded RNA intermediate. The remaining steps are essentially identical to part of the retrovirus replicative cycle (see Figure 17.7).

into an RNA intermediate **(Figure 18.8)**. To insert at another site, the RNA intermediate is first converted back to DNA by reverse transcriptase, an enzyme encoded by the retrotransposon. (Reverse transcriptase is also encoded by retroviruses, as you learned in Chapter 17. In fact, retroviruses may have evolved from retrotransposons.) Another cellular enzyme catalyzes insertion of the reverse-transcribed DNA at a new site.

Sequences Related to Transposable Elements

Multiple copies of transposable elements and sequences related to them are scattered throughout eukaryotic genomes. A single unit is usually hundreds to thousands of base pairs long, and the dispersed "copies" are similar but usually not identical to each other. Some of these are transposable elements that can move; the enzymes required for this movement may be encoded by any transposable element, including the one that is moving. Others are related sequences that have lost the ability to move altogether. Transposable elements and related sequences make up 25–50% of most mammalian genomes (see Figure 18.5) and even higher percentages in amphibians and many plants. In fact, the very large size of some plant genomes is accounted for not by extra genes, but by extra transposable elements. For example, such sequences make up 85% of the corn genome!

In humans and other primates, a large portion of transposable element–related DNA consists of a family of similar sequences called *Alu elements*. These sequences alone account for approximately 10% of the human genome. *Alu* elements are about 300 nucleotides long, much shorter than most functional transposable elements, and they do not code for any protein. However, many *Alu* elements are transcribed into RNA; its cellular function, if any, is currently unknown.

An even larger percentage (17%) of the human genome is made up of a type of retrotransposon called *LINE-1*, or *L1*. These sequences are much longer than *Alu* elements—about 6,500 base pairs—and have a low rate of transposition. An

accompanying genomic analysis found L1 sequences within the introns of nearly 80% of the human genes that were analyzed, suggesting that L1 may help regulate gene expression. Other researchers have proposed that L1 retrotransposons may have differential effects on gene expression in developing neurons, contributing to the great diversity of neuronal cell types (see Chapter 37).

Although many transposable elements encode proteins, these proteins do not carry out normal cellular functions. Therefore, transposable elements are usually included in the "noncoding" DNA category, along with other repetitive sequences.

Other Repetitive DNA, Including Simple Sequence DNA

Repetitive DNA that is not related to transposable elements probably arises due to mistakes during DNA replication or recombination. Such DNA accounts for about 14% of the human genome (see Figure 18.5). About a third of this (5–6% of the human genome) consists of duplications of long stretches of DNA, with each unit ranging from 10,000 to 300,000 base pairs. The large segments seem to have been copied from one chromosomal location to another site on the same or a different chromosome and probably include some functional genes.

In contrast to scattered copies of long sequences, **simple sequence DNA** contains many copies of tandemly repeated short sequences, as in the following example (showing one DNA strand only):

...GTTACGTTACGTTACGTTACGTTACGTTAC...

In this case, the repeated unit (GTTAC) consists of 5 nucleotides. Repeated units may contain as many as 500 nucleotides, but often contain fewer than 15 nucleotides, as in this example. When the unit contains 2–5 nucleotides, the series of repeats is called a **short tandem repeat (STR)**. The number of copies of the repeated unit can vary from site to site within a given genome. There could be as many as several hundred thousand repetitions of the GTTAC unit at one site, but only half that number at another.

The repeat number also varies from person to person, and since humans are diploid, each person has two alleles per site, which can differ. This diversity produces variation that can be used to identify a unique set of genetic markers for each individual, his or her **genetic profile**. Forensic scientists can use STR analysis on DNA extracted from samples of tissues or body fluids to identify victims of a crime scene or natural disaster. In such an application, STR analysis is performed on STR sites selected because they have relatively few repeats and are easily sequenced. This technique has also been used by The Innocence Project, a nonprofit organization, to free more than 250 wrongly convicted people from prison.

Altogether, simple sequence DNA makes up 3% of the human genome. Much of a genome's simple sequence DNA is located at chromosomal telomeres and centromeres, suggesting that this DNA plays a structural role for chromosomes. The DNA at centromeres is essential for the separation of chromatids in cell division (see Chapter 9). Centromeric DNA, along with simple sequence DNA located elsewhere, may also help organize the chromatin within the interphase nucleus. The simple sequence DNA located at telomeres, at the tips of chromosomes, binds proteins that protect the ends of a chromosome from degradation and from joining to other chromosomes.

Genes and Multigene Families

We finish our discussion of the various types of DNA sequences in eukaryotic genomes with a closer look at genes. Recall that DNA sequences that code for proteins or give rise to tRNA or rRNA compose a mere 1.5% of the human genome (see Figure 18.5). If we include introns and regulatory sequences associated with genes, the total amount of DNA that is gene related—coding and noncoding—constitutes about 25% of the human genome. Put another way, only about 6% (1.5% out of 25%) of the length of the average gene is represented in the final gene product.

Like the genes of bacteria, many eukaryotic genes are present as unique sequences, with only one copy per haploid set of chromosomes. But in the human genome and the genomes of many other animals and plants, solitary genes make up less than half of the total gene-related DNA. The rest occur in **multigene families**, collections of two or more identical or very similar genes.

In multigene families consisting of *identical* DNA sequences, those sequences are usually clustered tandemly and, with the notable exception of the genes for histone proteins, have RNAs as their final products. An example is the family of identical DNA sequences that are the genes for the three largest rRNA molecules (Figure 18.9a). These rRNA molecules are transcribed from a single transcription unit that is repeated tandemly hundreds to thousands of times in one or several clusters in the genome of a multicellular eukaryote. The many copies of this rRNA transcription unit help cells to quickly make the millions of ribosomes needed for active protein synthesis. The primary transcript is cleaved to yield the three rRNA molecules, which combine with proteins and one other kind of rRNA (5S rRNA) to form ribosomal subunits.

The classic examples of multigene families of *nonidentical* genes are two related families of genes that encode globins, a group of proteins that include the α and β polypeptide subunits of hemoglobin. One family, located on chromosome 16 in humans, encodes various forms of α-globin; the other, on chromosome 11, encodes forms of β-globin (Figure 18.9b). The different forms of each globin subunit are expressed at different times in development, allowing hemoglobin to function effectively in the changing environment of the developing animal. In humans, for example, the embryonic and fetal forms

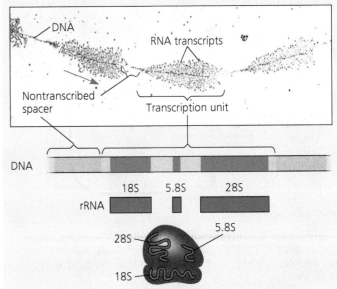

(a) Part of the ribosomal RNA gene family. The TEM at the top shows three of the hundreds of copies of rRNA transcription units in a salamander genome. Each "feather" corresponds to a single unit being transcribed by about 100 molecules of RNA polymerase (dark dots along the DNA), moving left to right (red arrow). The growing RNA transcripts extend from the DNA. In the diagram of a transcription unit below the TEM, the genes for three types of rRNA (blue) are adjacent to regions that are transcribed but later removed (yellow). A single transcript is processed to yield one of each of the three rRNAs (red), key components of the ribosome.

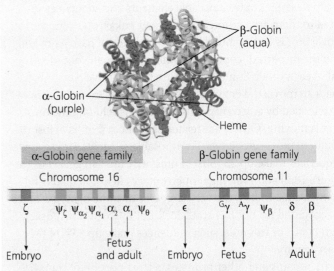

(b) The human α-globin and β-globin gene families. Adult hemoglobin is composed of two α-globin and two β-globin polypeptide subunits, as shown in the molecular model. The genes (dark blue) encoding α- and β-globins are found in two families, organized as shown here. The noncoding DNA separating the functional genes within each family includes pseudogenes (ψ; green), versions of the original genes that no longer produce functional proteins. Genes and pseudogenes are named with Greek letters. Some genes are expressed only in the embryo or fetus.

▲ Figure 18.9 **Gene families.**

? In (a), how could you determine the direction of transcription if it weren't indicated by the red arrow?

of hemoglobin have a higher affinity for oxygen than the adult forms, ensuring the efficient transfer of oxygen from mother to fetus. Also found in the globin gene family clusters are several pseudogenes (green in Figure 18.9b).

We'll return to the globin gene family to consider the evolutionary history of these gene clusters in the next section. We'll also consider some of the processes that have shaped the genomes of different species over evolutionary time.

CONCEPT CHECK 18.4

1. Discuss the characteristics of mammalian genomes that make them larger than prokaryotic genomes.
2. Which of the three mechanisms described in Figures 18.7 and 18.8 result(s) in a copy remaining at the original site as well as appearing in a new location?
3. Contrast the organizations of the rRNA gene family and the globin gene families. For each, explain how the existence of a family of genes benefits the organism.

   For suggested answers, see Appendix A.

CONCEPT 18.5

Duplication, rearrangement, and mutation of DNA contribute to genome evolution

EVOLUTION The basis of change at the genomic level is mutation, which underlies much of genome evolution. It seems likely that the earliest forms of life had a minimal number of genes—those necessary for survival and reproduction. If this were indeed the case, one aspect of evolution must have been an increase in the size of the genome, with the extra genetic material providing the raw material for gene diversification. In this section, we'll first describe how extra copies of all or part of a genome can arise and then consider subsequent processes that can lead to the evolution of proteins (or RNA products) with slightly different or entirely new functions.

Duplication of Entire Chromosome Sets

An accident in meiosis can result in one or more extra sets of chromosomes, a condition known as polyploidy. Although such accidents would most often be lethal, in rare cases they could facilitate the evolution of genes. In a polyploid organism, one set of genes can provide essential functions for the organism. The genes in the one or more extra sets can diverge by accumulating mutations; these variations may persist if the organism carrying them survives and reproduces. In this way, genes with novel functions can evolve. As long as one copy of an essential gene is expressed, the divergence of another copy can lead to its encoded protein acting in a novel way, thereby changing the organism's phenotype. The outcome of this accumulation of mutations may be the branching off of a new species, as happens often in flowering plants (see Chapter 22).

Polyploid animals also exist, but they are much rarer; the tetraploid model organism *Xenopus laevis*, the African clawed frog, is an example.

Alterations of Chromosome Structure

Scientists have long known that sometime in the last 6 million years, when the ancestors of humans and chimpanzees diverged as species, the fusion of two ancestral chromosomes in the human line led to different haploid numbers for humans ($n = 23$) and chimpanzees ($n = 24$). The banding patterns in stained chromosomes suggested that the ancestral versions of current chimp chromosomes 12 and 13 fused end to end, forming chromosome 2 in an ancestor of the human lineage. With the recent explosion in genomic sequence information, we can now compare the chromosomal organizations of many different species on a much finer scale. This information allows us to make inferences about the evolutionary processes that shape chromosomes and may drive speciation. Sequencing and analysis of human chromosome 2 provided very strong supporting evidence for the model we have just described **(Figure 18.10)**.

In another study of broader scope, researchers compared the DNA sequence of each human chromosome with the whole-genome sequence of the mouse. For human chromosome 16, the comparison revealed that large blocks of genes on this chromosome are found on four mouse chromosomes. This

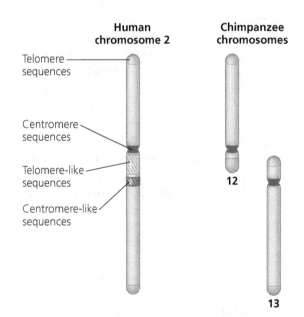

▲ **Figure 18.10 Related human and chimpanzee chromosomes.** The positions of telomere-like and centromere-like sequences on human chromosome 2 (left) match those of telomeres on chimp chromosome 13 (right). This suggests that chromosomes 12 and 13 in a human ancestor fused end-to-end to form human chromosome 2. The centromere from ancestral chromosome 12 remained functional on human chromosome 2, while the one from ancestral chromosome 13 did not. (Chimp chromosomes 12 and 13 have since been renamed 2a and 2b, respectively.)

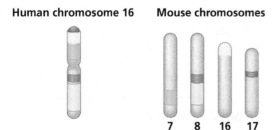

Human chromosome 16   **Mouse chromosomes**

7   8   16   17

▲ **Figure 18.11 A comparison of human and mouse chromosomes.** DNA sequences very similar to large blocks of human chromosome 16 (colored areas in this diagram) are found on mouse chromosomes 7, 8, 16, and 17. This suggests that the DNA sequence in each block has stayed together in the mouse and human lineages since the time they diverged from a common ancestor.

observation suggests that the genes in each block stayed together during the evolution of the mouse and human lineages (**Figure 18.11**). *transposable elements can provide sites for crossover between nonsister chromatids.*

Performing the same comparative analysis between chromosomes of humans and six other mammalian species allowed the researchers to reconstruct the evolutionary history of chromosomal rearrangements in these eight species. They found many duplications and inversions of large portions of chromosomes, the result of mistakes during meiotic recombination in which the DNA broke and was rejoined incorrectly. The rate of these events seems to have accelerated about 100 million years ago, around the time large dinosaurs became extinct and the number of mammalian species increased rapidly. The apparent coincidence is interesting because chromosomal rearrangements are thought to contribute to the generation of new species. Although two individuals with different arrangements could still mate and produce offspring, the offspring would have two nonequivalent sets of chromosomes, making meiosis inefficient or even impossible. Thus, chromosomal rearrangements would reduce the success of matings between members of the two populations, a step on the way to the populations becoming two separate species. (You'll learn more about this in Chapter 22.)

Duplication and Divergence of Gene-Sized Regions of DNA

Errors during meiosis can also lead to the duplication of chromosomal regions that are smaller than the ones we've just discussed, including segments the length of individual genes. Unequal crossing over during prophase I of meiosis, for instance, can result in one chromosome with a deletion and another with a duplication of a particular gene. As illustrated in **Figure 18.12**, transposable elements can provide homologous sites where nonsister chromatids can cross over, even when other chromatid regions are not correctly aligned.

Also, slippage can occur during DNA replication, such that the template shifts with respect to the new complementary strand, and a part of the template strand is either skipped by the replication machinery or used twice as a template. As a result,

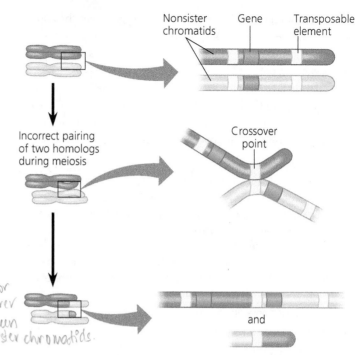

▲ **Figure 18.12 Gene duplication due to unequal crossing over.** One mechanism by which a gene (or other DNA segment) can be duplicated is recombination during meiosis between copies of a transposable element flanking the gene. Such recombination between misaligned nonsister chromatids of homologous chromosomes produces one chromatid with two copies of the gene and one chromatid with no copy.

MAKE CONNECTIONS *Recall how crossing over occurs (see Figure 10.11). In the middle panel above, draw a line along the portions that result in the upper chromatid in the bottom panel. Use a different color to do the same for the other chromatid.*

a segment of DNA is deleted or duplicated. It is easy to imagine how such errors could occur in regions of repeats. The variable number of repeated units of simple sequence DNA at a given site, used for STR analysis, is probably due to errors like these. Evidence that unequal crossing over and template slippage during DNA replication lead to duplication of genes is found in the existence of multigene families, such as the globin family.

Evolution of Genes with Related Functions: The Human Globin Genes

Duplication events can lead to the evolution of genes with related functions, such as those of the α-globin and β-globin gene families (see Figure 18.9b). A comparison of gene sequences within a multigene family can suggest the order in which the genes arose. This approach to re-creating the evolutionary history of the globin genes indicates that they all evolved from one common ancestral globin gene that underwent duplication and divergence into the α-globin and β-globin ancestral genes about 450–500 million years ago (**Figure 18.13**). Each of these genes was later duplicated several times, and the copies then diverged from each other in sequence, yielding the current family members. In fact, the common ancestral globin gene also gave rise to the oxygen-binding muscle protein myoglobin and to the plant protein

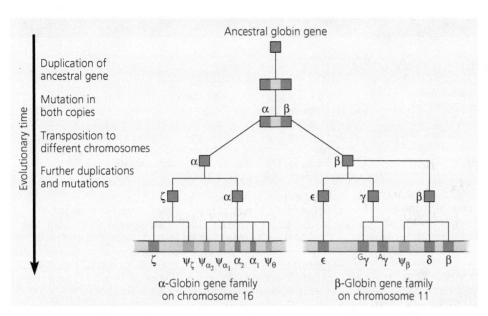

Evolutionary time →

Duplication of
ancestral gene

Mutation in
both copies

Transposition to
different chromosomes

Further duplications
and mutations

Ancestral globin gene

α β

α β

ζ α ϵ γ β

ζ ψ_ζ ψ_{α_2} ψ_{α_1} α_2 α_1 ψ_θ ϵ $^G\gamma$ $^A\gamma$ ψ_β δ β

α-Globin gene family
on chromosome 16

β-Globin gene family
on chromosome 11

▲ Figure 18.13 **A model for the evolution of the human α-globin and β-globin gene families from a single ancestral globin gene.**

? *The green elements are pseudogenes. Explain how they could have arisen after gene duplication.*

leghemoglobin. The latter two proteins function as monomers, and their genes are included in a "globin superfamily."

After the duplication events, the differences between the genes in the globin families undoubtedly arose from mutations that accumulated in the gene copies over many generations. The current model is that the necessary function provided by an α-globin protein, for example, was fulfilled by one gene, while other copies of the α-globin gene accumulated random mutations. Many mutations may have had an adverse effect on the organism and others may have had no effect, but a few mutations must have altered the function of the protein product in a way that was advantageous to the organism at a particular life stage without substantially changing the protein's oxygen-carrying function. Presumably, natural selection acted on these altered genes, maintaining them in the population.

In the **Scientific Skills Exercise**, you can compare amino acid sequences of the globin family members and see how such comparisons were used to generate the model for globin gene evolution shown in Figure 18.13. The existence of several pseudogenes among the functional globin genes provides additional evidence for this model (see Figure 18.9b): Random mutations in these "genes" over evolutionary time have destroyed their function.

Evolution of Genes with Novel Functions

In the evolution of the globin gene families, gene duplication and subsequent divergence produced family members whose protein products performed similar functions (oxygen transport). Alternatively, one copy of a duplicated gene can undergo alterations that lead to a completely new function for the protein product. The genes for lysozyme and α-lactalbumin are good examples.

Lysozyme is an enzyme that helps protect animals against bacterial infection by hydrolyzing bacterial cell walls; α-lactalbumin is a nonenzymatic protein that plays a role in milk production in mammals. The two proteins are quite similar in their amino acid sequences and three-dimensional structures. Both genes are found in mammals, whereas only the lysozyme gene is present in birds. These findings suggest that at some time after the lineages leading to mammals and birds had separated, the lysozyme gene was duplicated in the mammalian lineage but not in the avian lineage. Subsequently, one copy of the duplicated lysozyme gene evolved into a gene encoding α-lactalbumin, a protein with a completely different function.

Besides the duplication and divergence of whole genes, rearrangement of existing DNA sequences within genes has also contributed to genome evolution. The presence of introns may have promoted the evolution of new proteins by facilitating the duplication or shuffling of exons, as we'll discuss next.

Rearrangements of Parts of Genes: Exon Duplication and Exon Shuffling

Proteins often have a modular architecture consisting of discrete structural and functional regions called **domains**. One domain of an enzyme, for example, might include the active site, while another might allow the enzyme to bind to a cellular membrane. In quite a few cases, different exons code for the different domains of a protein.

We've already seen that unequal crossing over during meiosis can lead to duplication of a gene on one chromosome and its loss from the homologous chromosome (see Figure 18.12). By a similar process, a particular exon within a gene could be duplicated on one chromosome and deleted from the other. The gene with the duplicated exon would code for a protein containing a second copy of the encoded domain. This change in the protein's structure could augment its function by increasing its stability, enhancing its ability to bind a particular ligand, or altering some other property. Quite a few protein-coding genes have multiple copies of related exons, which presumably arose by duplication and then diverged. The gene encoding the extracellular matrix protein collagen is a good example. Collagen is a structural protein with a highly repetitive amino acid sequence, which is reflected in the repetitive pattern of exons in the collagen gene.

Alternatively, we can imagine the occasional mixing and matching of different exons either within a gene or between two different (nonallelic) genes owing to errors in meiotic recombination. This process, termed *exon shuffling*, could lead

Reading an Amino Acid Sequence Identity Table

How Have Amino Acid Sequences of Human Globin Genes Diverged During Their Evolution? To build a model of the evolutionary history of the globin genes (see Figure 18.13), researchers compared the amino acid sequences of the polypeptides they encode. In this exercise, you will analyze comparisons of the amino acid sequences of globin polypeptides to shed light on their evolutionary relationships.

How the Experiment Was Done Scientists obtained the DNA sequences for each of the eight globin genes and "translated" them into amino acid sequences. They then used a computer program to align the sequences and calculate a percent identity value for each pair. The percent identity reflects the number of positions with identical amino acids relative to the total number of amino acids in a globin polypeptide. The data were arranged in a table to show the pairwise comparisons.

Data from the Experiment The following table shows an example of a pairwise alignment—that of the α_1-globin (alpha-1 globin) and ζ-globin (zeta globin) amino acid sequences—using the standard single-letter codes for amino acids. To the left of each line of amino acid sequence is the number of the first amino acid in that line.

Globin	Alignment of Globin Amino Acid Sequences
α_1	1 MVLSPADKTNVKAAWGKVGAHAGEYGAEAL
ζ	1 MSLTKTERTIIVSMWAKISTQADTIGTETL
α_1	31 ERMFLSFPTTKTYFPHFDLSH-GSAQVKGH
ζ	31 ERLFLSHPQTKTYFPHFDL-HPGSAQLRAH
α_1	61 GKKVADALTNAVAHVDDMPNALSALSDLHA
ζ	61 GSKVVAAVGDAVKSIDDIGGALSKLSELHA
α_1	91 HKLRVDPVNFKLLSHCLLVTLAAHLPAEFT
ζ	91 YILRVDPVNFKLLSHCLLVTLAARFPADFT
α_1	121 PAVHASLDKFLASVSTVLTSKYR
ζ	121 AEAHAAWDKFLSVVSSVLTEKYR

The percent identity value for the α_1- and ζ-globin amino acid sequences was calculated by counting the number of matching amino acids (87), dividing by the total number of amino acid positions (143), and then multiplying by 100. This resulted in a 61% identity value for the α_1-ζ pair, as shown in the amino acid identity table at the bottom of the page. The values for other globin pairs were calculated in the same way.

Interpret the Data

1. Notice that in the table, the data are arranged so each globin pair can be compared. (a) Notice that some cells in the table have dashes. Given the pairs that are being compared for these cells, what percent identity value is implied by the dashes? (b) Notice that the cells in the lower left half of the table are blank. Using the information already provided in the table, fill in the missing values. Why does it make sense that these cells were left blank?

2. The earlier that two genes arose from a duplicated gene, the more divergent their bases can become, which may result in amino acid differences in the protein products. (a) Based on that premise, identify which two genes are most divergent from each other. What is the percent identity between them? (b) Using the same approach, identify which two globin genes are the most recently duplicated. What is the percent identity between them?

3. The model of globin gene evolution shown in Figure 18.13 suggests that an ancestral gene duplicated into α- and β-globin genes and then each one was further duplicated and modified by mutation. What features of the data set support the model?

4. Make a list of all the percent identity values from the table, starting with 100% at the top. Next to each number write the globin pair(s) with that percent identity value. Use one color for the globins from the α family and a different color for the globins from the β family. (a) Compare the order of pairs on your list with their position in the model shown in Figure 18.13. Does the order of pairs describe the same relative "closeness" of globin family members seen in the model? (b) Compare the percent identity values for pairs within the α or β group to the values for between-group pairs.

Further Reading R. C. Hardison, Globin genes on the move, *Journal of Biology* 7:35.1–35.5 (2008). doi:10.1186/jbiol92

(MB) A version of this Scientific Skills Exercise can be assigned in MasteringBiology.

Amino Acid Identity Table								
		α Family			β Family			
		α_1 (alpha 1)	α_2 (alpha 2)	ζ (zeta)	β (beta)	δ (delta)	ε (epsilon)	$^A\gamma$ (gamma A)	$^G\gamma$ (gamma G)
α Family	α_1	------	100	61	45	44	39	42	42
	α_2		------	61	45	44	39	42	42
	ζ			------	38	40	41	41	41
β Family	β				------	93	76	73	73
	δ					------	73	71	72
	ε						------	80	80
	$^A\gamma$							------	99
	$^G\gamma$								------

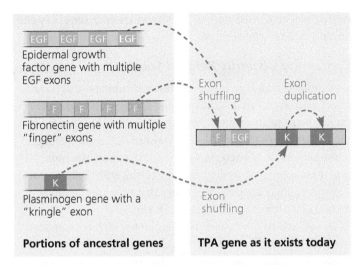

Epidermal growth factor gene with multiple EGF exons

Fibronectin gene with multiple "finger" exons

Plasminogen gene with a "kringle" exon

Exon shuffling

Exon duplication

Exon shuffling

Portions of ancestral genes

TPA gene as it exists today

▲ **Figure 18.14 Evolution of a new gene by exon shuffling.** Exon shuffling could have moved exons, each encoding a particular domain, from ancestral forms of the genes for epidermal growth factor, fibronectin, and plasminogen (left) into the evolving gene for tissue plasminogen activator, TPA (right). Duplication of the "kringle" exon from the plasminogen gene after its movement could account for the two copies of this exon in the TPA gene.

? *How could the presence of transposable elements in introns have facilitated the exon shuffling shown here?*

to new proteins with novel combinations of functions. As an example, let's consider the gene for tissue plasminogen activator (TPA). The TPA protein is an extracellular protein that helps control blood clotting. It has four domains of three types, each encoded by an exon; one exon is present in two copies. Because each type of exon is also found in other proteins, the gene for TPA is thought to have arisen by several instances of exon shuffling and duplication **(Figure 18.14)**.

How Transposable Elements Contribute to Genome Evolution

The persistence of transposable elements as a large fraction of some eukaryotic genomes is consistent with the idea that they play an important role in shaping a genome over evolutionary time. These elements can contribute to the evolution of the genome in several ways. They can promote recombination, disrupt cellular genes or control elements, and carry entire genes or individual exons to new locations.

Transposable elements of similar sequence scattered throughout the genome facilitate recombination between different chromosomes by providing homologous regions for crossing over. Most such recombination events are probably detrimental, causing chromosomal translocations and other changes in the genome that may be lethal to the organism. But over the course of evolutionary time, an occasional recombination event of this sort may be advantageous to the organism. (For the change to be heritable, of course, it must happen in a cell that will give rise to a gamete.)

The movement of a transposable element can have a variety of consequences. For instance, if a transposable element "jumps" into the middle of a protein-coding sequence, it will

prevent the production of a normal transcript of the gene. If a transposable element inserts within a regulatory sequence, the transposition may lead to increased or decreased production of one or more proteins. Transposition caused both types of effects on the genes coding for pigment-synthesizing enzymes in McClintock's corn kernels. Again, while such changes are usually harmful, in the long run some may prove beneficial by providing a survival advantage.

During transposition, a transposable element may carry along a gene or group of genes to a new position in the genome. This mechanism probably accounts for the location of the α-globin and β-globin gene families on different human chromosomes, as well as the dispersion of the genes of certain other gene families. By a similar tag-along process, an exon from one gene may be inserted into another gene in a mechanism similar to that of exon shuffling during recombination. For example, an exon may be inserted by transposition into the intron of a protein-coding gene. If the inserted exon is retained in the RNA transcript during RNA splicing, the protein that is synthesized will have an additional domain, which may confer a new function on the protein.

All the processes discussed in this section most often produce either harmful effects, which may be lethal, or no effect at all. In a few cases, however, small beneficial heritable changes may occur. Over many generations, the resulting genetic diversity provides valuable raw material for natural selection. Diversification of genes and their products is an important factor in the evolution of new species. Thus, the accumulation of changes in the genome of each species provides a record of its evolutionary history. To read this record, we must be able to identify genomic changes. Comparing the genomes of different species allows us to do that and has increased our understanding of how genomes evolve. You'll learn more about these topics in the final section.

CONCEPT CHECK 18.5

1. Describe three examples of errors in cellular processes that lead to DNA duplications.
2. Explain how multiple exons might have arisen in the ancestral EGF and fibronectin genes shown in Figure 18.14 (left).
3. What are three ways that transposable elements are thought to contribute to genome evolution?

For suggested answers, see Appendix A.

CONCEPT 18.6

Comparing genome sequences provides clues to evolution and development

EVOLUTION One researcher has likened the current state of biology to the Age of Exploration in the 15th century after major improvements in navigation and the building of faster ships. In the last 25 years, we have seen rapid advances in genome sequencing and data collection, new techniques for assessing gene activity across the whole genome, and refined approaches for understanding how genes and their products work together in complex systems. We are truly poised on the brink of a new world.

Comparisons of genome sequences from different species reveal much about the evolutionary history of life, from very ancient to more recent. Similarly, comparative studies of the genetic programs that direct embryonic development in different species are beginning to clarify the mechanisms that generated the great diversity of life-forms present today. In this final section of the chapter, we'll discuss what has been learned from these two approaches.

Comparing Genomes

The more similar in sequence the genes and genomes of two species are, the more closely related those species are in their evolutionary history. Comparing genomes of closely related species sheds light on more recent evolutionary events, whereas comparing genomes of very distantly related species helps us understand ancient evolutionary history. In either case, learning about characteristics that are shared or divergent between groups enhances our picture of the evolution of life-forms and biological processes. Evolutionary relationships between species can be represented by a diagram in the form of a tree (often turned sideways), where each branch point marks the divergence of two lineages (see Chapter 1). **Figure 18.15** shows the evolutionary relationships of some groups and spe-

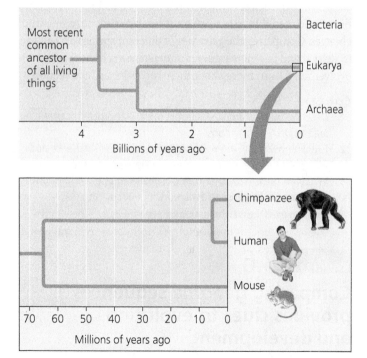

▲ **Figure 18.15 Evolutionary relationships of the three domains of life.** This tree diagram shows the ancient divergence of bacteria, archaea, and eukaryotes. A portion of the eukaryote lineage is expanded in the inset to show the more recent divergence of three mammalian species discussed in this chapter.

cies we will be discussing. We'll consider comparisons between distantly related species first.

Comparing Distantly Related Species

Determining which genes have remained similar—that is, are *highly conserved*—in distantly related species can help clarify evolutionary relationships among species that diverged from each other long ago. Indeed, comparisons of the complete genome sequences of bacteria, archaea, and eukaryotes indicate that these three groups diverged between 2 and 4 billion years ago and strongly support the theory that they are the fundamental domains of life (see Figure 18.15).

In addition to their value in evolutionary biology, comparative genomic studies confirm the relevance of research on model organisms to our understanding of biology in general and human biology in particular. Genes that evolved a very long time ago can still be surprisingly similar in disparate species. As a case in point, several genes in yeast are so similar to certain human disease genes that researchers have deduced the functions of the disease genes by studying their yeast counterparts. This striking similarity underscores the common origin of these two distantly related species.

Comparing Closely Related Species

The genomes of two closely related species are likely to be organized similarly because of their relatively recent divergence. This allows the fully sequenced genome of one species to be used as a scaffold for assembling the genomic sequences of a closely related species, accelerating mapping of the second genome. For instance, using the human genome sequence as a guide, researchers were able to quickly sequence the entire chimpanzee genome.

The recent divergence of two closely related species also underlies the small number of gene differences that are found when their genomes are compared. The particular genetic differences can therefore be more easily correlated with phenotypic differences between the two species. An exciting application of this type of analysis is seen as researchers compare the human genome with the genomes of the chimpanzee, mouse, rat, and other mammals. Identifying the genes shared by all of these species but not by nonmammals should give clues about what it takes to make a mammal, while finding the genes shared by chimpanzees and humans but not by rodents should tell us something about primates. And, of course, comparing the human genome with that of the chimpanzee should help us answer the tantalizing question we asked at the beginning of the chapter: What genomic information makes a human or a chimpanzee?

An analysis of the overall composition of the human and chimpanzee genomes, which are thought to have diverged only about 6 million years ago (see Figure 18.15), reveals some general differences. Considering single nucleotide substitutions, the two genomes differ by only 1.2%. When researchers looked at longer stretches of DNA, however, they were surprised to find a further 2.7% difference due to insertions or deletions of larger regions in the genome of one or the other species; many of the insertions were duplications or other repetitive DNA. In fact, a third of the human duplications are not present in the chimpanzee genome, and some of these duplications contain regions associated with human diseases. There are more *Alu* elements in the human genome than in the chimpanzee genome, and the latter contains many copies of a retroviral provirus not present in humans. All of these observations provide clues to the forces that might have swept the two genomes along different paths, but we don't have a complete picture yet. We also don't know how these differences might account for the distinct characteristics of each species.

To discover the basis for the phenotypic differences between the two species, biologists are studying specific genes and types of genes that differ between humans and chimpanzees and comparing them with their counterparts in other mammals. This approach has revealed a number of genes that are apparently changing (evolving) faster in the human than in either the chimpanzee or the mouse. Among them are genes involved in defense against malaria and tuberculosis and at least one gene that regulates brain size. When genes are classified by function, the genes that seem to be evolving the fastest are those that code for transcription factors. This discovery makes sense because transcription factors regulate gene expression and thus play a key role in orchestrating the overall genetic program.

One transcription factor whose gene shows evidence of rapid change in the human lineage is called *FOXP2*. Several lines of evidence suggest that the *FOXP2* gene functions in vocalization in vertebrates. For one thing, mutations in this gene can produce severe speech and language impairment in humans. Moreover, the *FOXP2* gene is expressed in the brains of zebra finches and canaries at the time when these songbirds are learning their songs. But perhaps the strongest evidence comes from a "knock-out" experiment in which researchers disrupted the *FOXP2* gene in mice and analyzed the resulting phenotype. Normal mice produce ultrasonic squeaks (whistles) to communicate stress, but mice that were homozygous for a mutated form of *FOXP2* had malformed brains and failed to vocalize normally (**Figure 18.16**). Heterozygous mice, with one faulty copy of the gene, also showed vocalization defects. These results augmented the evidence from birds and humans, supporting the idea that the *FOXP2* gene product turns on genes involved in vocalization.

The *FOXP2* story is an excellent example of how different approaches can complement each other in uncovering biological phenomena of widespread importance. The *FOXP2* experiments used mice as a model for humans because it would be unethical (as well as impractical) to carry out such experiments in humans. Mice and humans diverged about 65.5 million years ago (see Figure 18.15) and share about 85% of their genes. This genetic similarity can be exploited in studying

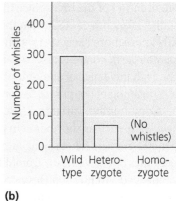

(a)   (b)

▲ **Figure 18.16 The function of *FOXP2*, a gene that is rapidly evolving in the human lineage. (a)** Wild-type mice emit ultrasonic squeaks (whistles) to communicate stress. **(b)** Researchers used genetic engineering to produce mice in which one or both copies of *FOXP2* were disrupted, separated each newborn pup from its mother, and recorded the number of ultrasonic whistles produced by the pup. No vocalization was observed in homozygous mutants, and the effect on heterozygotes was also extreme.

human genetic disorders. If researchers know the organ or tissue that is affected by a particular genetic disorder, they can look for genes that are expressed in these locations in mice.

Further research efforts are under way to extend genomic studies to many more microbial species, additional primates, and neglected species from diverse branches of the tree of life. These studies will advance our understanding of all aspects of biology, including health and ecology as well as evolution.

Comparing Genomes Within a Species

Another exciting consequence of our ability to analyze genomes is our growing understanding of the spectrum of genetic variation in humans. Because the history of the human species is so short—probably about 200,000 years—the amount of DNA variation among humans is small compared with that of many other species. Much of our diversity seems to be in the form of **single nucleotide polymorphisms** (**SNPs**, pronounced "snips"), defined as single base-pair sites where variation is found in at least 1% of the population. Usually detected by DNA sequencing, SNPs occur on average about once in 100–300 base pairs in the human genome. Scientists have already identified the location of several million human SNP sites and continue to find more.

In the course of this search, they have also found other variations—including inversions, deletions, and duplications. The most surprising discovery has been the widespread occurrence of *copy-number variants* (*CNVs*), loci where some individuals have one or multiple copies of a particular gene or genetic region, rather than the standard two copies (one on each homolog). CNVs result from regions of the genome being duplicated or deleted inconsistently within the population. One study of 40 people found more than 8,000 CNVs involving 13% of the genes in the genome, and these CNVs probably represent just a small subset of the total. Since these variants encompass much longer stretches of DNA than the single nucleotides of SNPs, CNVs are more likely to have phenotypic consequences and to play a role in complex diseases and disorders. At the very least, the high incidence of copy-number variation casts doubt on the meaning of the phrase "a normal human genome."

Copy-number variants, SNPs, and variations in repetitive DNA such as short tandem repeats (STRs) will be useful genetic markers for studying human evolution. In 2010, the genomes of two Africans from different communities were sequenced: Archbishop Desmond Tutu, the South African civil rights advocate and a member of the Bantu tribe, the majority population in southern Africa; and !Gubi, a hunter-gatherer from the Khoisan community in Namibia, a minority African population that is probably the human group with the oldest known lineage. The comparison revealed many differences, as you might expect. The analysis was then broadened to compare the protein-coding regions of !Gubi's genome with those of three other Khoisan community members (self-identified Bushmen) living nearby. Remarkably, these four Khoisan genomes differed more from each other than a European would from an Asian. These data highlight the extensive diversity among African genomes. Extending this approach will help us answer important questions about the differences between human populations and the migratory routes of human populations throughout history.

Comparing Developmental Processes

Biologists in the field of evolutionary developmental biology, or **evo-devo** as it is often called, compare developmental processes of different multicellular organisms. Their aim is to understand how these processes have evolved and how changes in them can modify existing organismal features or lead to new ones. With the advent of molecular techniques and the recent flood of genomic information, we are beginning to realize that the genomes of related species with strikingly different forms may have only minor differences in gene sequence or regulation. Discovering the molecular basis of these differences in turn helps us understand the origins of the myriad diverse forms that cohabit this planet, thus informing our study of evolution.

Widespread Conservation of Developmental Genes Among Animals

You may recall that the homeotic genes in *Drosophila* specify the identity of body segments in the fruit fly (see Figure 16.8). Molecular analysis of the homeotic genes in *Drosophila* has shown that they all include a 180-nucleotide sequence called a **homeobox**, which specifies a 60-amino-acid *homeodomain* in the encoded proteins. An identical or very similar nucleotide sequence has been discovered in the homeotic genes of many invertebrates and vertebrates. The sequences are so similar between humans and fruit flies, in fact, that one researcher has whimsically referred to flies as "little people with wings." The

resemblance even extends to the organization of these genes: The vertebrate genes homologous to the homeotic genes of fruit flies have kept the same chromosomal arrangement **(Figure 18.17)**. Homeobox-containing sequences have also been found in regulatory genes of much more distantly related eukaryotes, including plants and yeasts. From these similarities, we can deduce that the homeobox DNA sequence evolved very early in the history of life and was sufficiently beneficial to organisms to have been conserved in animals and plants virtually unchanged for hundreds of millions of years.

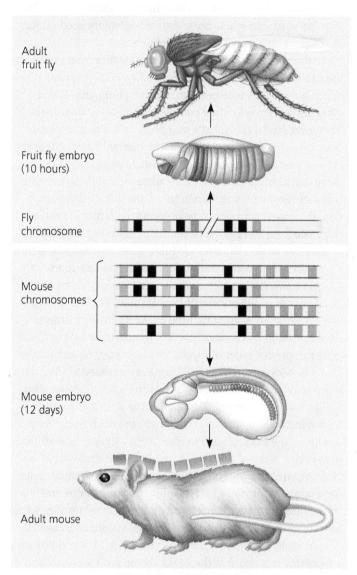

▲ **Figure 18.17 Conservation of homeotic genes in a fruit fly and a mouse.** Homeotic genes that control the form of anterior and posterior structures of the body occur in the same linear sequence on chromosomes in *Drosophila* and mice. Each colored band on the chromosomes shown here represents a homeotic gene. In fruit flies, all homeotic genes are found on one chromosome. The mouse and other mammals have the same or similar sets of genes on four chromosomes. The color code indicates the parts of the embryos in which these genes are expressed and the adult body regions that result. All of these genes are essentially identical in flies and mice, except for those represented by black bands, which are less similar in the two animals.

Homeotic genes in animals were named *Hox* genes, short for *homeobox*-containing genes, because homeotic genes were the first genes found to have this sequence. Other homeobox-containing genes were later found that do not act as homeotic genes; that is, they do not directly control the identity of body parts. However, most of these genes, in animals at least, are associated with development, suggesting their ancient and fundamental importance in that process. In *Drosophila*, for example, homeoboxes are present not only in the homeotic genes but also in the egg-polarity gene *bicoid* (see Figures 16.9 and 16.10), in several of the segmentation genes, and in a master regulatory gene for eye development.

Researchers have discovered that the homeobox-encoded homeodomain is the part of a protein that binds to DNA when the protein functions as a transcriptional regulator. However, the shape of the homeodomain allows it to bind to any DNA segment; its own structure is not specific for a particular sequence. Instead, other, more variable domains in a homeodomain-containing protein determine which genes the protein regulates. Interaction of these variable domains with still other transcription factors helps a homeodomain-containing protein recognize specific enhancers in the DNA. Proteins with homeodomains probably regulate development by coordinating the transcription of batteries of developmental genes, switching them on or off. In embryos of *Drosophila* and other animal species, different combinations of homeobox genes are active in different parts of the embryo. This selective expression of regulatory genes, varying over time and space, is central to pattern formation.

Developmental biologists have found that in addition to homeotic genes, many other genes involved in development are highly conserved from species to species. These include numerous genes encoding components of signaling pathways. The extraordinary similarity among particular developmental genes in different animal species raises a question: How can the same genes be involved in the development of animals whose forms are so very different from each other?

Ongoing studies are suggesting answers to this question. In some cases, small changes in regulatory sequences of particular genes cause changes in gene expression patterns that can lead to major changes in body form. For example, the differing patterns of expression of the *Hox* genes along the body axis in insects and crustaceans can explain the variation in the number of leg-bearing segments among these segmented animals (**Figure 18.18**). Also, recent research suggests that the same *Hox* gene product may have subtly dissimilar effects in different species, turning on new genes or turning on the same genes at higher or lower levels. In other cases, similar genes direct different developmental processes in different organisms, resulting in diverse body shapes. Several *Hox* genes, for instance, are expressed in the embryonic and larval stages of the sea urchin, a nonsegmented animal that has a body plan quite different from those of insects and mice. Sea urchin adults make the pincushion-shaped shells you may have seen on the

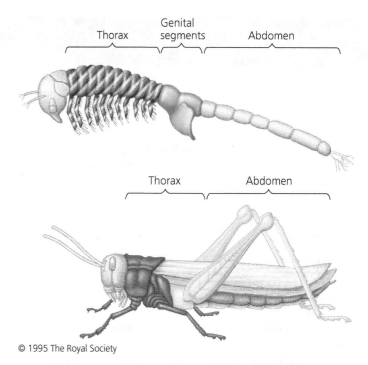

© 1995 The Royal Society

▲ **Figure 18.18 Effect of differences in *Hox* gene expression in crustaceans and insects.** Changes in the expression patterns of *Hox* genes have occurred over evolutionary time. These changes account in part for the different body plans of the brine shrimp *Artemia*, a crustacean (top), and the grasshopper, an insect. Shown here are regions of the adult body color-coded for expression of four *Hox* genes that determine formation of particular body parts during embryonic development. Each color represents a specific *Hox* gene. Colored stripes on the thorax of *Artemia* indicate co-expression of three *Hox* genes.

beach (see Figure 6.4). They are among the organisms long used in classical embryological studies (see Chapter 36).

In this final chapter of the genetics unit, you have learned how studying genomic composition and comparing the genomes of different species can disclose much about how genomes evolve. Further, comparing developmental programs, we can see that the unity of life is reflected in the similarity of molecular and cellular mechanisms used to establish body pattern, although the genes directing development may differ among organisms. The similarities between genomes reflect the common ancestry of life on Earth. But the differences are also crucial, for they have created the huge diversity of organisms that have evolved. In the remainder of the book, we expand our perspective beyond the level of molecules, cells, and genes to explore this diversity on the organismal level.

CONCEPT CHECK 18.6

1. Would you expect the genome of the macaque (a monkey) to be more similar to the mouse genome or the human genome? Why?
2. The DNA sequences called homeoboxes, which help homeotic genes in animals direct development, are common to flies and mice. Given this similarity, explain why these animals are so different.

For suggested answers, see Appendix A.

18 Chapter Review

SUMMARY OF KEY CONCEPTS

CONCEPT 18.1

The Human Genome Project fostered development of faster, less expensive sequencing techniques (pp. 344–345)

- The **Human Genome Project** was largely completed in 2003, aided by major advances in sequencing technology.
- In the **whole-genome shotgun approach**, the whole genome is cut into many small, overlapping fragments that are sequenced; computer software then assembles the complete sequence.

> **?** *How did the Human Genome Project result in more rapid, less expensive DNA sequencing?*

CONCEPT 18.2

Scientists use bioinformatics to analyze genomes and their functions (pp. 345–347)

- Computer analysis of genome sequences aids the identification of protein-coding sequences. Methods for determining gene function include comparing the sequences of newly discovered genes with those of known genes in other species, and also observing the phenotypic effects of experimentally inactivating genes whose functions are unknown.
- In **systems biology**, researchers aim to model the dynamic behavior of whole biological systems based on the study of the interactions among the system's parts. For example, scientists use the computer-based tools of **bioinformatics** to compare genomes and to study sets of genes and proteins as whole systems (**genomics** and **proteomics**). These studies include large-scale analyses of functional DNA elements.

> **?** *What was the most significant finding of the ENCODE pilot project? Why has the project been expanded to include other species?*

CONCEPT 18.3

Genomes vary in size, number of genes, and gene density (pp. 347–349)

	Bacteria	Archaea	Eukarya
Genome size	Most are 1–6 Mb		Most are 10–4,000 Mb, but a few are much larger
Number of genes	1,500–7,500		5,000–40,000
Gene density	Higher than in eukaryotes		Lower than in prokaryotes (Within eukaryotes, lower density is correlated with larger genomes.)
Introns	None in protein-coding genes	Present in some genes	Present in most genes of multicellular eukaryotes, but only in some genes of unicellular eukaryotes
Other noncoding DNA	Very little		Can be large amounts; generally more repetitive noncoding DNA in multicellular eukaryotes

> **?** *Compare genome size, gene number, and gene density (a) in the three domains and (b) among eukaryotes.*

CONCEPT 18.4

Multicellular eukaryotes have much noncoding DNA and many multigene families (pp. 349–353)

- Only 1.5% of the human genome codes for proteins or gives rise to rRNAs or tRNAs; the rest is noncoding DNA, including **pseudogenes** and **repetitive DNA** of unknown function.
- The most abundant type of repetitive DNA in multicellular eukaryotes consists of **transposable elements** and related sequences. In eukaryotes, there are two types of transposable elements: **transposons**, which move via a DNA intermediate, and **retrotransposons**, which are more prevalent and move via an RNA intermediate.
- Other repetitive DNA includes short noncoding sequences that are tandemly repeated thousands of times (**simple sequence DNA**, which includes **STRs**); these sequences are especially prominent in centromeres and telomeres, where they probably play structural roles in the chromosome.
- Though many eukaryotic genes are present in one copy per haploid chromosome set, others are members of a family of related genes, such as the human globin gene families:

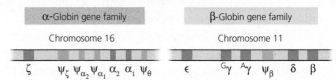

> **?** *Explain how the function of transposable elements might account for their prevalence in human noncoding DNA.*

CONCEPT 18.5

Duplication, rearrangement, and mutation of DNA contribute to genome evolution (pp. 353–357)

- Accidents in cell division can lead to extra copies of all or part of entire chromosome sets, which may then diverge if one set accumulates sequence changes.
- The chromosomal organization of genomes can be compared among species, providing information about evolutionary relationships. Within a given species, rearrangements of chromosomes are thought to contribute to the emergence of new species.
- The genes encoding the various globin proteins evolved from one common ancestral globin gene, which duplicated and diverged into α-globin and β-globin ancestral genes. Subsequent duplication and random mutation gave rise to the present globin genes, all of which code for oxygen-binding proteins. The copies of some duplicated genes have diverged so much that the functions of their encoded proteins (such as lysozyme and α-lactalbumin) are now substantially different.
- Each exon may code for a **domain**, a discrete structural and functional region of a protein. Rearrangement of exons within and between genes during evolution has led to genes containing multiple copies of similar exons and/or several different exons derived from other genes.
- Movement of transposable elements or recombination between copies of the same element can generate new sequence combinations that are beneficial to the organism, which can alter the functions of genes or their patterns of expression and regulation.

> **?** *How could chromosomal rearrangements lead to the emergence of new species?*

CONCEPT 18.6

Comparing genome sequences provides clues to evolution and development (pp. 357–361)

- Comparative studies of genomes from widely divergent and closely related species provide valuable information about ancient and more recent evolutionary history, respectively. Human and chimpanzee sequences are about 4% different. Along with nucleotide variations in specific genes, these differences may account for the distinct characteristics of the two species. Analysis of **single nucleotide polymorphisms (SNPs)** and copy-number variants (CNVs) within a species can also shed light on the evolution of that species.

- Evolutionary developmental (**evo-devo**) biologists have shown that homeotic genes and some other genes associated with animal development contain a **homeobox** region whose sequence is highly conserved among diverse species. Related sequences are present in the genes of plants and yeasts.

? *What type of information can be obtained by comparing the genomes of closely related species? Of very distantly related species?*

TEST YOUR UNDERSTANDING

Level 1: Knowledge/Comprehension

1. Bioinformatics includes all of the following except
   a. using computer programs to align DNA sequences.
   b. analyzing protein interactions in a species.
   c. using molecular biology to combine DNA from two different sources in a test tube.
   d. developing computer-based tools for genome analysis.
   e. using mathematical tools to make sense of biological systems.

2. One of the characteristics of retrotransposons is that
   a. they code for an enzyme that synthesizes DNA using an RNA template.
   b. they are found only in animal cells.
   c. they generally move by a cut-and-paste mechanism.
   d. they contribute a significant portion of the genetic variability seen within a population of gametes.
   e. their amplification is dependent on a retrovirus.

3. Homeotic genes
   a. encode transcription factors that control the expression of genes responsible for specific anatomical structures.
   b. are found only in *Drosophila* and other arthropods.
   c. are the only genes that contain the homeobox domain.
   d. encode proteins that form anatomical structures in the fly.
   e. are responsible for differentiation in muscle cells.

Level 2: Application/Analysis

4. Two eukaryotic proteins have one domain in common but are otherwise very different. Which of the following processes is most likely to have contributed to this similarity?
   a. gene duplication   d. histone modification
   b. alternative splicing   e. random point mutations
   c. exon shuffling

5. Two eukaryotic proteins are identical except for one domain in each protein, and these two domains are completely different from each other. Which of the following processes is most likely to have contributed to this difference?
   a. gene duplication   d. histone modification
   b. alternative splicing   e. random point mutations
   c. exon shuffling

6. **DRAW IT** Below are the amino acid sequences (using the single-letter code; see Figure 3.17) of four short segments of the *FOXP2* protein from six species: chimpanzee (C), orangutan (O), gorilla (G), rhesus macaque (R), mouse (M), and human (H). These segments contain all of the amino acid differences between the *FOXP2* proteins of these species.

   1. ATETI...PKSSD...TSSTT...NARRD
   2. ATETI...PKSSE...TSSTT...NARRD
   3. ATETI...PKSSD...TSSTT...NARRD
   4. ATETI...PKSSD...TSSNT...SARRD
   5. ATETI...PKSSD...TSSTT...NARRD
   6. VTETI...PKSSD...TSSTT...NARRD

   Use a highlighter to color any amino acid that varies among the species. (Color that amino acid in all sequences.)

   (a) The C, G, R sequences are identical. Which lines correspond to those sequences?

   (b) The H sequence differs from that of the C, G, R species at two amino acids. Underline the two differences in the H sequence.

   (c) The O sequence differs from the C, G, R sequences at one amino acid (having V instead of A) and from the H sequence at three amino acids. Which line is the O sequence?

   (d) In the M sequence, circle the amino acid(s) that differ from the C, G, R sequences, and draw a square around those that differ from the H sequence. Describe these differences.

   (e) Primates and rodents diverged between 60 and 100 million years ago, and chimpanzees and humans, about 6 million years ago. What can you conclude by comparing the amino acid differences between the mouse and the C, G, R species with those between the human and the C, G, R species?

Level 3: Synthesis/Evaluation

7. **SCIENTIFIC INQUIRY**
   The scientists mapping human SNPs noticed that groups of SNPs tended to be inherited together, in blocks known as haplotypes, ranging from 5,000 to 200,000 base pairs long. There are only four or five commonly occurring combinations of SNPs per haplotype. Propose an explanation, integrating what you've learned throughout this chapter and this unit.

8. **FOCUS ON EVOLUTION**
   Genes important in the embryonic development of animals, such as homeobox-containing genes, have been relatively well conserved during evolution; that is, they are more similar among different species than are many other genes. Why is this?

9. **FOCUS ON INFORMATION**
   The continuity of life is based on heritable information in the form of DNA. In a short essay (100–150 words), explain how mutations in protein-coding genes and regulatory DNA contribute to evolution.

For selected answers, see Appendix A.

MasteringBiology®

Students Go to **MasteringBiology** for assignments, the eText, and the Study Area with practice tests, animations, and activities.

Instructors Go to **MasteringBiology** for automatically graded tutorials and questions that you can assign to your students, plus Instructor Resources.

Unit 3 **Evolution**

20 Phylogeny

As organisms adapt to their environments over time, they become increasingly different from their ancestors. To reconstruct an organism's evolutionary history, or **phylogeny**, biologists use data ranging from fossils to molecules.

19 Descent with Modification

Darwin proposed that the diversity of life and the match between organisms and their environments arose through **natural selection** over time, as species adapted to their environments.

21 The Evolution of Populations

The evolutionary impact of natural selection appears in the genetic changes of a **population** of organisms over time.

22 The Origin of Species

Evolutionary changes in a population ultimately can result in **speciation**, a process in which one species gives rise to two or more species.

23 Broad Patterns of Evolution

As speciation occurs again and again, new groups of organisms arise while others disappear. These changes make up the **broad patterns of evolutionary change** documented in the fossil record.

Evolution

Descent with Modification — 19
Phylogeny — 20
The Evolution of Populations — 21
The Origin of Species — 22
Broad Patterns of Evolution — 23

Genetics
Chemistry and Cells
Ecology
Animals
Plants
History of Life

19

Descent with Modification

KEY CONCEPTS

19.1 The Darwinian revolution challenged traditional views of a young Earth inhabited by unchanging species

19.2 Descent with modification by natural selection explains the adaptations of organisms and the unity and diversity of life

19.3 Evolution is supported by an overwhelming amount of scientific evidence

OVERVIEW

Endless Forms Most Beautiful

A hungry bird would have to look very closely to spot this caterpillar of the moth *Synchlora aerata*, which blends in well with the flowers on which it feeds (**Figure 19.1**). The disguise is enhanced by the caterpillar's flair for "decorating"—it glues pieces of flower petals to its body, transforming itself into its own background.

This striking caterpillar is a member of a diverse group, the more than 120,000 species of lepidopteran insects (moths and butterflies). All lepidopteran species go through a juvenile stage characterized by a well-developed head with chewing mouthparts: the ravenous, efficient feeding machines we call caterpillars. As adults, all lepidopterans share other features, such as three pairs of legs and two pairs of wings covered with small scales. But the many lepidopteran species also differ from one another, in both their caterpillar and adult forms. How did there come to be so many different moths and butterflies, and what causes their similarities and differences?

The self-decorating caterpillar and its many close relatives illustrate three key observations about life:

- the striking ways in which organisms are suited for life in their environments*
- the many shared characteristics (unity) of life
- the rich diversity of life

A century and a half ago, Charles Darwin was inspired to develop a scientific explanation for these three broad observations. When he published his hypothesis in *The Origin of Species*, Darwin ushered in a scientific revolution—the era of evolutionary biology.

For now, we will define **evolution** as *descent with modification*, a phrase Darwin used in proposing that Earth's many species are descendants of ancestral species that were different from the present-day species. Evolution can also be defined more narrowly as a change in the genetic composition of a population from generation to generation (as discussed further in Chapter 21).

Whether it is defined broadly or narrowly, we can view evolution in two related but different ways: as a pattern and as a process. The *pattern* of evolutionary change is revealed by data from a range of scientific disciplines, including biology, geology, physics, and chemistry. These data are

▼ **Figure 19.1** How is this caterpillar protecting itself from predators?

*Here and throughout this book, the term *environment* refers to other organisms as well as to the physical aspects of an organism's surroundings.

facts—they are observations about the natural world. The *process* of evolution consists of the mechanisms that produce the observed pattern of change. These mechanisms represent natural causes of the natural phenomena we observe. Indeed, the power of evolution as a unifying theory is its ability to explain and connect a vast array of observations about the living world.

As with all general theories in science, we continue to test our understanding of evolution by examining whether it can account for new observations and experimental results. In this and the following chapters, we'll examine how ongoing discoveries shape what we know about the pattern and process of evolution. To set the stage, we'll first retrace Darwin's quest to explain the adaptations, unity, and diversity of what he called life's "endless forms most beautiful."

CONCEPT 19.1

The Darwinian revolution challenged traditional views of a young Earth inhabited by unchanging species

What impelled Darwin to challenge the prevailing views about Earth and its life? Darwin's revolutionary proposal developed over time, influenced by the work of others and by his travels (Figure 19.2). As we'll see, his ideas had deep historical roots.

Scala Naturae and Classification of Species

Long before Darwin was born, several Greek philosophers suggested that life might have changed gradually over time. But one philosopher who greatly influenced early Western science, Aristotle (384–322 BCE), viewed species as fixed (unchanging). Through his observations of nature, Aristotle recognized certain "affinities" among organisms. He concluded that life-forms could be arranged on a ladder, or scale, of increasing complexity, later called the *scala naturae* ("scale of nature"). Each form of life, perfect and permanent, had its allotted rung on this ladder.

These ideas were generally consistent with the Old Testament account of creation, which holds that species were individually designed by God and therefore perfect. In the 1700s, many scientists interpreted the often remarkable match of organisms to their environment as evidence that the Creator had designed each species for a particular purpose.

One such scientist was Carolus Linnaeus (1707–1778), a Swedish physician and botanist who sought to classify life's diversity, in his words, "for the greater glory of God." Linnaeus developed the two-part, or *binomial*, format for naming species (such as *Homo sapiens* for humans) that is still used today. In contrast to the linear hierarchy of the *scala naturae*, Linnaeus adopted a nested classification system, grouping similar species into increasingly general categories. For example, similar species are grouped in the same genus, similar genera (plural of genus) are grouped in the same family, and so on.

Linnaeus did not ascribe the resemblances among species to evolutionary kinship, but rather to the pattern of their creation. A century later, however, Darwin argued that classification should be based on evolutionary relationships. He also noted that scientists using the Linnaean system often grouped organisms in ways that reflected those relationships.

Ideas About Change over Time

Among other sources of information, Darwin drew from the work of scientists studying **fossils**, the remains or traces of organisms from the past. As depicted in **Figure 19.3**, many fossils are found in sedimentary rocks formed from the

▲ **Figure 19.2 Unusual species inspired novel ideas.** Darwin observed this species of marine iguana and many other unique animals when he visited the Galápagos Islands in 1835.

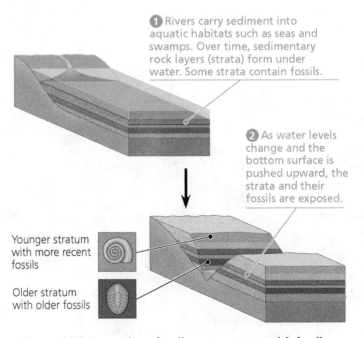

❶ Rivers carry sediment into aquatic habitats such as seas and swamps. Over time, sedimentary rock layers (strata) form under water. Some strata contain fossils.

❷ As water levels change and the bottom surface is pushed upward, the strata and their fossils are exposed.

Younger stratum with more recent fossils

Older stratum with older fossils

▲ **Figure 19.3 Formation of sedimentary strata with fossils.**

sand and mud that settle to the bottom of seas, lakes, and swamps. New layers of sediment cover older ones and compress them into layers of rock called **strata** (singular, *stratum*). The fossils in a particular stratum provide a glimpse of some of the organisms that populated Earth at the time that layer formed. Later, erosion may carve through upper (younger) strata, revealing deeper (older) strata that had been buried.

Paleontology, the study of fossils, was developed in large part by French scientist Georges Cuvier (1769–1832). In examining strata near Paris, Cuvier noted that the older the stratum, the more dissimilar its fossils were to current life-forms. He also observed that from one layer to the next, some new species appeared while others disappeared. He inferred that extinctions must have been a common occurrence, but he staunchly opposed the idea of evolution. Cuvier speculated that each boundary between strata represented a sudden catastrophic event, such as a flood, that had destroyed many of the species living in that area. Such regions, he reasoned, were later repopulated by different species immigrating from other areas.

In contrast, other scientists suggested that profound change could take place through the cumulative effect of slow but continuous processes. In 1795, Scottish geologist James Hutton (1726–1797) proposed that Earth's geologic features could be explained by gradual mechanisms, such as valleys being formed by rivers wearing through rocks. The leading geologist of Darwin's time, Charles Lyell (1797–1875), incorporated Hutton's thinking into his proposal that the same geologic processes are operating today as in the past, and at the same rate.

Hutton and Lyell's ideas strongly influenced Darwin's thinking. Darwin agreed that if geologic change results from slow, continuous actions rather than from sudden events, then Earth must be much older than the widely accepted age of a few thousand years. It would, for example, take a very long time for a river to carve a canyon by erosion. He later reasoned that perhaps similarly slow and subtle processes could produce substantial biological change. Darwin was not the first to apply the idea of gradual change to biological evolution, however.

Lamarck's Hypothesis of Evolution

Although some 18th-century naturalists suggested that life evolves as environments change, only one of Charles Darwin's predecessors proposed a mechanism for *how* life changes over time: French biologist Jean-Baptiste de Lamarck (1744–1829). Alas, Lamarck is primarily remembered today *not* for his visionary recognition that evolutionary change explains patterns in fossils and the match of organisms to their environments, but for the incorrect mechanism he proposed.

Lamarck published his hypothesis in 1809, the year Darwin was born. By comparing living species with fossil forms, Lamarck had found what appeared to be several lines

◀ **Figure 19.4 Acquired traits cannot be inherited.** This bonsai tree was "trained" to grow as a dwarf by pruning and shaping. However, seeds from this tree would produce offspring of normal size.

of descent, each a chronological series of older to younger fossils leading to a living species. He explained his findings using two principles that were widely accepted at the time. The first was *use and disuse*, the idea that parts of the body that are used extensively become larger and stronger, while those that are not used deteriorate. Among many examples, he cited a giraffe stretching its neck to reach leaves on high branches. The second principle, *inheritance of acquired characteristics*, stated that an organism could pass these modifications to its offspring. Lamarck reasoned that the long, muscular neck of the living giraffe had evolved over many generations as giraffes stretched their necks ever higher.

Lamarck also thought that evolution happens because organisms have an innate drive to become more complex. Darwin rejected this idea, but he, too, thought that variation was introduced into the evolutionary process in part through inheritance of acquired characteristics. Today, however, our understanding of genetics refutes this mechanism: Experiments show that traits acquired by use during an individual's life are not inherited in the way proposed by Lamarck (**Figure 19.4**).

Lamarck was vilified in his own time, especially by Cuvier, who denied that species ever evolve. In retrospect, however, Lamarck did recognize that the match of organisms to their environments can be explained by gradual evolutionary change, and he did propose a testable explanation for how this change occurs.

CONCEPT CHECK 19.1

1. How did Hutton's and Lyell's ideas influence Darwin's thinking about evolution?

2. **MAKE CONNECTIONS** Scientific hypotheses must be testable and falsifiable (see Concept 1.3). Applying these criteria, are Cuvier's explanation of the fossil record and Lamarck's hypothesis of evolution scientific? Explain your answer in each case.

For suggested answers, see Appendix A.

Descent with modification by natural selection explains the adaptations of organisms and the unity and diversity of life

As the 19th century dawned, it was generally thought that species had remained unchanged since their creation. A few clouds of doubt about the permanence of species were beginning to gather, but no one could have forecast the thundering storm just beyond the horizon. How did Charles Darwin become the lightning rod for a revolutionary view of life?

Darwin's Research

Charles Darwin (1809–1882) was born in Shrewsbury, England. He had a consuming interest in nature—reading nature books, fishing, hunting, and collecting insects. Darwin's father, a physician, could see no future for his son as a naturalist and sent him to medical school in Edinburgh. But Charles found medicine boring and surgery before the days of anesthesia horrifying. He enrolled at Cambridge University, intending to become a clergyman. (At that time many scholars of science belonged to the clergy.)

At Cambridge, Darwin became the protégé of John Henslow, a botany professor. Henslow recommended him to Captain Robert FitzRoy, who was preparing the survey ship HMS *Beagle* for a voyage around the world. FitzRoy, who was himself an accomplished scientist, accepted Darwin because he was a skilled naturalist and because they were of similar age and social class.

The Voyage of the Beagle

Darwin embarked on the *Beagle* in December 1831. The primary mission of the voyage was to chart poorly known stretches of the South American coastline. Darwin spent most of his time on shore, observing and collecting thousands of plants and animals. He noted the characteristics that made organisms well suited to such diverse environments as Brazil's humid jungles, Argentina's broad grasslands, and the Andes' towering peaks.

Darwin observed that the plants and animals in temperate regions of South America more closely resembled species living in the South American tropics than species living in temperate regions of Europe. Furthermore, the fossils he found, though clearly different from living species, distinctly resembled the living organisms of South America.

Darwin also read Lyell's *Principles of Geology* during the voyage. He experienced geologic change firsthand when a violent earthquake shook the coast of Chile, and he observed afterward that rocks along the coast had been thrust upward by several feet. Finding fossils of ocean organisms high in the Andes, Darwin inferred that the rocks containing the fossils must have been raised there by many similar earthquakes. These observations reinforced what he had learned from Lyell: Physical evidence did not support the traditional view that Earth was only a few thousand years old.

Darwin's interest in the geographic distribution of species was further stimulated by the *Beagle*'s stop at the Galápagos, a group of volcanic islands located near the equator about 900 km west of South America (Figure 19.5). Darwin was fascinated by the unusual organisms there. The birds he collected included several kinds of mockingbirds. These mockingbirds, though similar to each other, seemed to be different species.

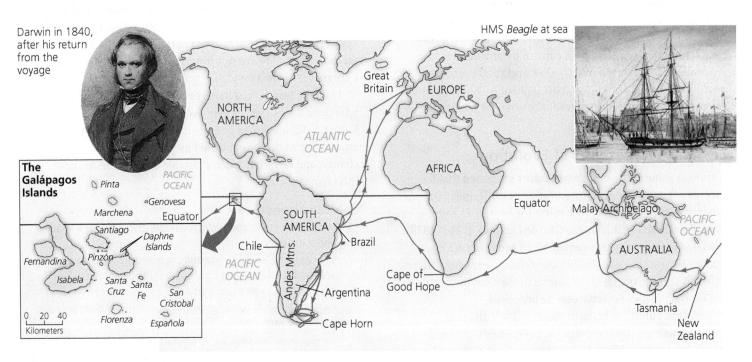

▲ Figure 19.5 **The voyage of HMS *Beagle*.**

Some were unique to individual islands, while others lived on two or more adjacent islands. Furthermore, although the animals on the Galápagos resembled species living on the South American mainland, most of the Galápagos species were not known from anywhere else in the world. Darwin hypothesized that the Galápagos had been colonized by organisms that had strayed from South America and then diversified, giving rise to new species on the various islands.

Darwin's Focus on Adaptation

During the voyage of the *Beagle*, Darwin observed many examples of **adaptations**, inherited characteristics of organisms that enhance their survival and reproduction in specific environments. Later, as he reassessed his observations, he began to perceive adaptation to the environment and the origin of new species as closely related processes. Could a new species arise from an ancestral form by the gradual accumulation of adaptations to a different environment? From studies made years after Darwin's voyage, biologists have concluded that this is indeed what happened to the diverse group of Galápagos finches (see Figure 1.16). The finches' various beaks and behaviors are adapted to the specific foods available on their home islands **(Figure 19.6)**. Darwin realized that explaining such adaptations was essential to understanding evolution. As we'll explore further, his explanation of how adaptations arise centered on **natural selection**, a process in which individuals that have certain inherited traits tend to survive and reproduce at higher rates than other individuals *because of* those traits.

By the early 1840s, Darwin had worked out the major features of his hypothesis. He set these ideas on paper in 1844, when he wrote a long essay on descent with modification and its underlying mechanism, natural selection. Yet he was still reluctant to publish his ideas, apparently because he anticipated the uproar they would cause. During this time, Darwin continued to compile evidence in support of his hypothesis. By the mid-1850s, he had described his ideas to Lyell and a few others. Lyell, who was not yet convinced of evolution, nevertheless urged Darwin to publish on the subject before someone else came to the same conclusions and published first.

In June 1858, Lyell's prediction came true. Darwin received a manuscript from Alfred Russel Wallace (1823–1913), a British naturalist working in the South Pacific islands of the Malay Archipelago **(Figure 19.7)**. Wallace had developed a hypothesis of natural selection nearly identical to Darwin's. He asked Darwin to evaluate his paper and forward it to Lyell if it merited publication. Darwin complied, writing to Lyell: "Your words have come

(a) Cactus-eater. The long, sharp beak of the cactus ground finch (*Geospiza scandens*) helps it tear and eat cactus flowers and pulp.

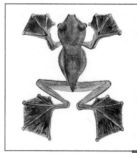

(c) Insect-eater. The green warbler finch (*Certhidea olivacea*) uses its narrow, pointed beak to grasp insects.

(b) Seed-eater. The large ground finch (*Geospiza magnirostris*) has a large beak adapted for cracking seeds on the ground.

▲ **Figure 19.6 Three examples of beak variation in Galápagos finches.** The Galápagos Islands are home to more than a dozen species of closely related finches, some found only on a single island. A striking difference among them is their beaks, which are adapted to specific diets.

MAKE CONNECTIONS *Review Figure 1.16. To which of the other two species shown above is the cactus-eater more closely related (that is, with which does it share a more recent common ancestor)?*

▶ **Figure 19.7 Alfred Russel Wallace.** The inset is a painting Wallace made of a flying tree frog from the Malay Archipelago.

true with a vengeance. . . . I never saw a more striking coincidence . . . so all my originality, whatever it may amount to, will be smashed." On July 1, 1858, Lyell and a colleague presented Wallace's paper, along with extracts from Darwin's unpublished 1844 essay, to the Linnean Society of London. Darwin quickly finished his book, titled *On the Origin of Species by Means of Natural Selection* (commonly referred to as *The Origin of Species*), and published it the next year. Although Wallace had submitted his ideas for publication first, he admired Darwin and thought that Darwin had developed the idea of natural selection so extensively that he should be known as its main architect.

Within a decade, Darwin's book and its proponents had convinced most scientists that life's diversity is the product of evolution. Darwin succeeded where previous evolutionists had failed, mainly by presenting a plausible scientific mechanism with immaculate logic and an avalanche of evidence.

Ideas from *The Origin of Species*

In his book, Darwin amassed evidence that descent with modification by natural selection explains the three broad observations about nature listed in the Overview: the unity of life, the diversity of life, and the match between organisms and their environments.

Descent with Modification

In the first edition of *The Origin of Species*, Darwin never used the word *evolution* (although the final word of the book is "evolved"). Rather, he discussed *descent with modification*, a phrase that summarized his view of life. Organisms share many characteristics, leading Darwin to perceive unity in life. He attributed the unity of life to the descent of all organisms from an ancestor that lived in the remote past. He also thought that as the descendants of that ancestral organism lived in various habitats over millions of years, they accumulated diverse modifications, or adaptations, that fit them to specific ways of life. Darwin reasoned that over a long time, descent with modification eventually led to the rich diversity of life today.

Darwin viewed the history of life as a tree, with multiple branchings from a common trunk out to the tips of the youngest twigs (**Figure 19.8**). In his diagram, the tips of the twigs that are labeled A, B, C, and D represent several groups of organisms living in the present day, while the unlabeled branches represent groups that are extinct. Each fork of the tree represents the most recent common ancestor of all the lines of evolution that subsequently branch from that point. Darwin reasoned that such a branching process, along with past extinction events, could explain the large morphological gaps (differences in form) that sometimes exist in between related groups of organisms.

As an example, consider the three living species of elephants: the Asian elephant (*Elephas maximus*) and two species of African elephants (*Loxodonta africana* and *L. cyclotis*). As shown in the tree diagram in **Figure 19.9**, these closely related species are very similar because they shared the same line of

▶ **Figure 19.8 "I think . . ."** In this 1837 sketch, Darwin envisioned the branching pattern of evolution. Branches that end in twigs labeled A–D represent particular groups of living organisms; all other branches represent extinct groups.

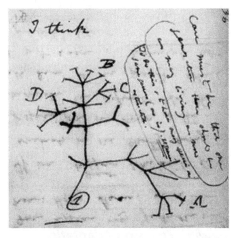

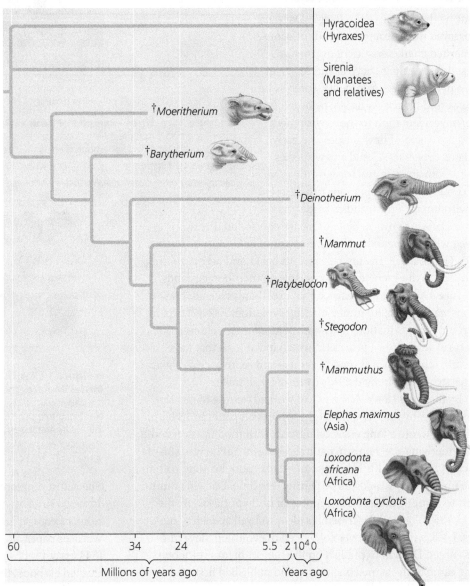

▲ **Figure 19.9 Descent with modification.** This evolutionary tree of elephants and their relatives is based mainly on fossils—their anatomy, order of appearance in strata, and geographic distribution. Note that most branches of descent ended in extinction (denoted by the dagger symbol †). (Time line not to scale.)

? *Based on the tree shown here, approximately when did the most recent ancestor shared by* Mammuthus *(woolly mammoths), Asian elephants, and African elephants live?*

descent until a relatively recent split from their common ancestor.

Note that seven lineages related to elephants have become extinct over the past 32 million years. As a result, there are no living species that fill the morphological gap between elephants and their nearest relatives today, the hyraxes and the manatees and their relatives. Such extinctions are not uncommon. In fact, many evolutionary branches, even some major ones, are dead ends: Scientists estimate that over 99% of all species that have ever lived are now extinct. As in Figure 19.9, fossils of extinct species can document the divergence of present-day groups by "filling in" gaps between them.

Artificial Selection, Natural Selection, and Adaptation

Darwin proposed the mechanism of natural selection to explain the observable patterns of evolution. He crafted his argument carefully, hoping to persuade even the most skeptical readers. First he discussed familiar examples of selective breeding of domesticated plants and animals. Humans have modified other species over many generations by selecting and breeding individuals that possess desired traits, a process called **artificial selection (Figure 19.10)**. As a result of artificial selection, crops, livestock animals, and pets often bear little resemblance to their wild ancestors.

Darwin then argued that a similar process occurs in nature. He based his argument on two observations, from which he drew two inferences.

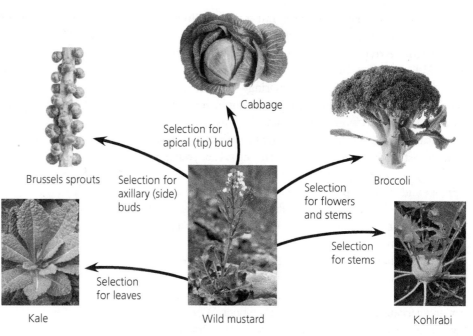

▲ **Figure 19.10 Artificial selection.** These different vegetables have all been selected from one species of wild mustard. By selecting variations in different parts of the plant, breeders have obtained these divergent results.

Observation #1: Members of a population often vary in their inherited traits **(Figure 19.11)**.

Observation #2: All species can produce more offspring than their environment can support **(Figure 19.12)**, and many of these offspring fail to survive and reproduce.

Inference #1: Individuals whose inherited traits give them a higher probability of surviving and reproducing in a given environment tend to leave more offspring than other individuals.

Inference #2: This unequal ability of individuals to survive and reproduce will lead to the accumulation of favorable traits in the population over generations.

▲ **Figure 19.11 Variation in a population.** Individuals in this population of Asian ladybird beetles vary in color and spot pattern. Natural selection may act on these variations only if (1) they are heritable and (2) they affect the beetles' ability to survive and reproduce.

◄ **Figure 19.12 Overproduction of offspring.** A single puffball fungus can produce billions of offspring. If all of these offspring and their descendants survived to maturity, they would carpet the surrounding land surface.

Spore cloud

371

As inferences #1 and #2 suggest, Darwin saw an important connection between natural selection and the capacity of organisms to "overreproduce." He began to make this connection after reading an essay by economist Thomas Malthus, who contended that much of human suffering—disease, famine, and war—resulted from the human population's potential to increase faster than food supplies and other resources. Similarly, Darwin realized that the capacity to overreproduce was characteristic of all species. Of the many eggs laid, young born, and seeds spread, only a tiny fraction complete their development and leave offspring of their own. The rest are eaten, starved, diseased, unmated, or unable to tolerate physical conditions of the environment such as salinity or temperature.

An organism's heritable traits can influence not only its own performance, but also how well its offspring cope with environmental challenges. For example, an organism might have a trait that gives its offspring an advantage in escaping predators, obtaining food, or tolerating physical conditions. When such advantages increase the number of offspring that survive and reproduce, the traits that are favored will likely appear at a greater frequency in the next generation. Thus, over time, natural selection resulting from factors such as predators, lack of food, or adverse physical conditions can lead to an increase in the proportion of favorable traits in a population.

How rapidly do such changes occur? Darwin reasoned that if artificial selection can bring about dramatic change in a relatively short period of time, then natural selection should be capable of substantial modification of species over many hundreds of generations. Even if the advantages of some heritable traits over others are slight, the advantageous variations will gradually accumulate in the population, and less favorable ones will diminish. Over time, this process will increase the frequency of individuals with favorable adaptations and refine the match between organisms and their environment.

Natural Selection: A Summary

Let's now recap the main ideas of natural selection:

- Natural selection is a process in which individuals that have certain heritable traits survive and reproduce at a higher rate than other individuals because of those traits.
- Over time, natural selection can increase the match between organisms and their environment (Figure 19.13).
- If an environment changes, or if individuals move to a new habitat, natural selection may result in adaptation to these new conditions, sometimes giving rise to new species.

One subtle but important point is that although natural selection occurs through interactions between individual organisms and their environment, *individuals do not evolve*. Rather, it is the population that evolves over time.

A second key point is that natural selection can amplify or diminish only those heritable traits that differ among the individuals in a population. Thus, even if a trait is heritable, if all

(a) A flower mantid in Malaysia

(b) A leaf mantid in Borneo

▲ **Figure 19.13 Camouflage as an example of evolutionary adaptation.** Related species of the insects called mantids have diverse shapes and colors that evolved in different environments.

> **?** *Explain how these mantids demonstrate the three key observations about life introduced in the Overview: the match between organisms and their environments, unity, and diversity.*

the individuals in a population are genetically identical for that trait, evolution by natural selection cannot occur.

Third, remember that environmental factors vary from place to place and over time. A trait that is favorable in one place or time may be useless—or even detrimental—in other places or times. Natural selection is always operating, but which traits are favored depends on the context in which a species lives and mates.

Next, we'll survey the wide range of observations that support a Darwinian view of evolution by natural selection.

CONCEPT CHECK 19.2

1. How does the concept of descent with modification explain both the unity and diversity of life?
2. **WHAT IF?** Predict whether a fossil of an extinct mammal that lived high in the Andes would more closely resemble present-day mammals that live in South American jungles or present-day mammals that live high in African mountains? Explain.
3. **MAKE CONNECTIONS** Review the relationship between genotype and phenotype (see Figure 11.6). Suppose that in a particular pea population, flowers with the white phenotype are favored by natural selection. Predict what would happen over time to the frequency of the p allele in the population, and explain your reasoning.

For suggested answers, see Appendix A.

CONCEPT 19.3

Evolution is supported by an overwhelming amount of scientific evidence

In *The Origin of Species*, Darwin marshaled a broad range of evidence to support the concept of descent with modification. Still—as he readily acknowledged—there were instances in which key evidence was lacking. For example, Darwin referred to the origin of flowering plants as an "abominable mystery," and he lamented the lack of fossils showing how earlier groups of organisms gave rise to new groups.

In the last 150 years, new discoveries have filled many of the gaps that Darwin identified. The origin of flowering plants, for example, is much better understood (see Chapter 26), and many fossils have been discovered that signify the origin of new groups of organisms (see Chapter 23). In this section, we'll consider four types of data that document the pattern of evolution and illuminate the processes by which it occurs.

Direct Observations of Evolutionary Change

Biologists have documented evolutionary change in thousands of scientific studies. We'll examine many such studies throughout this unit, but let's look at two examples here.

Natural Selection in Response to Introduced Plant Species

Animals that eat plants, called herbivores, often have adaptations that help them feed efficiently on their primary food sources. What happens when herbivores begin to feed on a plant species with different characteristics than their usual food source?

An opportunity to study this question in nature is provided by soapberry bugs, which use their "beak," a hollow, needlelike mouthpart, to feed on seeds located within the fruits of various plants. In southern Florida, the soapberry bug (*Jadera haematoloma*) feeds on the seeds of a native plant, the balloon vine (*Cardiospermum corindum*). In central Florida, however, balloon vines have become rare. Instead, soapberry bugs in that region now feed on seeds of the goldenrain tree (*Koelreuteria elegans*), a species recently introduced from Asia.

Soapberry bugs feed most effectively when their beak length closely matches the depth at which the seeds are found within the fruit. Goldenrain tree fruit consists of three flat lobes, and its seeds are much closer to the fruit surface than are the seeds of the plump, round native balloon vine fruit. Researchers at the University of Utah predicted that in populations that feed on goldenrain tree, natural selection would result in beaks that are *shorter* than those in populations that feed on balloon vine (**Figure 19.14**). Indeed, beak lengths are shorter in the populations that feed on goldenrain tree.

▼ **Figure 19.14** Inquiry

Can a change in a population's food source result in evolution by natural selection?

Field Study Soapberry bugs feed most effectively when the length of their "beak" closely matches the depth of the seeds within the fruit. Scott Carroll and his colleagues measured beak lengths in soapberry bug populations feeding on the native balloon vine. They also measured beak lengths in populations feeding on the introduced goldenrain tree. The researchers then compared the measurements with those of museum specimens collected in the two areas before the goldenrain tree was introduced.

Soapberry bug with beak inserted in balloon vine fruit

Results Beak lengths were shorter in populations feeding on the introduced species than in populations feeding on the native species, in which the seeds are buried more deeply. The average beak length in museum specimens from each population (indicated by red arrows) was similar to beak lengths in populations feeding on native species.

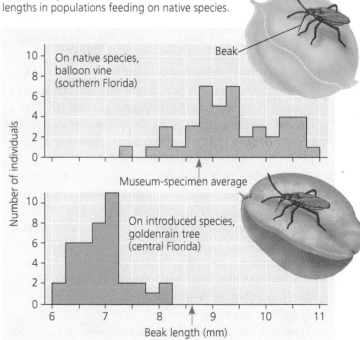

Conclusion Museum specimens and contemporary data suggest that a change in the size of the soapberry bug's food source can result in evolution by natural selection for matching beak size.

Source S. P. Carroll and C. Boyd, Host race radiation in the soapberry bug: natural history with the history, *Evolution* 46:1052–1069 (1992).

WHAT IF? Additional results showed that when soapberry bug eggs from a population fed on balloon vine fruits were reared on goldenrain tree fruits (or vice versa), the beak lengths of the adult insects matched those in the population from which the eggs were obtained. Interpret these results.

Researchers have also studied beak length evolution in soapberry bug populations that feed on plants introduced to Louisiana, Oklahoma, and Australia. In each of these locations, the fruit of the introduced plants is larger than the fruit of the native plant. Thus, in populations feeding on introduced species in these regions, the researchers predicted that natural selection would result in the evolution of *longer* beaks. Again, data from field studies upheld this prediction.

The adaptation observed in these soapberry bug populations had important consequences: In Australia, for example, the increase in beak length nearly doubled the success with which soapberry bugs could eat the seeds of the introduced species. Furthermore, since historical data show that the goldenrain tree reached central Florida just 35 years before the scientific studies were initiated, the results demonstrate that natural selection can cause rapid evolution in a wild population.

The Evolution of Drug-Resistant Bacteria

An example of ongoing natural selection that dramatically affects humans is the evolution of drug-resistant pathogens (disease-causing organisms and viruses). This is a particular problem with bacteria and viruses because resistant strains of these pathogens can proliferate very quickly.

Consider the evolution of drug resistance in the bacterium *Staphylococcus aureus*. About one in three people harbor this species on their skin or in their nasal passages with no negative effects. However, certain genetic varieties (strains) of this species, known as methicillin-resistant *S. aureus* (MRSA), are formidable pathogens. The past decade has seen an alarming increase in virulent forms of MRSA such as clone USA300, a strain that can cause "flesh-eating disease" and potentially fatal infections (**Figure 19.15**). How did clone USA300 and other strains of MRSA become so dangerous?

The story begins in 1943, when penicillin became the first widely used antibiotic. Although penicillin and other antibiotics have since saved millions of lives, by 1945, over 20% of the *S. aureus* strains seen in hospitals were resistant to penicillin. These bacteria had an enzyme, penicillinase, that could destroy penicillin. Researchers developed antibiotics that were not destroyed by penicillinase, but some *S. aureus* populations developed resistance to each new drug within a few years.

Then, in 1959, doctors began using the powerful antibiotic methicillin. But within two years, methicillin-resistant strains of *S. aureus* appeared. How did these resistant strains emerge? Methicillin works by deactivating a protein that bacteria use to synthesize their cell walls. However, *S. aureus* populations exhibited variations in how strongly their members were affected by the drug. In particular, some individuals were able to synthesize their cell walls using a different protein that was not affected by methicillin. These individuals survived the methicillin treatments and reproduced at higher rates than did other individuals. Over time, these resistant individuals became increasingly common, leading to the spread of MRSA.

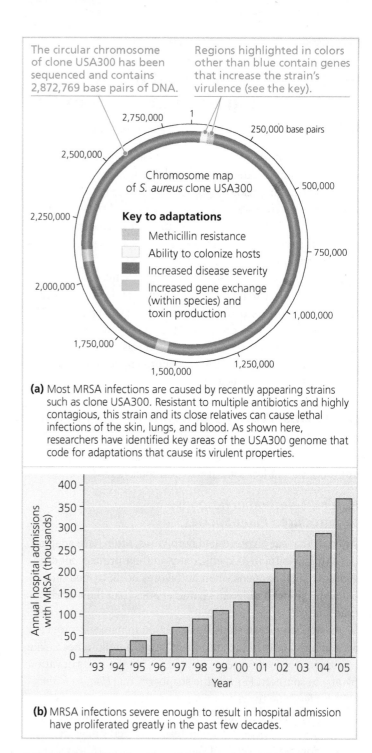

(a) Most MRSA infections are caused by recently appearing strains such as clone USA300. Resistant to multiple antibiotics and highly contagious, this strain and its close relatives can cause lethal infections of the skin, lungs, and blood. As shown here, researchers have identified key areas of the USA300 genome that code for adaptations that cause its virulent properties.

(b) MRSA infections severe enough to result in hospital admission have proliferated greatly in the past few decades.

▲ Figure 19.15 **The rise of methicillin-resistant *Staphylococcus aureus* (MRSA).**

Initially, MRSA could be controlled by antibiotics that work differently from the way methicillin works. But this has become increasingly difficult because some MRSA strains are resistant to multiple antibiotics—probably because bacteria can exchange genes with members of their own and other species (see Figure 24.17). Thus, the present-day multidrug-resistant strains may have emerged over time as MRSA strains that were resistant to different antibiotics exchanged genes.

The *S. aureus* and soapberry bug examples highlight two key points about natural selection. First, natural selection is a process of editing, not a creative mechanism. A drug does not *create* resistant pathogens; it *selects for* resistant individuals that are already present in the population. Second, natural selection depends on time and place. It favors those characteristics in a genetically variable population that provide advantage in the current, local environment. What is beneficial in one situation may be useless or even harmful in another. Beak lengths arise that match the size of the typical fruit eaten by a particular soapberry bug population. However, a beak length suitable for fruit of one size can be disadvantageous when the bug is feeding on fruit of another size.

Homology

A second type of evidence for evolution comes from analyzing similarities among different organisms. As we've discussed, evolution is a process of descent with modification: Characteristics present in an ancestral organism are altered (by natural selection) in its descendants over time as they face different environmental conditions. As a result, related species can have characteristics that have an underlying similarity yet function differently. Similarity resulting from common ancestry is known as **homology**. As we'll describe in this section, an understanding of homology can be used to make testable predictions and explain observations that are otherwise puzzling.

Anatomical and Molecular Homologies

The view of evolution as a remodeling process leads to the prediction that closely related species should share similar features—and they do. Of course, closely related species share the features used to determine their relationship, but they also share many other features. Some of these shared features make little sense except in the context of evolution. For example, the forelimbs of all mammals, including humans, cats, whales, and bats, show the same arrangement of bones from the shoulder to the tips of the digits, even though these appendages have very different functions: lifting, walking, swimming, and flying

(Figure 19.16). Such striking anatomical resemblances would be highly unlikely if these structures had arisen anew in each species. Rather, the underlying skeletons of the arms, forelegs, flippers, and wings of different mammals are **homologous structures** that represent variations on a structural theme that was present in their common ancestor.

Comparing early stages of development in different animal species reveals additional anatomical homologies not visible in adult organisms. For example, at some point in their development, all vertebrate embryos have a tail located posterior to (behind) the anus, as well as structures called pharyngeal (throat) arches (Figure 19.17). These homologous throat arches ultimately develop into structures with very different functions, such as gills in fishes and parts of the ears and throat in humans and other mammals.

Some of the most intriguing homologies concern "leftover" structures of marginal, if any, importance to the organism. These **vestigial structures** are remnants of features that served a function in the organism's ancestors. For instance, the

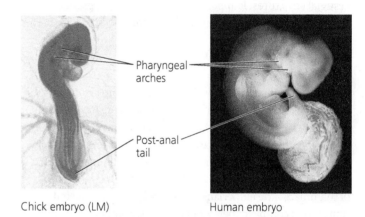

Chick embryo (LM)　　　　Human embryo

▲ **Figure 19.17 Anatomical similarities in vertebrate embryos.** At some stage in their embryonic development, all vertebrates have a tail located posterior to the anus (referred to as a post-anal tail), as well as pharyngeal (throat) arches. Descent from a common ancestor can explain such similarities.

▶ Figure 19.16 **Mammalian forelimbs: homologous structures.** Even though they have become adapted for different functions, the forelimbs of all mammals are constructed from the same basic skeletal elements: one large bone (purple), attached to two smaller bones (orange and tan), attached to several small bones (gold), attached to several metacarpals (green), attached to approximately five digits, each of which is composed of phalanges (blue).

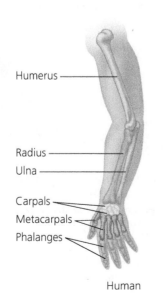
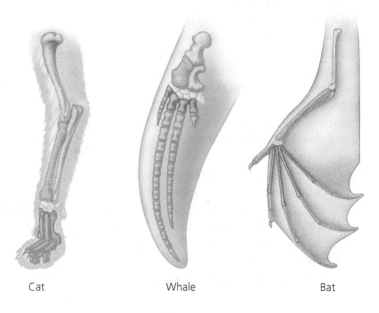

Human　　　　Cat　　　　Whale　　　　Bat

skeletons of some snakes retain vestiges of the pelvis and leg bones of walking ancestors. Another example is provided by eye remnants that are buried under scales in blind species of cave fishes. We would not expect to see these vestigial structures if snakes and blind cave fishes had origins separate from other vertebrate animals.

Biologists also observe similarities among organisms at the molecular level. All forms of life use the same genetic language of DNA and RNA, and the genetic code is essentially universal. Thus, it is likely that all species descended from common ancestors that used this code. But molecular homologies go beyond a shared code. For example, organisms as dissimilar as humans and bacteria share genes inherited from a very distant common ancestor. Some of these homologous genes have acquired new functions, while others, such as those coding for the ribosomal subunits used in protein synthesis (see Figure 14.17), have retained their original functions. It is also common for organisms to have genes that have lost their function, even though the homologous genes in related species may be fully functional. Like vestigial structures, it appears that such inactive "pseudogenes" may be present simply because a common ancestor had them.

A Different Cause of Resemblance: Convergent Evolution

Although organisms that are closely related share characteristics because of common descent, distantly related organisms can resemble one another for a different reason: **convergent evolution**, the independent evolution of similar features in different lineages. Consider marsupial mammals, many of which live in Australia. Marsupials are distinct from another group of mammals—the eutherians—few of which live in Australia. (Eutherians complete their embryonic development in the uterus, whereas marsupials are born as embryos and complete their development in an external pouch.) Some Australian marsupials have eutherian look-alikes with superficially similar adaptations.

For instance, a forest-dwelling Australian marsupial called the sugar glider looks very similar to flying squirrels, gliding eutherians that live in North American forests **(Figure 19.18)**. But the sugar glider has many other characteristics that make it a marsupial, much more closely related to kangaroos and other Australian marsupials than to flying squirrels or other eutherians. Again, our understanding of evolution can explain these observations: Although they evolved independently from different ancestors, these two mammals have adapted to similar environments in similar ways. In such examples in which species share features because of convergent evolution, the resemblance is said to be **analogous**, not homologous. Analogous features share similar function,

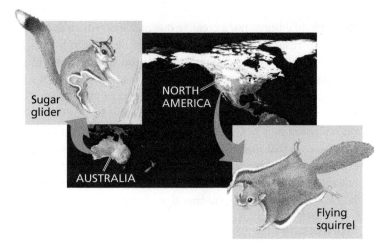

▲ **Figure 19.18 Convergent evolution.** The ability to glide through the air evolved independently in these two distantly related mammals.

but not common ancestry, while homologous features share common ancestry, but not necessarily similar function.

The Fossil Record

A third type of evidence for evolution comes from fossils. The fossil record documents the pattern of evolution, showing that past organisms differed from present-day organisms and that many species have become extinct. Fossils also show the evolutionary changes that have occurred in various groups of organisms. To give one of hundreds of examples, researchers found that the pelvic bone in fossil stickleback fish became greatly reduced in size over time in a number of different lakes. The consistent nature of this change suggests that the reduction in the size of the pelvic bone may have been driven by natural selection.

Fossils can also shed light on the origins of new groups of organisms. An example is the fossil record of cetaceans, the mammalian order that includes whales, dolphins, and porpoises. As shown in **Figure 19.19**, some of these fossils

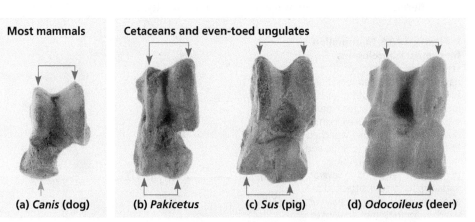

Most mammals	Cetaceans and even-toed ungulates		
(a) *Canis* (dog)	**(b)** *Pakicetus*	**(c)** *Sus* (pig)	**(d)** *Odocoileus* (deer)

▲ **Figure 19.19 Ankle bones: one piece of the puzzle.** Comparing fossils and present-day examples of the astragalus (a type of ankle bone) provides one line of evidence that cetaceans are closely related to even-toed ungulates. **(a)** In most mammals, the astragalus is shaped like that of a dog, with a double hump on one end (indicated by the red arrows) but not at the opposite end (blue arrow). **(b)** Fossils show that the early cetacean *Pakicetus* had an astragalus with double humps at both ends, a shape otherwise found only in even-toed ungulates, such as **(c)** pigs and **(d)** deer.

provided an unexpected line of support for a hypothesis based on DNA sequence data: that cetaceans are closely related to even-toed ungulates, a group that includes deer, pigs, camels, and cows. What else can fossils tell us about cetacean origins? The earliest cetaceans lived 50–60 million years ago. The fossil record indicates that prior to that time, most mammals were terrestrial. Although scientists had long realized that whales and other cetaceans originated from land mammals, few fossils had been found that revealed how cetacean limb structure had changed over time, leading eventually to the loss of hind limbs and the development of flippers and tail flukes. In the past few decades, however, a series of remarkable fossils have been discovered in Pakistan, Egypt, and North America. These fossils document steps in the transition from life on land to life in the sea, filling in some of the gaps between ancestral and living cetaceans (Figure 19.20).

Collectively, the recent fossil discoveries document the formation of new species and the origin of a major new group of mammals, the cetaceans. These discoveries also show that cetaceans and their close living relatives (hippopotamuses, pigs, deer, and other even-toed ungulates) are much more different

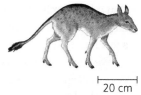

▲ *Diacodexis,* an early even-toed ungulate

from each other than were *Pakicetus* and early even-toed ungulates, such as *Diacodexis.* Similar patterns are seen in fossils documenting the origins of other major new groups of organisms, including mammals (see Chapter 23), flowering plants (see Chapter 26), and tetrapods (see Chapter 27). In each of these cases, the fossil record shows that over time, descent with modification produced increasingly large differences among related groups of organisms, ultimately resulting in the diversity of life we see today.

Biogeography

A fourth type of evidence for evolution has to do with **biogeography**, the scientific study of the geographic distributions of species. The geographic distributions of organisms are influenced by many factors, including *continental drift,* the slow movement of Earth's continents over time. About 250 million years ago, these movements united all of Earth's landmasses into a single large continent called **Pangaea** (see Figure 23.8).

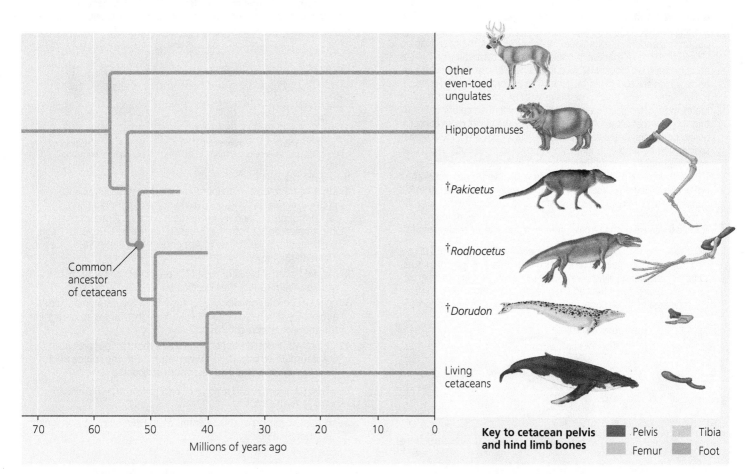

▲ Figure 19.20 **The transition to life in the sea.** Multiple lines of evidence support the hypothesis that cetaceans evolved from terrestrial mammals. Fossils document the reduction over time in the pelvis and hind limb bones of extinct cetacean ancestors, including *Pakicetus, Rodhocetus,* and *Dorudon.* DNA sequence data support the hypothesis that cetaceans are most closely related to hippopotamuses.

? *Which happened first during the evolution of cetaceans: changes in hind limb structure or the origin of tail flukes?*

Roughly 200 million years ago, Pangaea began to break apart; by 20 million years ago, the continents we know today were within a few hundred kilometers of their present locations.

We can use our understanding of evolution and continental drift to predict where fossils of different groups of organisms might be found. For example, scientists have constructed evolutionary trees for horses based on anatomical data. These trees and the ages of fossils of horse ancestors suggest that present-day horse species originated 5 million years ago in North America. At that time, North and South America were close to their present locations, but they were not yet connected, making it difficult for horses to travel between them. Thus, we would predict that the oldest horse fossils should be found only on the continent on which horses originated—North America. This prediction and others like it for differ-

ent groups of organisms have been upheld, providing more evidence for evolution.

We can also use our understanding of evolution to explain biogeographic data. For example, islands generally have many plant and animal species that are **endemic**—they are nowhere else in the world. Yet, as Darwin described in *The Origin of Species*, most island species are closely related to species from the nearest mainland or a neighboring island. He explained this observation by suggesting that islands are colonized by species from the nearest mainland. These colonists eventually give rise to new species as they adapt to their new environments. Such a process also explains why two islands with similar environments in distant parts of the world tend to be populated not by species that are closely related to each other, but rather by species related to those of the nearest mainland, where the environment is often quite different.

Scientific Skills Exercise

Making and Testing Predictions

Can Predation Result in Natural Selection for Color Patterns in Guppies? What we know about evolution changes constantly as new observations lead to new hypotheses—and hence to new ways to test our understanding of evolutionary theory. Consider the wild guppies (*Poecilia reticulata*) that live in pools connected by streams on the Caribbean island of Trinidad. Male guppies have highly varied color patterns, which are controlled by genes that are only expressed in adult males. Female guppies choose males with bright color patterns as mates more often than they choose males with drab coloring. But the bright colors that attract females also make the males more conspicuous to predators. Researchers observed that in pools with few predator species, the benefits of bright colors appear to "win out," and males are more brightly colored than in pools where predation is intense.

One guppy predator, the killifish, preys on juvenile guppies that have not yet displayed their adult coloration. Researchers predicted that if guppies with drab colors were transferred to a pool with only killifish, eventually the descendants of these guppies would be more brightly colored (because of the female preference for brightly colored males).

How the Experiment Was Done Researchers transplanted 200 guppies from pools containing pike-cichlid fish, intense guppy predators, to pools containing killifish, less active predators that prey mainly on juvenile guppies. They tracked the number of bright-colored spots and the total area of those spots on male guppies in each generation.

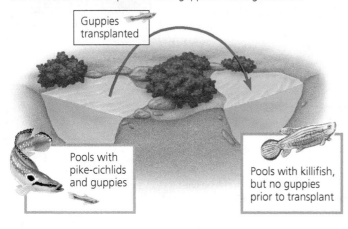

Guppies transplanted

Pools with pike-cichlids and guppies

Pools with killifish, but no guppies prior to transplant

Data from the Experiment After 22 months (15 generations), researchers compared the color pattern data for the source and transplanted populations.

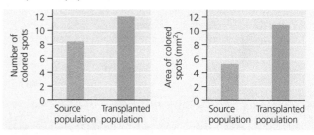

Interpret the Data

1. Identify the following elements of hypothesis-based science in this example: (a) question, (b) hypothesis, (c) prediction, (d) control group, and (e) experimental group. (For additional information about hypothesis-based science, see Chapter 1 and the Scientific Skills Review in Appendix F and in the Study Area in MasteringBiology.)

2. Explain how the types of data the researchers chose to collect enabled them to test their prediction.

3. (a) What conclusion would you draw from the data presented above? (b) What additional questions might you ask to determine the strength of this conclusion?

4. Predict what would happen if, after 22 months, guppies from the transplanted population were returned to the source pool. Describe an experiment to test your prediction.

Data from J.A. Endler, Natural selection on color patterns in Poecilia reticulata, Evolution 34:76–91 (1980).

(MB) A related version of this Scientific Skills Exercise can be assigned in MasteringBiology.

What Is Theoretical About Darwin's View of Life?

Some people dismiss Darwin's ideas as "just a theory." However, as we have seen, the *pattern* of evolution—the observation that life has evolved over time—has been documented directly and is supported by a great deal of evidence. In addition, Darwin's explanation of the *process* of evolution—that natural selection is the primary cause of the observed pattern of evolutionary change—makes sense of massive amounts of data. The effects of natural selection also can be observed and tested in nature.

What, then, is theoretical about evolution? Keep in mind that the scientific meaning of the term *theory* is very different from its meaning in everyday use. The colloquial use of the word *theory* comes close to what scientists mean by a hypothesis. In science, a theory is more comprehensive than a hypothesis. A theory, such as the theory of evolution by natural selection, accounts for many observations and explains and integrates a great variety of phenomena. Such a unifying theory does not become widely accepted unless its predictions stand up to thorough and continual testing by experiment and additional observation (see Chapter 1). As the rest of this unit demonstrates, this has certainly been the case with the theory of evolution by natural selection.

The skepticism of scientists as they continue to test theories prevents these ideas from becoming dogma. For example, although Darwin thought that evolution was a very slow process, we now know that this isn't always true. New species can form in relatively short periods of time—a few thousand years or less (see Chapter 22). Furthermore, evolutionary biologists now recognize that natural selection is not the only mechanism responsible for evolution. Indeed, the study of evolution today is livelier than ever as scientists use a wide range of experimental approaches and genetic analyses to test predictions based on natural selection and other evolutionary mechanisms. In the **Scientific Skills Exercise**, you'll work with data from an experiment on natural selection in wild guppies.

Although Darwin's theory attributes the diversity of life to natural processes, the diverse products of evolution nevertheless remain elegant and inspiring. As Darwin wrote in the final sentence of *The Origin of Species*, "There is grandeur in this view of life . . . [in which] endless forms most beautiful and most wonderful have been, and are being, evolved."

CONCEPT CHECK 19.3

1. Explain how the following statement is inaccurate: "Antibiotics have created drug resistance in MRSA."
2. How does evolution account for (a) the similar mammalian forelimbs with different functions shown in Figure 19.16 and (b) the similar forms of the two distantly related mammals shown in Figure 19.18?
3. **WHAT IF?** Fossils show that dinosaurs originated 250–200 million years ago. Would you expect the geographic distribution of early dinosaur fossils to be broad (on many continents) or narrow (on one or a few continents only)? Explain.

For suggested answers, see Appendix A.

19 Chapter Review

SUMMARY OF KEY CONCEPTS

CONCEPT 19.1

The Darwinian revolution challenged traditional views of a young Earth inhabited by unchanging species (pp. 366–367)

- Darwin proposed that life's diversity arose from ancestral species through natural selection, a departure from prevailing views.
- Cuvier studied fossils but denied that evolution occurs; he proposed that sudden catastrophic events in the past caused species to disappear from an area. Hutton and Lyell thought that geologic change could result from gradual, continuous mechanisms. Lamarck hypothesized that species evolve, but the underlying mechanisms he proposed are not supported by evidence.

? *Why was the age of Earth important for Darwin's ideas about evolution?*

CONCEPT 19.2

Descent with modification by natural selection explains the adaptations of organisms and the unity and diversity of life (pp. 368–372)

- Darwin's voyage on the *Beagle* gave rise to his idea that species originate from ancestral forms through the accumulation of **adaptations**. He refined his theory for many years and finally published it in 1859 after learning that Wallace had come to the same idea. In *The Origin of Species*, Darwin proposed that evolution occurs by **natural selection**.

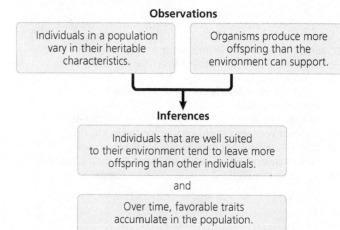

? *Describe how overreproduction and heritable variation relate to evolution by natural selection.*

CONCEPT 19.3

Evolution is supported by an overwhelming amount of scientific evidence (pp. 373–379)

- Researchers have directly observed natural selection leading to adaptive evolution in many studies, including research on soapberry bug populations and on MRSA.
- Organisms share characteristics because of common descent (**homology**) or because natural selection affects independently evolving species in similar environments in similar ways (**convergent evolution**).
- Fossils show that past organisms differed from living organisms, that many species have become extinct, and that species have evolved over long periods of time; fossils also document the origin of major new groups of organisms.
- Evolutionary theory can explain biogeographic patterns.

? *Summarize the different lines of evidence supporting the hypothesis that cetaceans descended from land mammals and are closely related to even-toed ungulates.*

TEST YOUR UNDERSTANDING

Level 1: Knowledge/Comprehension

1. Which of the following is *not* an observation or inference on which natural selection is based?
   a. There is heritable variation among individuals.
   b. Poorly adapted individuals never produce offspring.
   c. Species produce more offspring than the environment can support.
   d. Individuals whose characteristics are best suited to the environment generally leave more offspring than those whose characteristics are less well suited.
   e. Only a fraction of an individual's offspring may survive.

2. Which of the following observations helped Darwin shape his concept of descent with modification?
   a. Species diversity declines farther from the equator.
   b. Fewer species live on islands than on the nearest continents.
   c. Birds live on islands located farther from the mainland than the birds' maximum nonstop flight distance.
   d. South American temperate plants are more similar to the tropical plants of South America than to the temperate plants of Europe.
   e. Earthquakes reshape life by causing mass extinctions.

Level 2: Application/Analysis

3. Within six months of effectively using methicillin to treat *S. aureus* infections in a community, all new infections were caused by MRSA. How can this result best be explained?
   a. *S. aureus* can resist vaccines.
   b. A patient must have become infected with MRSA from another community.
   c. In response to the drug, *S. aureus* began making drug-resistant versions of the protein targeted by the drug.
   d. Some drug-resistant bacteria were present at the start of treatment, and natural selection increased their frequency.
   e. The drug caused the *S. aureus* DNA to change.

4. The upper forelimbs of humans and bats have fairly similar skeletal structures, whereas the corresponding bones in whales have very different shapes and proportions. However, genetic data suggest that all three kinds of organisms diverged from a common ancestor at about the same time. Which of the following is the most likely explanation for these data?
   a. Humans and bats evolved by natural selection, and whales evolved by Lamarckian mechanisms.
   b. Forelimb evolution was adaptive in people and bats, but not in whales.
   c. Natural selection in an aquatic environment resulted in significant changes to whale forelimb anatomy.
   d. Genes mutate faster in whales than in humans or bats.
   e. Whales are not properly classified as mammals.

5. DNA sequences in many human genes are very similar to the sequences of corresponding genes in chimpanzees. The most likely explanation for this result is that
   a. humans and chimpanzees share a relatively recent common ancestor.
   b. humans evolved from chimpanzees.
   c. chimpanzees evolved from humans.
   d. convergent evolution led to the DNA similarities.
   e. humans and chimpanzees are not closely related.

Level 3: Synthesis/Evaluation

6. **SCIENTIFIC INQUIRY**
   DRAW IT Mosquitoes resistant to the pesticide DDT first appeared in India in 1959, but now are found throughout the world. (a) Graph the data in the table below. (b) Examining the graph, hypothesize why the percentage of mosquitoes resistant to DDT rose rapidly. (c) Suggest an explanation for the global spread of DDT resistance.

Month	0	8	12
Mosquitoes Resistant* to DDT	4%	45%	77%

Source C. F. Curtis et al., Selection for and against insecticide resistance and possible methods of inhibiting the evolution of resistance in mosquitoes, *Ecological Entomology* 3:273–287 (1978).

*Mosquitoes were considered resistant if they were not killed within 1 hour of receiving a dose of 4% DDT.

7. **FOCUS ON EVOLUTION**
   Explain why anatomical and molecular features often fit a similar nested pattern. In addition, describe a process that can cause this not to be the case.

8. **FOCUS ON INTERACTIONS**
   Write a short essay (about 100–150 words) evaluating whether changes to an organism's physical environment are likely to result in evolutionary change. Use an example to support your reasoning.

For selected answers, see Appendix A.

MasteringBiology®

Students Go to **MasteringBiology** for assignments, the eText, and the Study Area with practice tests, animations, and activities.

Instructors Go to **MasteringBiology** for automatically graded tutorials and questions that you can assign to your students, plus Instructor Resources.

20

Phylogeny

KEY CONCEPTS

20.1 Phylogenies show evolutionary relationships

20.2 Phylogenies are inferred from morphological and molecular data

20.3 Shared characters are used to construct phylogenetic trees

20.4 Molecular clocks help track evolutionary time

20.5 New information continues to revise our understanding of evolutionary history

OVERVIEW

Investigating the Evolutionary History of Life

Look closely at the organism in **Figure 20.1**. Although it resembles a snake, this animal is actually a legless lizard known as the eastern glass lizard (*Ophisaurus ventralis*). Why isn't this glass lizard considered a snake? More generally, how do biologists distinguish and categorize the millions of species on Earth?

An understanding of evolutionary relationships suggests one way to address these questions: We can decide in which category to place a species by comparing its traits with those of potential close relatives. For example, the eastern glass lizard does not have a highly mobile jaw, a large number of vertebrae, or a short tail located behind the anus, three traits shared by all snakes. These and other characteristics suggest that despite a superficial resemblance, the glass lizard is not a snake.

Snakes and lizards are part of the continuum of life extending from the earliest organisms to the great variety of species alive today. To help make sense of that diversity, biologists trace **phylogeny**, the evolutionary history of a species or group of species. A phylogeny of lizards and snakes, for example, indicates that both the eastern glass lizard and snakes evolved from lizards with legs—but they evolved from different lineages of legged lizards (**Figure 20.2**). Thus, it appears that their limbless body forms evolved independently.

In fact, a broader survey of the lizards reveals that a snakelike body form has evolved in many different groups of lizards. Most lizards with such a body form are burrowers or live in grasslands. The repeated

▼ **Figure 20.1** What kind of organism is this?

▶ **Figure 20.2 Convergent evolution of limbless bodies.** A phylogeny based on DNA sequence data reveals that a legless body form evolved independently from legged ancestors in the lineages leading to the eastern glass lizard and to snakes.

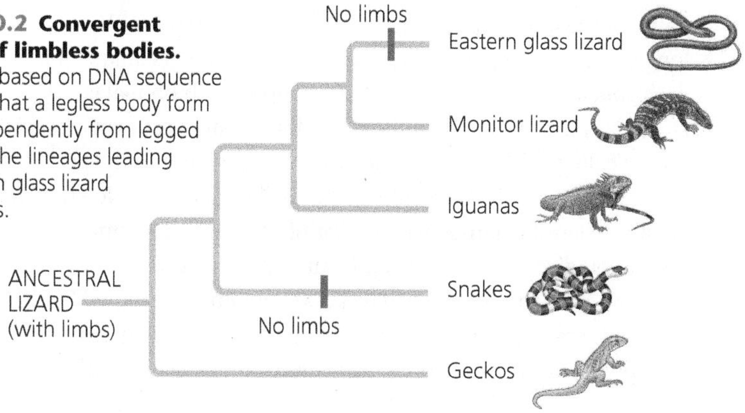

No limbs — Eastern glass lizard

Monitor lizard

Iguanas

ANCESTRAL LIZARD (with limbs)

No limbs — Snakes

Geckos

381

evolution of a snakelike body form in a consistent set of environments suggests that this change has been driven by natural selection: The legs of these organisms became reduced in size, or even disappeared, over generations as the species adapted to their environments.

In this chapter, we'll examine how biologists reconstruct and interpret phylogenies using **systematics**, a discipline focused on classifying organisms and determining their evolutionary relationships.

CONCEPT 20.1

Phylogenies show evolutionary relationships

Organisms share many characteristics because of common ancestry (see Chapter 19). As a result, we can learn a great deal about a species if we know its evolutionary history. For example, an organism is likely to share many of its genes, metabolic pathways, and structural proteins with its close relatives. We'll consider practical applications of such information later in this section, but first we'll examine how organisms are named and classified, the scientific discipline of **taxonomy**. We'll also look at how we can interpret and use diagrams that represent evolutionary history.

Binomial Nomenclature

Common names for organisms—such as monkey, finch, and lilac—convey meaning in casual usage, but they can also cause confusion. Each of these names, for example, refers to more than one species. Moreover, some common names do not accurately reflect the kind of organism they signify. Consider these three "fishes": jellyfish (a cnidarian), crayfish (a small lobsterlike crustacean), and silverfish (an insect). And of course, a given organism has different names in different languages.

To avoid ambiguity when communicating about their research, biologists refer to organisms by Latin scientific names. The two-part format of the scientific name, commonly called a **binomial**, was instituted in the 18th century by Carolus Linnaeus (see Chapter 19). The first part of a binomial is the name of the **genus** (plural, *genera*) to which the species belongs. The second part, called the specific epithet, is unique for each species within the genus. An example of a binomial is *Panthera pardus*, the scientific name for the large cat commonly called the leopard. Notice that the first letter of the genus is capitalized and the entire binomial is italicized. (Newly created scientific names are also "latinized": You can name an insect you discover after a friend, but you must add a Latin ending.) Many of the more than 11,000 binomials assigned by Linnaeus are still used today, including the optimistic name he gave our own species—*Homo sapiens*, meaning "wise man."

Hierarchical Classification

In addition to naming species, Linnaeus also grouped them into a hierarchy of increasingly inclusive categories. The first grouping is built into the binomial: Species that appear to be closely related are grouped into the same genus. For example, the leopard (*Panthera pardus*) belongs to a genus that also includes the African lion (*Panthera leo*), the tiger (*Panthera tigris*), and the jaguar (*Panthera onca*). Beyond genera, taxonomists employ progressively more comprehensive categories of classification. The taxonomic system named after Linnaeus, the Linnaean system, places related genera into the same **family**, families into **orders**, orders into **classes**, classes into **phyla** (singular, *phylum*), phyla into **kingdoms**, and, more recently, kingdoms into **domains (Figure 20.3)**. The resulting biological classification of a particular organism is somewhat like a postal address identifying a person in a particular apartment, in a building with many apartments, on a street with many apartment buildings, in a city with many streets, and so on.

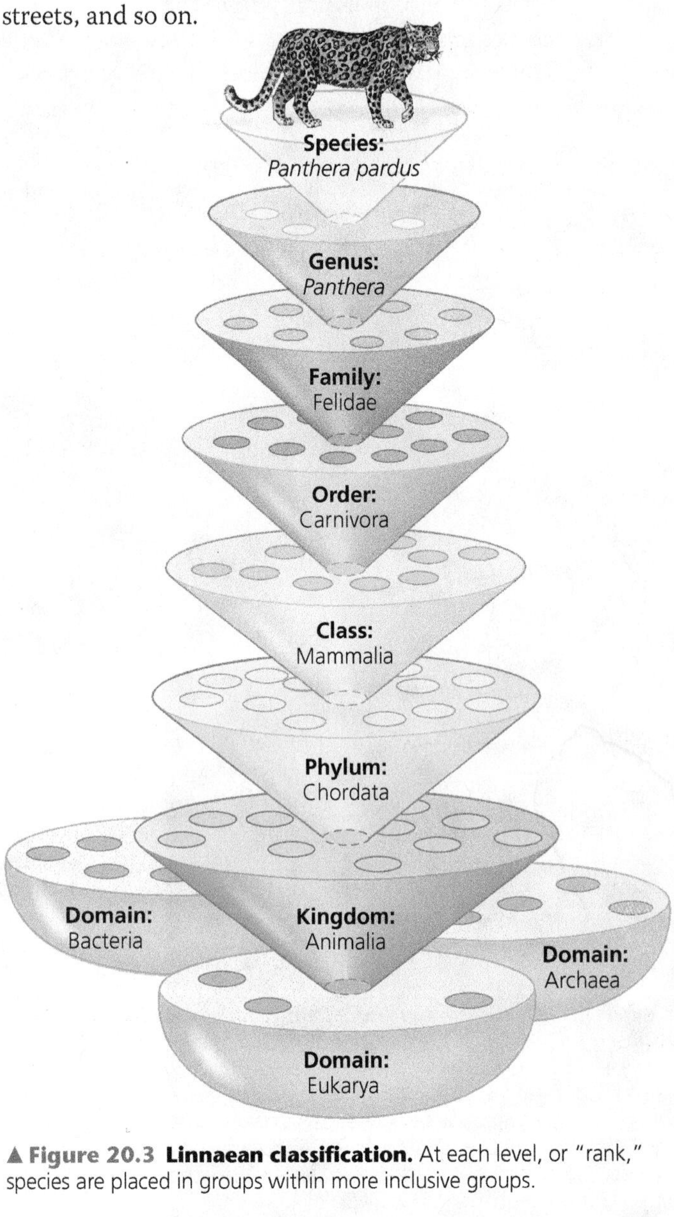

Species: *Panthera pardus*

Genus: Panthera

Family: Felidae

Order: Carnivora

Class: Mammalia

Phylum: Chordata

Domain: Bacteria

Kingdom: Animalia

Domain: Archaea

Domain: Eukarya

▲ **Figure 20.3 Linnaean classification.** At each level, or "rank," species are placed in groups within more inclusive groups.

The named taxonomic unit at any level of the hierarchy is called a **taxon** (plural, *taxa*). In the leopard example, *Panthera* is a taxon at the genus level, and Mammalia is a taxon at the class level that includes all the many orders of mammals. Note that in the Linnaean system, taxa broader than the genus are not italicized, though they are capitalized.

Classifying species is a way to structure our human view of the world. We lump together various species of trees to which we give the common name of pines and distinguish them from other trees that we call firs. Taxonomists have decided that pines and firs are different enough to be placed in separate genera, yet similar enough to be grouped into the same family, Pinaceae. As with pines and firs, higher levels of classification are usually defined by particular characters chosen by taxonomists. However, characters that are useful for classifying one group of organisms may not be appropriate for other organisms. For this reason, the larger categories often are not comparable between lineages; that is, an order of snails does not exhibit the same degree of morphological or genetic diversity as an order of mammals. Furthermore, as we'll see, the placement of species into orders, classes, and so on, does not necessarily reflect evolutionary history.

Linking Classification and Phylogeny

The evolutionary history of a group of organisms can be represented in a branching diagram called a **phylogenetic tree**. As in **Figure 20.4**, the branching pattern often matches how

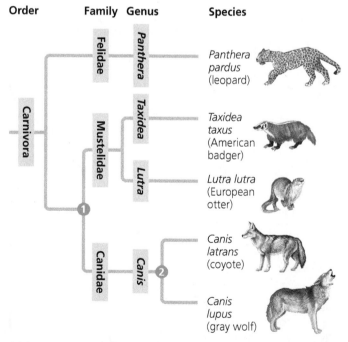

▲ **Figure 20.4 The connection between classification and phylogeny.** Hierarchical classification can reflect the branching patterns of phylogenetic trees. This tree traces possible evolutionary relationships between some of the taxa within order Carnivora, itself a branch of class Mammalia. The branch point ❶ represents the most recent common ancestor of all members of the weasel (Mustelidae) and dog (Canidae) families. The branch point ❷ represents the most recent common ancestor of coyotes and gray wolves.

taxonomists have classified groups of organisms nested within more inclusive groups. Sometimes, however, taxonomists have placed a species within a genus (or other group) to which it is *not* most closely related. One reason for such a mistake might be that over the course of evolution, a species has lost a key feature shared by its close relatives. If DNA or other new evidence indicates that an organism has been misclassified, the organism may be reclassified to accurately reflect its evolutionary history. Another issue is that while the Linnaean system may distinguish groups, such as amphibians, mammals, reptiles, and other classes of vertebrates, it tells us nothing about these groups' evolutionary relationships to one another. Such difficulties in aligning Linnaean classification with phylogeny have led many systematists to propose that classification be based entirely on evolutionary relationships.

Regardless of how groups are named, a phylogenetic tree represents a hypothesis about evolutionary relationships. These relationships often are depicted as a series of dichotomies, or two-way **branch points**. Each branch point represents the divergence of two evolutionary lineages from a common ancestor. In **Figure 20.5**, for example, branch point ❸ represents the common ancestor of taxa A, B, and C. The position of branch point ❹ to the right of ❸ indicates that taxa B and C diverged after their shared lineage split from that of taxon A. (Note also that tree branches can be rotated around a branch point without changing their evolutionary relationships.)

In Figure 20.5, taxa B and C are **sister taxa**, groups of organisms that share an immediate common ancestor (branch point ❹) and hence are each other's closest relatives. In addition, this tree, like most of the phylogenetic trees in this book, is **rooted**, which means that a branch point within the tree (often drawn farthest to the left) represents the most recent common ancestor of all taxa in the tree. The term **basal taxon**

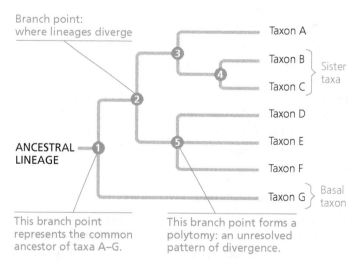

▲ **Figure 20.5 How to read a phylogenetic tree.**

DRAW IT *Redraw this tree, rotating the branches around branch points ❷ and ❹. Does your new version tell a different story about the evolutionary relationships between the taxa? Explain.*

refs to a lineage that diverges early in the history of a group and hence, like taxon G in Figure 20.5, lies on a branch that originates near the common ancestor of the group. Finally, the lineage leading to taxa D–F includes a **polytomy**, a branch point from which more than two descendant groups emerge. A polytomy signifies that evolutionary relationships among the taxa are not yet clear.

What We Can and Cannot Learn from Phylogenetic Trees

Let's summarize three key points about phylogenetic trees. First, they are intended to show patterns of descent, not phenotypic similarity. Although closely related organisms often resemble one another due to their common ancestry, they may not if their lineages have evolved at different rates or faced very different environmental conditions. For example, even though crocodiles are more closely related to birds than to lizards (see Figure 20.15), they look more like lizards because morphology has changed dramatically in the bird lineage.

Second, the sequence of branching in a tree does not necessarily indicate the actual (absolute) ages of the particular species. For example, the tree in Figure 20.4 does not indicate that the wolf evolved more recently than the European otter; rather, the tree shows only that the most recent common ancestor of the wolf and otter (branch point ❶) lived before the most recent common ancestor of the wolf and coyote (❷). To indicate when wolves and otters evolved, the tree would need to include additional divergences in each evolutionary lineage, as well as the dates when those splits occurred. Generally, unless given specific information about what the branch lengths in a phylogenetic tree mean—for example, that they are proportional to time—we should interpret the diagram solely in terms of patterns of descent. No assumptions should be made about when particular species evolved or how much change occurred in each lineage.

Third, we should not assume that a taxon on a phylogenetic tree evolved from the taxon next to it. Figure 20.4 does not indicate that wolves evolved from coyotes or vice versa. We can infer only that the lineage leading to wolves and the lineage leading to coyotes both evolved from the common ancestor ❷. That ancestor, which is now extinct, was neither a wolf nor a coyote. However, its descendants include the two *extant* (living) species shown here, wolves and coyotes.

Applying Phylogenies

Understanding phylogeny can have practical applications. Consider maize (corn), which originated in the Americas and is now an important food crop worldwide. From a phylogeny of maize based on DNA data, researchers have been able to identify two species of wild grasses that may be maize's closest living relatives. These two close relatives may be useful

as "reservoirs" of beneficial alleles that can be transferred to cultivated maize by cross-breeding or genetic engineering (see Concept 13.4).

A different use of phylogenetic trees is to infer species identities by analyzing the relatedness of DNA sequences from different organisms. Researchers have used this approach to investigate whether "whale meat" has been harvested illegally from whale species protected under international law rather than from species that can be harvested legally, such as Minke whales caught in the Southern Hemisphere **(Figure 20.6)**.

How do researchers construct trees like those we've considered here? In the next section, we'll begin to answer that question by examining the data used to determine phylogenies.

▼ Figure 20.6 Inquiry

What is the species identity of food being sold as whale meat?

Experiment C. S. Baker and S. R. Palumbi purchased 13 samples of "whale meat" from Japanese fish markets. They sequenced a specific part of the mitochondrial DNA (mtDNA) from each sample and compared their results with the comparable DNA sequence from known whale species. To infer the species identity of each sample, Baker and Palumbi constructed a *gene tree*, a phylogenetic tree that shows patterns of relatedness among DNA sequences rather than among taxa.

Results The analysis yielded the following gene tree:

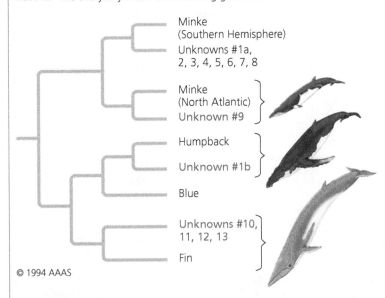

Minke (Southern Hemisphere)
Unknowns #1a, 2, 3, 4, 5, 6, 7, 8

Minke (North Atlantic)
Unknown #9

Humpback

Unknown #1b

Blue

Unknowns #10, 11, 12, 13

Fin

© 1994 AAAS

Conclusion This analysis indicated that mtDNA sequences of six of the unknown samples (in red) were most closely related to DNA sequences of whales that are not legal to harvest.

Source C. S. Baker and S. R. Palumbi, Which whales are hunted? A molecular genetic approach to monitoring whaling, *Science* 265:1538-1539 (1994).

WHAT IF? What diffferent results would have indicated that the whale meat had *not* been illegally harvested?

CONCEPT CHECK 20.1

1. Which levels of the classification in Figure 20.3 do humans share with leopards?

2. What does the phylogenetic tree in Figure 20.4 indicate about the evolutionary relationships between the leopard, badger, and wolf?

3. Which of the trees shown here depicts an evolutionary history different from the other two? Explain.

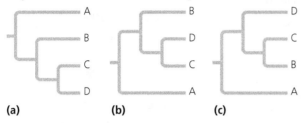

(a)　　　　　　(b)　　　　　　(c)

4. **WHAT IF?** Suppose new evidence indicates that taxon E in Figure 20.5 is the sister taxon of a group consisting of taxa D and F. Redraw the tree to accommodate this new finding.

For suggested answers, see Appendix A.

CONCEPT 20.2

Phylogenies are inferred from morphological and molecular data

To infer phylogeny, systematists must gather as much information as possible about the morphology, genes, and biochemistry of the relevant organisms. It is important to focus on features that result from common ancestry, because only such features reflect evolutionary relationships.

Morphological and Molecular Homologies

Recall that phenotypic and genetic similarities due to shared ancestry are called *homologies*. For example, the similarity in the number and arrangement of bones in the forelimbs of mammals is due to their descent from a common ancestor with the same bone structure; this is an example of a morphological homology (see Figure 19.16). In the same way, genes or other DNA sequences are homologous if they are descended from sequences carried by a common ancestor.

In general, organisms that share very similar morphologies or similar DNA sequences are likely to be more closely related than organisms with vastly different structures or sequences. In some cases, however, the morphological divergence between related species can be great and their genetic divergence small (or vice versa). Consider Hawaiian silversword plants: Some of these species are tall, twiggy trees, while others are dense, ground-hugging shrubs. But despite these striking phenotypic differences, the silverswords' genes are very similar. Based on these small molecular divergences, scientists estimate that the silversword group began to diverge 5 million years ago, which is also about the time when the oldest of the current Hawaiian islands formed. We'll discuss how scientists use molecular data to estimate such divergence times later in this chapter.

Sorting Homology from Analogy

A potential source of confusion in constructing a phylogeny is similarity due to convergent evolution—called **analogy**—rather than to shared ancestry (homology). Convergent evolution occurs when similar environmental pressures and natural selection produce similar (analogous) adaptations in organisms from different evolutionary lineages. For example, the two mole-like animals illustrated in **Figure 20.7** are similar in their external appearance. However, their internal anatomy, physiology, and reproductive systems are very dissimilar. Australian "moles" are marsupials; their young complete their embryonic development in a pouch on the outside of the mother's body. North American moles, in contrast, are eutherians; their young complete their embryonic development in the uterus within the mother's body. Indeed, genetic comparisons and the fossil record provide evidence that the common ancestor of these animals lived 140 million years ago, about the time the marsupial and eutherian mammals diverged. This common ancestor and most of its descendants were not mole-like, but analogous characteristics evolved independently in these two lineages as they became adapted to similar lifestyles.

Distinguishing between homology and analogy is critical in reconstructing phylogenies. To see why, consider bats and birds, both of which have adaptations that enable flight. This superficial resemblance might imply that bats are more closely related to birds than they are to cats, which cannot fly. But a closer examination reveals that a bat's wing is far more similar to the forelimbs of cats and other mammals than to

▲ Figure 20.7 **Convergent evolution of analogous burrowing characteristics.** An elongated body, enlarged front paws, small eyes, and a pad of thickened skin that protects a tapered nose all evolved independently in the marsupial Australian "mole" (top) and a eutherian North American mole (bottom).

a bird's wing. Bats and birds descended from a common tetrapod ancestor that lived about 320 million years ago. This common ancestor could not fly. Thus, although the underlying skeletal systems of bats and birds are homologous, their *wings* are not. Flight is enabled in different ways—stretched membranes in the bat wing versus feathers in the bird wing. Fossil evidence also documents that bat wings and bird wings arose independently from the forelimbs of different tetrapod ancestors. Thus, with respect to flight, a bat's wing is *analogous*, not homologous, to a bird's wing. Analogous structures that arose independently are also called **homoplasies** (from the Greek, meaning "to mold in the same way").

Besides corroborative similarities and fossil evidence, another clue to distinguishing between homology and analogy is the complexity of the characters being compared. The more elements that are similar in two complex structures, the more likely it is that they evolved from a common ancestor. For instance, the skulls of an adult human and an adult chimpanzee both consist of many bones fused together. The compositions of the skulls match almost perfectly, bone for bone. It is highly improbable that such complex structures, matching in so many details, have separate origins. More likely, the genes involved in the development of both skulls were inherited from a common ancestor. The same argument applies to comparisons at the gene level. Genes are sequences of thousands of nucleotides, each of which represents an inherited character in the form of one of the four DNA bases: A (adenine), G (guanine), C (cytosine), or T (thymine). If genes in two organisms share many portions of their nucleotide sequences, it is likely that the genes are homologous.

Evaluating Molecular Homologies

Comparing DNA molecules often poses technical challenges for researchers. The first step after sequencing the molecules is to align comparable sequences from the species being studied. If the species are very closely related, the sequences probably differ at only one or a few sites. In contrast, comparable nucleic acid sequences in distantly related species usually have different bases at many sites and may have different lengths. This is because insertions and deletions accumulate over long periods of time.

Suppose, for example, that certain noncoding DNA sequences near a particular gene are very similar in two species, except that the first base of the sequence has been deleted in one of the species. The effect is that the remaining sequence shifts back one notch. A comparison of the two sequences that does not take this deletion into account would overlook what in fact is a very good match. To address such problems, researchers have developed computer programs that estimate the best way to align comparable DNA segments of differing lengths **(Figure 20.8)**.

Such molecular comparisons reveal that many base substitutions and other differences have accumulated in the comparable genes of an Australian mole and a North American mole. The many differences indicate that their lineages have diverged

❶ These homologous DNA sequences are identical as species 1 and species 2 begin to diverge from their common ancestor.

1 CCATCAGAGTCC
2 CCATCAGAGTCC

❷ Deletion and insertion mutations shift what had been matching sequences in the two species.

Deletion
1 CCATCA(G)AGTCC
2 CCATCAGAGTCC
(G T A) Insertion

❸ Of the regions of the species 2 sequence that match the species 1 sequence, those shaded orange no longer align because of these mutations.

1 CCAT CAAGTCC
2 CCATGTACAGAGTCC

❹ The matching regions realign after a computer program adds gaps in sequence 1.

1 CCAT___CA_AGTCC
2 CCATGTACAGAGTCC

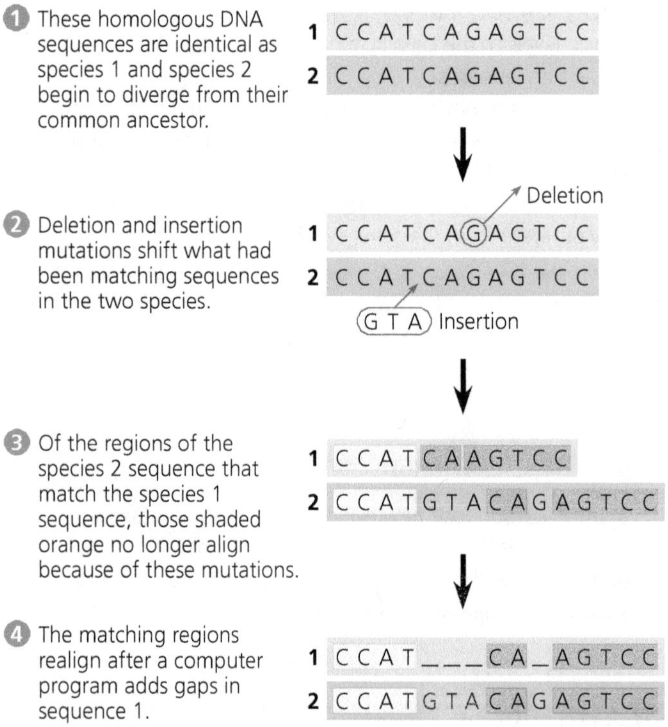

▲ **Figure 20.8 Aligning segments of DNA.** Systematists search for similar sequences along DNA segments from two species (only one DNA strand is shown for each species). In this example, 11 of the original 12 bases have not changed since the species diverged. Hence, those portions of the sequences still align once the length is adjusted.

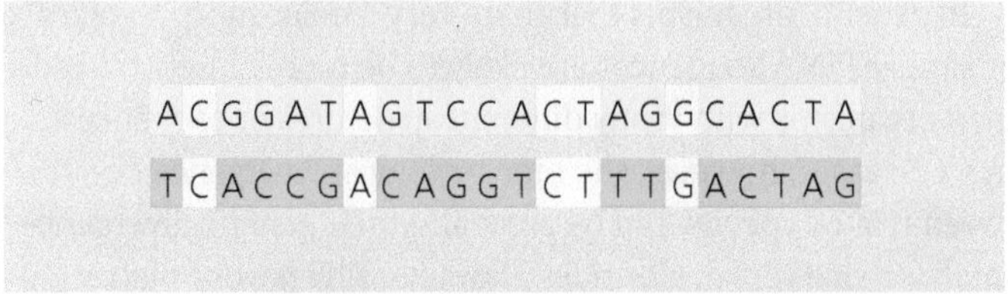

greatly since their common ancestor; thus, we say that the living species are not closely related. In contrast, the high degree of gene sequence similarity among the silversword plants indicates that they are all very closely related, in spite of their considerable morphological differences.

Just as with morphological characters, it is necessary to distinguish homology from analogy in evaluating molecular similarities for evolutionary studies. Two sequences that resemble each other at many points along their length most likely are homologous (see Figure 20.8). But in organisms that do not appear to be closely related, the bases that their otherwise very different sequences happen to share may simply be coincidental matches, called molecular homoplasies **(Figure 20.9)**.

ACGGATAGTCCACTAGGCACTA
TCACCGACAGGTCTTTGACTAG

▲ **Figure 20.9 A molecular homoplasy.** These two DNA sequences from organisms that are not closely related coincidentally share 23% of their bases. Statistical tools have been developed to determine whether DNA sequences that share more than 25% of their bases do so because they are homologous.

❓ *Why might you expect organisms that are not closely related to nevertheless share roughly 25% of their bases?*

Scientists have developed statistical tools that can help distinguish "distant" homologies from such coincidental matches in extremely divergent sequences.

CONCEPT CHECK 20.2

1. Decide whether each of the following pairs of structures more likely represents analogy or homology, and explain your reasoning: (a) a porcupine's quills and a cactus's spines; (b) a cat's paw and a human's hand; (c) an owl's wing and a hornet's wing.

2. **WHAT IF?** Suppose that species 1 and species 2 have similar appearances but very divergent gene sequences and that species 2 and species 3 have very different appearances but similar gene sequences. Which pair of species is more likely to be closely related: 1 and 2, or 2 and 3? Explain.

For suggested answers, see Appendix A.

CONCEPT 20.3

Shared characters are used to construct phylogenetic trees

In reconstructing phylogenies, the first step is to distinguish homologous features from analogous ones (since only homology reflects evolutionary history). Next we must choose a method of inferring phylogeny from these homologous characters. A widely used set of methods is known as cladistics.

Cladistics

In the approach to systematics called **cladistics**, common ancestry is the primary criterion used to classify organisms. Using this methodology, biologists attempt to place species into groups called **clades**, each of which includes an ancestral species and all of its descendants **(Figure 20.10a)**. Clades, like taxonomic ranks, are nested within larger clades. In Figure 20.4, for example, the cat group (Felidae) represents a clade within a larger clade (Carnivora) that also includes the dog group (Canidae).

However, a taxon is equivalent to a clade only if it is **monophyletic** (from the Greek, meaning "single tribe"), signifying that it consists of an ancestral species and all of its descendants (see Figure 20.10a). Contrast this with a **paraphyletic** ("beside the tribe") group, which consists of an ancestral species and some, but not all, of its descendants **(Figure 20.10b)**, or a **polyphyletic** ("many tribes") group, which includes taxa with different ancestors **(Figure 20.10c)**. Note also that in a paraphyletic group, the most recent common ancestor of all members of the group *is* part of the group, whereas in a polyphyletic group, the most recent common ancestor *is not* part of the group. Next we'll discuss how clades are identified using shared derived characters.

Shared Ancestral and Shared Derived Characters

As a result of descent with modification, organisms share some characteristics with their ancestors, and they also have some characteristics that differ from those of their ancestors. For example, all mammals have backbones, but a backbone does not distinguish mammals from other vertebrates because *all* vertebrates have backbones. The backbone predates the branching of mammals from other vertebrates. Thus, for mammals, the backbone is a **shared ancestral character**, a character that originated in an ancestor of the taxon. In contrast, hair is a character shared by all mammals but *not* found in their ancestors. Thus, in mammals, hair is considered a **shared derived character**, an evolutionary novelty unique to a clade.

▼ **Figure 20.10 Monophyletic, paraphyletic, and polyphyletic groups.**

(a) Monophyletic group (clade)

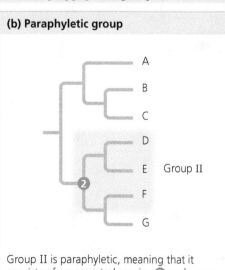

Group I, consisting of three species (A, B, C) and their common ancestor ①, is a clade, also called a monophyletic group. A monophyletic group consists of an ancestral species and *all* of its descendants.

(b) Paraphyletic group

Group II is paraphyletic, meaning that it consists of an ancestral species ② and some of its descendants (species D, E, F) but not all of them (missing species G).

(c) Polyphyletic group

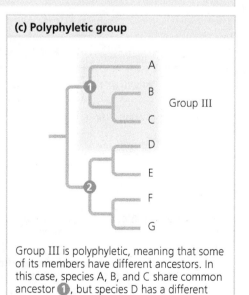

Group III is polyphyletic, meaning that some of its members have different ancestors. In this case, species A, B, and C share common ancestor ①, but species D has a different ancestor: ②.

Note that it is a relative matter whether a particular character is considered ancestral or derived. A backbone can also qualify as a shared derived character, but only at a deeper branch point that distinguishes all vertebrates from other animals.

Inferring Phylogenies Using Derived Characters

Shared derived characters are unique to particular clades. Because all features of organisms arose at some point in the history of life, it should be possible to determine the clade in which each shared derived character first appeared and to use that information to infer evolutionary relationships.

To see how this analysis is done, consider the set of characters shown in **Figure 20.11a** for each of five vertebrates—a leopard, turtle, frog, bass, and lamprey (a jawless aquatic vertebrate). As a basis of comparison, we need to select an outgroup. An **outgroup** is a species or group of species from an evolutionary lineage that is known to have diverged before the lineage that includes the species we are studying (the **ingroup**). A suitable outgroup can be determined based on evidence from morphology, paleontology, embryonic development, and gene sequences. An appropriate outgroup for our example is the lancelet, a small animal that lives in mudflats and (like vertebrates) is a member of the more inclusive group called the chordates. Unlike the vertebrates, however, the lancelet does not have a backbone.

By comparing members of the ingroup with each other and with the outgroup, we can determine which characters were derived at the various branch points of vertebrate evolution. For example, *all* of the vertebrates in the ingroup have backbones: This character was present in the ancestral vertebrate, but not in the outgroup. Now note that hinged jaws are a character absent in lampreys but present in other members of the ingroup; this character helps us to identify an early branch point in the vertebrate clade. Proceeding in this way, we can translate the data in our table of characters into a phylogenetic tree that groups all the ingroup taxa into a hierarchy based on their shared derived characters (**Figure 20.11b**).

Phylogenetic Trees with Proportional Branch Lengths

In the phylogenetic trees we have presented so far, the lengths of the tree's branches do not indicate the degree of evolutionary change in each lineage. Furthermore, the chronology represented by the branching pattern of the tree is relative (earlier versus later) rather than absolute (how many millions of years ago). But in some tree diagrams, branch lengths are proportional to amount of evolutionary change or to the times at which particular events occurred.

In **Figure 20.12**, for example, the branch length of the phylogenetic tree reflects the number of changes that have taken place in a particular DNA sequence in that lineage. Note that the total length of the horizontal lines from the base of the tree to the mouse is less than that of the line leading to the outgroup species, the fruit fly *Drosophila*. This implies that in the time since the mouse and fly diverged from a common ancestor, more genetic changes have occurred in the *Drosophila* lineage than in the mouse lineage.

Even though the branches of a phylogenetic tree may have different lengths, among organisms alive today, all the different lineages that descend from a common ancestor have survived

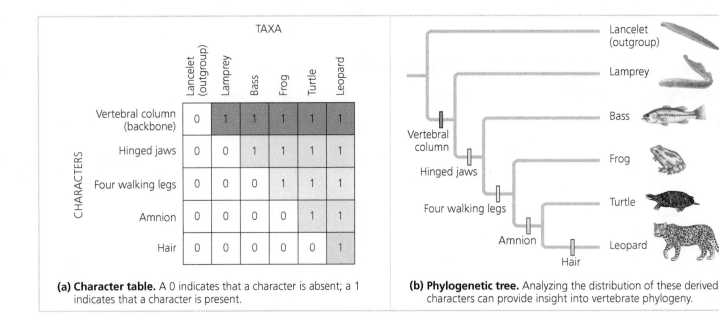

(a) **Character table.** A 0 indicates that a character is absent; a 1 indicates that a character is present.

(b) **Phylogenetic tree.** Analyzing the distribution of these derived characters can provide insight into vertebrate phylogeny.

▲ **Figure 20.11 Constructing a phylogenetic tree.** The characters used here include the amnion, a membrane that encloses the embryo inside a fluid-filled sac (see Figure 27.25).

DRAW IT *In (b), circle the most inclusive clade for which a hinged jaw is a shared ancestral character.*

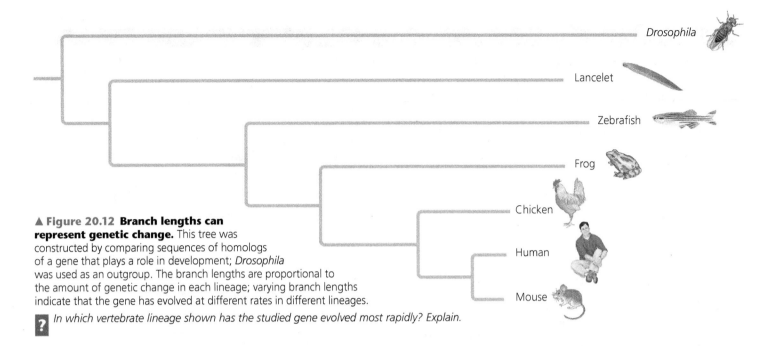

▲ **Figure 20.12 Branch lengths can represent genetic change.** This tree was constructed by comparing sequences of homologs of a gene that plays a role in development; *Drosophila* was used as an outgroup. The branch lengths are proportional to the amount of genetic change in each lineage; varying branch lengths indicate that the gene has evolved at different rates in different lineages.

? *In which vertebrate lineage shown has the studied gene evolved most rapidly? Explain.*

for the same number of years. To take an extreme example, humans and bacteria had a common ancestor that lived over 3 billion years ago. Fossils and genetic evidence indicate that this ancestor was a single-celled prokaryote. Even though bacteria have apparently changed little in their morphology since that common ancestor, there have nonetheless been 3 billion

years of evolution in the bacterial lineage, just as there have been 3 billion years of evolution in the lineage that ultimately gave rise to humans.

These equal spans of chronological time can be represented in a phylogenetic tree whose branch lengths are proportional to time **(Figure 20.13)**. Such a tree draws on fossil data to place

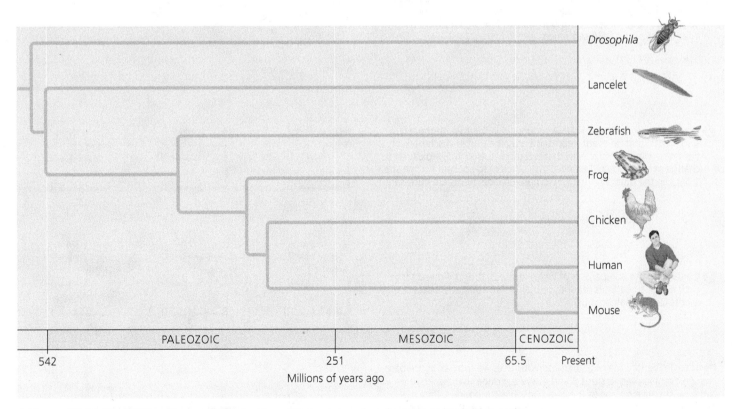

▲ **Figure 20.13 Branch lengths can indicate time.** This tree is based on the same molecular data as the tree in Figure 20.12, but here the branch points are mapped to dates based on fossil evidence. Thus, the branch lengths are proportional to time. Each lineage has the same total length from the base of the tree to the branch tip, indicating that all the lineages have diverged from the common ancestor for equal amounts of time.

Applying Parsimony to a Problem in Molecular Systematics

Application In considering possible phylogenies for a group of species, systematists compare molecular data for the species. An efficient way to begin is by identifying the most parsimonious hypothesis—the one that requires the fewest evolutionary events (molecular changes) to have occurred.

Technique Follow the numbered steps as we apply the principle of parsimony to a hypothetical phylogenetic problem involving three closely related bird species.

Species I   Species II   Species III

① First, draw the three possible phylogenies for the species. (Although only 3 trees are possible when ordering 3 species, the number of possible trees increases rapidly with the number of species: There are 15 trees for 4 species and 34,459,425 trees for 10 species.)

Three phylogenetic hypotheses:

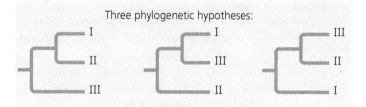

② Tabulate the molecular data for the species. In this simplified example, the data represent a DNA sequence consisting of just four nucleotide bases. Data from several outgroup species (not shown) were used to infer the ancestral DNA sequence.

	Site 1	2	3	4
Species I	C	T	A	T
Species II	C	T	T	C
Species III	A	G	A	C
Ancestral sequence	A	G	T	T

③ Now focus on site 1 in the DNA sequence. In the tree on the left, a single base-change event, represented by the purple hatchmark on the branch leading to species I and II (and labeled 1/C, indicating a change at site 1 to nucleotide C), is sufficient to account for the site 1 data. In the other two trees, two base-change events are necessary.

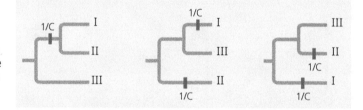

④ Continuing the comparison of bases at site 2, 3, and 4 reveals that each of the three trees requires a total of five additional base-change events (purple hatchmarks).

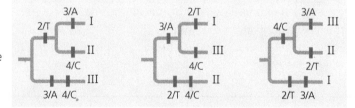

Results To identify the most parsimonious tree, we total all of the base-change events noted in steps 3 and 4. We conclude that the first tree is the most parsimonious of the three possible phylogenies. (In a real example, many more sites would be analyzed. Hence, the trees would often differ by more than one base-change event.)

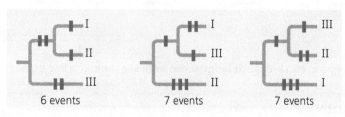

6 events   7 events   7 events

branch points in the context of geologic time. Additionally, it is possible to combine these two types of trees by labeling branch points with information about rates of genetic change or dates of divergence.

Maximum Parsimony

As the growing database of DNA sequences enables us to study more species, the difficulty of building the phylogenetic tree that best describes their evolutionary history also grows. What if you are analyzing data for 50 species? There are 3×10^{76} different ways to arrange 50 species into a tree! And which tree in this huge forest reflects the true phylogeny? Systematists can never be sure of finding the most accurate tree in such a large data set, but they can narrow the possibilities by applying the principle of maximum parsimony.

According to the principle of **maximum parsimony**, we should first investigate the simplest explanation that is consistent with the facts. (The parsimony principle is also called "Occam's razor" after William of Occam, a 14th-century English philosopher who advocated this minimalist problem-solving approach of "shaving away" unnecessary complications.) In the case of trees based on morphology, the most parsimonious tree requires the fewest evolutionary events, as measured by the origin of shared derived morphological characters. For phylogenies based on DNA, the most parsimonious tree requires the fewest base changes.

Scientists have developed many computer programs to search for trees that are parsimonious. When a large amount of accurate data is available, the methods used in these programs usually yield similar trees. As an example of one method, **Figure 20.14** walks you through the process of identifying the most parsimonious molecular tree for a three-species problem. Computer programs use the principle of parsimony to estimate phylogenies in a similar way: They examine large numbers of possible trees and select the tree or trees that require the fewest evolutionary changes.

Phylogenetic Trees as Hypotheses

This is a good place to reiterate that any phylogenetic tree represents a hypothesis about how the various organisms in the tree are related to one another. The best hypothesis is the one that best fits all the available data. A phylogenetic hypothesis may be modified when new evidence compels systematists to revise their trees. Indeed, while many older phylogenetic hypotheses have been supported by new morphological and molecular data, others have been changed or rejected.

Thinking of phylogenies as hypotheses also allows us to use them in a powerful way: We can make and test predictions based on the assumption that a phylogeny—our hypothesis—is correct. For example, in an approach known as *phylogenetic bracketing*, we can predict (by parsimony) that features shared by two groups of closely related organisms are present in their

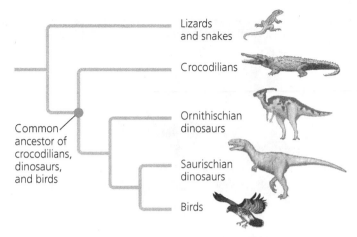

▲ **Figure 20.15 A phylogenetic tree of birds and their close relatives.**

? *What is the most basal taxon represented in this tree?*

common ancestor and all of its descendants unless independent data indicate otherwise. (Note that "prediction" can refer to unknown past events as well as to evolutionary changes yet to occur.)

This approach has been used to make novel predictions about dinosaurs. For example, there is evidence that birds descended from the theropods, a group of bipedal saurischian dinosaurs. As seen in **Figure 20.15**, the closest living relatives of birds are crocodiles. Birds and crocodiles share numerous features: They have four-chambered hearts, they "sing" to defend territories and attract mates (although a crocodile's "song" is more like a bellow), and they build nests **(Figure 20.16)**. Both birds and crocodiles also care for their eggs by *brooding*, a behavior in which a parent warms the eggs with its body. Birds brood by sitting on their eggs, whereas crocodiles cover their eggs with their neck. Reasoning that any feature shared by birds and crocodiles is likely to have been present in their common ancestor (denoted by the blue dot in Figure 20.15) and *all* of its descendants, biologists predicted that dinosaurs had four-chambered hearts, sang, built nests, and exhibited brooding.

▲ **Figure 20.16 A crocodile guards its nest.** After building its nest mound, this female African dwarf crocodile will care for the eggs until they hatch.

Front limb

Hind limb

Eggs

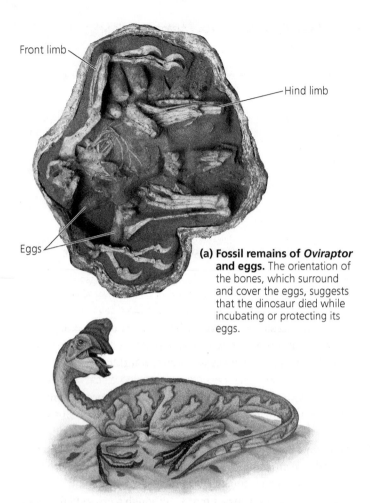

(a) Fossil remains of *Oviraptor* **and eggs.** The orientation of the bones, which surround and cover the eggs, suggests that the dinosaur died while incubating or protecting its eggs.

(b) Artist's reconstruction of the dinosaur's posture based on the fossil findings.

▲ **Figure 20.17 Fossil support for a phylogenetic prediction: Dinosaurs built nests and brooded their eggs.**

Internal organs, such as the heart, rarely fossilize, and it is, of course, difficult to test whether dinosaurs sang to defend territories and attract mates. However, fossilized dinosaur eggs and nests have provided evidence supporting the prediction of brooding in dinosaurs. First, a fossil embryo of an *Oviraptor* dinosaur was found, still inside its egg. This egg was identical to those found in another fossil, one that showed an adult *Oviraptor* crouching over a group of eggs in a posture similar to that seen in brooding birds today **(Figure 20.17)**. Researchers suggested that the *Oviraptor* dinosaur preserved in this second fossil died while incubating or protecting its eggs. The broader conclusion that emerged from this work—that dinosaurs built nests and exhibited brooding—has since been strengthened by additional fossil discoveries that show that other species of dinosaurs built nests and sat on their eggs. Finally, by supporting predictions based on the phylogenetic hypothesis shown in Figure 20.15, fossil discoveries of nests and brooding in dinosaurs provide independent data that suggest that the hypothesis is correct.

CONCEPT CHECK 20.3

1. To distinguish a particular clade of mammals within the larger clade that corresponds to class Mammalia, would hair be a useful character? Why or why not?

2. The most parsimonious tree of evolutionary relationships can be inaccurate. How can this occur?

3. **WHAT IF?** Draw a phylogenetic tree that includes the relationships from Figure 20.15 and those shown here. Traditionally, all the taxa shown besides birds and mammals were classified as reptiles. Would a cladistic approach support that classification? Explain.

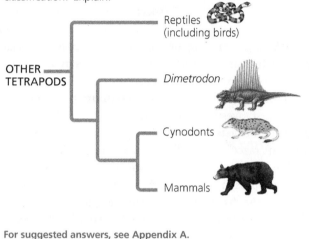

Reptiles (including birds)

OTHER TETRAPODS

Dimetrodon

Cynodonts

Mammals

For suggested answers, see Appendix A.

CONCEPT 20.4

Molecular clocks help track evolutionary time

One goal of evolutionary biology is to understand the relationships among all organisms, including those for which there is no fossil record. However, if we attempt to determine the timing of phylogenies that extend beyond the fossil record, we must rely on an important assumption about how change occurs at the molecular level.

Molecular Clocks

We stated earlier that researchers have estimated that the common ancestor of Hawaiian silversword plants lived about 5 million years ago. How did they make this estimate? They relied on the concept of a **molecular clock**, an approach for measuring the absolute time of evolutionary change based on the observation that some genes and other regions of genomes appear to evolve at constant rates. An assumption underlying the molecular clock is that the number of nucleotide substitutions in related genes is proportional to the time that has elapsed since the genes branched from their common ancestor (divergence time).

We can calibrate the molecular clock of a gene that has a reliable average rate of evolution by graphing the number of genetic differences—for example, nucleotide, codon, or amino acid differences—against the dates of evolutionary branch

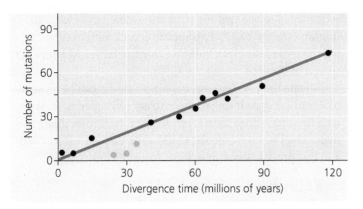

▲ **Figure 20.18 A molecular clock for mammals.** The number of accumulated mutations in seven proteins has increased over time in a consistent manner for most mammal species. The three green data points represent primate species, whose proteins appear to have evolved more slowly than those of other mammals. The divergence time for each data point was based on fossil evidence.

? *Use the graph to estimate the divergence time for a mammal with a total of 30 mutations in the seven proteins.*

points that are known from the fossil record (**Figure 20.18**). The average rates of genetic change inferred from such graphs can then be used to estimate the dates of events that cannot be discerned from the fossil record, such as the origin of the silverswords discussed earlier.

Of course, no gene marks time with complete precision. In fact, some portions of the genome appear to have evolved in irregular bursts that are not at all clocklike. And even those genes that seem to act as reliable molecular clocks are accurate only in the statistical sense of showing a fairly smooth *average* rate of change. Over time, there may still be deviations from that average rate. Furthermore, the same gene may evolve at different rates in different groups of organisms. Finally, when comparing genes that are clocklike, the rate of the clock may vary greatly from one gene to another; some genes evolve a million times faster than others.

Differences in Clock Speed

What causes such differences in the speed at which clocklike genes evolve? The answer relates to the fact that some mutations may be selectively neutral—neither beneficial nor detrimental. Of course, many new mutations are harmful and are removed quickly by selection. But if most of the rest are neutral and have little or no effect on fitness, then the rate of those neutral mutations should indeed be regular, like a clock. Differences in the clock rate for different genes are a function of how important a gene is. If the exact sequence of amino acids that a gene specifies is essential to survival, most of the mutational changes will be harmful and only a few will be neutral. As a result, such genes change only slowly. But if the exact sequence of amino acids is less critical, fewer of the new mutations will be harmful and more will be neutral. Such genes change more quickly.

Potential Problems with Molecular Clocks

In fact, molecular clocks do not run as smoothly as expected if the underlying mutations were selectively neutral. Many irregularities are likely to be the result of natural selection in which certain DNA changes are favored over others. Indeed, evidence suggests that almost half the amino acid differences in proteins of two *Drosophila* species, *D. simulans* and *D. yakuba*, are not neutral but have resulted from natural selection. But because the direction of natural selection may change repeatedly over long periods of time (and hence may average out), some genes experiencing selection can nevertheless serve as approximate markers of elapsed time.

Another question arises when researchers attempt to extend molecular clocks beyond the time span documented by the fossil record. Although some fossils are more than 3 billion years old, these are very rare. An abundant fossil record extends back only about 550 million years, but molecular clocks have been used to date evolutionary divergences that occurred a billion or more years ago. These estimates assume that the clocks have been constant for all that time. Such estimates are highly uncertain.

In some cases, problems may be avoided by calibrating molecular clocks with data on the rates at which genes have evolved in different taxa. In other cases, problems may be avoided by using many genes rather than the common approach of using just one or a few genes. By using many genes, fluctuations in evolutionary rate due to natural selection or other factors that vary over time may average out. For example, one group of researchers constructed molecular clocks of vertebrate evolution from published sequence data for 658 nuclear genes. Despite the broad period of time covered (nearly 600 million years) and the fact that natural selection probably affected some of these genes, their estimates of divergence times agreed closely with fossil-based estimates. As this example suggests, if used with care, molecular clocks can aid our understanding of evolutionary relationships.

Applying a Molecular Clock: Dating the Origin of HIV

Researchers have used a molecular clock to date the origin of HIV infection in humans. Phylogenetic analysis shows that HIV, the virus that causes AIDS, is descended from viruses that infect chimpanzees and other primates. (Most of these viruses do not cause AIDS-like diseases in their native hosts.) When did HIV jump to humans? There is no simple answer, because the virus has spread to humans more than once. The multiple origins of HIV are reflected in the variety of strains (genetic types) of the virus. HIV's genetic material is made of RNA, and like other RNA viruses, it evolves quickly.

The most widespread strain in humans is HIV-1 M. To pinpoint the earliest HIV-1 M infection, researchers compared samples of the virus from various times during the epidemic, including a sample from 1959. A comparison of gene

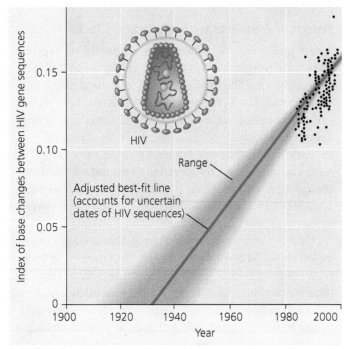

© 2000 AAAS

▲ **Figure 20.19 Dating the origin of HIV-1 M.** The black data points are based on DNA sequences of an HIV gene in patients' blood samples. (The dates when these individual HIV gene sequences arose are not certain because a person can harbor the virus for years before symptoms occur.) Projecting the gene's rate of change in the 1980s and 1990s backward in time suggests that the virus originated in the 1930s.

sequences showed that the virus has evolved in a clocklike fashion **(Figure 20.19)**. Extrapolating backward in time using the molecular clock indicates that the HIV-1 M strain first spread to humans during the 1930s.

Despite their limitations, molecular clocks can be a useful tool for biologists trying to reconstruct phylogenies. As with data from any other source, researchers must re-evaluate their hypotheses when molecular clocks provide new information—and this process sometimes leads to significant changes.

CONCEPT CHECK 20.4

1. What is a molecular clock? What assumption underlies the use of a molecular clock?
2. **MAKE CONNECTIONS** Review Concept 14.5. Explain how numerous base changes could occur in an organism's DNA yet have no effect on its fitness.
3. **WHAT IF?** Suppose a molecular clock dates the divergence of two taxa at 80 million years ago, but new fossil evidence shows that the taxa diverged at least 120 million years ago. Explain how this could happen.

For suggested answers, see Appendix A.

Scientific Skills Exercise

Interpreting Data in a Phylogenetic Tree

What Are the Evolutionary Relationships among Bears? Researchers have long debated different hypotheses for the phylogeny and classification of species in the bear family, Ursidae. In this exercise, you will interpret the results of one study using DNA sequence data to infer relationships among living bear species.

How the Study Was Done In 2008, researchers obtained complete mitochondrial DNA (mtDNA) genome sequences for the eight living species of bears. The mtDNA sequences were aligned and compared using maximum parsimony and other methods. The researchers then constructed the phylogenetic tree shown below.

Data from the Study

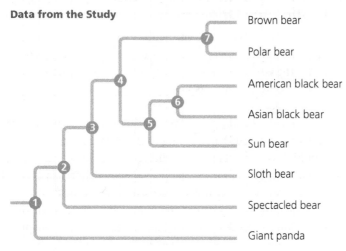

Interpret the Data

1. First, practice reading phylogenetic relationships from the tree. Which number represents the most recent common ancestor of (a) all bears, (b) sloth bears and spectacled bears, and (c) the Asian black bear and the brown bear?
2. Is this phylogenetic tree rooted? Explain.
3. According to the data represented in this tree, is the sun bear more closely related to the sloth bear or the polar bear? Explain.
4. Which species is a basal taxon among the bears? What does this mean about its evolution compared with that of the others?

In a study published in 2000, researchers sequenced part of the mitochondrial cytochrome *b* gene from 61 brown bears; 31 of these bears were from coastal mainland Alaska, while the rest were from the ABC islands in southeastern Alaska. Mainland and ABC brown bears differ by 11 fixed nucleotide substitutions in the cytochrome *b* gene. The researchers compared the sequences of the brown bears with those of 55 polar bears. They found that polar bears and ABC brown bears differ at only three nucleotides in this gene, whereas polar bears and mainland brown bears had more differences.

5. (a) Do the results from the 2000 study indicate that brown bears are monophyletic, paraphyletic, or polyphyletic? Explain. (b) Redraw the tree to reflect the hypothesis supported by the 2000 study, and circle the sister taxon of polar bears.
6. Describe in words how the two trees differ.

Data from J. Krause et al., Mitochondrial genomes reveal an explosive radiation of extinct and extant bears near the Miocene-Pliocene boundary, *BMC Evolutionary Biology* 8: 220 (2008).

(MB) A related version of this Scientific Skills Exercise can be assigned in MasteringBiology.

New information continues to revise our understanding of evolutionary history

The discovery that the glass lizard in Figure 20.1 evolved from a different lineage of legless lizards than did snakes is one example of how our understanding of life's diversity is affected by systematics. The **Scientific Skills Exercise** describes another example and gives you an opportunity to interpret phylogenetic data from bear species. Indeed, in recent decades, systematists have gained insight into even the very deepest branches of the tree of life by analyzing DNA sequence data.

From Two Kingdoms to Three Domains

Taxonomists once classified all known species into two kingdoms: plants and animals. Classification schemes with more than two kingdoms gained broad acceptance in the late 1960s, when many biologists recognized five kingdoms: Monera (prokaryotes), Protista (a diverse kingdom consisting mostly of unicellular organisms), Plantae, Fungi, and Animalia. This system highlighted the two fundamentally different types of cells, prokaryotic and eukaryotic, and set the prokaryotes apart from all eukaryotes by placing them in their own kingdom, Monera.

However, phylogenies based on genetic data soon began to reveal a problem with this system: Some prokaryotes differ as much from each other as they do from eukaryotes. Such difficulties have led biologists to adopt a three-domain system **(Figure 20.20)**. The three domains—Bacteria, Archaea, and Eukarya—are a taxonomic level higher than the kingdom level. The validity of these domains is supported by many studies, including a recent study that analyzed nearly 100 completely sequenced genomes.

The domain Bacteria contains most of the currently known prokaryotes, while the domain Archaea consists of a diverse group of prokaryotic organisms that inhabit a wide variety of environments. The domain Eukarya consists of all the organisms that have cells containing true nuclei. This domain includes many groups of single-celled organisms as well as multicellular plants, fungi, and animals. Figure 20.20 represents one possible phylogenetic tree for the three domains and the many lineages they encompass.

The three-domain system highlights the fact that much of the history of life has been about single-celled organisms. The two prokaryotic domains consist entirely of single-celled organisms, and even in Eukarya, only the branches labeled in red type (land plants, fungi, and animals) are dominated by multicellular organisms. Of the five kingdoms previously recognized by taxonomists, most biologists continue to recognize Plantae, Fungi, and Animalia, but not Monera and Protista. The kingdom Monera is obsolete because it would

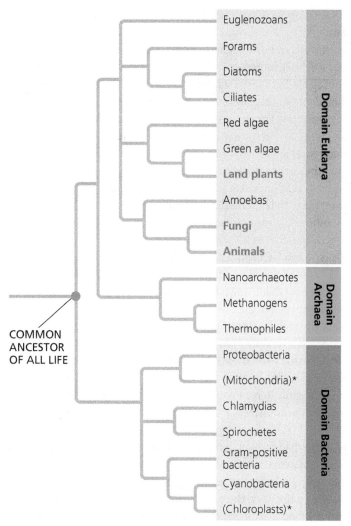

▲ **Figure 20.20 The three domains of life.** This phylogenetic tree is based on sequence data for rRNA and other genes. For simplicity, only some of the major branches in each domain are shown. The lineages within Eukarya that are dominated by multicellular organisms (plants, fungi, and animals) are indicated by blue type. The two lineages denoted by an asterisk are based on DNA from cellular organelles. All other lineages consist solely or mainly of single-celled organisms.

MAKE CONNECTIONS *After reviewing endosymbiont theory (see Figure 4.16), explain the specific positions of the mitochondrion and chloroplast lineages on this tree.*

have members in two different domains. The kingdom Protista has also crumbled because it includes members that are more closely related to plants, fungi, or animals than to other protists (see Chapter 25).

The Important Role of Horizontal Gene Transfer

In the phylogeny shown in Figure 20.20, the first major split in the history of life occurred when bacteria diverged from other organisms. If this tree is correct, eukaryotes and archaea are more closely related to each other than either is to bacteria.

This reconstruction of the tree of life is based largely on sequence comparisons of rRNA genes, which code for the

RNA components of ribosomes. Because ribosomes are fundamental to the workings of the cell, rRNA genes have evolved so slowly that homologies between distantly related organisms can still be detected, making these genes very useful for determining evolutionary relationships between deep branches in the history of life. However, other genes reveal a different set of relationships. For example, researchers have found that many of the genes that influence metabolism in yeast (a unicellular eukaryote) are more similar to genes in the domain Bacteria than they are to genes in the domain Archaea—a finding that suggests that the eukaryotes may share a more recent common ancestor with bacteria than with archaea. As we'll discuss in Chapter 25, these conflicting results may reflect how eukaryotes originated: as a "fusion" between two prokaryotes, one of which was a bacterium and the other an archaean.

Comparisons of complete genomes from the three domains show that there have been substantial movements of genes between organisms in the different domains. These took place through **horizontal gene transfer**, a process in which genes are transferred from one genome to another through mechanisms such as exchange of transposable elements and plasmids, viral infection (see Chapter 17), and perhaps fusions of organisms. Recent research reinforces the view that horizontal gene transfer is important. For example, a 2008 analysis indicated that, on average, 80% of the genes in 181 prokaryotic genomes had moved between species at some point during the course of evolution. Because phylogenetic trees are based on the assumption that genes are passed vertically from one generation to the next, the occurrence of such horizontal transfer events helps to explain why trees built using different genes can give inconsistent results.

Horizontal gene transfer has played a key role throughout the evolutionary history of life, and it continues to occur today. Some biologists have argued that horizontal gene transfer is so common that the early history of life should be represented not as a dichotomously branching tree like that in Figure 20.20, but rather as a tangled network of connected branches (**Figure 20.21**). Although scientists continue to debate whether early steps in the history of life are best represented as a tree or a tangled web, in recent decades there have been many exciting discoveries about evolutionary events that

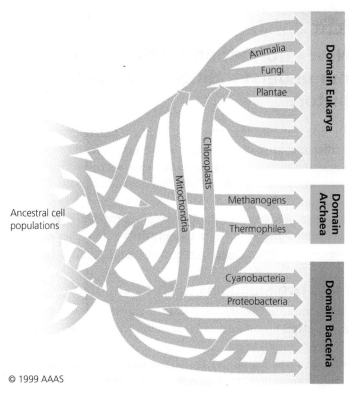

© 1999 AAAS

▲ **Figure 20.21 A tangled web of life.** Horizontal gene transfer may have been so common in the early history of life that the base of a "tree of life" might be more accurately portrayed as a tangled web.

occurred later in time. We'll explore the mechanisms that underlie such events in the rest of this unit's chapters, beginning with factors that cause genetic change in populations.

CONCEPT CHECK 20.5

1. Why is the kingdom Monera no longer considered a valid taxon?
2. Explain why phylogenies based on different genes can yield different branching patterns for the tree of all life.
3. **WHAT IF?** Draw the three possible dichotomously branching trees showing evolutionary relationships for the domains Bacteria, Archaea, and Eukarya. Two of these trees have been supported by genetic data. Is it likely that the third tree might also receive such support? Explain your answer.

For suggested answers, see Appendix A.

20 Chapter Review

SUMMARY OF KEY CONCEPTS

CONCEPT 20.1

Phylogenies show evolutionary relationships (pp. 382–385)

- Linnaeus's **binomial** classification system gives organisms two-part names: a **genus** plus a specific epithet.

- In the Linnaean system, species are grouped into increasingly broad taxa: Related genera are placed into the same family, families into orders, orders into classes, classes into phyla, phyla into kingdoms, and (more recently) kingdoms into domains.
- Systematists depict evolutionary relationships as branching **phylogenetic trees**. Many systematists propose that classification be based entirely on evolutionary relationships.

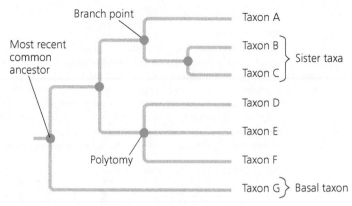

- Unless branch lengths are proportional to time or amount of genetic change, a phylogenetic tree indicates only patterns of descent.
- Much information can be learned about a species from its evolutionary history; hence, phylogenies are useful in a wide range of applications.

? *Humans and chimpanzees are sister species. Explain what that means.*

CONCEPT 20.2

Phylogenies are inferred from morphological and molecular data (pp. 385–387)

- Organisms with similar morphologies or DNA sequences are likely to be more closely related than organisms with very different structures and genetic sequences.
- To infer phylogeny, **homology** (similarity due to shared ancestry) must be distinguished from **analogy** (similarity due to convergent evolution).
- Computer programs are used to align comparable DNA sequences and to distinguish molecular homologies from coincidental matches between taxa that diverged long ago.

? *Why is it necessary to distinguish homology from analogy to infer phylogeny?*

CONCEPT 20.3

Shared characters are used to construct phylogenetic trees (pp. 387–392)

- A **clade** is a monophyletic grouping that includes an ancestral species and all of its descendants.
- Clades can be distinguished by their **shared derived characters**.

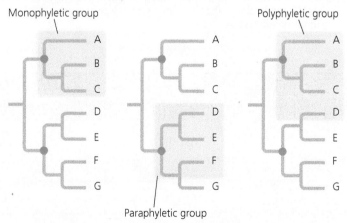

- Branch lengths can be proportional to amount of evolutionary change or time.

- Among phylogenies, the most parsimonious tree is the one that requires the fewest evolutionary changes.
- Well-supported phylogenetic hypotheses are consistent with a wide range of data.

? *Explain the logic of using shared derived characters to infer phylogeny.*

CONCEPT 20.4

Molecular clocks help track evolutionary time (pp. 392–394)

- Some regions of DNA change at a rate consistent enough to serve as a **molecular clock**, in which the amount of genetic change is used to estimate the date of past evolutionary events. Other DNA regions change in a less predictable way.
- A molecular clock analysis suggests that the most common strain of HIV jumped from primates to humans in the 1930s.

? *Describe some assumptions and limitations of molecular clocks.*

CONCEPT 20.5

New information continues to revise our understanding of evolutionary history (pp. 394–396)

- Past classification systems have given way to the current view of the tree of life, which consists of three great **domains**: Bacteria, Archaea, and Eukarya.
- Phylogenies based on rRNA genes suggest that eukaryotes are most closely related to archaea, while data from some other genes suggest a closer relationship to bacteria.
- Genetic analyses indicate that extensive horizontal gene transfer has occurred throughout the evolutionary history of life.

? *Why was the five-kingdom system abandoned for a three-domain system?*

TEST YOUR UNDERSTANDING

Level 1: Knowledge/Comprehension

1. In a comparison of birds and mammals, the condition of having four limbs is
   a. a shared ancestral character.
   b. a shared derived character.
   c. a character useful for distinguishing birds from mammals.
   d. an example of analogy rather than homology.
   e. a character useful for sorting bird species.

2. To apply parsimony to constructing a phylogenetic tree,
   a. choose the tree that assumes all evolutionary changes are equally probable.
   b. choose the tree in which the branch points are based on as many shared derived characters as possible.
   c. base phylogenetic trees only on the fossil record, as this provides the simplest explanation for evolution.
   d. choose the tree that represents the fewest evolutionary changes in either DNA sequences or morphology.
   e. choose the tree with the fewest branch points.

Level 2: Application/Analysis

3. In Figure 20.4, which similarly inclusive taxon descended from the same common ancestor as Canidae?
   a. Felidae
   b. Mustelidae
   c. Carnivora
   d. *Canis*
   e. *Lutra*

4. Three living species X, Y, and Z share a common ancestor T, as do extinct species U and V. A grouping that consists of species T, X, Y, and Z (but not U or V) makes up
   a. a monophyletic taxon.
   b. a clade.
   c. an ingroup, with species U as the outgroup.
   d. a paraphyletic group.
   e. a polyphyletic group.

5. Based on the tree below, which statement is *not* correct?

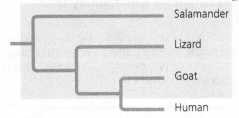

   a. The salamander lineage is a basal taxon.
   b. Salamanders are a sister group to the group containing lizards, goats, and humans.
   c. Salamanders are as closely related to goats as to humans.
   d. Lizards are more closely related to salamanders than to humans.
   e. The group highlighted by shading is paraphyletic.

6. If you were using cladistics to build a phylogenetic tree of cats, which of the following would be the best outgroup?
   a. lion
   b. domestic cat
   c. wolf
   d. leopard
   e. tiger

7. The relative lengths of the frog and mouse branches in the phylogenetic tree in Figure 20.12 indicate that
   a. frogs evolved before mice.
   b. mice evolved before frogs.
   c. the genes of frogs and mice have only coincidental homoplasies.
   d. the homolog has evolved more slowly in mice.
   e. the homolog has evolved more rapidly in mice.

Level 3: Synthesis/Evaluation

8. **SCIENTIFIC INQUIRY**
   DRAW IT (a) Draw a phylogenetic tree based on characters 1–5 in the table below. Place hatch marks on the tree to indicate the origin(s) of characters 1–6. (b) Assume that tuna and dolphins are sister species, and redraw the phylogenetic tree accordingly. Place hatch marks on the tree to indicate the origin(s) of characters 1–6. (c) How many evolutionary changes are required in each tree? Which tree is most parsimonious?

Character	Lancelet (outgroup)	Lamprey	Tuna	Salamander	Turtle	Leopard	Dolphin
1. Backbone	0	1	1	1	1	1	1
2. Hinged jaw	0	0	1	1	1	1	1
3. Four limbs	0	0	0	1	1	1	1*
4. Amnion	0	0	0	0	1	1	1
5. Milk	0	0	0	0	0	1	1
6. Dorsal (back) fin	0	0	1	0	0	0	1

*Although adult dolphins have only two obvious limbs (their flippers), as embryos they have two hind-limb buds, for a total of four limbs.

9. **FOCUS ON EVOLUTION**
   Darwin suggested looking at a species' close relatives to learn what its ancestors may have been like. How does his suggestion anticipate recent methods, such as phylogenetic bracketing and the use of outgroups in cladistic analysis?

10. **FOCUS ON INFORMATION**
    In a short essay (100–150 words), explain how genetic information—along with the process of descent with modification—enables scientists to construct phylogenies that extend hundreds of millions of years back in time.

For selected answers, see Appendix A.

MasteringBiology®

Students Go to **MasteringBiology** for assignments, the eText, and the Study Area with practice tests, animations, and activities.

Instructors Go to **MasteringBiology** for automatically graded tutorials and questions that you can assign to your students, plus Instructor Resources.

21

The Evolution of Populations

KEY CONCEPTS

21.1 Genetic variation makes evolution possible

21.2 The Hardy-Weinberg equation can be used to test whether a population is evolving

21.3 Natural selection, genetic drift, and gene flow can alter allele frequencies in a population

21.4 Natural selection is the only mechanism that consistently causes adaptive evolution

OVERVIEW

The Smallest Unit of Evolution

One common misconception about evolution is that individual organisms evolve. It is true that natural selection acts on individuals: Each organism's traits affect its survival and reproductive success compared with that of other individuals. But the evolutionary impact of natural selection is only apparent in the changes in a *population* of organisms over time.

Consider the medium ground finch (*Geospiza fortis*), a seed-eating bird that inhabits the Galápagos Islands **(Figure 21.1)**. In 1977, the *G. fortis* population on the island of Daphne Major was decimated by a long period of drought: Of some 1,200 birds, only 180 survived. Researchers Peter and Rosemary Grant observed that during the drought, small, soft seeds were in short supply. The finches mostly fed on large, hard seeds that were more plentiful. Birds with larger, deeper beaks were better able to crack and eat these larger seeds, and they survived at a higher rate than finches with smaller beaks. Since beak depth is an inherited trait in these birds, the average beak depth in the next generation of *G. fortis* was greater than it had been in the pre-drought population **(Figure 21.2)**. The finch population had evolved by natural selection. However, the *individual* finches did not evolve. Each bird had a beak of a particular size, which did not grow larger during the drought. Rather, the proportion of large beaks in the population increased from generation to generation: The population evolved, not its individual members.

▼ **Figure 21.1** Is this finch evolving?

▶ Figure 21.2 **Evidence of selection by food source.** The data represent adult beak depth measurements of medium ground finches hatched in the generations before and after the 1977 drought. In a single generation, evolution by natural selection resulted in a larger average beak size in the population.

(MB) A related Experimental Inquiry Tutorial can be assigned in MasteringBiology.

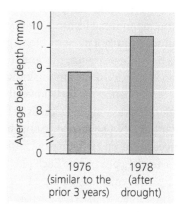

Focusing on evolutionary change in populations, we can define evolution on its smallest scale, called **microevolution**, as a change in allele frequencies in a population over generations. As you will see in this chapter, natural selection is not the only cause of microevolution. In fact, there are three main mechanisms that can cause allele frequency change: natural selection, genetic drift (chance events that alter allele frequencies), and gene flow (the transfer of alleles between populations). Each of these mechanisms has distinctive effects on the genetic composition of populations. However, only natural selection consistently improves the match between organisms and their environment (adaptation). Before we examine natural selection and adaptation more closely, let's revisit a prerequisite for these processes in a population: genetic variation.

▲ **Figure 21.3 Phenotypic variation in horses.** In horses, coat color varies along a continuum and is influenced by multiple genes.

CONCEPT 21.1

Genetic variation makes evolution possible

In *The Origin of Species*, Darwin provided abundant evidence that life on Earth has evolved over time, and he proposed natural selection as the primary mechanism for that change. He observed that individuals differ in their inherited traits and that selection acts on such differences, leading to evolutionary change. Although Darwin realized that variation in heritable traits is a prerequisite for evolution, he did not know precisely how organisms pass heritable traits to their offspring.

Just a few years after Darwin published *The Origin of Species*, Gregor Mendel wrote a groundbreaking paper on inheritance in pea plants (see Chapter 11). In that paper, Mendel proposed a model of inheritance in which organisms transmit discrete heritable units (now called genes) to their offspring. Although Darwin did not know about genes, Mendel's paper set the stage for understanding the genetic differences on which evolution is based. Here we'll examine such genetic differences and how they are produced.

Genetic Variation

Individuals within a species vary in their specific characteristics. Among humans, you can easily observe phenotypic variation in facial features, height, and voice. And though you cannot identify a person's blood group (A, B, AB, or O) from his or her appearance, this and many other molecular traits also vary extensively among individuals.

Such phenotypic variations often reflect **genetic variation**, differences among individuals in the composition of their genes or other DNA sequences. Some heritable phenotypic differences occur on an "either-or" basis, such as the flower colors of Mendel's pea plants: Each plant had flowers that were either purple or white (see Figure 11.3). Characters that vary in this

way are typically determined by a single gene locus, with different alleles producing distinct phenotypes. In contrast, other phenotypic differences vary in gradations along a continuum. Such variation usually results from the influence of two or more genes on a single phenotypic character. In fact, many phenotypic characters are influenced by multiple genes, including coat color in horses (**Figure 21.3**), seed number in maize (corn), and height in humans.

How much do genes and other DNA sequences vary from one individual to another? Genetic variation at the whole-gene level (*gene variability*) can be quantified as the average percentage of loci that are heterozygous. (Recall that a heterozygous individual has two different alleles for a given locus, whereas a homozygous individual has two identical alleles for that locus.) As an example, on average the fruit fly *Drosophila melanogaster* is heterozygous for about 1,920 of its 13,700 loci (14%) and homozygous for all the rest.

Considerable genetic variation can also be measured at the molecular level of DNA (*nucleotide variability*). But little of this variation results in phenotypic variation because many of the differences occur within *introns*, noncoding segments of DNA lying between *exons*, the regions retained in mRNA after RNA processing (see Figure 14.12). And of the variations that occur within exons, most do not cause a change in the amino acid sequence of the protein encoded by the gene. In the sequence comparison summarized in **Figure 21.4**, there are 43 nucleotide sites with variable base pairs (where substitutions have occurred), as well as several sites where insertions or deletions have occurred. Although 18 variable sites occur within the four exons of the *Adh* gene, only one of these variations—at site 1,490—results in an amino acid change. Note, however, that this single variable site is enough to cause genetic variation at the level of the gene, and two different forms of the Adh enzyme are produced.

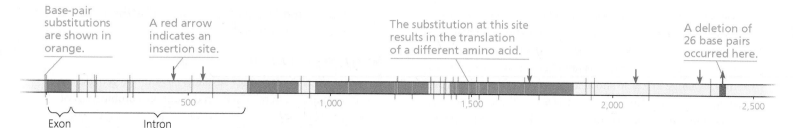

Base-pair substitutions are shown in orange.

A red arrow indicates an insertion site.

The substitution at this site results in the translation of a different amino acid.

A deletion of 26 base pairs occurred here.

Exon   Intron

▲ **Figure 21.4 Extensive genetic variation at the molecular level.** This diagram summarizes data from a study comparing the DNA sequence of the alcohol dehydrogenase (*Adh*) gene in several fruit flies (*Drosophila melanogaster*). The *Adh* gene has four exons (dark blue) separated by introns (light blue); the exons include the coding regions that are ultimately translated into the amino acids of the Adh enzyme. Only one substitution has a phenotypic effect, producing a different form of the Adh enzyme.

MAKE CONNECTIONS *Review Figures 14.6 and 14.12. Explain how a base-pair substitution that alters a coding region of the* Adh *locus could have no effect on amino acid sequence. Then explain how an insertion in an exon could have no effect on the protein produced.*

It is important to bear in mind that some phenotypic variation is not heritable (**Figure 21.5** shows a striking example in a caterpillar of the southwestern United States). Phenotype is the product of an inherited genotype and many environmental influences (see Concept 11.3). In a human example, bodybuilders alter their phenotypes dramatically but do not pass their huge muscles on to the next generation. In general, only the genetically determined part of phenotypic variation can have evolutionary consequences. As such, genetic variation provides the raw material for evolutionary change: Without genetic variation, evolution cannot occur.

Sources of Genetic Variation

The genetic variation on which evolution depends originates when mutation, gene duplication, or other processes produce new alleles and new genes. Genetic variants can be produced in short periods of time in organisms that reproduce rapidly. Sexual reproduction can also result in genetic variation as existing genes are arranged in new ways.

Formation of New Alleles

New alleles can arise by *mutation*, a change in the nucleotide sequence of an organism's DNA. A mutation is like a shot in the dark—we cannot predict accurately which segments of DNA will be altered or in what way. In multicellular organisms, only mutations in cell lines that produce gametes can be passed to offspring. In plants and fungi, this is not as limiting as it may sound, since many different cell lines can produce gametes. But in most animals, the majority of mutations occur in somatic cells and are lost when the individual dies.

A change of as little as one base in a gene, called a "point mutation," can have a significant impact on phenotype, as in sickle-cell disease (see Figure 14.25). Organisms reflect many generations of past selection, and hence their phenotypes tend to be well matched to their environments. As a result, it's unlikely that a new mutation that alters a phenotype will improve it. In fact, most such mutations are at least slightly harmful. But since much of the DNA in eukaryotic genomes does not code for protein products, point mutations in these noncoding

(a)

(b)

▲ **Figure 21.5 Nonheritable variation.** These caterpillars of the moth *Nemoria arizonaria* owe their different appearances to chemicals in their diets, not to differences in their genotypes. **(a)** Caterpillars raised on a diet of oak flowers resemble the flowers, whereas **(b)** their siblings raised on oak leaves resemble oak twigs.

regions are generally harmless. Also, because of the redundancy in the genetic code, even a point mutation in a gene that encodes a protein will have no effect on the protein's function if the amino acid composition is not changed. And even where there is a change in the amino acid, it may not affect the protein's shape and function. However, as you will see later in this chapter, a mutant allele may on rare occasions actually make its bearer better suited to the environment, enhancing reproductive success.

Altering Gene Number or Position

Chromosomal changes that delete, disrupt, or rearrange many loci at once are usually harmful. However, when such large-scale changes leave genes intact, they may not affect the organisms' phenotypes. In rare cases, chromosomal rearrangements may even be beneficial. For example, the translocation of part of one chromosome to a different chromosome could link DNA segments in a way that produces a positive effect.

A key potential source of variation is the duplication of genes due to errors in meiosis (such as unequal crossing over), slippage during DNA replication, or the activities of transposable elements (see Concept 18.4). Duplications of large chromosome segments, like other chromosomal aberrations, are often harmful, but the duplication of smaller pieces of DNA may not be. Gene duplications that do not have severe effects can persist over generations, allowing mutations to accumulate. The result is an expanded genome with new genes that may take on new functions.

Such increases in gene number appear to have played a major role in evolution. For example, the remote ancestors of mammals had a single gene for detecting odors that has since been duplicated many times: Humans today have about 350 functional olfactory receptor genes, and mice have 1,000. This proliferation of olfactory genes probably helped mammals over the course of evolution, enabling them to detect faint odors and to distinguish among many different smells.

Rapid Reproduction

Mutation rates tend to be low in plants and animals, averaging about one mutation in every 100,000 genes per generation, and they are often even lower in prokaryotes. But prokaryotes have many more generations per unit of time, so mutations can quickly generate genetic variation in populations of these organisms. The same is true of viruses. For instance, HIV has a generation span of about two days. It also has an RNA genome, which has a much higher mutation rate than a typical DNA genome because of the lack of RNA repair mechanisms in host cells (see Chapter 17). For this reason, it is unlikely that a single-drug treatment would ever be effective against HIV; mutant forms of the virus that are resistant to a particular drug would no doubt proliferate in relatively short order. The most effective AIDS treatments to date have been drug "cocktails" that combine several medications. It is less likely that a set of

mutations that together confer resistance to *all* the drugs will occur in a short time period.

Sexual Reproduction

In organisms that reproduce sexually, most of the genetic variation in a population results from the unique combination of alleles that each individual receives from its parents. Of course, at the nucleotide level, all the differences among these alleles have originated from past mutations. Sexual reproduction then shuffles existing alleles and deals them at random to produce individual genotypes.

Three mechanisms contribute to this shuffling: crossing over, independent assortment of chromosomes, and fertilization (see Chapter 10). During meiosis, homologous chromosomes, one inherited from each parent, trade some of their alleles by crossing over. These homologous chromosomes and the alleles they carry are then distributed at random into gametes. Then, because myriad possible mating combinations exist in a population, fertilization brings together gametes that are likely to have different genetic backgrounds. The combined effects of these three mechanisms ensure that sexual reproduction rearranges existing alleles into fresh combinations each generation, providing much of the genetic variation that makes evolution possible.

CONCEPT CHECK 21.1

1. Explain why genetic variation within a population is a prerequisite for evolution.
2. Of all the mutations that occur in a population, why do only a small fraction become widespread?
3. **MAKE CONNECTIONS** If a population stopped reproducing sexually (but still reproduced asexually), how would its genetic variation be affected over time? Explain. (See Concept 10.4.)

For suggested answers, see Appendix A.

CONCEPT 21.2

The Hardy-Weinberg equation can be used to test whether a population is evolving

Although the individuals in a population must differ genetically for evolution to occur, the presence of genetic variation does not guarantee that a population will evolve. For that to happen, one of the factors that cause evolution must be at work. In this section, we'll explore one way to test whether evolution is occurring in a population. First, let's clarify what we mean by a population.

Gene Pools and Allele Frequencies

A **population** is a group of individuals of the same species that live in the same area and interbreed, producing fertile offspring. Different populations of a single species may

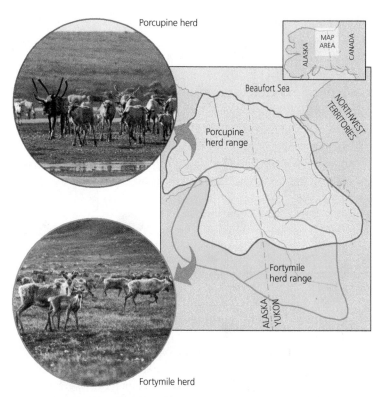

▲ Figure 21.6 One species, two populations. These two caribou populations in the Yukon are not totally isolated; they sometimes share the same area. Still, members of either population are most likely to breed within their own population.

be isolated geographically from one another, exchanging genetic material only rarely. Such isolation is common for species that live on widely separated islands or in different lakes. But not all populations are isolated, nor must populations have sharp boundaries (Figure 21.6). Still, members of a population typically breed with one another and thus on average are more closely related to each other than to members of other populations.

We can characterize a population's genetic makeup by describing its **gene pool**, which consists of all copies of every type of allele at every locus in all members of the population. If only one allele exists for a particular locus in a population, that allele is said to be *fixed* in the gene pool, and all individuals are homozygous for that allele. But if there are two or more alleles for a particular locus in a population, individuals may be either homozygous or heterozygous.

Each allele has a frequency (proportion) in the population. For example, imagine a population of 500 wildflower plants with two alleles, C^R and C^W, for a locus that codes for flower pigment. These alleles show incomplete dominance (see Figure 11.10); thus, each genotype has a distinct phenotype. Plants homozygous for the C^R allele ($C^R C^R$) produce red pigment and have red flowers; plants homozygous for the C^W allele ($C^W C^W$) produce no red pigment and have

 $C^R C^R$

 $C^W C^W$

 $C^R C^W$

white flowers; and heterozygotes ($C^R C^W$) produce some red pigment and have pink flowers.

In our population, suppose there are 320 plants with red flowers, 160 with pink flowers, and 20 with white flowers. Because these are diploid organisms, these 500 individuals have a total of 1,000 copies of the gene for flower color. The C^R allele accounts for 800 of these copies ($320 \times 2 = 640$ for $C^R C^R$ plants, plus $160 \times 1 = 160$ for $C^R C^W$ plants). Thus, the frequency of the C^R allele is $800/1,000 = 0.8$ (80%).

When studying a locus with two alleles, the convention is to use p to represent the frequency of one allele and q to represent the frequency of the other allele. Thus, p, the frequency of the C^R allele in the gene pool of this population, is $p = 0.8$ (80%). And because there are only two alleles for this gene, the frequency of the C^W allele, represented by q, must be $q = 1 - p = 0.2$ (20%). For loci that have more than two alleles, the sum of all allele frequencies must still equal 1 (100%).

Next we'll see how allele and genotype frequencies can be used to test whether evolution is occurring in a population.

The Hardy-Weinberg Principle

One way to assess whether natural selection or other factors are causing evolution at a particular locus is to determine what the genetic makeup of a population would be if it were *not* evolving at that locus. We can then compare that scenario with the data that we actually observe for the population. If there are no differences, we can conclude that the population is not evolving. If there are differences, this suggests that the population may be evolving—and then we can try to figure out why.

Hardy-Weinberg Equilibrium

The gene pool of a population that is not evolving can be described by the **Hardy-Weinberg principle**, named for the British mathematician and German physician, respectively, who independently derived it in 1908. This principle states that the frequencies of alleles and genotypes in a population will remain constant from generation to generation, provided that only Mendelian segregation and recombination of alleles are at work. Such a gene pool is in *Hardy-Weinberg equilibrium*.

To use the Hardy-Weinberg principle, it is helpful to think about genetic crosses in a new way. Previously, we used Punnett squares to determine the genotypes of offspring in a genetic cross (see Figure 11.5). Here, instead of considering the possible allele combinations from one cross, we'll consider the combination of alleles in *all* of the crosses in a population.

Imagine that all the alleles for a given locus from all the individuals in a population are placed in a large bin. We can think of this bin as holding the population's gene pool for that locus. "Reproduction" occurs by selecting alleles at random from the bin; somewhat similar events occur in nature when fish release sperm and eggs into the water or when pollen (containing plant sperm) is blown about by the wind. By viewing reproduction as a process of randomly selecting and combining alleles from

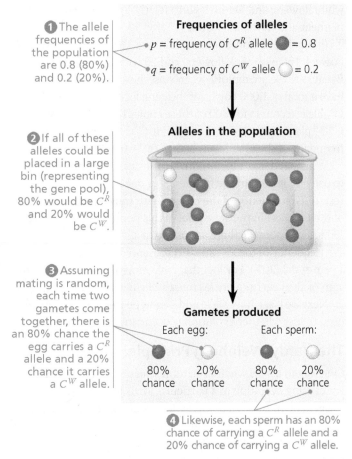

Frequencies of alleles

1. The allele frequencies of the population are 0.8 (80%) and 0.2 (20%).

p = frequency of C^R allele ● = 0.8

q = frequency of C^W allele ○ = 0.2

Alleles in the population

2. If all of these alleles could be placed in a large bin (representing the gene pool), 80% would be C^R and 20% would be C^W.

Gametes produced

3. Assuming mating is random, each time two gametes come together, there is an 80% chance the egg carries a C^R allele and a 20% chance it carries a C^W allele.

Each egg:

80% chance   20% chance

Each sperm:

80% chance   20% chance

4. Likewise, each sperm has an 80% chance of carrying a C^R allele and a 20% chance of carrying a C^W allele.

▲ **Figure 21.7 Selecting alleles at random from a gene pool.**

the bin (the gene pool), we are in effect assuming that mating occurs at random—that is, that all male-female matings are equally likely.

Let's apply the bin analogy to the hypothetical wildflower population discussed earlier (**Figure 21.7**). In that population of 500 flowers, the frequency of the allele for red flowers (C^R) is $p = 0.8$, and the frequency of the allele for white flowers (C^W) is $q = 0.2$. In other words, a bin holding all 1,000 copies of the flower-color gene in the population would contain 800 C^R alleles and 200 C^W alleles. Assuming that gametes are formed by selecting alleles at random from the bin, the probability that an egg or sperm contains a C^R or C^W allele is equal to the frequency of these alleles in the bin. Thus, as shown in Figure 21.7, each egg has an 80% chance of containing a C^R allele and a 20% chance of containing a C^W allele; the same is true for each sperm.

Using the rule of multiplication (see Figure 11.9), we can now calculate the frequencies of the three possible genotypes, assuming random unions of sperm and eggs. The probability that two C^R alleles will come together is $p \times p = p^2 = 0.8 \times 0.8 = 0.64$. Thus, about 64% of the plants in the next generation will have the genotype $C^R C^R$. The frequency of $C^W C^W$ individuals is expected to be about $q \times q = q^2 = 0.2 \times 0.2 = 0.04$, or 4%. $C^R C^W$ heterozygotes can arise in two different

Gametes for each generation are drawn at random from the gene pool of the previous generation:

80% C^R ($p = 0.8$)   20% C^W ($q = 0.2$)

Sperm

C^R $p = 0.8$ C^W $q = 0.2$

C^R $p = 0.8$

Eggs

C^W $q = 0.2$

0.64 (p^2) $C^R C^R$ 0.16 (pq) $C^R C^W$

0.16 (qp) $C^R C^W$ 0.04 (q^2) $C^W C^W$

If the gametes come together at random, the genotype frequencies of this generation are in Hardy-Weinberg equilibrium:

64% $C^R C^R$, 32% $C^R C^W$, and 4% $C^W C^W$

Gametes of this generation:

64% C^R (from $C^R C^R$ plants) + 16% C^R (from $C^R C^W$ plants) = 80% $C^R = 0.8 = p$

4% C^W (from $C^W C^W$ plants) + 16% C^W (from $C^R C^W$ plants) = 20% $C^W = 0.2 = q$

With random mating, these gametes will result in the same mix of genotypes in the next generation:

64% $C^R C^R$, 32% $C^R C^W$, and 4% $C^W C^W$ plants

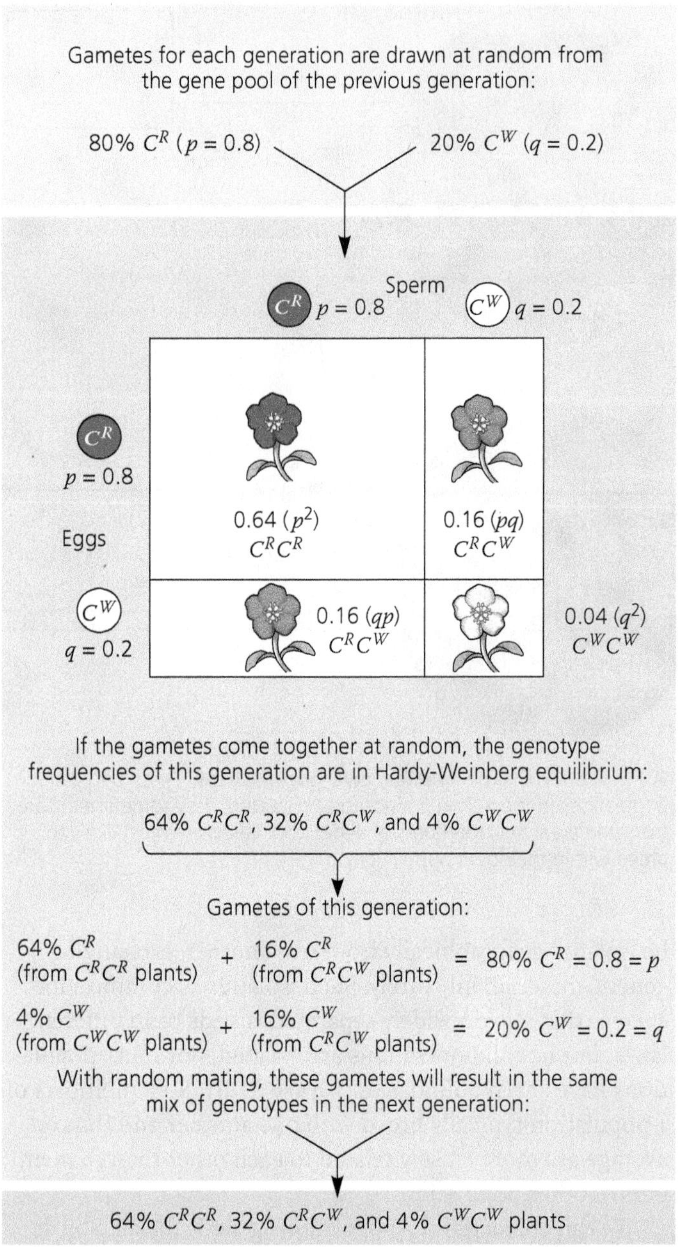

▲ **Figure 21.8 The Hardy-Weinberg principle.** In our wildflower population, the gene pool remains constant from one generation to the next. Mendelian processes alone do not alter frequencies of alleles or genotypes.

? *If the frequency of the C^R allele is 0.6, predict the frequencies of the $C^R C^R$, $C^R C^W$, and $C^W C^W$ genotypes.*

ways. If the sperm provides the C^R allele and the egg provides the C^W allele, the resulting heterozygotes will be $p \times q = 0.8 \times 0.2 = 0.16$, or 16% of the total. If the sperm provides the C^W allele and the egg the C^R allele, the heterozygous offspring will make up $q \times p = 0.2 \times 0.8 = 0.16$, or 16%. The frequency of heterozygotes is thus the sum of these possibilities: $pq + qp = 2pq = 0.16 + 0.16 = 0.32$, or 32%.

As shown in **Figure 21.8**, the genotype frequencies in the next generation must add up to 1 (100%). Thus, the equation for Hardy-Weinberg equilibrium states that at a locus with two alleles, the three genotypes will appear in the following proportions:

$$\underbrace{p^2}_{\substack{\text{Expected} \\ \text{frequency} \\ \text{of genotype} \\ C^R C^R}} + \underbrace{2pq}_{\substack{\text{Expected} \\ \text{frequency} \\ \text{of genotype} \\ C^R C^W}} + \underbrace{q^2}_{\substack{\text{Expected} \\ \text{frequency} \\ \text{of genotype} \\ C^W C^W}} = 1$$

Note that for a locus with two alleles, only three genotypes are possible (in this case, $C^R C^R$, $C^R C^W$, and $C^W C^W$). As a result, the sum of the frequencies of the three genotypes must equal 1 (100%) in *any* population—regardless of whether the population is in Hardy-Weinberg equilibrium. A population is in Hardy-Weinberg equilibrium only if the genotype frequencies are such that the actual frequency of one homozygote is p^2, the actual frequency of the other homozygote is q^2, and the actual frequency of heterozygotes is $2pq$. Finally, as suggested by Figure 21.8, if a population such as our wildflowers is in Hardy-Weinberg equilibrium and its members continue to mate randomly generation after generation, allele and genotype frequencies will remain constant. The system operates somewhat like a deck of cards: No matter how many times the deck is reshuffled to deal out new hands, the deck itself remains the same. Aces do not grow more numerous than jacks. And the repeated shuffling of a population's gene pool over the generations cannot, in itself, change the frequency of one allele relative to another.

Conditions for Hardy-Weinberg Equilibrium

The Hardy-Weinberg principle describes a hypothetical population that is not evolving. But in real populations, the allele and genotype frequencies often *do* change over time. Such changes can occur when at least one of the following five conditions of Hardy-Weinberg equilibrium is not met:

1. **No mutations.** The gene pool is modified if mutations alter alleles or if entire genes are deleted or duplicated.
2. **Random mating.** If individuals tend to mate within a subset of the population, such as their near neighbors or close relatives (inbreeding), random mixing of gametes does not occur, and genotype frequencies change.
3. **No natural selection.** Differences in the survival and reproductive success of individuals carrying different genotypes can alter allele frequencies.
4. **Extremely large population size.** The smaller the population, the more likely it is that allele frequencies will fluctuate by chance from one generation to the next (a process called genetic drift).
5. **No gene flow.** By moving alleles into or out of populations, gene flow can alter allele frequencies.

Departure from these conditions usually results in evolutionary change, which, as we've already described, is common in natural populations. But it is also common for natural populations to be in Hardy-Weinberg equilibrium for specific genes. This apparent contradiction occurs because a population can be evolving at some loci, yet simultaneously be in Hardy-Weinberg equilibrium at other loci. In addition, some populations evolve so slowly that the changes in their allele and genotype frequencies are difficult to distinguish from those predicted for a nonevolving population.

Applying the Hardy-Weinberg Principle

The Hardy-Weinberg equation is often used as an initial test of whether evolution is occurring in a population (you'll encounter an example in Concept Check 21.2, question 3). The equation also has medical applications, such as estimating the percentage of a population carrying the allele for an inherited disease. For example, consider phenylketonuria (PKU), a metabolic disorder that results from homozygosity for a recessive allele and occurs in about one out of every 10,000 babies born in the United States. Left untreated, PKU results in mental disability and other problems. (Newborns are now tested for PKU, and symptoms can be largely avoided with a diet very low in phenylalanine. For this reason, products that contain phenylalanine, such as diet colas, carry warning labels.)

To apply the Hardy-Weinberg equation, we must assume that no new PKU mutations are being introduced into the population (condition 1), and that people neither choose their mates on the basis of whether or not they carry this gene nor generally mate with close relatives (condition 2). We must also ignore any effects of differential survival and reproductive success among PKU genotypes (condition 3) and assume that there are no effects of genetic drift (condition 4) or of gene flow from other populations into the United States (condition 5). These assumptions are reasonable: The mutation rate for the PKU gene is low, inbreeding and other forms of nonrandom mating are not common in the United States, selection occurs only against the rare homozygotes (and then only if dietary restrictions are not followed), the U.S. population is very large, and populations outside the country have PKU allele frequencies similar to those seen in the United States. If all these assumptions hold, then the frequency of individuals in the population born with PKU will correspond to q^2 in the Hardy-Weinberg equation (q^2 = frequency of homozygotes). Because the allele is recessive, we must estimate the number of heterozygotes rather than counting them directly as we did with the pink flowers. Since we know there is one PKU occurrence per 10,000 births (q^2 = 0.0001), the frequency (q) of the recessive allele for PKU is

$$q = \sqrt{0.0001} = 0.01$$

and the frequency of the dominant allele is

$$p = 1 - q = 1 - 0.01 = 0.99$$

Using the Hardy-Weinberg Equation to Interpret Data and Make Predictions

Is Evolution Occurring in a Soybean Population? One way to test whether evolution is occurring in a population is to compare the observed genotype frequencies at a locus with those expected for a nonevolving population based on the Hardy-Weinberg equation. In this exercise, you'll test whether a soybean population is evolving at a locus with two alleles, C^G and C^Y, that affect chlorophyll production and hence leaf color.

How the Experiment Was Done Students planted soybean seeds and then counted the number of seedlings of each genotype at day 7 and again at day 21. Seedlings of each genotype could be distinguished visually because the C^G and C^Y alleles show incomplete dominance: $C^G C^G$ seedlings have green leaves, $C^G C^Y$ seedlings have green-yellow leaves, and $C^Y C^Y$ seedlings have yellow leaves.

Data from the Experiment

	Number of Seedlings			
Time (days)	Green ($C^G C^G$)	Green-yellow ($C^G C^Y$)	Yellow ($C^Y C^Y$)	Total
7	49	111	56	216
21	47	106	20	173

Interpret the Data

1. Use the observed genotype frequencies from the day 7 data to calculate the frequencies of the C^G allele (p) and the C^Y allele (q). (Remember that the frequency of an allele in a gene pool is the number of copies of that allele divided by the total number of copies of all alleles at that locus.)

2. Next, use the Hardy-Weinberg equation ($p^2 + 2pq + q^2 = 1$) to calculate the expected frequencies of genotypes $C^G C^G$, $C^G C^Y$, and $C^Y C^Y$ for a population in Hardy-Weinberg equilibrium.

3. Calculate the observed frequencies of genotypes $C^G C^G$, $C^G C^Y$, and $C^Y C^Y$ at day 7. (The observed frequency of a genotype in a gene pool is the number of individuals with that genotype divided by the total number of individuals.) Compare these frequencies to the expected frequencies calculated in step 2. Is the seedling population in Hardy-Weinberg equilibrium at day 7, or is evolution occurring? Explain your reasoning and identify which genotypes, if any, appear to be selected for or against.

4. Calculate the observed frequencies of genotypes $C^G C^G$, $C^G C^Y$, and $C^Y C^Y$ at day 21. Compare these frequencies to the expected frequencies calculated in step 2 and the observed frequencies at day 7. Is the seedling population in Hardy-Weinberg equilibrium at day 21, or is evolution occurring? Explain your reasoning and identify which genotypes, if any, appear to be selected for or against.

5. Homozygous $C^Y C^Y$ individuals cannot produce chlorophyll. The ability to photosynthesize becomes more critical as seedlings age and begin to exhaust the supply of food that was stored in the seed from which they emerged. Develop a hypothesis that explains the data for days 7 and 21. Based on this hypothesis, predict how the frequencies of the C^G and C^Y alleles will change beyond day 21.

(MB) A version of this Scientific Skills Exercise can be assigned in MasteringBiology.

The frequency of carriers, heterozygous people who do not have PKU but may pass the PKU allele to offspring, is

$$2pq = 2 \times 0.99 \times 0.01 = 0.0198$$
(approximately 2% of the U.S. population)

Remember, the assumption of Hardy-Weinberg equilibrium yields an approximation; the real number of carriers may differ. Still, our calculations suggest that harmful recessive alleles at this and other loci can be concealed in a population because they are carried by healthy heterozygotes. The **Scientific Skills Exercise** provides another opportunity for you to apply the Hardy-Weinberg principle to allele data for a population.

CONCEPT CHECK 21.2

1. A population has 700 individuals, 85 of genotype AA, 320 of genotype Aa, and 295 of genotype aa. What are the frequencies of alleles A and a?

2. The frequency of allele a is 0.45 for a population in Hardy-Weinberg equilibrium. What are the expected frequencies of genotypes AA, Aa, and aa?

3. **WHAT IF?** A locus that affects susceptibility to a degenerative brain disease has two alleles, V and v. In a population, 16 people have genotype VV, 92 have genotype Vv, and 12 have genotype vv. Is this population evolving? Explain.

For suggested answers, see Appendix A.

CONCEPT 21.3

Natural selection, genetic drift, and gene flow can alter allele frequencies in a population

Note again the five conditions required for a population to be in Hardy-Weinberg equilibrium. A deviation from any of these conditions is a potential cause of evolution. New mutations (violation of condition 1) can alter allele frequencies, but because mutations are rare, the change from one generation to the next is likely to be very small. Nonrandom mating (violation of condition 2) can affect the frequencies of homozygous and heterozygous genotypes but by itself has no effect on allele frequencies in the gene pool. (Allele frequencies can change if individuals with certain inherited traits are more likely than other individuals to obtain mates. However, such a situation not only causes a deviation from random mating; it also violates condition 3, no natural selection.) For the rest of this section, we will focus on the three mechanisms that alter allele frequencies directly and cause most evolutionary change: natural selection, genetic drift, and gene flow (violations of conditions 3–5).

Natural Selection

The concept of natural selection is based on differential success in survival and reproduction: Individuals in a population exhibit variations in their heritable traits, and those with traits that are better suited to their environment tend to produce more offspring than those with traits that are not as well suited (see Chapter 19).

In genetic terms, we now know that selection results in alleles being passed to the next generation in proportions that differ from those in the present generation. For example, the fruit fly *D. melanogaster* has an allele that confers resistance to several insecticides, including DDT. This allele has a frequency of 0% in laboratory strains of *D. melanogaster* established from flies collected in the wild in the early 1930s, prior to DDT use. However, in strains established from flies collected after 1960 (following 20 or more years of DDT use), the allele frequency is 37%. We can infer that this allele either arose by mutation between 1930 and 1960 or was present in 1930, but very rare. In any case, the rise in frequency of this allele most likely occurred because DDT is a powerful poison that is a strong selective force in exposed fly populations.

As the *D. melanogaster* example shows, an allele that confers resistance to an insecticide will increase in frequency in a population exposed to that insecticide. Such changes are not coincidental. By consistently favoring some alleles over others, natural selection can cause *adaptive evolution* (evolution that results in a better match between organisms and their environment). We'll explore this process in more detail a little later in this chapter.

Genetic Drift

If you flip a coin 1,000 times, a result of 700 heads and 300 tails might make you suspicious about that coin. But if you flip a coin only 10 times, an outcome of 7 heads and 3 tails would not be surprising. The smaller the number of coin flips, the more likely it is that chance alone will cause a deviation from the predicted result. (In this case, the prediction is an equal number of heads and tails.) Chance events can also cause allele frequencies to fluctuate unpredictably from one generation to the next, especially in small populations—a process called **genetic drift**.

Figure 21.9 models how genetic drift might affect a small population of our wildflowers. In this example, drift leads to the loss of an allele from the gene pool, but it is a matter of chance that the C^W allele is lost and not the C^R allele. Such unpredictable changes in allele frequencies can be caused by chance events associated with survival and reproduction. Perhaps a large animal such as a moose stepped on the three $C^W C^W$ individuals in generation 2, killing them and increasing the chance that only the C^R allele would be passed to the next generation. Allele frequencies can also be affected by chance events that occur during fertilization. For example, suppose two individuals

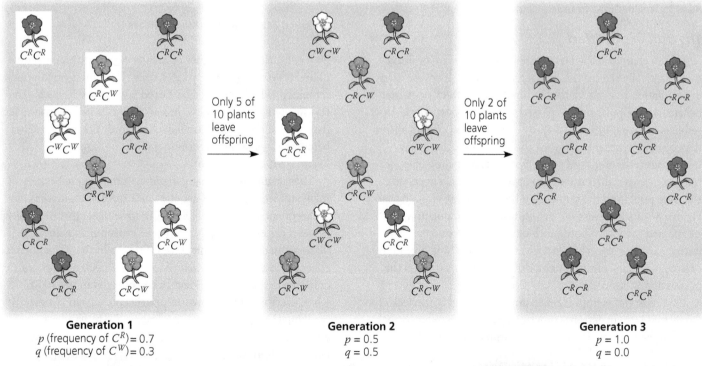

Generation 1
p (frequency of C^R) = 0.7
q (frequency of C^W) = 0.3

Generation 2
p = 0.5
q = 0.5

Generation 3
p = 1.0
q = 0.0

▲ **Figure 21.9 Genetic drift.** This small wildflower population has a stable size of ten plants. Suppose that by chance only five plants of generation 1 (those in white boxes) produce fertile offspring. (This could occur, for example, if only those plants happened to grow in a location that provided enough nutrients to support the production of offspring.) Again by chance, only two plants of generation 2 leave fertile offspring. As a result, by chance the frequency of the C^W allele first increases in generation 2, then falls to zero in generation 3.

BioFlix Visit the Study Area in **MasteringBiology** for the BioFlix® 3-D Animation on Mechanisms of Evolution.

of genotype $C^R C^W$ had a small number of offspring. By chance alone, every egg and sperm pair that generated offspring could happen to have carried the C^R allele and not the C^W allele.

Certain circumstances can result in genetic drift having a significant impact on a population. Two examples are the founder effect and the bottleneck effect.

The Founder Effect

When a few individuals become isolated from a larger population, this smaller group may establish a new population whose gene pool differs from the source population; this is called the **founder effect**. The founder effect might occur, for example, when a few members of a population are blown by a storm to a new island. Genetic drift, in which chance events alter allele frequencies, will occur in such a case if the storm indiscriminately transports some individuals (and their alleles), but not others, from the source population.

The founder effect probably accounts for the relatively high frequency of certain inherited disorders among isolated human populations. For example, in 1814, 15 British colonists founded a settlement on Tristan da Cunha, a group of small islands in the Atlantic Ocean midway between Africa and South America. Apparently, one of the colonists carried a recessive allele for retinitis pigmentosa, a progressive form of blindness that afflicts homozygous individuals. Of the founding colonists' 240 descendants on the island in the late 1960s, 4 had retinitis pigmentosa. The frequency of the allele that causes this disease is ten times higher on Tristan da Cunha than in the populations from which the founders came.

The Bottleneck Effect

A sudden change in the environment, such as a fire or flood, may drastically reduce the size of a population. A severe drop in population size can cause the **bottleneck effect**, so named because the population has passed through a "bottleneck" that reduces its size (**Figure 21.10**). By chance alone, certain alleles may be overrepresented among the survivors, others may be underrepresented, and some may be absent altogether. Ongoing genetic drift is likely to have substantial effects on the gene pool until the population becomes large enough that chance events have less impact. But even if a population that has passed through a bottleneck ultimately recovers in size, it may have low levels of genetic variation for a long period of time—a legacy of the genetic drift that occurred when the population was small.

One reason it is important to understand the bottleneck effect is that human actions sometimes create severe bottlenecks for other species, as the following example shows.

Case Study: *Impact of Genetic Drift on the Greater Prairie Chicken*

Millions of greater prairie chickens (*Tympanuchus cupido*) once lived on the prairies of Illinois. As these prairies were converted to farmland and other uses during the 19th and

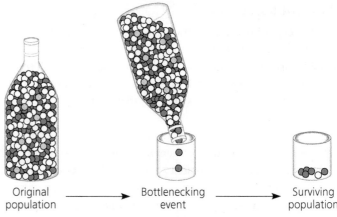

(a) Shaking just a few marbles through the narrow neck of a bottle is analogous to a drastic reduction in the size of a population. By chance, blue marbles are overrepresented in the surviving population, and gold marbles are absent.

(b) Similarly, bottlenecking a wild population tends to reduce genetic variation, as in the Florida panther (*Puma concolor coryi*), a subspecies in danger of extinction.

▲ **Figure 21.10 The bottleneck effect.**

20th centuries, the number of greater prairie chickens plummeted (**Figure 21.11a**). By 1993, only two Illinois populations remained, which together harbored fewer than 50 birds. The few surviving birds had low levels of genetic variation, and less than 50% of their eggs hatched, compared with much higher hatching rates of the larger populations in Kansas and Nebraska (**Figure 21.11b**).

These data suggest that genetic drift during the bottleneck may have led to a loss of genetic variation and an increase in the frequency of harmful alleles. To investigate this hypothesis, researchers extracted DNA from 15 museum specimens of Illinois greater prairie chickens. Of the 15 birds, 10 had been collected in the 1930s, when there were 25,000 greater prairie chickens in Illinois, and 5 had been collected in the 1960s, when there were 1,000 greater prairie chickens in Illinois. By studying the DNA of these specimens, the researchers were able to obtain a minimum, baseline estimate of how much genetic variation was present in the Illinois population *before* the population shrank to extremely low numbers. This baseline estimate is a key piece of information that is not usually available in cases of population bottlenecks.

The researchers surveyed six loci and found that the 1993 Illinois greater prairie chicken population had lost nine alleles

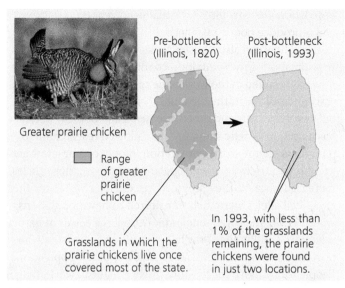

Greater prairie chicken

Pre-bottleneck (Illinois, 1820)

Post-bottleneck (Illinois, 1993)

Range of greater prairie chicken

Grasslands in which the prairie chickens live once covered most of the state.

In 1993, with less than 1% of the grasslands remaining, the prairie chickens were found in just two locations.

(a) The Illinois population of greater prairie chickens dropped from millions of birds in the 1800s to fewer than 50 birds in 1993.

Location	Population size	Number of alleles per locus	Percentage of eggs hatched
Illinois			
1930–1960s	1,000–25,000	5.2	93
1993	<50	3.7	<50
Kansas, 1998 (no bottleneck)	750,000	5.8	99
Nebraska, 1998 (no bottleneck)	75,000–200,000	5.8	96

(b) As a consequence of the drastic reduction in the size of the Illinois population, genetic drift resulted in a drop in the number of alleles per locus (averaged across six loci studied) and a decrease in the percentage of eggs that hatched.

▲ **Figure 21.11 Genetic drift and loss of genetic variation.**

that were present in the museum specimens. The 1993 population also had fewer alleles per locus than the pre-bottleneck Illinois or the current Kansas and Nebraska populations (see Figure 21.11b). Thus, as predicted, drift had reduced the genetic variation of the small 1993 population. Drift may also have increased the frequency of harmful alleles, leading to the low egg-hatching rate. To counteract these negative effects, 271 birds from neighboring states were added to the Illinois population over four years. This strategy succeeded: New alleles entered the population, and the egg-hatching rate improved to over 90%. Overall, studies on the Illinois greater prairie chicken illustrate the powerful effects of genetic drift in small populations and provide hope that in at least some populations, these effects can be reversed.

Effects of Genetic Drift: A Summary

The examples we've described highlight four key points:

1. **Genetic drift is significant in small populations.** Chance events can cause an allele to be disproportionately over- or underrepresented in the next generation. Although chance events occur in populations of all sizes, they tend to alter allele frequencies substantially only in small populations.
2. **Genetic drift can cause allele frequencies to change at random.** Because of genetic drift, an allele may increase in frequency one year, then decrease the next; the change from year to year is not predictable. Thus, unlike natural selection, which in a given environment consistently favors some alleles over others, genetic drift causes allele frequencies to change at random over time.
3. **Genetic drift can lead to a loss of genetic variation within populations.** By causing allele frequencies to fluctuate randomly over time, genetic drift can eliminate alleles from a population. Because evolution depends on genetic variation, such losses can influence how effectively a population can adapt to a change in the environment.
4. **Genetic drift can cause harmful alleles to become fixed.** Alleles that are neither harmful nor beneficial can be lost or become fixed entirely by chance through genetic drift. In very small populations, genetic drift can also cause alleles that are slightly harmful to become fixed. When this occurs, the population's survival can be threatened (as in the case of the greater prairie chicken).

Gene Flow

Natural selection and genetic drift are not the only phenomena affecting allele frequencies. Allele frequencies can also change by **gene flow**, the transfer of alleles into or out of a population due to the movement of fertile individuals or their gametes. For example, suppose that near our original hypothetical wildflower population there is another population consisting primarily of white-flowered individuals ($C^W C^W$). Insects carrying pollen from these plants may fly to and pollinate plants in our original population. The introduced C^W alleles would modify our original population's allele frequencies in the next generation. Because alleles are transferred between populations, gene flow tends to reduce the genetic differences between populations. In fact, if it is extensive enough, gene flow can result in two populations combining into a single population with a common gene pool.

Alleles transferred by gene flow can also affect how well populations are adapted to local environmental conditions. Researchers studying the songbird *Parus major* (great tit) on the small Dutch island of Vlieland noted survival differences between two populations on the island. Females born in the eastern population survive twice as well as females born in the central population, regardless of where the females eventually

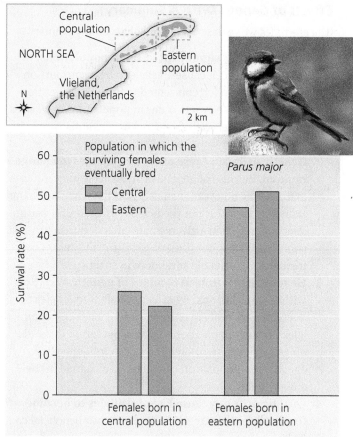

Parus major

© 2005 Macmillan Publishers Ltd.

▲ **Figure 21.12 Gene flow and local adaptation.** In *Parus major* populations on Vlieland, the yearly survival rate of females born in the eastern population is higher than that of females born in the central population. Gene flow from the mainland to the central population is 3.3 times higher than gene flow to the eastern population, and birds from the mainland are selected against in both populations. These data suggest that gene flow from the mainland has prevented the central population from adapting fully to its local conditions.

settle and raise offspring (**Figure 21.12**). This finding suggests that females born in the eastern population are better adapted to life on the island than females born in the central population. But extensive field studies also showed that the two populations are connected by high levels of gene flow (mating), which should reduce genetic differences between them.

So how can the eastern population be better adapted to life on Vlieland than the central population? The answer lies in the unequal amounts of gene flow from the mainland. In any given year, 43% of the first-time breeders in the central population are immigrants from the mainland, compared with only 13% in the eastern population. Birds with mainland genotypes survive and reproduce poorly on Vlieland, and in the eastern population, selection reduces the frequency of these genotypes. In the central population, however, gene flow from the mainland is so high that it overwhelms the effects of selection. As a result, females born in the central population have many immigrant genes, reducing the degree to which members of that population are adapted to life on the island. Researchers are currently investigating why gene flow is so much higher in the central

population and why birds with mainland genotypes survive and reproduce poorly on Vlieland.

Gene flow can also transfer alleles that improve the ability of populations to adapt to local conditions. For example, gene flow has resulted in the worldwide spread of some insecticide-resistance alleles in the mosquito *Culex pipiens*, a vector of West Nile virus and other diseases. Each of these alleles has a unique genetic signature that allowed researchers to document that it arose by mutation in only one or a few geographic locations. In their population of origin, these alleles increased because they provided insecticide resistance. These beneficial alleles were then transferred to new populations, where again, their frequencies increased as a result of natural selection. Finally, gene flow has become an increasingly important agent of evolutionary change in human populations. People today move much more freely about the world than in the past. As a result, mating is more common between members of populations that previously had very little contact, leading to an exchange of alleles and fewer genetic differences between those populations.

CONCEPT CHECK 21.3

1. In what sense is natural selection more "predictable" than genetic drift?

2. Distinguish genetic drift from gene flow in terms of (a) how they occur and (b) their implications for future genetic variation in a population.

3. **WHAT IF?** Suppose two plant populations exchange pollen and seeds. In one population, individuals of genotype *AA* are most common (9,000 *AA*, 900 *Aa*, 100 *aa*), while the opposite is true in the other population (100 *AA*, 900 *Aa*, 9,000 *aa*). If neither allele has a selective advantage, what will happen over time to the allele and genotype frequencies of these populations?

For suggested answers, see Appendix A.

CONCEPT 21.4

Natural selection is the only mechanism that consistently causes adaptive evolution

Evolution by natural selection is a blend of chance and "sorting": chance in the creation of new genetic variations (as in mutation) and sorting as natural selection favors some alleles over others. Because of this favoring process, the outcome of natural selection is *not* random. Instead, natural selection consistently increases the frequencies of alleles that provide reproductive advantage and thus leads to **adaptive evolution**.

Natural Selection: *A Closer Look*

In examining how natural selection brings about adaptive evolution, we'll begin with the concept of relative fitness and the different ways that an organism's phenotype is subject to natural selection.

Relative Fitness

The phrases "struggle for existence" and "survival of the fittest" are commonly used to describe natural selection, but these expressions are misleading if taken to mean direct competitive contests among individuals. There *are* animal species in which individuals, usually males, lock horns or otherwise spar to determine mating privilege. But reproductive success is generally more subtle and depends on many factors besides outright battle. For example, a barnacle that is more efficient at collecting food than its neighbors may have greater stores of energy and hence be able to produce more eggs. A moth may have more offspring than other moths in the same population because its body colors more effectively conceal it from predators, improving its chance of surviving long enough to produce more offspring. These examples illustrate how in a given environment, certain traits can lead to greater **relative fitness**: the contribution an individual makes to the gene pool of the next generation *relative to* the contributions of other individuals.

Although we often refer to the relative fitness of a genotype, remember that the entity that is subjected to natural selection is the whole organism, not the underlying genotype. Thus, selection acts more directly on the phenotype than on the genotype; it acts on the genotype indirectly, via how the genotype affects the phenotype.

Directional, Disruptive, and Stabilizing Selection

Natural selection can occur in three ways, depending on which phenotypes in a population are favored. These three modes of selection are called directional selection, disruptive selection, and stabilizing selection.

Directional selection occurs when conditions favor individuals at one extreme of a phenotypic range, thereby shifting a population's frequency curve for the phenotypic character in one direction or the other **(Figure 21.13a)**. Directional selection is common when a population's environment changes or when members of a population migrate to a different habitat. For instance, an increase in the relative abundance of large seeds over small seeds led to increased beak depth in a population of Galápagos finches (see Figure 21.2).

▼ **Figure 21.13 Modes of selection.** These cases describe three ways in which a hypothetical deer mouse population with heritable variation in fur coloration from light to dark might evolve. The graphs show how the frequencies of individuals with different fur colors change over time. The large white arrows symbolize selective pressures against certain phenotypes.

MAKE CONNECTIONS *Review Figure 19.14. Which mode of selection has occurred in soapberry bug populations that feed on the introduced goldenrain tree? Explain.*

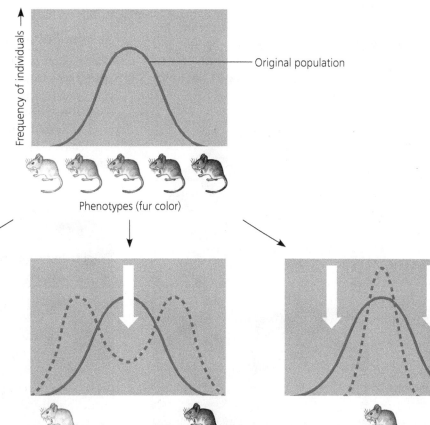

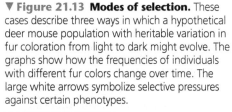

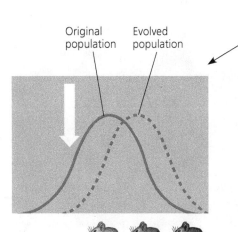

(a) Directional selection shifts the overall makeup of the population by favoring variants that are at one extreme of the distribution. In this case, lighter mice are selected against because they live among dark rocks, making it harder for them to hide from predators.

(b) Disruptive selection favors variants at both ends of the distribution. These mice have colonized a patchy habitat made up of light and dark rocks, with the result that mice of an intermediate color are selected against.

(c) Stabilizing selection removes extreme variants from the population and preserves intermediate types. If the environment consists of rocks of an intermediate color, both light and dark mice will be selected against.

Disruptive selection (Figure 21.13b) occurs when conditions favor individuals at both extremes of a phenotypic range over individuals with intermediate phenotypes. One example is a population of black-bellied seedcracker finches in Cameroon whose members display two distinctly different beak sizes. Small-billed birds feed mainly on soft seeds, whereas large-billed birds specialize in cracking hard seeds. It appears that birds with intermediate-sized bills are relatively inefficient at cracking both types of seeds and thus have lower relative fitness.

Stabilizing selection (Figure 21.13c) acts against both extreme phenotypes and favors intermediate variants. This mode of selection reduces variation and tends to maintain the status quo for a particular phenotypic character. For example, the birth weights of most human babies lie in the range of 3–4 kg (6.6–8.8 pounds); babies who are either much smaller or much larger suffer higher rates of mortality.

Regardless of the mode of selection, however, the basic mechanism remains the same. Selection favors individuals whose heritable phenotypic traits provide higher reproductive success than do the traits of other individuals.

The Key Role of Natural Selection in Adaptive Evolution

The adaptations of organisms include many striking examples. Certain octopuses, for instance, can change color rapidly, enabling them to blend into different backgrounds. Another example is the remarkable jaws of snakes (Figure 21.14), which allow them to swallow prey much larger than their own head (a feat analogous to a person swallowing a whole watermelon). Other adaptations, such as a version of an enzyme that shows improved function in cold environments, may be less visually dramatic but just as important for survival and reproduction.

Such adaptations can arise gradually over time as natural selection increases the frequencies of alleles that enhance survival and reproduction. As the proportion of individuals that have favorable traits increases, the match between a species and its environment improves; that is, adaptive evolution occurs. Note, however, that the physical and biological components of an organism's environment may change over time. As a result, what constitutes a "good match" between an organism and its environment can be a moving target, making adaptive evolution a continuous, dynamic process.

And what about genetic drift and gene flow? Both can, in fact, increase the frequencies of alleles that improve the match between organisms and their environment, but neither does so consistently. Genetic drift can cause the frequency of a slightly beneficial allele to increase, but it also can cause the frequency of such an allele to decrease. Similarly, gene flow may introduce alleles that are advantageous or ones that are disadvantageous. Natural selection is the only evolutionary mechanism that consistently leads to adaptive evolution.

Sexual Selection

Charles Darwin was the first to explore the implications of **sexual selection**, a form of natural selection in which individuals with certain inherited characteristics are more likely than other individuals to obtain mates. Sexual selection can result in **sexual dimorphism**, a difference in secondary sexual characteristics between males and females of the same species (Figure 21.15). These distinctions include differences in size, color, ornamentation, and behavior.

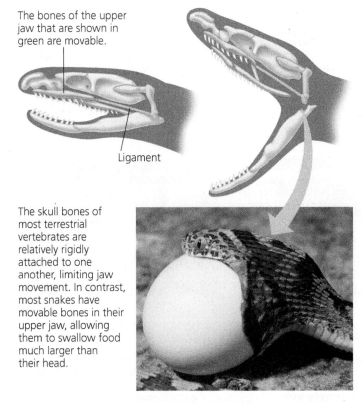

The bones of the upper jaw that are shown in green are movable.

Ligament

The skull bones of most terrestrial vertebrates are relatively rigidly attached to one another, limiting jaw movement. In contrast, most snakes have movable bones in their upper jaw, allowing them to swallow food much larger than their head.

▲ Figure 21.14 **Movable jaw bones in snakes.**

▲ Figure 21.15 **Sexual dimorphism and sexual selection.** Peacocks (above left) and peahens (above right) show extreme sexual dimorphism. There is intrasexual selection between competing males, followed by intersexual selection when the females choose among the showiest males.

How does sexual selection operate? There are several ways. In *intrasexual selection*, meaning selection within the same sex, individuals of one sex compete directly for mates of the opposite sex. In many species, intrasexual selection occurs among males. For example, a single male may patrol a group of females and prevent other males from mating with them. The patrolling male may defend his status by defeating smaller, weaker, or less fierce males in combat. More often, this male is the psychological victor in ritualized displays that discourage would-be competitors but do not risk injury that would reduce his own fitness. Intrasexual selection has also been observed among females in a variety of species, including ring-tailed lemurs and broad-nosed pipefish.

In *intersexual selection*, also called *mate choice*, individuals of one sex (usually the females) are choosy in selecting their mates from the other sex. In many cases, the female's choice depends on the showiness of the male's appearance or behavior (see Figure 21.15). What intrigued Darwin about mate choice is that male showiness may not seem adaptive in any other way and may in fact pose some risk. For example, bright plumage may make male birds more visible to predators. But if such characteristics help a male gain a mate, and if this benefit outweighs the risk from predation, then both the bright plumage and the female preference for it will be reinforced because they enhance overall reproductive success.

How do female preferences for certain male characteristics evolve in the first place? One hypothesis is that females prefer male traits that are correlated with "good genes." If the trait preferred by females is indicative of a male's overall genetic quality, both the male trait and female preference for it should increase in frequency. **Figure 21.16** describes one experiment testing this hypothesis in gray tree frogs (*Hyla versicolor*).

Other researchers have shown that in several bird species, the traits preferred by females are related to overall male health. Here, too, female preference appears to be based on traits that reflect "good genes," in this case alleles indicative of a robust immune system.

The Preservation of Genetic Variation

Some of the genetic variation in populations represents **neutral variation**, differences in DNA sequence that do not confer a selective advantage or disadvantage. But variation is also found at loci affected by selection. What prevents natural selection from reducing genetic variation at those loci by culling all unfavorable alleles? The tendency for directional and stabilizing selection to reduce variation is countered by mechanisms that preserve or restore it, such as diploidy and balancing selection.

Diploidy

In diploid organisms, a considerable amount of genetic variation is hidden from selection in the form of recessive alleles. Recessive alleles that are less favorable than their dominant

▼ **Figure 21.16** **Inquiry**

Do females select mates based on traits indicative of "good genes"?

Experiment Female gray tree frogs (*Hyla versicolor*) prefer to mate with males that give long mating calls. Allison Welch and colleagues, at the University of Missouri, tested whether the genetic makeup of long-calling (LC) males is superior to that of short-calling (SC) males. The researchers fertilized half the eggs of each female with sperm from an LC male and fertilized the remaining eggs with sperm from an SC male. In two separate experiments (one in 1995, the other in 1996), the resulting half-sibling offspring were raised in a common environment and their survival and growth were monitored.

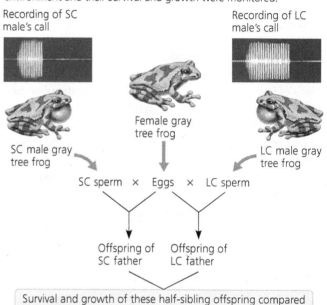

Survival and growth of these half-sibling offspring compared

Results

Offspring Performance	1995	1996
Larval survival	LC better	NSD
Larval growth	NSD	LC better
Time to metamorphosis	LC better (shorter)	LC better (shorter)

NSD = no significant difference; LC better = offspring of LC males superior to offspring of SC males.

Conclusion Because offspring fathered by an LC male outperformed their half-siblings fathered by an SC male, the team concluded that the duration of a male's mating call is indicative of the male's overall genetic quality. This result supports the hypothesis that female mate choice can be based on a trait that indicates whether the male has "good genes."

Source A. M. Welch et al., Call duration as an indicator of genetic quality in male gray tree frogs, *Science* 280:1928–1930 (1998).

Inquiry in Action Read and analyze the original paper in *Inquiry in Action: Interpreting Scientific Papers.*

WHAT IF? Why did the researchers split each female frog's eggs into two batches for fertilization by different males? Why didn't they mate each female with a single male frog?

counterparts or even harmful in the current environment can persist by propagation in heterozygous individuals. This latent variation is exposed to natural selection only when both parents carry the same recessive allele and two copies end up in the same zygote. This happens only rarely if the frequency of the recessive allele is very low. Heterozygote protection maintains a huge pool of alleles that might not be favored under present conditions, but which could bring new benefits if the environment changes.

Balancing Selection

Selection itself may preserve variation at some loci. **Balancing selection** occurs when natural selection maintains two or more forms in a population. This type of selection includes heterozygote advantage and frequency-dependent selection.

Heterozygote Advantage If individuals who are heterozygous at a particular locus have greater fitness than do both kinds of homozygotes, they exhibit **heterozygote advantage**. In such a case, natural selection tends to maintain two or more alleles at that locus. Note that heterozygote advantage is defined in terms of *genotype*, not phenotype. Thus, whether heterozygote advantage represents stabilizing or directional selection depends on the relationship between the genotype and the phenotype. For example, if the phenotype of a heterozygote is intermediate to the phenotypes of both homozygotes, heterozygote advantage is a form of stabilizing selection.

An example of heterozygote advantage occurs at the locus in humans that codes for the β polypeptide subunit of hemoglobin, the oxygen-carrying protein of red blood cells. In homozygous individuals, a certain recessive allele at that locus causes sickle-cell disease. The red blood cells of people with sickle-cell disease become distorted in shape, or *sickled*, under low-oxygen conditions (see Figure 3.22), as occurs in the capillaries. These sickled cells can clump together and block the flow of blood in the capillaries, resulting in serious damage to organs such as the kidney, heart, and brain. Although some red blood cells become sickled in heterozygotes, not enough become sickled to cause sickle-cell disease.

Heterozygotes for the sickle-cell allele are protected against the most severe effects of malaria, a disease caused by a parasite that infects red blood cells (see Figure 25.26). One reason for this partial protection is that the body destroys sickled red blood cells rapidly, killing the parasites they harbor (but not affecting parasites inside normal red blood cells). Protection against malaria is important in tropical regions where the disease is a major killer. In such regions, selection favors heterozygotes over homozygous dominant individuals, who are more vulnerable to the effects of malaria, and also over homozygous recessive individuals, who develop sickle-cell disease. The frequency of the sickle-cell allele in Africa is generally highest in areas where the malaria parasite is most common **(Figure 21.17)**. In some populations, it accounts for 20% of the hemoglobin alleles in the gene pool, a very high frequency for such a harmful allele.

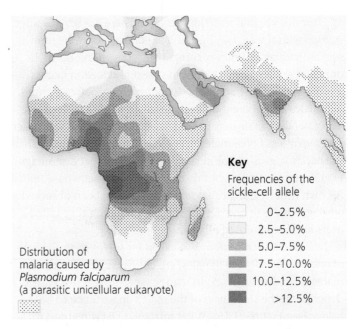

Key
Frequencies of the sickle-cell allele

☐ 0–2.5%
▨ 2.5–5.0%
▨ 5.0–7.5%
▨ 7.5–10.0%
▨ 10.0–12.5%
▨ >12.5%

Distribution of malaria caused by *Plasmodium falciparum* (a parasitic unicellular eukaryote)

▲ **Figure 21.17 Mapping malaria and the sickle-cell allele.** The sickle-cell allele is most common in Africa, but it is not the only case of heterozygote advantage providing protection against malaria. Alleles at other loci (not shown on this map) are also favored by heterozygote advantage in populations near the Mediterranean Sea and in Southeast Asia where malaria is widespread.

Frequency-Dependent Selection In **frequency-dependent selection**, the fitness of a phenotype depends on how common it is in the population. Consider the scale-eating fish (*Perissodus microlepis*) of Lake Tanganyika, in Africa. These fish attack other fish from behind, darting in to remove a few scales from the flank of their prey. Of interest here is a peculiar feature of the scale-eating fish: Some are "left-mouthed" and some are "right-mouthed." Simple Mendelian inheritance determines these phenotypes, with the right-mouthed allele being dominant to the left-mouthed allele. Because their mouth twists to the left, left-mouthed fish always attack their prey's right flank **(Figure 21.18)**. (To see why, twist your lower jaw and lips to the left and imagine trying to take a bite from the left side of a fish, approaching it from behind.) Similarly, right-mouthed fish always attack from the left. Prey species guard against attack from whatever phenotype of scale-eating fish is most common in the lake. Thus, from year to year, selection favors whichever mouth phenotype is least common. As a result, the frequency of left- and right-mouthed fish oscillates over time, and balancing selection (due to frequency dependence) keeps the frequency of each phenotype close to 50%.

Why Natural Selection Cannot Fashion Perfect Organisms

Though natural selection leads to adaptation, nature abounds with examples of organisms that are less than ideally suited for their lifestyles. There are several reasons why.

1. **Selection can act only on existing variations.** Natural selection favors only the fittest phenotypes among those

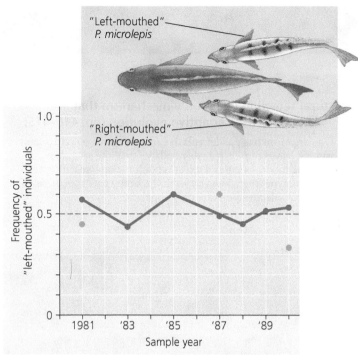

"Left-mouthed"
P. microlepis

"Right-mouthed"
P. microlepis

© 1993 AAAS

▲ **Figure 21.18 Frequency-dependent selection.** In a population of the scale-eating fish *Perissodus microlepis*, the frequency of left-mouthed individuals rises and falls in a regular manner (shown in red). At each of three time periods when the phenotypes of breeding adults were assessed, a majority of the adults that reproduced (represented by green dots) had the opposite phenotype of that which was most common in the population. Thus, it appears that right-mouthed individuals were favored by selection when left-mouthed individuals were more common, and vice versa.

? *What did the researchers measure to determine which phenotype was favored by selection? Are any assumptions implied by this choice? Explain.*

currently in the population, which may not be the ideal traits. New advantageous alleles do not arise on demand.

2. **Evolution is limited by historical constraints.** Each species has a legacy of descent with modification from ancestral forms. Evolution does not scrap the ancestral anatomy and build each new complex structure from scratch; rather, evolution co-opts existing structures and adapts them to new situations. We could imagine that if a terrestrial animal were to adapt to an environment in which flight would be advantageous, it might be best just to grow an extra pair of limbs that would serve as wings. However, evolution does not work this way; instead, it operates on the traits an organism already has. Thus, in birds and bats, an existing pair of limbs took on new functions for flight as these organisms evolved from nonflying ancestors.

3. **Adaptations are often compromises.** Each organism must do many different things. A seal spends part of its time on rocks; it could probably walk better if it had legs instead of flippers, but then it would not swim nearly as well. We humans owe much of our versatility and athleticism to our prehensile hands and flexible limbs, but these

▲ **Figure 21.19 Evolutionary compromise.** The loud call that enables a Túngara frog to attract mates also attracts more dangerous characters in the neighborhood—in this case, a bat about to seize a meal.

also make us prone to sprains, torn ligaments, and dislocations: Structural reinforcement has been compromised for agility. **Figure 21.19** depicts another example of evolutionary compromise.

4. **Chance, natural selection, and the environment interact.** Chance events can affect the subsequent evolutionary history of populations. For instance, when a storm blows insects or birds hundreds of kilometers over an ocean to an island, the wind does not necessarily transport those individuals that are best suited to the new environment. Thus, not all alleles present in the founding population's gene pool are better suited to the new environment than the alleles that are "left behind." In addition, the environment at a particular location may change unpredictably from year to year, again limiting the extent to which adaptive evolution results in a close match between the organism and current environmental conditions.

With these four constraints, evolution does not tend to craft perfect organisms. Natural selection operates on a "better than" basis. We can, in fact, see evidence for evolution in the many imperfections of the organisms it produces.

CONCEPT CHECK 21.4

1. What is the relative fitness of a sterile mule? Explain.
2. Explain why natural selection is the only evolutionary mechanism that consistently leads to adaptive evolution.
3. **WHAT IF?** Consider a population in which heterozygotes at a certain locus have an extreme phenotype (such as being larger than homozygotes) that confers a selective advantage. Does such a situation represent directional, disruptive, or stabilizing selection? Explain your answer.
4. **WHAT IF?** Would individuals who are heterozygous for the sickle-cell allele be selected for or against in a region free from malaria? Explain.

For suggested answers, see Appendix A.

21 Chapter Review

SUMMARY OF KEY CONCEPTS

CONCEPT 21.1

Genetic variation makes evolution possible (pp. 400–402)

- **Genetic variation** refers to genetic differences among individuals within a population.
- The nucleotide differences that provide the basis of genetic variation originate when mutation and gene duplication produce new alleles and new genes.
- New genetic variants are produced rapidly in organisms with short generation times. In sexually reproducing organisms, most of the genetic differences among individuals result from crossing over, the independent assortment of chromosomes, and fertilization.

? *Typically, most of the nucleotide variability that occurs within a genetic locus does not affect the phenotype. Explain why.*

CONCEPT 21.2

The Hardy-Weinberg equation can be used to test whether a population is evolving (pp. 402–406)

- A **population**, a localized group of organisms belonging to one species, is united by its **gene pool**, the aggregate of all the alleles in the population.
- The **Hardy-Weinberg principle** states that the allele and genotype frequencies of a population will remain constant if the population is large, mating is random, mutation is negligible, there is no gene flow, and there is no natural selection. For such a population, if p and q represent the frequencies of the only two possible alleles at a particular locus, then p^2 is the frequency of one kind of homozygote, q^2 is the frequency of the other kind of homozygote, and $2pq$ is the frequency of the heterozygous genotype.

? *Is it circular reasoning to calculate* p *and* q *from observed genotype frequencies and then use those values of* p *and* q *to test if the population is in Hardy-Weinberg equilibrium? Explain your answer.* (Hint: *Consider a specific case, such as a population with 195 individuals of genotype* AA, *10 of genotype* Aa, *and 195 of genotype* aa.)

CONCEPT 21.3

Natural selection, genetic drift, and gene flow can alter allele frequencies in a population (pp. 406–410)

- In natural selection, individuals that have certain inherited traits tend to survive and reproduce at higher rates than other individuals *because of* those traits.
- In **genetic drift**, chance fluctuations in allele frequencies over generations tend to reduce genetic variation.
- **Gene flow**, the transfer of alleles between populations, tends to reduce genetic differences between populations over time.

? *Would two small, geographically isolated populations in very different environments be likely to evolve in similar ways? Explain.*

CONCEPT 21.4

Natural selection is the only mechanism that consistently causes adaptive evolution (pp. 410–415)

- One organism has greater **relative fitness** than a second organism if it leaves more fertile descendants than the second organism. The modes of natural selection differ in how selection acts on phenotype (the white arrows in the summary diagram below represent selective pressure on a population).

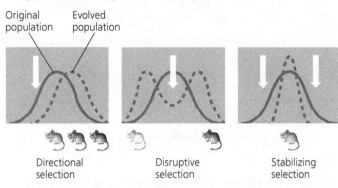

Original population | Evolved population

Directional selection | Disruptive selection | Stabilizing selection

- Unlike genetic drift and gene flow, natural selection consistently increases the frequencies of alleles that enhance survival and reproduction, thus improving the match between organisms and their environment.
- **Sexual selection** influences evolutionary change in secondary sex characteristics that can give individuals advantages in mating.
- Despite the winnowing effects of selection, populations have considerable genetic variation. Some of this variation represents **neutral variation**; additional variation can be maintained by diploidy and **balancing selection**.
- There are constraints to evolution: Natural selection can act only on available variation; structures result from modified ancestral anatomy; adaptations are often compromises; and chance, natural selection, and the environment interact.

? *How might secondary sex characteristics differ between males and females in a species in which females compete for mates?*

TEST YOUR UNDERSTANDING

Level 1: Knowledge/Comprehension

1. Natural selection changes allele frequencies because some _____ survive and reproduce more successfully than others.
   - **a.** alleles
   - **b.** loci
   - **c.** gene pools
   - **d.** species
   - **e.** individuals

2. No two people are genetically identical, except for identical twins. The main source of genetic variation among human individuals is
   - **a.** new mutations that occurred in the preceding generation.
   - **b.** genetic drift due to the small size of the population.
   - **c.** the reshuffling of alleles in sexual reproduction.
   - **d.** natural selection.
   - **e.** environmental effects.

3. Sparrows with average-sized wings survive severe storms better than those with longer or shorter wings, illustrating
   - **a.** the bottleneck effect.
   - **b.** disruptive selection.
   - **c.** frequency-dependent selection.
   - **d.** neutral variation.
   - **e.** stabilizing selection.

Level 2: Application/Analysis

4. If the nucleotide variability of a locus equals 0%, what is the gene variability and number of alleles at that locus?
  a. gene variability = 0%; number of alleles = 0
  b. gene variability = 0%; number of alleles = 1
  c. gene variability = 0%; number of alleles = 2
  d. gene variability > 0%; number of alleles = 2
  e. Without more information, gene variability and number of alleles cannot be determined.

5. There are 25 individuals in population 1, all with genotype *AA*, and there are 40 individuals in population 2, all with genotype *aa*. Assume that these populations are located far from each other and that their environmental conditions are very similar. Based on the information given here, the observed genetic variation most likely resulted from
  a. genetic drift.
  b. gene flow.
  c. disruptive selection.
  d. nonrandom mating.
  e. directional selection.

6. A fruit fly population has a gene with two alleles, *A1* and *A2*. Tests show that 70% of the gametes produced in the population contain the *A1* allele. If the population is in Hardy-Weinberg equilibrium, what proportion of the flies carry both *A1* and *A2*?
  a. 0.7
  b. 0.49
  c. 0.21
  d. 0.42
  e. 0.09

Level 3: Synthesis/Evaulation

7. SCIENTIFIC INQUIRY
  DRAW IT Researchers studied genetic variation in the marine mussel *Mytilus edulis* around Long Island, New York. They measured the frequency of a particular allele (lap^{94}) for an enzyme involved in regulating the mussel's internal saltwater balance. The researchers presented their data as a series of pie charts linked to sampling sites within Long Island Sound, where the salinity is highly variable, and along the coast of the open ocean, where salinity is constant:

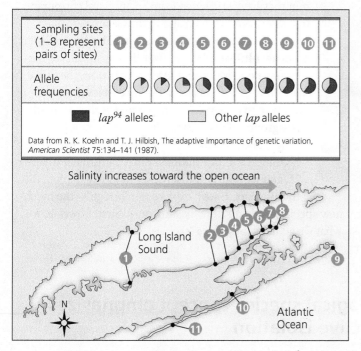

Data from R. K. Koehn and T. J. Hilbish, The adaptive importance of genetic variation, *American Scientist* 75:134–141 (1987).

Create a data table for the 11 sampling sites by estimating the frequency of lap^{94} from the pie charts. (*Hint*: Think of each pie chart as a clock face to help you estimate the proportion of the shaded area.) Then graph the frequencies for sites 1–8 to show how the frequency of this allele changes with increasing salinity in Long Island Sound (from southwest to northeast). How do the data from sites 9–11 compare with the data from the sites within the Sound?

Construct a hypothesis that explains the patterns you observe in the data and that accounts for the following observations: (1) The lap^{94} allele helps mussels maintain osmotic balance in water with a high salt concentration but is costly to use in less salty water; and (2) mussels produce larvae that can disperse long distances before they settle on rocks and grow into adults.

8. FOCUS ON EVOLUTION
Using at least two examples, explain how the process of evolution is revealed by the imperfections of living organisms.

9. FOCUS ON ORGANIZATION
Heterozygotes at the sickle-cell locus produce both normal and abnormal (sickle-cell) hemoglobin (see Concept 11.4). When hemoglobin molecules are packed into a heterozygote's red blood cells, some cells receive relatively large quantities of abnormal hemoglobin, making these cells prone to sickling. In a short essay (approximately 100–150 words), explain how these molecular and cellular events lead to emergent properties at the individual and population levels of biological organization.

For selected answers, see Appendix A.

MasteringBiology®

Students Go to **MasteringBiology** for assignments, the eText, and the Study Area with practice tests, animations, and activities.

Instructors Go to **MasteringBiology** for automatically graded tutorials and questions that you can assign to your students, plus Instructor Resources.

22 The Origin of Species

KEY CONCEPTS

22.1 The biological species concept emphasizes reproductive isolation
22.2 Speciation can take place with or without geographic separation
22.3 Hybrid zones reveal factors that cause reproductive isolation
22.4 Speciation can occur rapidly or slowly and can result from changes in few or many genes

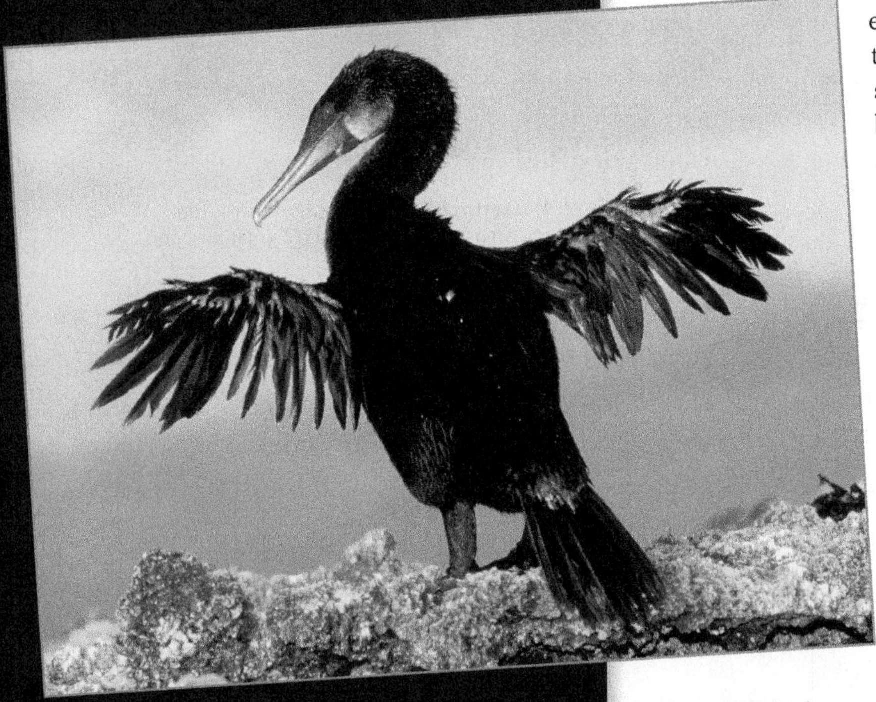

▼ **Figure 22.1** How did this flightless bird come to live on the isolated Galápagos Islands?

OVERVIEW

That "Mystery of Mysteries"

When Darwin came to the Galápagos, he noted that these volcanic islands, despite their geologic youth, were teeming with plants and animals found nowhere else in the world (**Figure 22.1**). Later he realized that these species had formed relatively recently. He wrote in his diary: "Both in space and time, we seem to be brought somewhat near to that great fact—that mystery of mysteries—the first appearance of new beings on this Earth."

The "mystery of mysteries" that captivated Darwin is **speciation**, the process by which one species splits into two or more species. Speciation fascinated Darwin (and many biologists since) because it leads to the tremendous diversity of life, repeatedly yielding new species that differ from existing ones. Speciation also explains the many features that organisms share (the unity of life). When a species splits, the species that result share many characteristics because they are descended from this common ancestor. At the DNA sequence level, such similarities indicate that the flightless cormorant (*Phalacrocorax harrisi*) in Figure 22.1 is closely related to flying cormorants found in the Americas. This suggests that the flightless cormorant may have originated from an ancestral cormorant that flew from the mainland to the Galápagos.

Speciation also forms a conceptual bridge between **microevolution**, changes over time in allele frequencies in a population, and **macroevolution**, the broad pattern of evolution above the species level. An example of macroevolutionary change is the origin of new groups of organisms, such as mammals or flowering plants, through a series of speciation events. We examined microevolutionary mechanisms in Chapter 21, and we'll turn to macroevolution in Chapter 23. In this chapter, we'll explore the "bridge"—the mechanisms by which new species originate from existing ones. First, however, we need to establish what we actually mean by a "species."

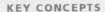

CONCEPT 22.1

The biological species concept emphasizes reproductive isolation

The word *species* is Latin for "kind" or "appearance." In daily life, we commonly distinguish between various "kinds" of organisms—dogs and cats, for instance—from differences in their appearance. But are organisms truly divided into the discrete units we call species, or is this classification an arbitrary attempt to impose order on the natural world? To answer this question, biologists compare not only the morphology (body form) of different groups of organisms but also less obvious differences in physiology, biochemistry, and DNA sequences. The results generally confirm that morphologically distinct species are indeed discrete groups, differing in many ways besides their body forms.

The Biological Species Concept

The primary definition of species used in this textbook is the **biological species concept**. According to this concept, a **species** is a group of populations whose members have the potential to interbreed in nature and produce viable, fertile offspring—but do not produce viable, fertile offspring with members of other such groups **(Figure 22.2)**. Thus, the members of a biological species are united by being reproductively compatible, at least potentially. All human beings, for example, belong to the same species. A businesswoman in Manhattan may be unlikely to meet a dairy farmer in Mongolia, but if the two should happen to meet and mate, they could have viable babies that develop into fertile adults. In contrast, humans and chimpanzees remain distinct biological species even where they live in the same region, because many factors keep them from interbreeding and producing fertile offspring.

What holds the gene pool of a species together, causing its members to resemble each other more than they resemble members of other species? To answer this question, we need to return to the evolutionary mechanism called *gene flow*, the transfer of alleles into or out of a population (see Concept 21.3). Typically, gene flow occurs between the different populations of a species. This ongoing transfer of alleles tends to hold the populations together genetically. As we'll explore in the following sections, the absence of gene flow plays a key role in the formation of new species, as well as in keeping them apart once their potential to interbreed has been reduced.

Reproductive Isolation

Because biological species are defined in terms of reproductive compatibility, the formation of a new species hinges on **reproductive isolation**—the existence of biological barriers that impede members of two species from interbreeding and producing viable, fertile offspring. Such barriers block gene flow between the species and limit the formation of **hybrids**, offspring that result from an interspecific mating. Although a single barrier may not prevent all gene flow, a combination of several barriers can effectively isolate a species' gene pool.

Clearly, a fly cannot mate with a frog or a fern, but the reproductive barriers between more closely related species are not so obvious. These barriers can be classified according to whether they contribute to reproductive isolation before or after fertilization. **Prezygotic barriers** ("before the zygote") block fertilization from occurring. Such barriers typically act in one of three ways: by impeding members of different species

(a) Similarity between different species. The eastern meadowlark (*Sturnella magna*, left) and the western meadowlark (*Sturnella neglecta*, right) have similar body shapes and colorations. Nevertheless, they are distinct biological species because their songs and other behaviors are different enough to prevent interbreeding should they meet in the wild.

(b) Diversity within a species. As diverse as we may be in appearance, all humans belong to a single biological species (*Homo sapiens*), defined by our capacity to interbreed successfully.

▲ **Figure 22.2 The biological species concept is based on the potential to interbreed rather than on physical similarity.**

from attempting to mate, by preventing an attempted mating from being completed successfully, or by hindering fertilization if mating is completed successfully. If a sperm cell from one species overcomes prezygotic barriers and fertilizes an ovum from another species, a variety of **postzygotic barriers** ("after the zygote") may contribute to reproductive isolation after the hybrid zygote is formed. For example, developmental errors may reduce survival among hybrid embryos. Or problems after birth may cause hybrids to be infertile or may decrease their chance of surviving long enough to reproduce. **Figure 22.3** describes prezygotic and postzygotic barriers in more detail.

Prezygotic barriers impede mating or hinder fertilization if mating does occur

Habitat Isolation	Temporal Isolation	Behavioral Isolation	Mechanical Isolation

Individuals of different species

MATING ATTEMPT

Two species that occupy different habitats within the same area may encounter each other rarely, if at all, even though they are not isolated by obvious physical barriers, such as mountain ranges.

Species that breed during different times of the day, different seasons, or different years cannot mix their gametes.

Courtship rituals that attract mates and other behaviors unique to a species are effective reproductive barriers, even between closely related species. Such behavioral rituals enable *mate recognition*—a way to identify potential mates of the same species.

Mating is attempted, but morphological differences prevent its successful completion.

Example: Two species of garter snakes in the genus *Thamnophis* occur in the same geographic areas, but one lives mainly in water (a) while the other is primarily terrestrial (b).

Example: In North America, the geographic ranges of the eastern spotted skunk (*Spilogale putorius*) (c) and the western spotted skunk (*Spilogale gracilis*) (d) overlap, but *S. putorius* mates in late winter and *S. gracilis* mates in late summer.

Example: Blue-footed boobies, inhabitants of the Galápagos, mate only after a courtship display unique to their species. Part of the "script" calls for the male to high-step (e), a behavior that calls the female's attention to his bright blue feet.

Example: The shells of two species of snails in the genus *Bradybaena* spiral in different directions: Moving inward to the center, one spirals in a counterclockwise direction (f, left), the other in a clockwise direction (f, right). As a result, the snails' genital openings (indicated by arrows) are not aligned, and mating cannot be completed.

(a)

(c)

(e)

(f)

(b)

(d)

Postzygotic barriers prevent a hybrid zygote from developing into a viable, fertile adult

Gametic Isolation	Reduced Hybrid Viability	Reduced Hybrid Fertility	Hybrid Breakdown

FERTILIZATION → VIABLE, FERTILE OFFSPRING

Sperm of one species may not be able to fertilize the eggs of another species. For instance, sperm may not be able to survive in the reproductive tract of females of the other species, or biochemical mechanisms may prevent the sperm from penetrating the membrane surrounding the other species' eggs.

The genes of different parent species may interact in ways that impair the hybrid's development or survival in its environment.

Even if hybrids are vigorous, they may be sterile. If the chromosomes of the two parent species differ in number or structure, meiosis in the hybrids may fail to produce normal gametes. Since the infertile hybrids cannot produce offspring when they mate with either parent species, genes cannot flow freely between the species.

Some first-generation hybrids are viable and fertile, but when they mate with one another or with either parent species, offspring of the next generation are feeble or sterile.

Example: Gametic isolation separates certain closely related species of aquatic animals, such as sea urchins (g). Sea urchins release their sperm and eggs into the surrounding water, where they fuse and form zygotes. It is difficult for gametes of different species, such as the red and purple urchins shown here, to fuse because proteins on the surfaces of the eggs and sperm bind very poorly to each other.

Example: Some salamander subspecies of the genus *Ensatina* live in the same regions and habitats, where they may occasionally hybridize. But most of the hybrids do not complete development, and those that do are frail (h).

Example: The hybrid offspring of a male donkey (i) and a female horse (j) is a mule (k), which is robust but sterile. A "hinny" (not shown), the offspring of a female donkey and a male horse, is also sterile.

Example: Strains of cultivated rice have accumulated different mutant recessive alleles at two loci in the course of their divergence from a common ancestor. Hybrids between them are vigorous and fertile (l, left and right), but plants in the next generation that carry too many of these recessive alleles are small and sterile (l, center). Although these rice strains are not yet considered different species, they have begun to be separated by postzygotic barriers.

(i)

(g)

(h)

(j)

(l)

(k)

Limitations of the Biological Species Concept

One strength of the biological species concept is that it directs our attention to a way by which speciation can occur: by the evolution of reproductive isolation. However, the number of species to which this concept can be usefully applied is limited. There is, for example, no way to evaluate the reproductive isolation of fossils. The biological species concept also does not apply to organisms that reproduce asexually all or most of the time, such as prokaryotes. (Many prokaryotes do transfer genes among themselves, as we will discuss in Chapter 24, but this is not part of their reproductive process.) Furthermore, in the biological species concept, species are designated by the *absence* of gene flow. But there are many pairs of species that are morphologically and ecologically distinct, and yet gene flow occurs between them. An example is the grizzly bear (*Ursus arctos*) and polar bear (*Ursus maritimus*), whose hybrid offspring have been dubbed "grolar bears" **(Figure 22.4)**. As we'll discuss, natural selection can cause such species to remain distinct even though some gene flow occurs between them. This observation has led some researchers to argue that the biological species concept overemphasizes gene flow and downplays the role of natural selection. Because of the limitations to the biological species concept, alternative species concepts are useful in certain situations.

◄ Grizzly bear (*U. arctos*)

▼ Polar bear (*U. maritimus*)

▲ Hybrid "grolar bear"

▲ **Figure 22.4 Hybridization between two species of bears in the genus *Ursus*.**

Other Definitions of Species

While the biological species concept emphasizes the *separateness* of species from one another due to reproductive barriers, several other definitions emphasize the *unity within* a species. For example, the **morphological species concept** characterizes a species by body shape and other structural features. The morphological species concept can be applied to asexual and sexual organisms, and it can be useful even without information on the extent of gene flow. In practice, scientists often distinguish species using morphological criteria. A disadvantage of this approach, however, is that it relies on subjective criteria; researchers may disagree on which structural features distinguish a species.

The **ecological species concept** views a species in terms of its ecological niche, the sum of how members of the species interact with the nonliving and living parts of their environment (see Chapter 41). For example, two species of oak trees might differ in their size or in their ability to tolerate dry conditions, yet still occasionally interbreed. Because they occupy different ecological niches, these oaks would be considered two separate species even though some gene flow occurs between them. Unlike the biological species concept, the ecological species concept can accommodate asexual as well as sexual species. It also emphasizes the role of disruptive natural selection as organisms adapt to different environmental conditions.

The **phylogenetic species concept** defines a species as the smallest group of individuals that share a common ancestor, forming one branch on the tree of life. Biologists trace the phylogenetic history of a species by comparing its characteristics, such as morphology or molecular sequences, with those of other organisms. Such analyses can distinguish groups of individuals that are sufficiently different to be considered separate species. Of course, the difficulty with this species concept is determining the degree of difference required to indicate separate species.

In addition to those discussed here, more than 20 other species definitions have been proposed. The usefulness of each definition depends on the situation and the research questions being asked. For our purposes of studying how species originate, the biological species concept, with its focus on reproductive barriers, is particularly helpful.

CONCEPT CHECK 22.1

1. (a) Which species concept(s) could you apply to both asexual and sexual species? (b) Which would be most useful for identifying species in the field? Explain.
2. **WHAT IF?** Suppose you are studying two bird species that live in a forest and are not known to interbreed. One species feeds and mates in the treetops and the other on the ground. But in captivity, the birds can interbreed and produce viable, fertile offspring. What type of reproductive barrier most likely keeps these species separate in nature? Explain.

For suggested answers, see Appendix A.

Speciation can take place with or without geographic separation

Now that we have a clearer sense of what constitutes a unique species, let's return to our discussion of the process by which such species arise from existing species. Speciation can occur in two main ways, depending on how gene flow is interrupted between populations of the existing species (**Figure 22.5**).

Allopatric ("Other Country") Speciation

In **allopatric speciation** (from the Greek *allos*, other, and *patra*, homeland), gene flow is interrupted when a population is divided into geographically isolated subpopulations. For example, the water level in a lake may subside, resulting in two or more smaller lakes that are now home to separated populations (see Figure 22.5a). Or a river may change course and divide a population of animals that cannot cross it. Allopatric speciation can also occur without geologic remodeling, such as when individuals colonize a remote area and their descendants become isolated from the parent population. The flightless cormorant in Figure 22.1 likely originated in this way from an ancestral flying species that reached the Galápagos Islands.

The Process of Allopatric Speciation

How formidable must a geographic barrier be to promote allopatric speciation? The answer depends on the ability of the organisms to move about. Birds, mountain lions, and coyotes can cross rivers and canyons—as can the windblown pollen of pine trees and the seeds of many flowering plants. In contrast, small rodents may find a wide river or deep canyon a formidable barrier.

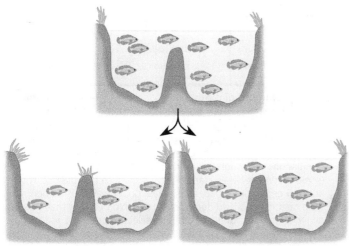

(a) Allopatric speciation. A population forms a new species while geographically isolated from its parent population.

(b) Sympatric speciation. A subset of a population forms a new species without geographic separation.

▲ **Figure 22.5 Two main modes of speciation.**

(a) Under high predation   **(b) Under low predation**

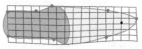 

In ponds with predatory fishes, the head region of the mosquitofish is streamlined and the tail region is powerful, enabling rapid bursts of speed.

In ponds without predatory fishes, mosquitofish have a different body shape that favors long, steady swimming.

▲ **Figure 22.6 Reproductive isolation as a by-product of selection.** Bringing together mosquitofish from different ponds indicates that selection for traits that enable mosquitofish in high-predation ponds to avoid predators has isolated them reproductively from mosquitofish in low-predation ponds.

Once geographic separation has occurred, the separated gene pools may diverge. Different mutations arise, and natural selection and genetic drift may alter allele frequencies in different ways in the separated populations. Reproductive isolation may then arise as a by-product of the genetic divergence that results from selection or drift.

Let's consider an example. On Andros Island, in the Bahamas, populations of the mosquitofish *Gambusia hubbsi* colonized a series of ponds that later became isolated from one another. Genetic analyses indicate that little or no gene flow currently occurs between the ponds. The environments of these ponds are very similar except that some contain many predatory fishes, while others do not. In the "high-predation" ponds, selection has favored the evolution of a mosquitofish body shape that enables rapid bursts of speed (**Figure 22.6**). In low-predation ponds, selection has favored a different body shape, one that improves the ability to swim for long periods of time. How have these different selective pressures affected the evolution of reproductive barriers? Researchers studied this question by bringing together mosquitofish from the two types of ponds. They found that female mosquitofish prefer to mate with males whose body shape is similar to their own. This preference establishes a behavioral barrier to reproduction between mosquitofish from high-predation and low-predation ponds. Thus, as a by-product of selection for avoiding predators, reproductive barriers have started to form in these allopatric populations.

Evidence of Allopatric Speciation

Many studies provide evidence that speciation can occur in allopatric populations. Consider the 30 species of snapping shrimp in the genus *Alpheus* that live off the Isthmus of Panama, the land bridge that connects South and North America. Fifteen of these species live on the Atlantic side of the isthmus, while the other 15 live on the Pacific side. Before the isthmus formed, gene flow could occur between the Atlantic and Pacific populations of snapping shrimp. Did the species

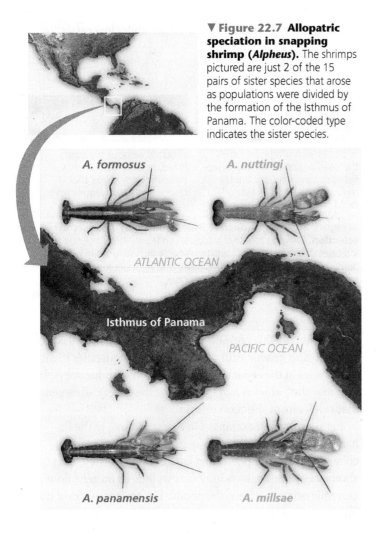

▼ Figure 22.7 Allopatric speciation in snapping shrimp (*Alpheus*). The shrimps pictured are just 2 of the 15 pairs of sister species that arose as populations were divided by the formation of the Isthmus of Panama. The color-coded type indicates the sister species.

A. formosus

A. nuttingi

ATLANTIC OCEAN

Isthmus of Panama

PACIFIC OCEAN

A. panamensis

A. millsae

on different sides of the isthmus originate by allopatric speciation? Morphological and genetic data group these shrimp into 15 pairs of *sister species*, pairs whose member species are each other's closest relative (see Figure 20.5). In each of these 15 pairs, one of the sister species lives on the Atlantic side of the isthmus, while the other lives on the Pacific side (**Figure 22.7**), strongly suggesting that the two species arose as a consequence of geographic separation. Furthermore, genetic analyses indicate that the *Alpheus* species originated from 9 million to 3 million years ago, with the sister species that live in the deepest water diverging first. These divergence times are consistent with geologic evidence that the isthmus formed gradually, starting 10 million years ago and closing completely about 3 million years ago.

The importance of allopatric speciation is also suggested by the fact that regions that are isolated or highly subdivided by barriers typically have more species than do otherwise similar regions that lack such features. For example, many unique plants and animals are found on the geographically isolated Hawaiian Islands (we'll return to the origin of Hawaiian species in Chapter 23). Similarly, unusually high numbers of butterfly species are found in regions of South America that are subdivided by many rivers.

▼ Figure 22.8 Inquiry

Can divergence of allopatric populations lead to reproductive isolation?

Experiment A researcher divided a laboratory population of the fruit fly *Drosophila pseudoobscura*, raising some flies on a starch medium and others on a maltose medium. After one year (about 40 generations), natural selection resulted in divergent evolution: Populations raised on starch digested starch more efficiently, while those raised on maltose digested maltose more efficiently. The researcher then put flies from the same or different populations in mating cages and measured mating frequencies. All flies used in the mating preference tests were reared for one generation on a standard cornmeal medium.

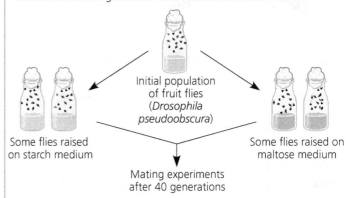

Some flies raised on starch medium

Initial population of fruit flies (*Drosophila pseudoobscura*)

Some flies raised on maltose medium

Mating experiments after 40 generations

Results Mating patterns among populations of flies raised on different media are shown below. When flies from "starch populations" were mixed with flies from "maltose populations," the flies tended to mate with like partners. But in the control group (shown on the right), flies from different populations adapted to starch were about as likely to mate with each other as with flies from their own population; similar results were obtained for control groups adapted to maltose.

		Female	
		Starch	Maltose
Male	Starch	22	9
	Maltose	8	20

Number of matings in experimental group

		Female	
		Starch population 1	Starch population 2
Male	Starch population 1	18	15
	Starch population 2	12	15

Number of matings in control group

Conclusion In the experimental group, the strong preference of "starch flies" and "maltose flies" to mate with like-adapted flies indicates that a reproductive barrier was forming between these fly populations. Although this reproductive barrier was not absolute (some mating between starch flies and maltose flies did occur), after 40 generations it appeared to be under way. This barrier may have been caused by differences in courtship behavior that arose as an incidental by-product of differing selective pressures as these allopatric populations adapted to different sources of food.

Source D. M. B. Dodd, Reproductive isolation as a consequence of adaptive divergence in *Drosophila pseudoobscura*, *Evolution* 43:1308–1311 (1989).

WHAT IF? Why were all flies used in the mating preference tests reared on a standard medium (rather than on a starch or maltose medium)?

Field observations show that reproductive isolation between two populations generally increases as the geographic distance between them increases. Researchers have also tested whether intrinsic reproductive barriers develop when populations are isolated experimentally and subjected to different environmental conditions. In such cases, too, the results provide strong support for allopatric speciation (**Figure 22.8**, on the preceding page).

We need to emphasize here that although geographic isolation prevents interbreeding between allopatric populations, physical separation is not a biological barrier to reproduction. Biological reproductive barriers such as those described in Figure 22.3 are intrinsic to the organisms themselves. Hence, it is biological barriers that can prevent interbreeding when members of different populations come into contact with one another.

Sympatric ("Same Country") Speciation

In **sympatric speciation** (from the Greek *syn*, together), speciation occurs in populations that live in the same geographic area. How can reproductive barriers form between sympatric populations while their members remain in contact with each other? Although such contact (and the ongoing gene flow that results) makes sympatric speciation less common than allopatric speciation, sympatric speciation can occur if gene flow is reduced by such factors as polyploidy, habitat differentiation, and sexual selection. (Note that these factors can also promote allopatric speciation.)

Polyploidy

A species may originate from an accident during cell division that results in extra sets of chromosomes, a condition called **polyploidy**. Polyploid speciation occasionally occurs in animals; for example, the gray tree frog *Hyla versicolor* (see Figure 21.16) is thought to have originated in this way. However, polyploidy is far more common in plants. Botanists estimate that more than 80% of the plant species alive today are descended from ancestors that formed by polyploid speciation.

Two distinct forms of polyploidy have been observed in plant (and a few animal) populations. An **autopolyploid** (from the Greek *autos*, self) is an individual that has more than two chromosome sets that are all derived from a single species. In plants, for example, a failure of cell division could double a cell's chromosome number from the diploid number ($2n$) to a tetraploid number ($4n$).

A tetraploid can produce fertile tetraploid offspring by

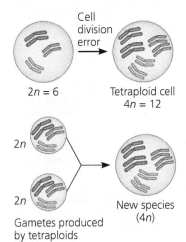

self-pollinating or by mating with other tetraploids. In addition, the tetraploids are reproductively isolated from diploid plants of the original population, because the triploid ($3n$) offspring of such unions have reduced fertility. Thus, in just one generation, autopolyploidy can generate reproductive isolation without any geographic separation.

A second form of polyploidy can occur when two different species interbreed and produce hybrid offspring. Most such hybrids are sterile because the set of chromosomes from one species cannot pair during meiosis with the set of chromosomes from the other species. However, an infertile hybrid may be able to propagate itself asexually (as many plants can do). In subsequent generations, various mechanisms can change a sterile hybrid into a fertile polyploid called an **allopolyploid** (**Figure 22.9**). The allopolyploids are fertile when mating with

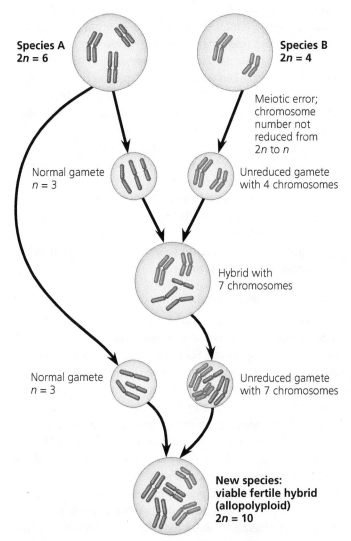

▲ **Figure 22.9 One mechanism for allopolyploid speciation in plants.** Most hybrids are sterile because their chromosomes are not homologous and cannot pair during meiosis. However, such a hybrid may be able to reproduce asexually. This diagram traces one mechanism that can produce fertile hybrids (allopolyploids) as new species. The new species has a diploid chromosome number equal to the sum of the diploid chromosome numbers of the two parent species.

each other but cannot interbreed with either parent species; thus, they represent a new biological species.

Although polyploid speciation is relatively rare, even in plants, scientists have documented that at least five new plant species have originated in this way since 1850. One of these examples involves the origin of a new species of goatsbeard plant (genus *Tragopogon*) in the Pacific Northwest. *Tragopogon* first arrived in the region when humans introduced three European species in the early 1900s. These three species are now common weeds in abandoned parking lots and other urban sites. In 1950, a new *Tragopogon* species was discovered near the Idaho-Washington border, a region where all three European species also were found. Genetic analyses revealed that this new species, *Tragopogon miscellus*, is a tetraploid hybrid of two of the European species. Although the *T. miscellus* population grows mainly by reproduction of its own members, additional episodes of hybridization between the parent species continue to add new members to the *T. miscellus* population—just one of many examples in which scientists have observed speciation in progress.

Many important agricultural crops—such as oats, cotton, potatoes, tobacco, and wheat—are polyploids. The wheat used for bread, *Triticum aestivum*, is an allohexaploid (six sets of chromosomes, two sets from each of three different species). The first of the polyploidy events that eventually led to modern wheat probably occurred about 8,000 years ago in the Middle East as a spontaneous hybrid of an early cultivated wheat species and a wild grass. Today, plant geneticists generate new polyploids in the laboratory by using chemicals that induce meiotic and mitotic errors. By harnessing the evolutionary process, researchers can produce new hybrid species with desired qualities, such as a hybrid that combines the high yield of wheat with the hardiness of rye.

Habitat Differentiation

Sympatric speciation can also occur when genetic factors enable a subpopulation to exploit a habitat or resource not used by the parent population. Such is the case with the North American apple maggot fly (*Rhagoletis pomonella*), a pest of apples. The fly's original habitat was the native hawthorn tree, but about 200 years ago, some populations colonized apple trees that had been introduced by European settlers. As apples mature more quickly than hawthorn fruit, natural selection has favored apple-feeding flies with rapid development. These apple-feeding populations now show temporal isolation from the hawthorn-feeding *R. pomonella*, providing a prezygotic restriction to gene flow between the two populations. Researchers also have identified alleles that benefit the flies that use one host plant but harm the flies that use the other host plant. As a result, natural selection operating on these alleles provides a postzygotic barrier to reproduction, further limiting gene flow. Altogether, although the two populations are still classified as subspecies rather than separate species, sympatric speciation appears to be well under way.

Sexual Selection

There is evidence that sympatric speciation can also be driven by sexual selection. Clues to how this can occur have been found in cichlid fishes from one of Earth's hot spots of animal speciation, East Africa's Lake Victoria. This lake was once home to as many as 600 species of cichlids. Genetic data indicate that these species originated within the last 100,000 years from a small number of colonizing species that arrived from rivers and lakes located elsewhere. How did so many species—more than double the number of freshwater fish species known in all of Europe—originate within a single lake?

One hypothesis is that subgroups of the original cichlid populations adapted to different food sources and that the resulting genetic divergence contributed to speciation in Lake Victoria.

▼ **Figure 22.10** Inquiry

Does sexual selection in cichlids result in reproductive isolation?

Experiment Researchers placed males and females of *Pundamilia pundamilia* and *P. nyererei* together in two aquarium tanks, one with natural light and one with a monochromatic orange lamp. Under normal light, the two species are noticeably different in male breeding coloration; under monochromatic orange light, the two species are very similar in color. The researchers then observed the mate choices of the females in each tank.

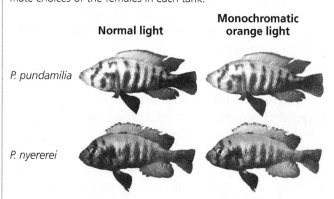

Results Under normal light, females of each species strongly preferred males of their own species. But under orange light, females of each species responded indiscriminately to males of both species. The resulting hybrids were viable and fertile.

Conclusion The researchers concluded that mate choice by females based on male breeding coloration is the main reproductive barrier that normally keeps the gene pools of these two species separate. Since the species can still interbreed when this prezygotic behavioral barrier is breached in the laboratory, the genetic divergence between the species is likely to be small. This suggests that speciation in nature has occurred relatively recently.

Source O. Seehausen and J. J. M. van Alphen, The effect of male coloration on female mate choice in closely related Lake Victoria cichlids (*Haplochromis nyererei* complex), *Behavioral Ecology and Sociobiology* 42:1–8 (1998).

WHAT IF? Suppose that female cichlids living in the murky waters of a polluted lake could not distinguish colors well. How might the gene pools of these species change over time?

But sexual selection, in which (typically) females select males based on their appearance (see Chapter 21), may also have been a factor. Researchers have studied two closely related sympatric species of cichlids that differ mainly in the coloration of breeding males: Breeding *Pundamilia pundamilia* males have a blue-tinged back, whereas breeding *Pundamilia nyererei* males have a red-tinged back (**Figure 22.10**, on the preceding page). Their results suggest that mate choice based on male breeding coloration is the main reproductive barrier that normally keeps the gene pools of these two species separate.

Allopatric and Sympatric Speciation: *A Review*

Now let's recap the two main modes by which new species form. In allopatric speciation, a new species forms in geographic isolation from its parent population. Geographic isolation severely restricts gene flow. As a result, other reproductive barriers from the ancestral species may arise as a by-product of genetic changes that occur within the isolated population. Many different processes can produce such genetic changes, including natural selection under different environmental conditions, genetic drift, and sexual selection. Once formed, intrinsic reproductive barriers that arise in allopatric populations can prevent interbreeding with the parent population even if the populations come back into contact. In the **Scientific Skills Exercise**, you will interpret data from a study of reproductive isolation in geographically separated salamander populations.

Sympatric speciation, in contrast, requires the emergence of a reproductive barrier that isolates a subset of a population from the remainder of the population in the same area. Though rarer than allopatric speciation, sympatric speciation can occur when gene flow to and from the isolated subpopulation is blocked. This can occur as a result of polyploidy, a condition in which an organism has extra sets of chromosomes.

Scientific Skills Exercise

Identifying Independent and Dependent Variables, Making a Scatter Plot, and Interpreting Data

Does Distance Between Salamander Populations Increase Their Reproductive Isolation? The process of allopatric speciation begins when populations become geographically isolated, preventing mating between individuals in different populations and thus stopping gene flow. It seems logical that as distance between populations increases, so will their degree of reproductive isolation. To test this hypothesis, researchers studied populations of the dusky salamander (*Desmognathus ochrophaeus*) living on different mountain ranges in the southern Appalachian Mountains.

How the Experiment Was Done The researchers tested the reproductive isolation of pairs of salamander populations by leaving one male and one female together and later checking the females for the presence of sperm. Four mating combinations were tested for each pair of populations (A and B)—two *within* the same population (female A with male A and female B with male B) and two *between* populations (female A with male B and female B with male A).

Data from the Experiment The researchers used an index of reproductive isolation that ranged from a value of 0 (no isolation) to a value of 2 (full isolation). The proportion of successful matings for each mating combination was measured, with 100% success = 1 and no success = 0. The reproductive isolation value for two populations is the sum of the proportion of successful matings of each type within populations (AA + BB) minus the sum of the proportion of successful matings of each type between populations (AB + BA). The following table provides data for 27 pairs of dusky salamander populations:

Interpret the Data

1. State the researchers' hypothesis, and identify the independent and dependent variables in this study. Explain why the researchers used four mating combinations for each pair of populations.

2. Calculate the value of the reproductive isolation index if (a) *all* of the matings within a population were successful, but *none* of the matings between populations were successful; (b) salamanders are equally successful in mating with members of their own population and members of another population.

3. Make a scatter plot of one variable against the other to help you visualize whether or not there is a relationship between the variables. (For additional information about graphs, see the Scientific Skills Review in Appendix F and in the Study Area in MasteringBiology.) Plot the dependent variable on the *y*-axis and the independent variable on the *x*-axis.

4. Interpret your graph by (a) explaining in words the relationship between the variables that can be visualized by graphing the data and (b) hypothesizing the possible cause of this relationship.

Data from S. G. Tilley, P. A. Verrell, and S. J. Arnold, Correspondence between sexual isolation and allozyme differentiation: A test in the salamander *Desmognathus ochrophaeus*, *Proceedings of the National Academy of Sciences USA.* 87:2715–2719 (1990).

(MB) A version of this Scientific Skills Exercise can be assigned in MasteringBiology.

Geographic Distance (km)	15	32	40	47	42	62	63	81	86	107	107	115	137	147
Reproductive Isolation Value	0.32	0.54	0.50	0.50	0.82	0.37	0.67	0.53	1.15	0.73	0.82	0.81	0.87	0.87
Distance (continued)	137	150	165	189	219	239	247	53	55	62	105	179	169	
Isolation (continued)	0.50	0.57	0.91	0.93	1.50	1.22	0.82	0.99	0.21	0.56	0.41	0.72	1.15	

Sympatric speciation also can occur when a subset of a population becomes reproductively isolated because of natural selection that results from a switch to a habitat or food source not used by the parent population. Finally, sympatric speciation can result from sexual selection.

Having reviewed the geographic context in which species originate, we'll next explore in more detail what can happen when new or partially formed species come into contact.

CONCEPT CHECK 22.2

1. Summarize key differences between allopatric and sympatric speciation. Which type of speciation is more common, and why?

2. Describe two mechanisms that can decrease gene flow in sympatric populations, thereby making sympatric speciation more likely to occur.

3. **WHAT IF?** Is allopatric speciation more likely to occur on an island close to a mainland or on a more isolated island of the same size? Explain your prediction.

4. **MAKE CONNECTIONS** Review meiosis in Figure 10.8. Describe how an error during meiosis could lead to polyploidy.

For suggested answers, see Appendix A.

Hybrid zones reveal factors that cause reproductive isolation

What happens if species with incomplete reproductive barriers come into contact with one another? One possible outcome is the formation of a **hybrid zone**, a region in which members of different species meet and mate, producing at least some offspring of mixed ancestry. In this section, we'll explore hybrid zones and what they reveal about factors that cause the evolution of reproductive isolation.

Patterns Within Hybrid Zones

Some hybrid zones form as narrow bands, such as the one depicted in **Figure 22.11** for two species of toads in the genus *Bombina*, the yellow-bellied toad (*B. variegata*) and the fire-bellied toad (*B. bombina*). This hybrid zone, represented by the red line on the map, extends for 4,000 km but is less than 10 km wide in most places. The hybrid zone occurs where the higher-altitude habitat of the yellow-bellied toad meets the

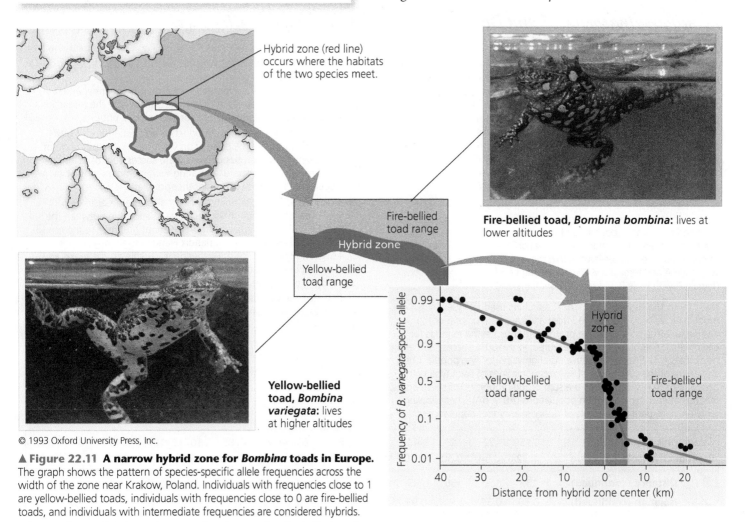

Hybrid zone (red line) occurs where the habitats of the two species meet.

Fire-bellied toad range
Hybrid zone
Yellow-bellied toad range

Fire-bellied toad, *Bombina bombina*: lives at lower altitudes

Yellow-bellied toad, *Bombina variegata*: lives at higher altitudes

© 1993 Oxford University Press, Inc.

▲ **Figure 22.11 A narrow hybrid zone for *Bombina* toads in Europe.** The graph shows the pattern of species-specific allele frequencies across the width of the zone near Krakow, Poland. Individuals with frequencies close to 1 are yellow-bellied toads, individuals with frequencies close to 0 are fire-bellied toads, and individuals with intermediate frequencies are considered hybrids.

? *Does the graph indicate that gene flow is spreading fire-bellied toad alleles into the range of the yellow-bellied toad? Explain.*

Graph: Frequency of *B. variegata*-specific allele (y-axis: 0.99, 0.9, 0.5, 0.1, 0.01) vs Distance from hybrid zone center (km) (x-axis: 40, 30, 20, 10, 0, 10, 20). Yellow-bellied toad range, Hybrid zone, Fire-bellied toad range labeled.

lowland habitat of the fire-bellied toad. Across a given "slice" of the zone, the frequency of alleles specific to yellow-bellied toads typically decreases from about 90% at the edge where only yellow-bellied toads are found, to 50% in the central portion of the zone, to less than 10% at the edge where only fire-bellied toads are found.

What causes such a pattern of allele frequencies across a hybrid zone? We can infer that there is an obstacle to gene flow—otherwise, alleles from one parent species would also be common in the gene pool of the other parent species. Are geographic barriers reducing gene flow? Not in this case, since the toads can move throughout the hybrid zone. A more important factor is that hybrid toads have increased rates of embryonic mortality and a variety of morphological abnormalities, including ribs that are fused to the spine and malformed tadpole mouthparts. Because the hybrids have poor survival and reproduction, they produce few viable offspring with members of the parent species. As a result, hybrid individuals rarely serve as a stepping-stone from which alleles are passed from one species to the other. Outside the hybrid zone, additional obstacles to gene flow may be provided by natural selection in the different environments in which the parent species live.

Hybrid zones typically are located wherever the habitats of the interbreeding species meet. Those regions often resemble a group of isolated patches scattered across the landscape—more like the complex pattern of spots on a Dalmatian than

the continuous band shown in Figure 22.11. But regardless of whether they have complex or simple spatial patterns, hybrid zones form when two species lacking complete barriers to reproduction come into contact. Once formed, how does a hybrid zone change over time?

Hybrid Zones over Time

Studying a hybrid zone is like observing a naturally occurring experiment on speciation. Will the hybrids become reproductively isolated from their parents and form a new species, as occurred by polyploidy in the goatsbeard plant of the Pacific Northwest? If not, there are three possible outcomes for the hybrid zone over time: reinforcement of barriers, fusion of species, or stability (Figure 22.12). We'll discuss each of these outcomes in turn.

- **Reinforcement:** When hybrids are less fit than members of their parent species, natural selection tends to strengthen prezygotic barriers to reproduction, thus reducing the formation of unfit hybrids. Because this process involves *reinforcing* reproductive barriers, it is called reinforcement. If reinforcement is occurring, a logical prediction is that barriers to reproduction between species should be stronger for sympatric populations than for allopatric populations. Evidence in support of this prediction has been observed in birds, fishes, insects, plants, and other organisms.

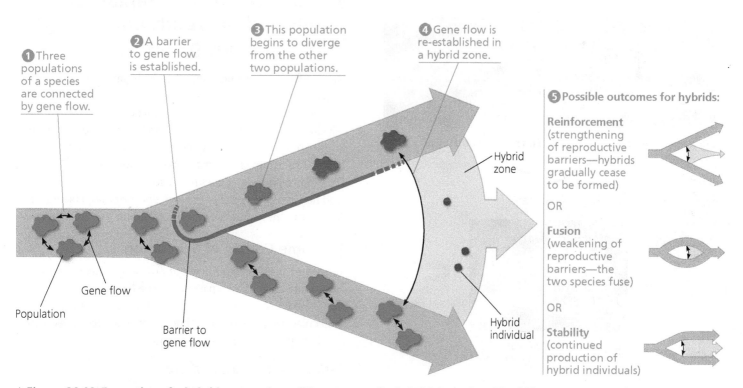

▲ Figure 22.12 **Formation of a hybrid zone and possible outcomes for hybrids over time.** The thick colored arrows represent the passage of time.

WHAT IF? *Predict what might happen if gene flow were re-established at step 3 in this process.*

- **Fusion:** Barriers to reproduction may be weak when two species meet in a hybrid zone. Indeed, so much gene flow may occur that reproductive barriers weaken further and the gene pools of the two species become increasingly alike. In effect, the speciation process reverses, eventually causing the two hybridizing species to fuse into a single species. Such a situation may be occurring among Lake Victoria cichlids. Many pairs of ecologically similar cichlid species are reproductively isolated because the females of one species prefer to mate with males of one color, while females of the other species prefer to mate with males of a different color (see Figure 22.10). Murky waters caused by pollution may have reduced the ability of females to use color to distinguish males of their own species from males of closely related species. In some polluted waters, many hybrids have been produced, leading to fusion of the parent species' gene pools and a loss of species **(Figure 22.13)**.

- **Stability:** Many hybrid zones are stable in the sense that hybrids continue to be produced. In some cases, this occurs because the hybrids survive or reproduce better than members of either parent species, at least in certain habitats or years. But stable hybrid zones have also been observed in cases where the hybrids are selected *against*—an unexpected result. For example, hybrids continue to be formed in the *Bombina* hybrid zone even though they are strongly selected against. What could explain this finding? One possibility relates to the narrowness of the *Bombina* hybrid

Pundamilia nyererei

Pundamilia pundamilia

Pundamilia "turbid water,"
hybrid offspring from a location
with turbid water

▲ **Figure 22.13 Fusion: The breakdown of reproductive barriers.** Increasingly cloudy water in Lake Victoria over the past 30 years may have weakened reproductive barriers between *P. nyererei* and *P. pundamilia*. In areas of cloudy water, the two species have hybridized extensively, causing their gene pools to fuse.

zone (see Figure 22.11). Evidence suggests that members of both parent species migrate into the zone from the parent populations located outside the zone, thus leading to the continued production of hybrids. If the hybrid zone were wider, this would be less likely to occur, since the center of the zone would receive little gene flow from distant parent populations located outside the hybrid zone.

As we've seen, events in hybrid zones can shed light on how barriers to reproduction between closely related species change over time. In the next section, we'll examine how interactions between hybridizing species can also provide a glimpse into the speed and genetic control of speciation.

CONCEPT CHECK 22.3

1. What are hybrid zones, and why can they be viewed as "natural laboratories" in which to study speciation?

2. **WHAT IF?** Consider two species that diverged while geographically separated but resumed contact before reproductive isolation was complete. Predict what would happen over time if the two species mated indiscriminately and (a) hybrid offspring survived and reproduced more poorly than offspring from intraspecific matings or (b) hybrid offspring survived and reproduced as well as offspring from intraspecific matings.

For suggested answers, see Appendix A.

CONCEPT 22.4

Speciation can occur rapidly or slowly and can result from changes in few or many genes

Darwin faced many questions when he began to ponder that "mystery of mysteries"—speciation. He found answers to some of those questions when he realized that evolution by natural selection helps explain both the diversity of life and the adaptations of organisms (see Chapter 19). But biologists since Darwin have continued to ask fundamental questions about speciation. For example, how long does it take for new species to form? And how many genes change when one species splits into two? Answers to these questions are also beginning to emerge.

The Time Course of Speciation

We can gather information about how long it takes new species to form from broad patterns in the fossil record and from studies that use morphological data (including fossils) or molecular data to assess the time interval between speciation events in particular groups of organisms.

Patterns in the Fossil Record

The fossil record includes many episodes in which new species appear suddenly in a geologic stratum, persist essentially unchanged through several strata, and then disappear. For example, there are dozens of species of marine invertebrates that make

(a) In a punctuated model, new species change most as they branch from a parent species and then change little for the rest of their existence.

Time

(b) In a gradual model, species diverge from one another more slowly and steadily over time.

▲ Figure 22.14 **Two models for the tempo of speciation, based on patterns observed in the fossil record.**

their debut in the fossil record with novel morphologies, but then change little for millions of years before becoming extinct. Paleontologists Niles Eldredge and Stephen Jay Gould coined the term **punctuated equilibria** to describe these patterns in the fossil record: periods of apparent stasis punctuated by sudden change **(Figure 22.14a)**. Other species do not show a punctuated pattern; instead, they appear to have changed more gradually over long periods of time **(Figure 22.14b)**. For example, the fossil record shows that many species of trilobites (early arthropods) changed gradually over the course of 10–20 million years.

What might punctuated and gradual patterns tell us about how long it takes new species to form? Suppose that a species survived for 5 million years, but most of the morphological changes that caused it to be designated a new species occurred during the first 50,000 years of its existence—just 1% of its total lifetime. Time periods this short (in geologic terms) often cannot be distinguished in fossil strata, in part because the rate of sediment accumulation may be too slow to separate layers formed so close together in time. Thus, based on its fossils, the species would seem to have appeared suddenly and then lingered with little or no change before becoming extinct. Even though such a species may have originated more slowly than its fossils suggest (in this case taking up to 50,000 years), a punctuated pattern indicates that speciation occurred relatively rapidly. For species whose fossils changed much more gradually, we also cannot tell exactly when a new biological species formed, since information about reproductive isolation does not fossilize. However, it is likely that speciation in such groups occurred relatively slowly, perhaps taking millions of years.

Speciation Rates

The existence of fossils that display a punctuated pattern suggests that once the process of speciation begins, it can be completed relatively rapidly—a suggestion supported by recent studies. For example, rapid speciation appears to have produced the wild sunflower *Helianthus anomalus*. Genetic evidence indicates that this species originated by the hybridization of two other sunflower species, *H. annuus* and *H. petiolaris*. The hybrid species *H. anomalus* is ecologically distinct and reproductively isolated from both parent species **(Figure 22.15)**. Unlike the outcome of allopolyploid speciation, in which there is a change in chromosome number after hybridization, in these sunflowers the two parent species and the hybrid all have the same number of chromosomes ($2n = 34$). How, then, did speciation occur? To study this question, researchers performed an experiment designed to mimic events in nature: They crossed the

▲ Figure 22.15 **A hybrid sunflower species and its dry sand dune habitat.** The wild sunflower *Helianthus anomalus* originated via the hybridization of two other sunflowers, *H. annuus* and *H. petiolaris*, which live in nearby but moister environments.

two parent species and followed the fate of the hybrid offspring over several generations (**Figure 22.16**). Their results indicated that natural selection could produce extensive genetic changes in hybrid populations over short periods of time. These changes appear to have caused the hybrids to diverge reproductively from their parents and form a new species, *H. anomalus*.

The sunflower example, along with the apple maggot fly, Lake Victoria cichlid, and fruit fly examples discussed earlier, suggests that new species can arise rapidly *once divergence begins*. But what is the total length of time between speciation events? This interval consists of the time that elapses before populations of a newly formed species start to diverge from one another plus the time it takes for speciation to be complete once divergence begins. It turns out that the total time between speciation events varies considerably. For example, in a survey of data from 84 groups of plants and animals, the interval between speciation events ranged from 4,000 years (in cichlids of Lake Nabugabo, Uganda) to 40 million years (in some beetles). Overall, the time between speciation events in the groups studied averaged 6.5 million years and was rarely less than 500,000 years.

These data suggest that on average, millions of years may pass before a newly formed plant or animal species will itself give rise to another new species. As we'll see in Chapter 23, this finding has implications for how long it takes life on Earth to recover from mass extinction events. Moreover, the extreme variability in the time it takes new species to form indicates that organisms do not have a "speciation clock" ticking inside them, causing them to produce new species at regular time intervals. Instead, speciation begins only after gene flow between populations is interrupted, perhaps by changing environmental conditions or by unpredictable events, such as a storm that transports a few individuals to an isolated area. Furthermore, once gene flow is interrupted, the populations must diverge genetically to such an extent that they become reproductively isolated—all before other events cause gene flow to resume, possibly reversing the speciation process (see Figure 22.13).

Studying the Genetics of Speciation

The central quest of studying the genetics of speciation is to identify genes that cause reproductive isolation. In general, genes that influence a particular trait can be identified by performing genetic crosses and analyzing gene linkages—but such studies are by definition hard to do when studying different species (since they do not interbreed). However, studies of ongoing speciation (as in hybrid zones) have uncovered specific traits that cause reproductive isolation. By identifying the genes that control those traits, scientists can explore a fundamental question of evolutionary biology: How many genes change when a new species forms?

In a few cases, the evolution of reproductive isolation is due to a change in a single gene. For example, in Japanese snails of the genus *Euhadra*, a change in a single gene results in a

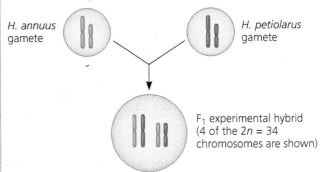
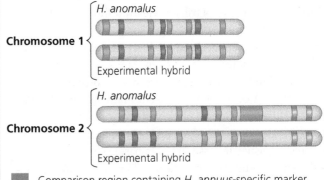

mechanical barrier to reproduction. This gene controls the direction in which the shells spiral. When their shells spiral in different directions, the snails' genitalia are oriented in a manner that prevents mating (Figure 22.3f shows a similar example in a different genus of snail).

A major barrier to reproduction between two closely related species of monkey flower, *Mimulus cardinalis* and *M. lewisii*, also appears to be influenced by a relatively small number of genes. These two species are isolated by several prezygotic and postzygotic barriers. Of these, one prezygotic barrier, pollinator choice, accounts for most of the isolation: In a hybrid zone between *M. cardinalis* and *M. lewisii*, nearly 98% of pollinator visits were restricted to one species or the other.

The two monkey flower species are visited by different pollinators: Hummingbirds prefer the red-flowered *M. cardinalis*, and bumblebees prefer the pink-flowered *M. lewisii*. Pollinator choice is affected by at least two loci in the monkey flowers, one of which, the "yellow upper," or *yup*, locus, influences flower color (Figure 22.17). By crossing the two parent species to produce F_1 hybrids and then performing repeated backcrosses of these F_1 hybrids to each parent species, researchers succeeded in transferring the *M. cardinalis* allele at this locus into *M. lewisii*, and vice versa. In a field experiment, *M. lewisii* plants with the *M. cardinalis yup* allele received 68-fold more visits from hummingbirds than did wild-type *M. lewisii*. Similarly, *M. cardinalis* plants with the *M. lewisii yup* allele received 74-fold more visits from bumblebees than did wild-type *M. cardinalis*. Thus, a mutation at a single locus can influence pollinator preference and hence contribute to reproductive isolation in monkey flowers.

In other organisms, the speciation process is influenced by larger numbers of genes and gene interactions. For example, hybrid sterility between two subspecies of the fruit fly *Drosophila pseudoobscura* results from gene interactions among at least four loci, and postzygotic isolation in the sunflower hybrid zone discussed earlier is influenced by at least 26 chromosome segments (and an unknown number of genes). Overall, studies suggest that few or many genes can influence the evolution of reproductive isolation and hence the emergence of a new species.

From Speciation to Macroevolution

As you've seen, speciation may begin with differences as seemingly small as the color on a cichlid's back. However, as speciation occurs again and again, such differences can accumulate and become more pronounced, eventually leading to the formation of new groups of organisms that differ greatly from their ancestors (as in the origin of whales from land-dwelling mammals; see Figure 19.20). Furthermore, as one group of organisms increases in size by producing many new species, another group of organisms may shrink, losing species to extinction. The cumulative effects of many such speciation and extinction events have helped shape the sweeping evolutionary

(a) Typical *Mimulus lewisii*

(b) *M. lewisii* with an *M. cardinalis* flower-color allele

(c) Typical *Mimulus cardinalis*

(d) *M. cardinalis* with an *M. lewisii* flower-color allele

▲ **Figure 22.17 A locus that influences pollinator choice.** Pollinator preferences provide a strong barrier to reproduction between *Mimulus lewisii* and *M. cardinalis*. After transferring the *M. lewisii* allele for a flower-color locus into *M. cardinalis* and vice versa, researchers observed a shift in some pollinators' preferences.

WHAT IF? *If* M. cardinalis *individuals that had the* M. lewisii yup *allele were planted in an area that housed both monkey flower species, how might the production of hybrid offspring be affected?*

changes that are documented in the fossil record. In the next chapter, we turn to such large-scale evolutionary changes as we begin our study of macroevolution.

CONCEPT CHECK 22.4

1. Speciation can occur rapidly between diverging populations, yet the length of time between speciation events is often more than a million years. Explain this apparent contradiction.

2. Summarize evidence that the *yup* locus acts as a prezygotic barrier to reproduction in two species of monkey flowers. Do these results demonstrate that the *yup* locus alone controls barriers to reproduction between these species? Explain.

3. **MAKE CONNECTIONS** Compare Figure 10.11 with Figure 22.16. What cellular process could cause the hybrid chromosomes in Figure 22.16 to contain DNA from both parent species? Explain.

For suggested answers, see Appendix A.

22 Chapter Review

SUMMARY OF KEY CONCEPTS

CONCEPT 22.1

The biological species concept emphasizes reproductive isolation (pp. 418–422)

- A biological **species** is a group of populations whose individuals have the potential to interbreed and produce viable, fertile offspring with each other but not with members of other species. The **biological species concept** emphasizes reproductive isolation through prezygotic and postzygotic barriers that separate gene pools.
- Although helpful in thinking about how speciation occurs, the biological species concept has limitations. For instance, it cannot be applied to organisms known only as fossils or to organisms that reproduce only asexually. Thus, scientists use other species concepts, such as the **morphological species concept**, in certain circumstances.

? *Explain the importance of gene flow to the biological species concept.*

CONCEPT 22.2

Speciation can take place with or without geographic separation (pp. 423–428)

- In **allopatric speciation**, gene flow is reduced when two populations of one species become geographically separated from each other. One or both populations may undergo evolutionary change during the period of separation, resulting in the establishment of prezygotic or postzygotic barriers to reproduction.
- In **sympatric speciation**, a new species originates while remaining in the same geographic area as the parent species. Plant species (and, more rarely, animal species) have evolved sympatrically through polyploidy. Sympatric speciation can also result from habitat shifts and sexual selection.

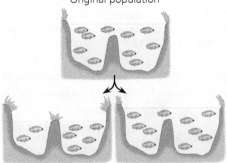

Original population

Allopatric speciation   Sympatric speciation

? *Can factors that cause sympatric speciation also cause allopatric speciation? Explain.*

CONCEPT 22.3

Hybrid zones reveal factors that cause reproductive isolation (pp. 428–430)

- Many groups of organisms form **hybrid zones** in which members of different species meet and mate, producing at least some offspring of mixed ancestry.

- Many hybrid zones exhibit **stability** in that hybrid offspring continue to be produced over time. In others, **reinforcement** strengthens prezygotic barriers to reproduction, thus decreasing the formation of unfit hybrids. In still other hybrid zones, barriers to reproduction may weaken over time, resulting in the **fusion** of the species' gene pools (reversing the speciation process).

? *What factors can support the long-term stability of a hybrid zone if the parent species live in different environments?*

CONCEPT 22.4

Speciation can occur rapidly or slowly and can result from changes in few or many genes (pp. 430–433)

- New species can form rapidly once divergence begins—but it can take millions of years for that to happen. The time interval between speciation events varies considerably, from a few thousand years to tens of millions of years.
- New developments in genetics have enabled researchers to identify specific genes involved in some cases of speciation. Results show that speciation can be driven by few or many genes.

? *Is speciation something that happened only in the distant past, or are new species continuing to arise today? Explain.*

TEST YOUR UNDERSTANDING

Level 1: Knowledge/Comprehension

1. The *largest* unit within which gene flow can readily occur is a
   a. population.
   b. species.
   c. genus.
   d. hybrid.
   e. phylum.

2. Males of different species of the fruit fly *Drosophila* that live in the same parts of the Hawaiian Islands have different elaborate courtship rituals. These rituals involve fighting other males and making stylized movements that attract females. What type of reproductive isolation does this represent?
   a. habitat isolation
   b. temporal isolation
   c. behavioral isolation
   d. gametic isolation
   e. postzygotic barriers

3. According to the punctuated equilibria model,
   a. natural selection is unimportant as a mechanism of evolution.
   b. given enough time, most existing species will branch gradually into new species.
   c. most new species accumulate their unique features relatively rapidly as they come into existence, then change little for the rest of their duration as a species.
   d. most evolution occurs in sympatric populations.
   e. speciation is usually due to a single mutation.

Level 2: Application/Analysis

4. Bird guides once listed the myrtle warbler and Audubon's warbler as distinct species. Recently, these birds have been reclassified as eastern and western forms of a single species, the

yellow-rumped warbler. Which of the following pieces of evidence, if true, would be cause for this reclassification?
- **a.** The two forms interbreed often in nature, and their offspring survive and reproduce well.
- **b.** The two forms live in similar habitats.
- **c.** The two forms have many genes in common.
- **d.** The two forms have similar food requirements.
- **e.** The two forms are very similar in coloration.

5. Which of the following factors would *not* contribute to allopatric speciation?
- **a.** A population becomes geographically isolated from the parent population.
- **b.** The separated population is small, and genetic drift occurs.
- **c.** The isolated population is exposed to different selection pressures than the ancestral population.
- **d.** Different mutations begin to distinguish the gene pools of the separated populations.
- **e.** Gene flow between the two populations is extensive.

6. Plant species A has a diploid number of 12. Plant species B has a diploid number of 16. A new species, C, arises as an allopolyploid from A and B. The diploid number for species C would probably be
- **a.** 12.
- **b.** 14.
- **c.** 16.
- **d.** 28.
- **e.** 56.

Level 3: Synthesis/Evaluation

7. **SCIENTIFIC INQUIRY**
   DRAW IT In this chapter, you read that bread wheat (*Triticum aestivum*) is an allohexaploid, containing two sets of chromosomes from each of three different parent species. Genetic analysis suggests that the three species pictured following this question each contributed chromosome sets to *T. aestivum*. (The capital letters here represent sets of chromosomes rather than individual genes.) Evidence also indicates that the first polyploidy event was a spontaneous hybridization of the early cultivated wheat species *T. monococcum* and a wild *Triticum* grass species. Based on this information, draw a diagram of one possible chain of events that could have produced the allohexaploid *T. aestivum*.

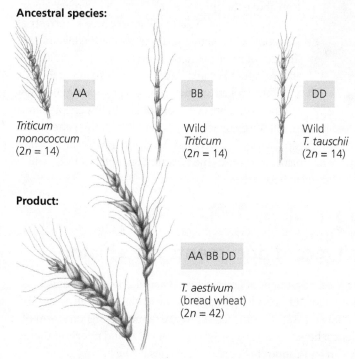

Ancestral species:

AA — *Triticum monococcum* ($2n = 14$)

BB — Wild *Triticum* ($2n = 14$)

DD — Wild *T. tauschii* ($2n = 14$)

Product:

AA BB DD — *T. aestivum* (bread wheat) ($2n = 42$)

8. **SCIENCE, TECHNOLOGY, AND SOCIETY**
   In the United States, the rare red wolf (*Canis lupus*) has been known to hybridize with coyotes (*Canis latrans*), which are much more numerous. Although red wolves and coyotes differ in terms of morphology, DNA, and behavior, genetic evidence suggests that living red wolf individuals are actually hybrids. Red wolves are designated as an endangered species and hence receive legal protection under the Endangered Species Act. Some people think that their endangered status should be withdrawn because the remaining red wolves are hybrids, not members of a "pure" species. Do you agree? Why or why not?

9. **FOCUS ON EVOLUTION**
   What is the biological basis for assigning all human populations to a single species? Can you think of a scenario by which a second human species could originate in the future?

10. **FOCUS ON INFORMATION**
    In sexually reproducing species, each individual begins life with DNA inherited from both parent organisms. In a short essay (100–150 words), apply this idea to what occurs when organisms of two species that have homologous chromosomes mate and produce (F_1) hybrid offspring. What percentage of the DNA in the F_1 hybrids' chromosomes comes from each parent species? As the hybrids mate and produce F_2 and later-generation hybrid offspring, describe how recombination and natural selection may affect whether the DNA in hybrid chromosomes is derived from one parent species or the other.

For selected answers, see Appendix A.

MasteringBiology®

Students Go to **MasteringBiology** for assignments, the eText, and the Study Area with practice tests, animations, and activities.

Instructors Go to **MasteringBiology** for automatically graded tutorials and questions that you can assign to your students, plus Instructor Resources.

23 Broad Patterns of Evolution

OVERVIEW

Lost Worlds

▲ *Cryolophosaurus* skull

▼ **Figure 23.1** On what continent did these dinosaurs roam?

Early Antarctic explorers encountered one of Earth's harshest, most barren environments, a land of extreme cold and almost no liquid water. Antarctic life is sparse and small—the largest fully terrestrial animal is a fly 5 mm long. But even as they struggled to survive, some of these explorers made an astonishing discovery: fossil evidence that life once thrived where it now barely exists. Fossils reveal that 500 million years ago, the ocean around Antarctica was warm and teeming with tropical invertebrates. Later, the continent was covered in forests for hundreds of millions of years. At various times, diverse animals stalked through these forests, including 3-m-tall predatory "terror birds" and giant dinosaurs, such as the voracious *Cryolophosaurus* (**Figure 23.1**), a relative of *Tyrannosaurus rex*.

Fossils discovered in other parts of the world tell a similar, if not quite as surprising, story: Past organisms were very different from those presently living. The sweeping changes in life on Earth as revealed by fossils illustrate **macroevolution**, the broad pattern of evolution above the species level. Examples of macroevolutionary change include the emergence of terrestrial vertebrates through a series of speciation events, the impact of mass extinctions on the diversity of life, and the origin of key adaptations, such as flight in birds.

Taken together, such changes provide a grand view of the evolutionary history of life. In this chapter, we'll examine how fossils form and the evidence they provide about the pattern of life's evolution, focusing on factors that have helped shape the rise and fall of different groups of organisms over time. The next unit (Chapters 24–27) will explore major steps in the history of life.

CONCEPT 23.1

The fossil record documents life's history

Starting with the earliest traces of life, the fossil record opens a window into the world of long ago and provides glimpses of the evolution of life over billions of years (**Figure 23.2**). In this section, we'll examine fossils as a form of scientific evidence: how fossils form, how scientists date and interpret them, and what they can and cannot tell us about changes in the history of life.

▼ **Figure 23.2 Documenting the history of life.** These fossils illustrate representative organisms from different points in time. Although prokaryotes and unicellular eukaryotes are shown only at the base of the diagram, these organisms continue to thrive today. In fact, most organisms on Earth are unicellular.

▼ *Dimetrodon*, the largest known carnivore of its day, was more closely related to mammals than to reptiles. The spectacular "sail" on its back may have functioned in temperature regulation.

0.5 m

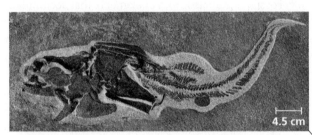

4.5 cm

▲ *Coccosteus cuspidatus*, a placoderm (fishlike vertebrate) that had a bony shield covering its head and front end

▲ Some prokaryotes bind thin films of sediments together, producing layered rocks called stromatolites, such as these in Shark Bay, Australia.

▲ A section through a fossilized stromatolite

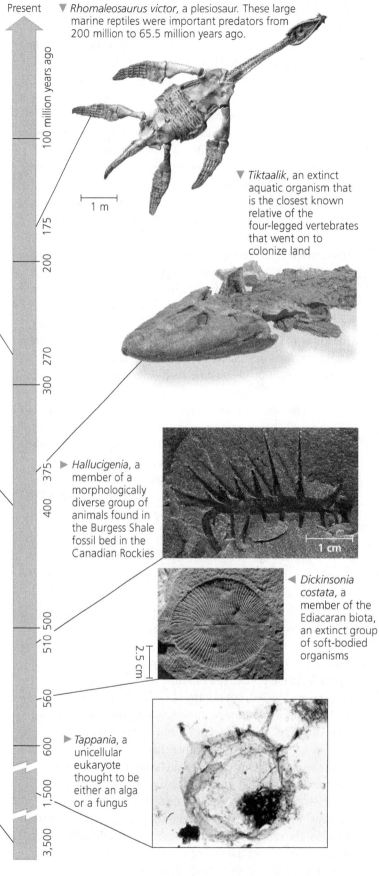

Present

▼ *Rhomaleosaurus victor*, a plesiosaur. These large marine reptiles were important predators from 200 million to 65.5 million years ago.

1 m

▼ *Tiktaalik*, an extinct aquatic organism that is the closest known relative of the four-legged vertebrates that went on to colonize land

▶ *Hallucigenia*, a member of a morphologically diverse group of animals found in the Burgess Shale fossil bed in the Canadian Rockies

1 cm

◀ *Dickinsonia costata*, a member of the Ediacaran biota, an extinct group of soft-bodied organisms

2.5 cm

▶ *Tappania*, a unicellular eukaryote thought to be either an alga or a fungus

100 million years ago

175

200

270

300

375

400

500

510

560

600

1,500

3,500

The Fossil Record

Sedimentary rocks are the richest source of fossils. As a result, the fossil record is based primarily on the sequence in which fossils have accumulated in sedimentary rock layers, called *strata* (see Figure 19.3). Useful information is also provided by other types of fossils, such as insects preserved in amber (fossilized tree sap) and mammals frozen in ice.

The fossil record shows that there have been great changes in the kinds of organisms on Earth at different points in time (Figure 23.2). Many past organisms were unlike organisms living today, and many organisms that once were common are now extinct. As we'll see later in this section, fossils also document how new groups of organisms arose from previously existing ones.

As substantial and significant as the fossil record is, keep in mind that it is an incomplete chronicle of evolutionary change. Many of Earth's organisms did not die in the right place at the right time to be preserved as fossils. Of those fossils that were formed, many were destroyed by later geologic processes, and only a fraction of the others have been discovered. As a result, the known fossil record is biased in favor of species that existed for a long time, were abundant and widespread in certain kinds of environments, and had hard shells, skeletons, or other parts that facilitated their fossilization. Even with its limitations, however, the fossil record is a remarkably detailed account of biological change over the vast scale of geologic time. Furthermore, as shown by the recently unearthed fossils of whale ancestors with hind limbs (see Figures 19.18 and 19.19), gaps in the fossil record continue to be filled by new discoveries. Although some of these discoveries are fortuitous, others illustrate the predictive nature of paleontology (see Figure 27.22).

How Rocks and Fossils Are Dated

Fossils are valuable data for reconstructing the history of life, but only if we can determine where they fit in that unfolding story. While the order of fossils in rock strata tells us the sequence in which the fossils were laid down—their relative ages—it does not tell us their actual (absolute) ages. Examining the relative positions of fossils is like peeling off layers of wallpaper in an old house. You can infer the sequence in which the layers were applied, but not the year each layer was added.

How can we determine the absolute age of a fossil? (Note that "absolute" dating does not mean errorless dating, but only that an age is given in years rather than relative terms such as *before* and *after*.) One of the most common techniques is **radiometric dating**, which is based on the decay of radioactive isotopes (see Chapter 2). In this process, a radioactive "parent" isotope decays to a "daughter" isotope at a characteristic rate. The rate of decay is expressed by the **half-life**, the time required for 50% of the parent isotope to decay **(Figure 23.3)**. Each type of radioactive isotope has a characteristic half-life, which is not affected by temperature, pressure, or other environmental variables. For example, carbon-14 decays relatively

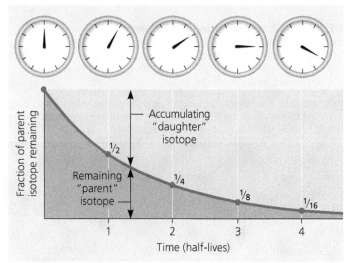

© 1976 Pearson Education, Inc.

▲ **Figure 23.3 Radiometric dating.** In this diagram, each division of the clock face represents a half-life.

quickly; it has a half-life of 5,730 years. Uranium-238 decays slowly; its half-life is 4.5 billion years.

Fossils contain isotopes of elements that accumulated in the organisms when they were alive. For example, a living organism contains the most common carbon isotope, carbon-12, as well as a radioactive isotope, carbon-14. When the organism dies, it stops accumulating carbon, and the amount of carbon-12 in its tissues does not change over time. However, the carbon-14 that it contains at the time of death slowly decays into another element, nitrogen-14. Thus, by measuring the ratio of carbon-14 to carbon-12 in a fossil, we can determine the fossil's age. This method works for fossils up to about 75,000 years old; fossils older than that contain too little carbon-14 to be detected with current techniques. Radioactive isotopes with longer half-lives are used to date older fossils.

Determining the age of these older fossils in sedimentary rocks is challenging. Organisms do not use radioisotopes with long half-lives, such as uranium-238, to build their bones or shells. In addition, the sedimentary rocks themselves tend to consist of sediments of differing ages. So while we may not be able to date these older fossils directly, an indirect method can be used to infer the age of fossils that are sandwiched between two layers of volcanic rock. As lava cools into volcanic rock, radioisotopes from the surrounding environment become trapped in the newly formed rock. Some of the trapped radioisotopes have long half-lives, allowing geologists to estimate the ages of ancient volcanic rocks. If two volcanic layers surrounding fossils are determined to be 525 million and 535 million years old, for example, then the fossils are roughly 530 million years old.

The Geologic Record

The study of fossils has helped geologists establish a **geologic record**, a standard time scale that divides Earth's history into four eons and further subdivisions **(Table 23.1)**. The first three

Table 23.1 The Geologic Record

Relative Duration of Eons	Era	Period	Epoch	Age (Millions of Years Ago)	Some Important Events in the History of Life
Phanerozoic	Cenozoic	Quaternary	Holocene		Historical time
				0.01	
			Pleistocene		Ice ages; origin of genus *Homo*
				2.6	
		Neogene	Pliocene		Appearance of bipedal human ancestors
				5.3	
			Miocene		Continued radiation of mammals and angiosperms; earliest direct human ancestors
				23	
		Paleogene	Oligocene		Origins of many primate groups
				33.9	
			Eocene		Angiosperm dominance increases; continued radiation of most present-day mammalian orders
				55.8	
			Paleocene		Major radiation of mammals, birds, and pollinating insects
				65.5	
Proterozoic	Mesozoic	Cretaceous			Flowering plants (angiosperms) appear and diversify; many groups of organisms, including most dinosaurs, become extinct at end of period
				145.5	
		Jurassic			Gymnosperms continue as dominant plants; dinosaurs abundant and diverse
				199.6	
		Triassic			Cone-bearing plants (gymnosperms) dominate landscape; dinosaurs evolve and radiate; origin of mammals
				251	
	Paleozoic	Permian			Radiation of reptiles; origin of most present-day groups of insects; extinction of many marine and terrestrial organisms at end of period
				299	
		Carboniferous			Extensive forests of vascular plants form; first seed plants appear; origin of reptiles; amphibians dominant
				359	
		Devonian			Diversification of bony fishes; first tetrapods and insects appear
				416	
		Silurian			Diversification of early vascular plants
				444	
		Ordovician			Marine algae abundant; colonization of land by diverse fungi, plants, and animals
				488	
Archaean		Cambrian			Sudden increase in diversity of many animal phyla (Cambrian explosion)
				542	
		Ediacaran			Diverse algae and soft-bodied invertebrate animals appear
				635	
				1,800	Oldest fossils of eukaryotic cells appear
				2,500	
				2,700	Concentration of atmospheric oxygen begins to increase
				3,500	Oldest fossils of cells (prokaryotes) appear
Hadean				3,850	Oldest known rocks on Earth's surface
				Approx. 4,600	Origin of Earth

eons—the Hadean, Archaean, and Proterozoic—together lasted about 4 billion years. The Phanerozoic eon, roughly the last half billion years, encompasses most of the time that animals have existed on Earth. It is divided into three eras: the Paleozoic, Mesozoic, and Cenozoic. Each era represents a distinct age in the history of Earth and its life. For example, the Mesozoic era is sometimes called the "age of reptiles" because of its abundance of reptilian fossils, including those of dinosaurs. The boundaries between the eras correspond to major extinction events seen in the fossil record, when many forms of life disappeared and were replaced by forms that evolved from the survivors.

The earliest direct evidence of life comes from the Archaean eon, based on 3.5 billion-year-old fossils of stromatolites (see Figure 23.2). **Stromatolites** are layered rocks that form when certain prokaryotes bind thin films of sediment together. These and other early prokaryotes were Earth's sole inhabitants for more than 1.5 billion years. Early prokaryotes transformed life on our planet by releasing oxygen to the atmosphere during the water-splitting step of photosynthesis (see Chapter 24).

The ensuing increase in atmospheric oxygen—a process that began about 2.4 billion years ago—led to the extinction of some organisms and the proliferation of others. One group that flourished was the eukaryotes, which originated about 1.8 billion years ago (see Chapter 25). The rise of the eukaryotes was associated with a series of other key events in the history of life, including the origin of multicellular organisms and the colonization of land. Fossil evidence and molecular clock estimates based on DNA sequence data suggest that simple multicellular organisms emerged about 1.5 billion years ago. Later, more complex multicellular organisms arose independently in several groups of eukaryotes, including those that eventually moved onto land: plants, fungi, and animals (see Chapters 26 and 27).

The Origin of New Groups of Organisms

Some fossils provide a detailed look at the origin of new groups of organisms. Such fossils are central to our understanding of evolution; they illustrate how new features arise and how long it takes for such changes to occur. We'll examine one such case here: the origin of mammals.

Along with amphibians and reptiles, mammals belong to the group of animals called *tetrapods* (from the Greek *tetra*, four, and *pod*, foot), named for having four limbs. Mammals have a number of unique anatomical features that fossilize readily, allowing scientists to trace their origin. For example, the lower jaw is composed of one bone (the dentary) in mammals but several bones in other tetrapods. In addition, the lower and upper jaws hinge between a different set of bones in mammals than in other tetrapods. Mammals also have a unique set of three bones that transmit sound in the middle ear (the hammer, anvil, and stirrup), whereas other tetrapods have only one such bone (the stirrup). Finally, the teeth of mammals are differentiated into incisors (for tearing), canines (for piercing), and the multi-pointed premolars and molars (for crushing and grinding). In

contrast, the teeth of other tetrapods usually consist of a row of undifferentiated, single-pointed teeth.

As detailed in **Figure 23.4**, the fossil record shows that the unique features of mammalian jaws and teeth evolved gradually over time, in a series of steps. As you study Figure 23.4, bear in mind that it includes just a few examples of the fossil skulls that document the origin of mammals. If all the known fossils in the sequence were arranged by shape and placed side by side, their features would blend smoothly from one group to the next. Some of these fossils would reflect how the features of a group that dominates life today, the mammals, gradually arose in a previously existing group, the cynodonts. Others would reveal side branches on the tree of life—groups of organisms that thrived for millions of years but ultimately left no descendants that survive today.

CONCEPT CHECK 23.1

1. Your measurements indicate that a fossilized skull you unearthed has a carbon-14/carbon-12 ratio about 1/16 that of the skulls of present-day animals. What is the approximate age of the fossilized skull?

2. Describe an example from the fossil record that shows how life has changed over time.

3. **DRAW IT** Relabel the x-axis of the graph in Figure 23.3 with time measurements in years to illustrate the radioactive decay of uranium-238 (half-life = 4.5 billion years).

4. **WHAT IF?** What would a fossil record of life today look like?

5. **WHAT IF?** Suppose researchers discover a fossil of an organism that lived 300 million years ago but had mammalian teeth and a mammalian jaw hinge. What inferences might you draw from this fossil about the origin of mammals and the evolution of novel skeletal structures? Explain.

For suggested answers, see Appendix A.

CONCEPT 23.2

The rise and fall of groups of organisms reflect differences in speciation and extinction rates

From its beginnings, life on Earth has been marked by the rise and fall of groups of organisms. Anaerobic prokaryotes originated, flourished, and then declined as the oxygen content of the atmosphere rose. Billions of years later, the first tetrapods emerged from the sea, giving rise to several major new groups of organisms. One of these, the amphibians, went on to dominate life on land for 100 million years, until other tetrapods (including dinosaurs and, later, mammals) replaced them as the dominant terrestrial vertebrates.

The rise and fall of these and other major groups of organisms have shaped the history of life. Narrowing our focus, we can also see that the rise or fall of any particular group of organisms is related to the speciation and extinction rates of

Over the course of 120 million years, mammals originated gradually from a group of tetrapods called synapsids. Shown here are a few of the many fossil organisms whose morphological features represent intermediate steps between living mammals and their early synapsid ancestors. The evolutionary context of the origin of mammals is shown in the tree diagram at right (the dagger symbol † indicates extinct lineages).

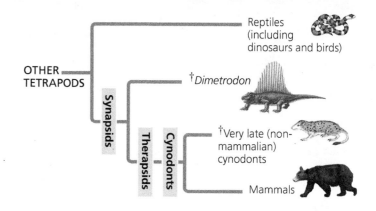

Key to skull bones

- Articular
- Quadrate
- Dentary
- Squamosal

Synapsid (300 mya)

Early synapsids had multiple bones in the lower jaw and single-pointed teeth. The jaw hinge was formed by the articular and quadrate bones. Early synapsids also had an opening called the *temporal fenestra* behind the eye socket. Powerful cheek muscles for closing the jaws probably passed through the temporal fenestra. Over time, this opening enlarged and moved in front of the hinge between the lower and upper jaws, thereby increasing the power and precision with which the jaws could be closed (much as moving a doorknob away from the hinge makes a door easier to close).

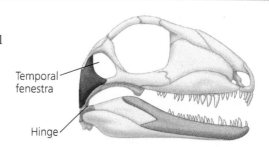

Temporal fenestra

Hinge

Therapsid (280 mya)

Later, a group of synapsids called therapsids appeared. Therapsids had large dentary bones, long faces, and the first examples of specialized teeth, large canines. These trends continued in a group of therapsids called cynodonts.

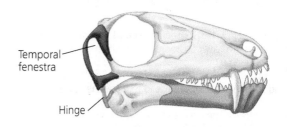

Temporal fenestra

Hinge

Early cynodont (260 mya)

In early cynodont therapsids, the dentary was the largest bone in the lower jaw, the temporal fenestra was large and positioned forward of the jaw hinge, and teeth with several cusps first appeared (not visible in the diagram). As in earlier synapsids, the jaw had an articular-quadrate hinge.

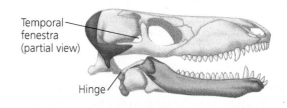

Temporal fenestra (partial view)

Hinge

Later cynodont (220 mya)

Later cynodonts had teeth with complex cusp patterns and their lower and upper jaws hinged in two locations: They retained the original articular-quadrate hinge and formed a new, second hinge between the dentary and squamosal bones. (The temporal fenestra is not visible in this or the below cynodont skull at the angles shown.)

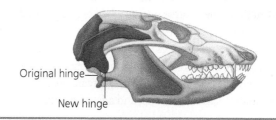

Original hinge

New hinge

Very late cynodont (195 mya)

In some very late (non-mammalian) cynodonts and early mammals, the original articular-quadrate hinge was lost, leaving the dentary-squamosal hinge as the only hinge between the lower and upper jaws, as in living mammals. The articular and quadrate bones migrated into the ear region (not shown), where they functioned in transmitting sound. In the mammal lineage, these two bones later evolved into the familiar hammer (malleus) and anvil (incus) bones of the ear.

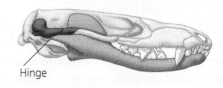

Hinge

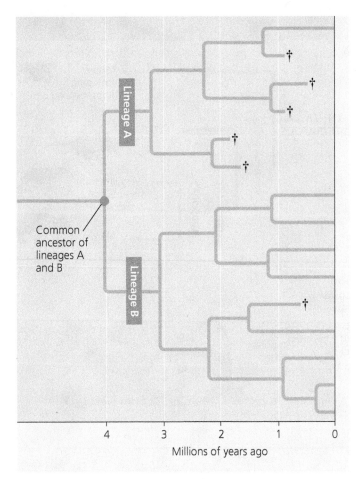

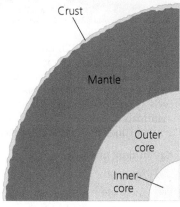

▶ **Figure 23.6 Cutaway view of Earth.** The thickness of the crust is exaggerated here.

Crust

Mantle

Outer core

Inner core

▲ **Figure 23.5 How speciation and extinction affect diversity.** The species diversity of a particular evolutionary lineage will increase when more new member species originate than are lost to extinction. In the hypothetical example shown here, by 2 million years ago both lineage A and lineage B have given rise to four species, and no species have become extinct (denoted by a dagger symbol †). Over the next 2 million years, however, lineage A experiences higher extinction rates than lineage B. As a result, after 4 million years (that is, by time 0), lineage A contains only one species while lineage B contains eight species.

? *Consider the period between 2 million and 1 million years ago. For each lineage, count the number of speciation and extinction events that occur during that time.*

its member species **(Figure 23.5)**. Just as a population grows when there are more births than deaths, a group of organisms grows (rises) when more new species appear than are lost to extinction. The reverse occurs when a group is in decline. In the **Scientific Skills Exercise**, you will interpret data from the fossil record about changes in a group of snail species in the early Paleogene period. Such changes in the fates of groups of organisms have been influenced by large-scale processes such as plate tectonics, mass extinctions, and adaptive radiations.

Plate Tectonics

If photographs of Earth were taken from space every 10,000 years and spliced together to make a movie, it would show something many of us find hard to imagine: The seemingly "rock solid" continents we live on move over time. Since the

origin of multicellular eukaryotes roughly 1.5 billion years ago, there have been three occasions (1.1 billion, 600 million, and 250 million years ago) when most of the landmasses of Earth came together to form a supercontinent, then later broke apart. Each time, this breakup yielded a different configuration of continents. Looking into the future, some geologists have estimated that the continents will come together again and form a new supercontinent roughly 250 million years from now.

According to the theory of **plate tectonics**, the continents are part of great plates of Earth's crust that essentially float on the hot, underlying portion of the mantle **(Figure 23.6)**. Movements in the mantle cause the plates to move over time in a process called *continental drift*. Geologists can measure the rate at which the plates are moving now, usually only a few centimeters per year. They can also infer the past locations of the continents using the magnetic signal recorded in rocks at the time of their formation. This method works because as a continent shifts its position over time, the direction of magnetic north recorded in its newly formed rocks also changes.

Earth's major tectonic plates are shown in **Figure 23.7**. Many important geologic processes, including the formation of mountains and islands, occur at plate boundaries. In some cases, two plates are moving away from each other, as are the North American and Eurasian plates, which are currently drifting apart at a rate of about 2 cm per year. In other cases, two plates slide past each other, forming regions where earthquakes are common. California's infamous San Andreas Fault is part of a border where two plates slide past each other. In still other cases, two plates collide, producing violent upheavals and forming new mountains along the plate boundaries. One spectacular example of this occurred 45 million years ago, when the Indian plate crashed into the Eurasian plate, starting the formation of the Himalayan mountains.

Consequences of Continental Drift

Plate movements rearrange geography slowly, but their cumulative effects are dramatic. In addition to reshaping the physical features of our planet, continental drift also has a major impact on life on Earth.

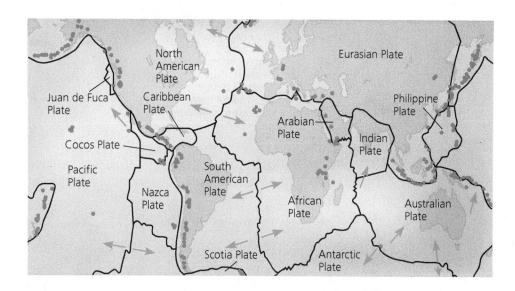

► **Figure 23.7 Earth's major tectonic plates.** The arrows indicate direction of movement. The reddish orange dots represent zones of violent tectonic activity.

Labels on map: North American Plate, Juan de Fuca Plate, Caribbean Plate, Cocos Plate, Pacific Plate, Nazca Plate, South American Plate, Scotia Plate, Eurasian Plate, Arabian Plate, Indian Plate, Philippine Plate, African Plate, Antarctic Plate, Australian Plate

Scientific Skills Exercise

Estimating Quantitative Data from a Graph and Developing Hypotheses

Do Ecological Factors Affect Evolutionary Rates? Researchers studied the fossil record to investigate whether differing modes of dispersal could explain differences in the longevity of species within one taxon of marine snails, the family Volutidae. Some volute snails had planktonic larvae that could disperse over great distances on ocean currents. Other volute snails had nonplanktonic larvae, which developed directly into adults without a swimming stage. The dispersal of snails with nonplanktonic larvae was limited by the distance they can crawl as adults.

How the Research Was Done The researchers studied the distribution of volute snail fossils in outcrops of sedimentary rocks located along North America's Gulf Coast. These rocks, which formed during the early Paleogene period, between 65 and 37 million years ago, contain many well-preserved snail fossils. Based on features of

the snail's shell, the researchers classified each fossil species as having planktonic or nonplanktonic larvae. Each bar in the graph shows how long one snail species persisted in the fossil record.

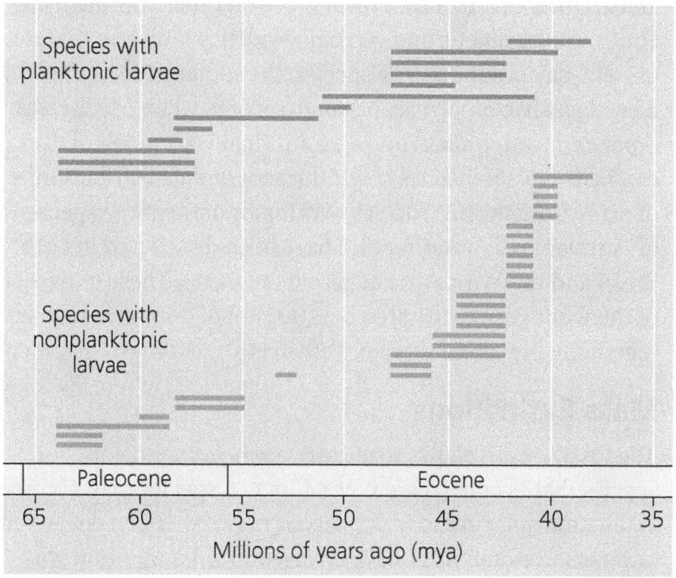

Interpret the Data

1. Here's a method for estimating quantitative data (fairly precisely) from a graph:

   (a) The first step is to measure along an axis that has a scale to obtain a conversion factor. In this case, 25 million years (my; from 40 to 65 million years ago (mya) on the x-axis) is represented by a distance of 7.0 cm.

   This yields a conversion factor (a ratio) of

   $$25 \text{ my} / 7.0 \text{ cm} = 3.6 \text{ my/cm}$$

   (b) Each horizontal bar represents the timespan during which a given snail species appears in the fossil record—the species' persistence time. To estimate the time period represented by a horizontal bar on this graph, measure the length of that bar in cm and multiply that measurement by the conversion factor, 3.6 my/cm. For example, the top (planktonic) bar on the graph has a length of about 1.1 cm; thus, that bar represents 1.1 cm x 3.6 my/cm = 4.0 million years persistence time.

2. Calculate the mean persistence times for species with planktonic larvae and species with nonplanktonic larvae.

3. Count the number of new species that form in each group beginning at 60 mya (the first three species in each group were present around 64 mya, the first time period sampled, so we don't know when those species first appear in the fossil record).

4. Propose a hypothesis to explain the difference in mean longevity of snail species with planktonic and nonplanktonic larvae.

Data from T. Hansen, Larval dispersal and species longevity in Lower Tertiary gastropods, *Science* 199:885–887 (1978).

(MB) A version of this Scientific Skills Exercise can be assigned in MasteringBiology.

Graph: Species with planktonic larvae; Species with nonplanktonic larvae. X-axis: Millions of years ago (mya), 65, 60, 55, 50, 45, 40, 35. Periods: Paleocene, Eocene.

© 1978 AAAS

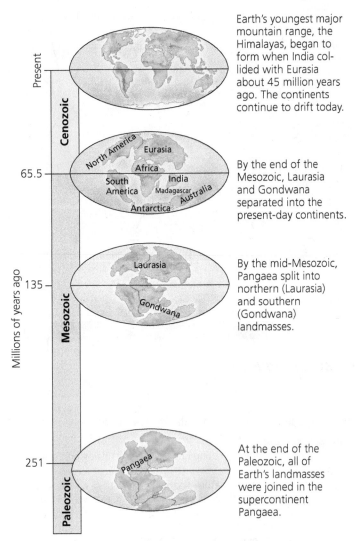

Earth's youngest major mountain range, the Himalayas, began to form when India collided with Eurasia about 45 million years ago. The continents continue to drift today.

By the end of the Mesozoic, Laurasia and Gondwana separated into the present-day continents.

By the mid-Mesozoic, Pangaea split into northern (Laurasia) and southern (Gondwana) landmasses.

At the end of the Paleozoic, all of Earth's landmasses were joined in the supercontinent Pangaea.

▲ Figure 23.8 **The history of continental drift during the Phanerozoic eon.**

? *Is the Australian plate's current direction of movement (see Figure 23.7) similar to the direction it traveled over the past 65 million years?*

One reason for its great impact on life is that continental drift alters the habitats in which organisms live. Consider the changes shown in **Figure 23.8**. About 250 million years ago, plate movements brought all the previously separated landmasses together into a supercontinent named **Pangaea**. Ocean basins became deeper, which lowered sea level and drained shallow coastal seas. At that time, as now, most marine species inhabited shallow waters, and the formation of Pangaea destroyed a considerable amount of that habitat. The interior of the vast continent was cold and dry, probably an even more severe environment than that of central Asia today. Overall, the formation of Pangaea had a tremendous impact on the physical environment and climate, which drove some species to extinction and provided new opportunities for groups of organisms that survived the crisis.

Another aspect of continental drift that affects organisms is the climate change that results when a continent shifts its location. The southern tip of Labrador, Canada, for example,

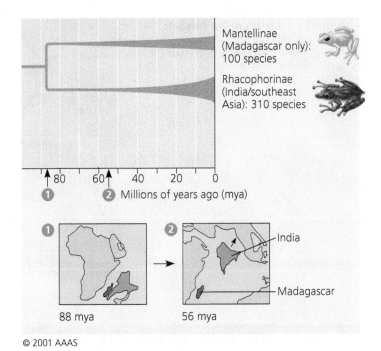

© 2001 AAAS

▲ Figure 23.9 **Speciation in frogs as a result of continental drift.** When present-day Madagascar began to separate from India ❶, the frog subfamilies Mantellinae and Rhacophorinae started to diverge, ultimately forming hundreds of new species in each location. The maps show the movement of Madagascar (red) and India (blue) over time.

once was located in the tropics but has moved 40° to the north over the last 200 million years. When faced with the changes in climate that such shifts in position entail, organisms adapt, move to a new location, or become extinct (this last outcome occurred for many organisms stranded on Antarctica).

Continental drift also promotes allopatric speciation on a grand scale. When supercontinents break apart, regions that once were connected become geographically isolated. As the continents drifted apart over the last 200 million years, each became a separate evolutionary arena, with lineages of plants and animals that diverged from those on other continents. For example, genetic and geologic evidence indicates that two present-day groups of frog species, the subfamilies Mantellinae and Rhacophorinae, began to diverge when Madagascar separated from India **(Figure 23.9)**. Finally, continental drift can help explain puzzles about the geographic distribution of extinct organisms, such as why fossils of the same species of Permian freshwater reptiles have been discovered in both Brazil and the West African nation of Ghana. These two parts of the world, now separated by 3,000 km of ocean, were joined together when these reptiles were living.

Mass Extinctions

The fossil record shows that the overwhelming majority of species that ever lived are now extinct. A species may become extinct for many reasons. Its habitat may have been destroyed, or its environment may have changed in a manner unfavorable to the species. For example, if ocean temperatures fall by even a few degrees, species that are otherwise well adapted may perish. Even if physical factors in the environment remain

▶ **Figure 23.10 Mass extinction and the diversity of life.** The five generally recognized mass extinction events, indicated by red arrows, represent peaks in the extinction rate of marine animal families (red line and left vertical axis). These mass extinctions interrupted the overall increase in the number of marine animal families over time (blue line and right vertical axis).

? *96% of marine animal species became extinct in the Permian mass extinction. Explain why the blue curve shows only a 50% drop at that time.*

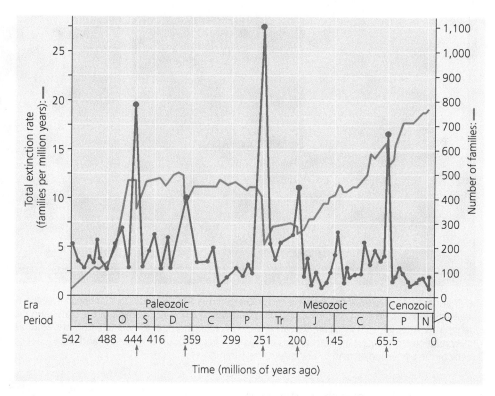

stable, biological factors may change—the origin of one species can spell doom for another.

Although extinction occurs on a regular basis, at certain times disruptive changes to the global environment have caused the rate of extinction to increase dramatically. When this occurs, a **mass extinction** results, in which large numbers of species become extinct worldwide.

The "Big Five" Mass Extinction Events

Patterns of the disappearance of species from the fossil record reveal that five mass extinctions have occurred during the past 500 million years (**Figure 23.10**). These events are particularly well documented for the decimation of hard-bodied animals that lived in shallow seas, the organisms for which the fossil record is most complete. In each mass extinction, 50% or more of Earth's marine species became extinct.

Two mass extinctions—the Permian and the Cretaceous—have received the most attention. The Permian mass extinction, which defines the boundary between the Paleozoic and Mesozoic eras (251 million years ago), claimed about 96% of marine animal species and drastically altered life in the ocean. Terrestrial life was also affected. For example, 8 out of 27 known orders of insects were wiped out. This mass extinction occurred in less than 500,000 years, possibly in just a few thousand years—an instant in the context of geologic time.

The Permian mass extinction occurred at a time of enormous volcanic eruptions in what is now Siberia. This period was the most extreme episode of volcanism to have occurred during the past half billion years. Geologic data indicate that an area of 1.6 million km^2 (roughly half the size of western Europe) was covered with a layer of lava hundreds to thousands

of meters thick. Besides spewing enormous amounts of lava and ash, the eruptions may have produced enough carbon dioxide to warm the global climate by an estimated 6°C. If this hypothesis is correct, reduced temperature differences between the equator and the poles could have slowed the mixing of ocean water, which in turn could have led to a widespread drop in oxygen concentrations. The resulting low-oxygen condition, called *ocean anoxia*, would have suffocated oxygen-breathers and promoted the growth of anaerobic bacteria that emit a poisonous metabolic by-product, hydrogen sulfide (H_2S) gas. As this gas bubbled into the atmosphere, it could have caused further extinctions by directly killing land plants and animals and by initiating chemical reactions that destroy the ozone layer, a "shield" that ordinarily protects organisms from life-threatening levels of UV radiation.

The Cretaceous mass extinction occurred about 65.5 million years ago and marks the boundary between the Mesozoic and Cenozoic eras. This event extinguished more than half of all marine species and eliminated many families of terrestrial plants and animals, including all dinosaurs (except birds, which are members of the same group; see Chapter 27). One clue to a possible cause of the Cretaceous mass extinction is a thin layer of clay enriched in iridium that separates sediments from the Mesozoic and Cenozoic eras. Iridium is an element that is very rare on Earth but common in many of the meteorites and other extraterrestrial objects that occasionally fall to Earth. This suggests that the high-iridium clay may be fallout from a huge cloud of debris that billowed into the atmosphere when an asteroid or large comet collided with Earth. This cloud would have blocked sunlight and severely disturbed the global climate for several months.

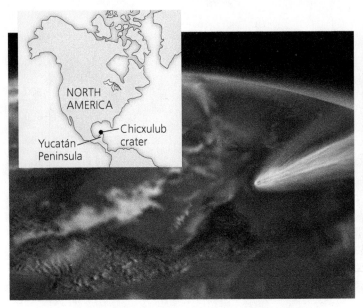
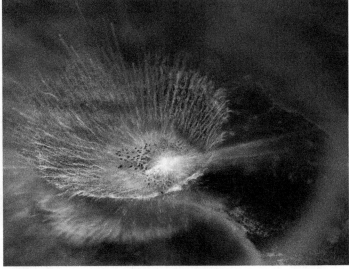

▲ **Figure 23.11 Trauma for Earth and its Cretaceous life.** Beneath the Caribbean Sea, the 65-million-year-old Chicxulub impact crater measures 180 km across. The horseshoe shape of the crater and the pattern of debris in sedimentary rocks indicate that an asteroid or comet struck at a low angle from the southeast. This artist's interpretation represents the impact and its immediate effect: a cloud of hot vapor and debris that could have killed many of the plants and animals in North America within hours.

Is there evidence of such an asteroid or comet? Research has focused on the Chicxulub crater, a 65-million-year-old scar beneath sediments off the Yucatán coast of Mexico **(Figure 23.11)**. The crater is the right size to have been caused by an object with a diameter of 10 km. Critical evaluation of this and other hypotheses for mass extinctions continues.

Is a Sixth Mass Extinction Under Way?

As you will read further in Chapter 43, human actions, such as habitat destruction, are modifying the global environment to such an extent that many species are threatened with extinction. More than a thousand species have become extinct in the last 400 years. Scientists estimate that this rate is 100 to 1,000 times the typical background rate seen in the fossil record. Is a sixth mass extinction now in progress?

This question is difficult to answer, in part because it is hard to document the number of extinctions occurring today. Tropical rain forests, for example, harbor many undiscovered species; destroying tropical forest may drive species to extinction before we even learn of their existence. Such uncertainties make it hard to assess the extent of the current extinction crisis. Even so, it is clear that losses have not reached those of the "big five" mass extinctions, in which large percentages of Earth's species became extinct. This does not discount the seriousness of today's situation. Monitoring programs show that many species are declining at an alarming rate due to habitat loss, introduced species, overharvesting, and other factors. Ongoing climate change may hasten some of these declines. Indeed, the fossil record indicates that over the last 500 million years, extinction rates have tended to increase when global temperatures were high **(Figure 23.12)**. Overall, evidence suggests that unless

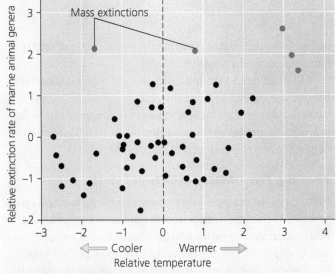

© 2008 The Royal Society

▲ **Figure 23.12 Fossil extinctions and temperature.** Extinction rates increased when global temperatures were high. Temperatures were estimated using ratios of oxygen isotopes and converted to an index in which 0 is the overall average temperature.

dramatic actions are taken, a sixth, human-caused mass extinction is likely to occur within the next few centuries or millennia.

Consequences of Mass Extinctions

Mass extinctions have significant and long-term effects. By eliminating large numbers of species, a mass extinction can reduce a thriving and complex ecological community to a pale shadow of its former self. And once an evolutionary lineage disappears, it cannot reappear; the course of evolution is changed forever. Consider what would have happened if the early primates living 66 million years ago had died out in the

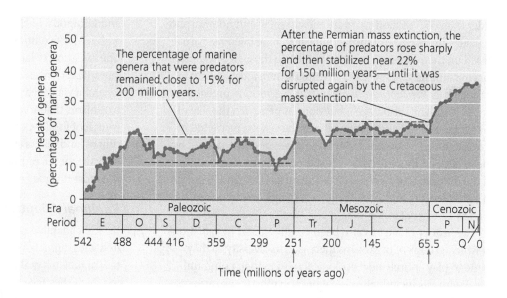

▶ **Figure 23.13 Mass extinctions and ecology.** The Permian and Cretaceous mass extinctions (indicated by red arrows) altered the ecology of the oceans by increasing the percentage of marine genera that were predators.

The percentage of marine genera that were predators remained close to 15% for 200 million years.

After the Permian mass extinction, the percentage of predators rose sharply and then stabilized near 22% for 150 million years—until it was disrupted again by the Cretaceous mass extinction.

Cretaceous mass extinction. Humans would not exist, and life on Earth would differ greatly from what it is today.

The fossil record shows that 5–10 million years typically pass after a mass extinction before the diversity of life recovers to previous levels. In some cases, it has taken much longer: It took about 100 million years for the number of marine families to recover after the Permian mass extinction (see Figure 23.10). These data have sobering implications. If a sixth mass extinction occurs, it will take millions of years for life on Earth to recover its diversity.

Mass extinctions can also alter ecological communities by changing the types of organisms residing there. For example, after the Permian and Cretaceous mass extinctions, the percentage of marine organisms that were predators grew substantially **(Figure 23.13)**. An increase in predators can increase both the pressures faced by prey and the competition among predators for food. In addition, mass extinctions can curtail lineages with novel and advantageous features. For example, in the late Triassic, a group of gastropods (snails and their relatives) arose that could drill through the shells of bivalves (such as clams) and feed on the animals inside. Although shell drilling provided access to a new and abundant source of food, this newly formed group was wiped out during the Triassic mass extinction (about 200 million years ago). Another 120 million years passed before another group of gastropods (the oyster drills) exhibited this drilling ability. As their predecessors might have done if they had not originated at an unfortunate time, oyster drills have since diversified into many new species. Finally, by eliminating so many species, mass extinctions can pave the way for adaptive radiations, in which new groups of organisms proliferate.

Adaptive Radiations

The fossil record indicates that the diversity of life has increased over the past 250 million years (see blue line in Figure 23.10). This increase has been fueled by **adaptive radiations**, periods of evolutionary change in which groups of organisms form many new species whose adaptations allow them to fill different ecological roles, or niches, in their communities. Large-scale adaptive radiations occurred after each of the big five mass extinctions, when survivors became adapted to the many vacant ecological niches. Adaptive radiations have also occurred in groups of organisms that possessed major evolutionary innovations, such as seeds or armored body coverings, or that colonized regions in which they faced little competition from other species.

Worldwide Adaptive Radiations

Fossil evidence indicates that mammals underwent a dramatic adaptive radiation after the extinction of terrestrial dinosaurs 65.5 million years ago **(Figure 23.14)**. Although mammals originated about 180 million years ago, the mammal fossils

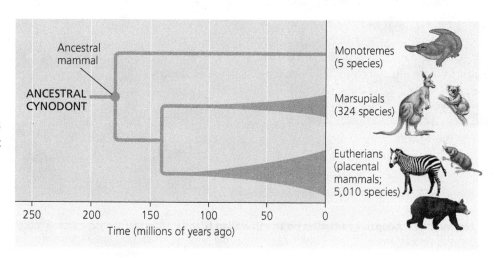

▲ **Figure 23.14 Adaptive radiation of mammals.**

older than 65.5 million years are mostly small and not morphologically diverse. Many species appear to have been nocturnal based on their large eye sockets, similar to those in living nocturnal mammals. A few early mammals were intermediate in size, such as *Repenomamus giganticus*, a 1-m-long predator that lived 130 million years ago—but none approached the size of many dinosaurs. Early mammals may have been restricted in size and diversity because they were eaten or outcompeted by the larger and more diverse dinosaurs. With the disappearance of the dinosaurs (except for birds), mammals expanded greatly in both diversity and size, filling the ecological roles once occupied by terrestrial dinosaurs.

The history of life has also been greatly altered by radiations in which groups of organisms increased in diversity as they came to play entirely new ecological roles in their communities. Examples include the rise of photosynthetic prokaryotes, the evolution of large predators in the early Cambrian, and the radiations following the colonization of land by plants, insects,

and tetrapods. Each of these last three radiations was associated with major evolutionary innovations that facilitated life on land. The radiation of land plants, for example, was associated with key adaptations, such as stems that support plants against gravity and a waxy coat that protects leaves from water loss. Finally, organisms that arise in an adaptive radiation can serve as a new source of food for still other organisms. In fact, the diversification of land plants stimulated a series of adaptive radiations in insects that ate or pollinated plants, one reason that insects are the most diverse group of animals on Earth today.

Regional Adaptive Radiations

Striking adaptive radiations have also occurred over more limited geographic areas. Such radiations can be initiated when a few organisms make their way to a new, often distant location in which they face relatively little competition from other organisms. The Hawaiian archipelago is one of the world's great showcases of this type of adaptive radiation (Figure 23.15).

▲ **Figure 23.15 Adaptive radiation on the Hawaiian Islands.** Molecular analysis indicates that these remarkably varied Hawaiian plants, known collectively as the "silversword alliance," are all descended from an ancestral tarweed that arrived on the islands about 5 million years ago from North America. Members of the silversword alliance have since spread into different habitats and formed new species with strikingly different adaptations.

Located about 3,500 km from the nearest continent, the volcanic islands are progressively older as one follows the chain toward the northwest; the youngest island, Hawaii, is less than a million years old and still has active volcanoes. Each island was born "naked" and was gradually populated by stray organisms that rode the ocean currents and winds either from far-distant land areas or from older islands of the archipelago itself. The physical diversity of each island, including immense variation in elevation and rainfall, provides many opportunities for evolutionary divergence by natural selection. Multiple invasions followed by speciation events have ignited an explosion of adaptive radiation in Hawaii. As a result, most of the thousands of species that inhabit the islands are found nowhere else on Earth. Besides the silverswords in Figure 23.15, organisms unique to Hawaii include a large group of colorful birds called Hawaiian honeycreepers and hundreds of fruit fly species.

CONCEPT CHECK 23.2

1. Explain the evolutionary consequences of continental drift for life on Earth.
2. Summarize how mass extinctions affect the evolutionary history of life.
3. What factors promote adaptive radiations?
4. **WHAT IF?** Suppose that an invertebrate species was lost in a mass extinction caused by a sudden catastrophic event. Would the last appearance of this species in the fossil record necessarily be close to when the extinction actually occurred? Would the answer to this question differ depending on whether the species was common (abundant and widespread) or rare? Explain.

For suggested answers, see Appendix A.

CONCEPT 23.3

Major changes in body form can result from changes in the sequences and regulation of developmental genes

The fossil record tells us what the great changes in the history of life have been and when they occurred. Moreover, an understanding of plate tectonics, mass extinction, and adaptive radiation provides a picture of how those changes came about. But we can also seek to understand the intrinsic biological mechanisms that underlie changes seen in the fossil record. For this, we turn to genetic mechanisms of change, paying particular attention to genes that influence development.

Effects of Developmental Genes

As you read in Chapter 15, evo-devo—research at the interface between evolutionary biology and developmental biology—is

illuminating how slight genetic differences can produce major morphological differences between species. Genes that control development influence the rate, timing, and spatial pattern of change in an organism's form as it develops from a zygote into an adult.

Changes in Rate and Timing

Many striking evolutionary transformations are the result of **heterochrony** (from the Greek *hetero*, different, and *chronos*, time), an evolutionary change in the rate or timing of developmental events. For example, an organism's shape depends in part on the relative growth rates of different body parts during development. Changes to these rates can alter the adult form substantially, as seen in the contrasting shapes of human and chimpanzee skulls **(Figure 23.16)**.

Other examples of the dramatic evolutionary effects of heterochrony include how increased growth rates of finger bones yielded the skeletal structure of wings in bats

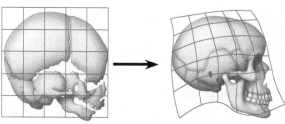

Chimpanzee infant Chimpanzee adult

Chimpanzee fetus Chimpanzee adult

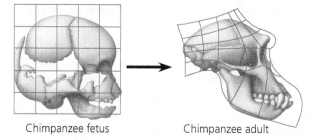

Human fetus Human adult

▲ **Figure 23.16 Relative skull growth rates.** In the human evolutionary lineage, mutations slowed the growth of the jaw relative to other parts of the skull. As a result, in humans the skull of an adult is more similar to the skull of an infant than is the case for chimpanzees.

▲ **Figure 23.17 Elongated hand and finger bones in a bat wing.** Heterochrony is responsible for the increased total length of hand and finger bones in a bat compared to that of other mammals.

MAKE CONNECTIONS *Locate the bat's wrist and elbow joints (see Figure 19.16). Calculate the ratio of the length of the bat's longest set of hand and finger bones to the length of its radius. Compare this ratio to the ratio of the bones in your own hand and arm.*

(Figure 23.17) and how slowed growth of leg and pelvic bones led to the reduction and eventual loss of hind limbs in whales (see Figure 19.19).

Heterochrony can also alter the timing of reproductive development relative to the development of nonreproductive organs. If reproductive organ development accelerates compared with other organs, the sexually mature stage of a species may retain body features that were juvenile structures in an ancestral species, a condition called **paedomorphosis** (from the Greek *paedos*, of a child, and *morphosis*, formation). For example, most salamander species have aquatic larvae that undergo metamorphosis in becoming adults. But some species grow to adult size and become sexually mature while retaining gills and other larval features (Figure 23.18). Such an evolutionary alteration of developmental timing can produce animals that appear very different from their ancestors, even though the overall genetic change may be small. Indeed, recent evidence indicates that a change at a single locus was probably sufficient to bring about paedomorphosis in the axolotl salamander, although other genes may have contributed as well.

Changes in Spatial Pattern

Substantial evolutionary changes can also result from alterations in genes that control the placement and spatial organization of body parts. For example, master regulatory genes called **homeotic genes** (described in Chapters 16 and 18) determine such basic features as where a pair of wings and a pair of legs will develop on a bird or how a plant's flower parts are arranged.

The products of one class of homeotic genes, the *Hox* genes, provide positional information in an animal embryo. This

▲ **Figure 23.18 Paedomorphosis.** The adults of some species retain features that were juvenile in ancestors. This salamander is an axolotl, an aquatic species that grows to full size, becomes sexually mature, and reproduces while retaining certain larval (tadpole) characteristics, including gills.

information prompts cells to develop into structures appropriate for a particular location. Changes in *Hox* genes or in how they are expressed can have a profound impact on morphology. For example, among crustaceans, a change in the location where two *Hox* genes (*Ubx* and *Scr*) are expressed correlates with the conversion of a swimming appendage to a feeding appendage. Large effects are also seen in snakes, where changes in how two *Hox* genes (*HoxC6* and *HoxC8*) are expressed suppress limb formation. Similarly, when comparing plant species, changes to the expression of homeotic genes known as *MADS-box* genes can produce flowers that differ dramatically in form (see Chapter 28).

The Evolution of Development

Large members of most animal phyla appear suddenly in fossils formed 535-525 million years ago. This rapid diversification of animals is referred to as the *Cambrian explosion* (see Concept 27.2). Yet the discovery of 560-million-year-old fossils of Ediacaran animals (see Figure 23.2) suggests that a set of genes sufficient to produce complex animals existed at least 25 million years before that time. If such genes have existed for so long, how can we explain the astonishing increases in diversity seen during and since the Cambrian explosion?

Adaptive evolution by natural selection provides one answer to this question. As we've seen throughout this unit, by sorting among differences in the sequences of protein-encoding genes, selection can improve adaptations rapidly. In addition, new genes (created by gene duplication events) can take on a wide range of new metabolic and structural functions. Thus, adaptive evolution of both new and existing genes may have played a key role in shaping the great diversity of life.

Examples in the previous section suggest that developmental genes may be particularly important. Next we'll examine how new morphological forms arise from changes in the nucleotide sequences or regulation of developmental genes.

Changes in Gene Sequence

New developmental genes arising after gene duplication events very likely facilitated the origin of novel morphological forms. But since other genetic changes also may have occurred at such times, it can be difficult to establish causal links between genetic and morphological changes that occurred in the past.

This difficulty was sidestepped in a recent study of developmental changes associated with the divergence of six-legged insects from crustacean-like ancestors that had more than six legs. In insects, such as *Drosophila*, the *Ubx* gene is expressed in the abdomen, while in crustaceans, such as *Artemia*, it is expressed in the main trunk of the body (**Figure 23.19**). When expressed, the *Ubx* gene suppresses leg formation in insects but not in crustaceans. To examine the workings of this gene, researchers cloned the *Ubx* gene from *Drosophila* and *Artemia*. Next, they genetically engineered fruit fly embryos to express either the *Drosophila Ubx* gene or the *Artemia Ubx* gene throughout their bodies. The *Drosophila* gene suppressed 100% of the limbs in the embryos, as expected, whereas the *Artemia* gene suppressed only 15%.

The researchers then sought to uncover key steps involved in the evolutionary transition from a crustacean *Ubx* gene to an insect *Ubx* gene. Their approach was to identify mutations that would cause the *Artemia Ubx* gene to suppress leg formation, thus making the crustacean gene act more like an insect *Ubx* gene. To do this, they constructed a series of "hybrid" *Ubx* genes, each of which contained known segments of the *Drosophila Ubx* gene and known segments of the *Artemia Ubx* gene. By inserting these hybrid genes into fruit fly embryos (one hybrid gene per embryo) and observing their effects on

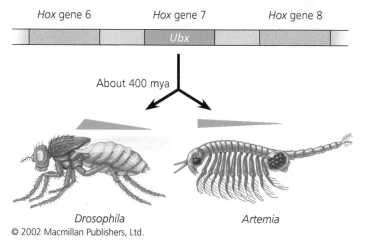

© 2002 Macmillan Publishers, Ltd.

▲ **Figure 23.19 Origin of the insect body plan.** Expression of the *Hox* gene *Ubx* suppresses the formation of legs in fruit flies (*Drosophila*) but not in brine shrimp (*Artemia*), thus helping to build the insect body plan. Fruit fly and brine shrimp *Hox* genes have evolved independently for 400 million years. The green triangles indicate the relative amounts of *Ubx* expression in different body regions.

leg development, the researchers were able to pinpoint the exact amino acid changes responsible for the suppression of additional limbs in insects. In so doing, this study provided evidence linking a particular change in the nucleotide sequence of a developmental gene to a major evolutionary change: the origin of the six-legged insect body plan.

Changes in Gene Regulation

Changes in the nucleotide sequence or regulation of developmental genes can result in morphological changes that harm the organism (see Chapter 16). However, a change in the nucleotide sequence of a gene may affect its function wherever the gene is expressed, while changes in the regulation of gene expression can be limited to a single cell type. Thus, a change in the regulation of a developmental gene may have fewer harmful side effects than a change to the sequence of the gene. This line of reasoning has prompted researchers to suggest that changes in the form of organisms may often be caused by mutations that affect the regulation of developmental genes—not their sequences.

This idea is supported by studies of a variety of species, including threespine stickleback fish. These fish live in the open ocean and in shallow, coastal waters. In western Canada, they also live in lakes formed when the coastline receded during the past 12,000 years. Marine stickleback fish have a pair of spines on their ventral (lower) surface, which deter some predators. These spines are often reduced or absent in stickleback fish living in lakes that lack predatory fishes and that are also low in calcium. Spines may have been lost in such lakes because they are not advantageous in the absence of predators, and the limited calcium is needed for purposes other than constructing spines.

▲ **Threespine stickleback (*Gasterosteus aculeatus*)**

At the genetic level, the developmental gene *Pitx1* was known to influence whether stickleback fish have ventral spines. Was the reduction of spines in some lake populations due to changes in the sequence of the *Pitx1* gene or to changes in how the gene is expressed? **Figure 23.20**, on the next page, describes an experiment designed to study this question. The researchers' results indicate that the regulation of gene expression has changed, not the DNA sequence of the gene. Furthermore, lake stickleback fish do express the *Pitx1* gene in tissues not related to the production of spines (for example, the mouth), illustrating how morphological change can be caused by altering the expression of a developmental gene in some parts of the body but not others.

What caused the loss of spines in lake stickleback fish?

Experiment Marine populations of the threespine stickleback fish have a set of protective spines on their lower (ventral) surface; however, these spines have been lost or reduced in some lake populations of this fish. Researchers performed genetic crosses and found that most of the reduction in spine size resulted from the effects of a single developmental gene, *Pitx1*. The researchers then tested two hypotheses about how *Pitx1* causes this morphological change.

Hypothesis A: A change in the DNA sequence of *Pitx1* caused spine reduction in lake populations. To test this idea, the team used DNA sequencing to compare the coding sequence of the *Pitx1* gene between marine and lake stickleback populations.

Hypothesis B: A change in the regulation of the expression of *Pitx1* caused spine reduction. To test this idea, the researchers monitored where in the developing embryo the *Pitx1* gene was expressed. They conducted whole-body *in situ* hybridization experiments (see Chapter 16) using *Pitx1* DNA as a probe to detect *Pitx1* mRNA in the fish.

Results

Test of Hypothesis A: Are there differences in the coding sequence of the *Pitx1* gene in marine and lake stickleback fish?

Result: No → The 283 amino acids of the *Pitx1* protein are identical in marine and lake stickleback populations.

Test of Hypothesis B: Are there any differences in the regulation of expression of *Pitx1*?

Result: Yes → Red arrows (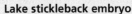) indicate regions of *Pitx1* gene expression in the photographs below. *Pitx1* is expressed in the ventral spine and mouth regions of developing marine stickleback fish but only in the mouth region of developing lake stickleback fish.

Marine stickleback embryo　　　　**Lake stickleback embryo**

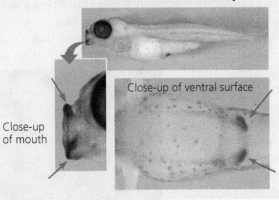

Close-up of ventral surface

Close-up of mouth

Conclusion The loss or reduction of ventral spines in lake populations of threespine stickleback fish appears to have resulted primarily from a change in the regulation of *Pitx1* gene expression, not from a change in the gene's sequence.

Source M. D. Shapiro et al., Genetic and developmental basis of evolutionary pelvic reduction in three-spine sticklebacks, *Nature* 428:717–723 (2004).

WHAT IF? What results would have led researchers to conclude that a change in the coding sequence of *Pitx1* was more important than a change in regulation of gene expression?

CONCEPT CHECK 23.3

1. How can heterochrony cause evolution of novel body forms?
2. Why is it likely that *Hox* genes have played a major role in the evolution of novel morphological forms?
3. **MAKE CONNECTIONS** Given that changes in morphology are often caused by changes in the regulation of gene expression, predict whether noncoding DNA is likely to be affected by natural selection. (Review Concept 15.3.)

For suggested answers, see Appendix A.

CONCEPT 23.4

Evolution is not goal oriented

What does our study of macroevolution tell us about how evolution works? One lesson is that throughout the history of life, the origin of new species has been affected by both small-scale factors (described in Chapter 21), such as natural selection operating in populations, and the large-scale factors described in this chapter, such as continental drift promoting bursts of speciation throughout the globe. Moreover, to paraphrase the Nobel Prize–winning geneticist François Jacob, evolution is like tinkering—a process in which new forms arise by the slight modification of existing forms. Even large changes, like the ones that produced the first mammals or the six-legged body plan of insects, can result from the modification of existing structures or existing developmental genes. Over time, such tinkering has led to three key features of the natural world (see Chapter 19): the striking ways in which organisms are suited for life in their environments; the many shared characteristics of life; and the rich diversity of life.

Evolutionary Novelties

François Jacob's view of evolution harkens back to Darwin's concept of descent with modification. As new species form, novel and complex structures can arise as gradual modifications of ancestral structures. In many cases, complex structures have evolved in increments from simpler versions that performed the same basic function. For example, consider the human eye, an intricate organ constructed from numerous parts that work together in forming an image and transmitting it to the brain. How could the human eye have evolved in gradual increments? Some argue that if the eye needs all of its components to function, a partial eye could not have been of use to our ancestors.

The flaw in this argument, as Darwin himself noted, lies in the assumption that only complicated eyes are useful. In fact, many animals depend on eyes that are far less complex than our own **(Figure 23.21)**. The simplest eyes that we know of are patches of light-sensitive photoreceptor cells. These simple eyes appear to have had a single evolutionary origin and are now found in a variety of animals, including small molluscs called limpets. Such eyes have no equipment for focusing images, but they do enable the animal to distinguish light from dark. Limpets cling more tightly to their rock when a shadow falls on them, a behavioral adaptation that reduces the risk of being eaten. Because limpets have had a long evolutionary history, we can conclude that their "simple" eyes are quite adequate to support their survival and reproduction.

In the animal kingdom, complex eyes have evolved independently from such basic structures many times. Some molluscs, such as squids and octopuses, have eyes as complex as those of humans and other vertebrates (see Figure 23.21). Although complex mollusc eyes evolved independently of vertebrate eyes, both evolved from a simple cluster of photoreceptor cells present in a common ancestor. In each case, the complex eye evolved through a series of incremental modifications that benefited the eyes' owners at every stage. Evidence of their independent evolution may also be found in their structure: Vertebrate eyes detect light at the back layer of the retina and conduct nerve impulses toward the front, while complex mollusc eyes do the reverse.

▼ **Figure 23.21 A range of eye complexity in molluscs.**

(a) Patch of pigmented cells

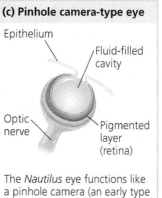

Pigmented cells (photoreceptors)
Epithelium
Nerve fibers

The limpet *Patella* has a simple patch of photoreceptors.

(b) Eyecup

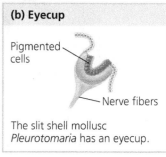

Pigmented cells
Nerve fibers

The slit shell mollusc *Pleurotomaria* has an eyecup.

(c) Pinhole camera-type eye

Epithelium
Fluid-filled cavity
Optic nerve
Pigmented layer (retina)

The *Nautilus* eye functions like a pinhole camera (an early type of camera lacking a lens).

(d) Eye with primitive lens

Cellular mass (lens)
Cornea
Optic nerve

The marine snail *Murex* has a primitive lens consisting of a mass of crystal-like cells. The cornea is a transparent region of tissue that protects the eye and helps focus light.

(e) Complex camera lens-type eye

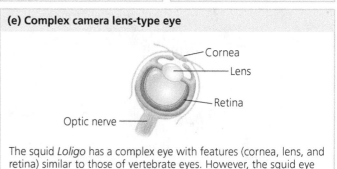

Cornea
Lens
Retina
Optic nerve

The squid *Loligo* has a complex eye with features (cornea, lens, and retina) similar to those of vertebrate eyes. However, the squid eye evolved independently from vertebrate eyes.

Throughout their evolutionary history, eyes retained their basic function of vision. But evolutionary novelties can also arise when structures that originally played one role gradually acquire a different one. For example, as cynodonts gave rise to early mammals, bones that formerly comprised the jaw hinge (the articular and quadrate; see Figure 23.4) were incorporated into the ear region of mammals, where they eventually took on a new function: the transmission of sound. Structures that evolve in one context but become co-opted for another function are sometimes called *exaptations* to distinguish them from the adaptive origin of the original structure. Note that the concept of exaptation does not imply that a structure somehow evolves in anticipation of future use. Natural selection cannot predict the future; it can only improve a structure in the context of its *current* utility. Novel features, such as the new jaw hinge and ear bones of early mammals, can arise gradually via a series of intermediate stages, each of which has some function in the organism's current context.

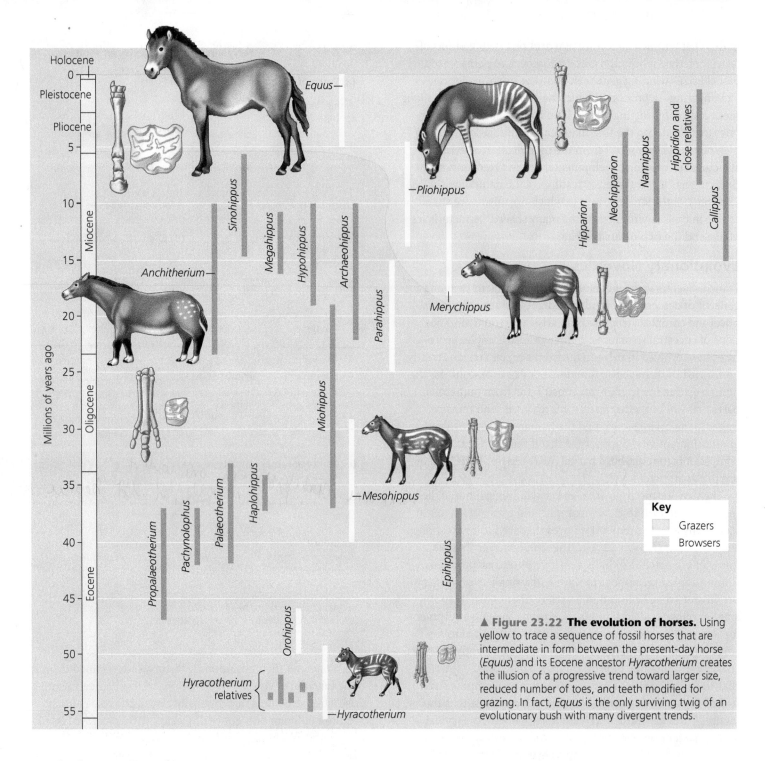

Key
Grazers
Browsers

▲ **Figure 23.22 The evolution of horses.** Using yellow to trace a sequence of fossil horses that are intermediate in form between the present-day horse (*Equus*) and its Eocene ancestor *Hyracotherium* creates the illusion of a progressive trend toward larger size, reduced number of toes, and teeth modified for grazing. In fact, *Equus* is the only surviving twig of an evolutionary bush with many divergent trends.

Evolutionary Trends

What else can we learn from patterns of macroevolution? Consider evolutionary "trends" observed in the fossil record. For instance, some evolutionary lineages exhibit a trend toward larger or smaller body size. An example is the evolution of the present-day horse (genus *Equus*), a descendant of the 55-million-year-old *Hyracotherium* (**Figure 23.22**). About the size of a large dog, *Hyracotherium* had four toes on its front feet, three toes on its hind feet, and teeth adapted for browsing on bushes and trees. In comparison, present-day horses are larger, have only one toe on each foot, and possess teeth modified for grazing on grasses.

Extracting a single evolutionary progression from the fossil record can be misleading, however; it is like describing a bush as growing toward a single point by tracing only the branches that lead to that twig. For example, by selecting certain species from the available fossils, it is possible to arrange a succession of animals intermediate between *Hyracotherium* and living horses that shows a trend toward large, single-toed species (follow the yellow highlighting in Figure 23.22). However, if we consider *all* fossil horses known today, this apparent trend vanishes. The genus *Equus* did not evolve in a straight line; it is the only surviving twig of an evolutionary tree that is so branched that it is more like a bush. *Equus* actually descended through a series of speciation episodes that included several adaptive radiations, not all of which led to large, one-toed, grazing horses. In fact, phylogenetic analyses suggest that all lineages that include grazers are closely related to *Parahippus*; the many other horse lineages, all of which are now extinct, remained multi-toed browsers for 35 million years.

Branching evolution *can* result in a real evolutionary trend even if some species counter the trend. One model of long-term trends views species as analogous to individuals: Speciation is their birth, extinction is their death, and new species that diverge from them are their offspring. In this model, just as populations of individual organisms undergo natural selection, species undergo *species selection*. The species that endure the longest and generate the most new offspring species determine the direction of major evolutionary trends. The species selection model suggests that "differential speciation success" plays a role in macroevolution similar to the role of differential reproductive success in microevolution. Evolutionary trends can also result directly from natural selection. For example, when horse ancestors invaded the grasslands that spread during the mid-Cenozoic, there was strong selection for grazers that could escape

predators by running faster. This trend would not have occurred without open grasslands.

Whatever its cause, an evolutionary trend does not imply that there is some intrinsic drive toward a particular phenotype. Evolution is the result of the interactions between organisms and their current environments; if environmental conditions change, an evolutionary trend may cease or even reverse itself. The cumulative effect of these ongoing interactions between organisms and their environments is enormous: It is through them that the staggering diversity of life— Darwin's "endless forms most beautiful"—has arisen.

CONCEPT CHECK 23.4

1. How can the Darwinian concept of descent with modification explain the evolution of such complex structures as the vertebrate eye?
2. **WHAT IF?** The myxoma virus kills up to 99.8% of infected European rabbits in populations with no previous exposure to the virus. The virus is transmitted by mosquitoes, which only bite living rabbits. Describe an evolutionary trend (in either the rabbit or virus) that might occur after a rabbit population first encounters the virus.

For suggested answers, see Appendix A.

23 Chapter Review

SUMMARY OF KEY CONCEPTS

CONCEPT 23.1

The fossil record documents life's history (pp. 436–440)

- The **fossil record**, based largely on fossils found in sedimentary rocks, documents the rise and fall of different groups of organisms over time. Sedimentary strata reveal the relative ages of **fossils**. The absolute ages of fossils can be estimated by radiometric dating and other methods.
- The study of fossils has helped geologists establish a **geologic record** of Earth's history.
- The fossil record shows how new groups of organisms can arise via the gradual modification of preexisting organisms.

? *What are the challenges of estimating the absolute ages of old fossils? Explain how these challenges may be overcome in some circumstances.*

CONCEPT 23.2

The rise and fall of groups of organisms reflect differences in speciation and extinction rates (pp. 440–449)

- In **plate tectonics**, continental plates move gradually over time, altering the physical geography and climate of Earth. These changes lead to extinctions in some groups of organisms and bursts of speciation in others.
- Evolutionary history has been punctuated by five **mass extinctions** that radically altered the history of life. Some of these extinctions may have been caused by changes in

continent positions, volcanic activity, or impacts from meteorites or comets.
- Large increases in the diversity of life have resulted from **adaptive radiations** that followed mass extinctions. Adaptive radiations have also occurred in groups of organisms that possessed major evolutionary innovations or that colonized new regions in which there was little competition from other organisms.

? *Explain how the broad evolutionary changes seen in the fossil record are the cumulative result of speciation and extinction events.*

CONCEPT 23.3

Major changes in body form can result from changes in the sequences and regulation of developmental genes (pp. 449–452)

- Developmental genes affect morphological differences between species by influencing the rate, timing, and spatial patterns of change in an organism's form as it develops into an adult.
- The evolution of new forms can be caused by changes in the nucleotide sequences or regulation of developmental genes.

? *How could changes in a single gene or DNA region ultimately lead to the origin of a new group of organisms?*

CONCEPT 23.4

Evolution is not goal oriented (pp. 452–455)

- Novel and complex biological structures can evolve through a series of incremental modifications, each of which benefits the organism that possesses it.

- Evolutionary trends can be caused by factors such as natural selection in a changing environment or species selection. Like all aspects of evolution, evolutionary trends result from interactions between organisms and their current environments.

? *Explain the reasoning behind the statement "Evolution is not goal oriented."*

TEST YOUR UNDERSTANDING

Level 1: Knowledge/Comprehension

1. Which factor most likely caused animals and plants in India to differ greatly from species in nearby Southeast Asia?
   a. The species became separated by convergent evolution.
   b. The climates of the two regions are similar.
   c. India is in the process of separating from the rest of Asia.
   d. Life in India was wiped out by ancient volcanic eruptions.
   e. India was a separate continent until 45 million years ago.

2. Adaptive radiations can be a direct consequence of four of the following five factors. Select the exception.
   a. vacant ecological niches
   b. genetic drift
   c. colonization of an isolated region that contains suitable habitat and few competitor species
   d. evolutionary innovation
   e. an adaptive radiation in a group of organisms (such as plants) that another group uses as food

3. A researcher discovers a fossil of what appears to be one of the oldest-known multicellular organisms. The researcher could estimate the age of this fossil based on
   a. the amount of carbon-14 in the fossil.
   b. the amount of uranium-238 in the fossil.
   c. the amount of carbon-14 in the sedimentary rocks in which the fossil was found.
   d. the amount of uranium-238 in volcanic layers surrounding the fossil.
   e. the amount of uranium-238 in the sedimentary rocks in which the fossil was found.

Level 2: Application/Analysis

4. A genetic change that caused a certain *Hox* gene to be expressed along the tip of a vertebrate limb bud instead of farther back helped make possible the evolution of the tetrapod limb. This type of change is illustrative of
   a. the influence of environment on development.
   b. paedomorphosis.
   c. a change in a developmental gene or in its regulation that altered the spatial organization of body parts.
   d. heterochrony.
   e. gene duplication.

5. A swim bladder is a gas-filled sac that helps fish maintain buoyancy. The evolution of the swim bladder from the air-breathing organ (a simple lung) of an ancestral fish is an example of
   a. an evolutionary trend.
   b. exaptation.
   c. changes in *Hox* gene expression.
   d. paedomorphosis.
   e. adaptive radiation.

6. **MAKE CONNECTIONS** Review Figure 20.10. Based on the phylogeny shown in Figure 23.4, identify the most inclusive clade to which both *Dimetrodon* and mammals belong. Explain.

Level 3: Synthesis/Evaluation

7. **SCIENTIFIC INQUIRY**
   Herbivory (plant eating) has evolved repeatedly in insects, typically from meat-eating or detritus-feeding ancestors (detritus is dead organic matter). Moths and butterflies, for example, eat plants, whereas their "sister group" (the insect group to which they are most closely related), the caddisflies, feed on animals, fungi, or detritus. As illustrated in the phylogenetic tree below, the combined moth/butterfly and caddisfly group shares a common ancestor with flies and fleas. Like caddisflies, flies and fleas are thought to have evolved from ancestors that did not eat plants.

   There are 140,000 species of moths and butterflies and 7,000 species of caddisflies. State a hypothesis about the impact of herbivory on adaptive radiations in insects. How could this hypothesis be tested?

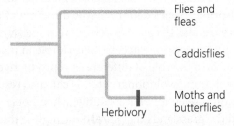

Flies and fleas

Caddisflies

Moths and butterflies

Herbivory

8. **SCIENCE, TECHNOLOGY, AND SOCIETY**
   Experts estimate that human activities cause the extinction of hundreds of species every year. In contrast, the natural rate of extinction is thought to average only a few species per year. If human actions continue to alter the global environment, especially by destroying tropical rain forests and changing Earth's climate, the likely result will be a wave of extinctions that could rival those at the end of the Cretaceous period. Considering that life has endured five mass extinctions, should we be concerned that we may cause a sixth mass extinction? How would such an extinction differ from previous extinctions? What might be some of the consequences?

9. **FOCUS ON EVOLUTION**
   Describe how gene flow, genetic drift, and natural selection all can influence macroevolution.

10. **FOCUS ON ORGANIZATION**
    You have seen many examples of how form fits function at all levels of the biological hierarchy. However, we can imagine forms that would function better than some forms actually found in nature. For example, if the wings of a bird were not formed from its forelimbs, such a hypothetical bird could fly yet also hold objects with its forelimbs. In a short essay (100–150 words), use the concept of "evolution as tinkering" to explain why there are limits to the functionality of forms in nature.

For selected answers, see Appendix A.

MasteringBiology®

Students Go to **MasteringBiology** for assignments, the eText, and the Study Area with practice tests, animations, and activities.

Instructors Go to **MasteringBiology** for automatically graded tutorials and questions that you can assign to your students, plus Instructor Resources.

Unit 4 The Evolutionary History of Life

24 Early Life and the Diversification of Prokaryotes

Life on Earth began 3.5 billion years ago with the origin of single-celled **prokaryotes**. Over this long history, a wide range of metabolic adaptations have evolved in prokaryotes, enabling them to thrive throughout the biosphere.

25 The Origin and Diversification of Eukaryotes

Following the metabolic diversification of prokaryotes, the origin of **eukaryotes** 1.8 billion years ago led to the evolution of a vast array of structurally complex organisms—the protists, plants, fungi, and animals that fill our world today.

26 The Colonization of Land by Plants and Fungi

The **colonization of land** by plants and fungi 500 million years ago transformed terrestrial environments from a "green slime" consisting of bacteria and single-celled eukaryotes to lush forests and other plant communities.

27 The Rise of Animal Diversity

The earliest animals were microscopic and lived in marine environments. By 530 million years ago, the origin of larger, mobile animals with complex nervous and digestive systems led to an explosive **radiation of animals**, transforming the microbe-only world to a world filled with predators, prey, and other large eukaryotes.

The Evolutionary History of Life

24 Early Life and the Diversification of Prokaryotes
25 The Origin and Diversification of Eukaryotes
26 The Colonization of Land by Plants and Fungi
27 The Rise of Animal Diversity

Evolution
Genetics
Chemistry and Cells
Ecology
Animals
Plants

24 Early Life and the Diversification of Prokaryotes

KEY CONCEPTS

24.1 Conditions on early Earth made the origin of life possible

24.2 Diverse structural and metabolic adaptations have evolved in prokaryotes

24.3 Rapid reproduction, mutation, and genetic recombination promote genetic diversity in prokaryotes

24.4 Prokaryotes have radiated into a diverse set of lineages

24.5 Prokaryotes play crucial roles in the biosphere

OVERVIEW

The First Cells

Our planet formed 4.6 billion years ago, condensing from a vast cloud of dust and rocks that surrounded the young sun. For its first few hundred million years, Earth was bombarded by huge chunks of rock and ice left over from the birth of the solar system. The collisions generated so much heat that all of the available water was vaporized, preventing the formation of seas and lakes. As a result, life probably could not have originated or survived during this time.

▼ **Figure 24.1** What organisms lived on early Earth?

This massive bombardment ended about 4 billion years ago, setting the stage for the origin of life on our young planet. While chemical signatures of life date back to 3.8 billion years ago, the earliest direct evidence comes from fossils that are 3.5 billion years old. These fossils are of **prokaryotes**, an informal term for single-celled organisms in domains Bacteria and Archaea (see Figure 20.20). Some of the earliest prokaryotic cells lived in dense mats similar to those that resemble stepping stones in **Figure 24.1**; others lived as free-floating, individual cells. These early prokaryotes were Earth's first organisms, and their descendants had the planet to themselves for about 1.5 billion years—until eukaryotes first appeared about 1.8 billion years ago (see Concept 25.1).

Over their long evolutionary history, descendants of Earth's first cells have given rise to the vast diversity of prokaryotes living today. This diversity includes "extreme" species such as *Deinococcus radiodurans*, which can survive 3 million rads of radiation (3,000 times the dose fatal to humans). Other prokaryotes live in environments that are too cold or hot or salty for most other organisms, and some have even been found living in rocks 3.2 km (2 miles) below Earth's surface.

But prokaryotic species also thrive in more "normal" habitats—the lands and waters in which most other species are found. And within these lands and waters, prokaryotes have colonized the bodies of other organisms that live there, including humans **(Figure 24.2)**. Their ability to live in a broad range of habitats helps explain why prokaryotes are the most abundant organisms on Earth—indeed, the number of prokaryotes in a handful of fertile soil is greater than the number of people who have ever lived. In this chapter, we'll examine the origin, adaptations, diversity, and enormous ecological impact of these remarkable organisms.

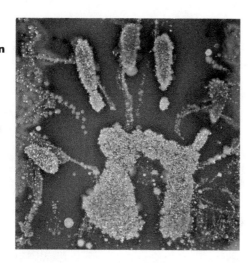

► **Figure 24.2 Bacteria that inhabit the human body.** Touching an agar gel led to the handprint-shaped growth of *Staphylococcus epidermidis*, just one of more than 1,000 species of bacteria that live on or in the human body.

CONCEPT 24.1

Conditions on early Earth made the origin of life possible

The earliest fossils are of prokaryotes that lived 3.5 billion years ago. But how did the first living cells appear? Observations and experiments in chemistry, geology, and physics have led scientists to propose one scenario that we'll examine here. They hypothesize that chemical and physical processes could have produced simple cells through a sequence of four main stages:

1. The abiotic (nonliving) synthesis of small organic molecules, such as amino acids and nitrogenous bases
2. The joining of these small molecules into macromolecules, such as proteins and nucleic acids
3. The packaging of these molecules into **protocells**, droplets with membranes that maintained an internal chemistry different from that of their surroundings
4. The origin of self-replicating molecules that eventually made inheritance possible

Though speculative, this scenario leads to predictions that can be tested in the laboratory. In this section, we'll examine some of the evidence for each stage.

Synthesis of Organic Compounds on Early Earth

As the bombardment of early Earth ended, the first atmosphere had little oxygen and was probably thick with water vapor, along with compounds released by volcanic eruptions, including nitrogen and its oxides, carbon dioxide, methane, ammonia, and hydrogen. As Earth cooled, the water vapor condensed into oceans, and much of the hydrogen escaped into space.

During the 1920s, Russian chemist A. I. Oparin and British scientist J. B. S. Haldane independently hypothesized that Earth's early atmosphere was a reducing (electron-adding) environment, in which organic compounds could have formed

from simpler molecules. The energy for this organic synthesis could have come from lightning and intense UV radiation. Haldane suggested that the early oceans were a solution of organic molecules, a "primitive soup" from which life arose.

In 1953, Stanley Miller, working under the guidance of Harold Urey at the University of Chicago, tested the Oparin-Haldane hypothesis by creating laboratory conditions comparable to those that scientists at the time thought existed on early Earth. His apparatus yielded a variety of amino acids found in organisms today, along with other organic compounds. Many laboratories have since repeated Miller's classic experiment using different recipes for the atmosphere, some of which also produced organic compounds.

However, some evidence suggests that the early atmosphere was made up primarily of nitrogen and carbon dioxide and was neither reducing nor oxidizing (electron removing). Recent Miller-Urey-type experiments using such "neutral" atmospheres have also produced organic molecules. In addition, small pockets of the early atmosphere—such as those near the openings of volcanoes—may have been reducing. Perhaps the first organic compounds formed near volcanoes or deep-sea vents, where hot water and minerals gush into the ocean from Earth's interior. In a 2008 test of the volcanic-atmosphere hypothesis, researchers used modern equipment to reanalyze molecules that Miller had saved from one of his experiments. The study found that numerous amino acids had formed under conditions that simulated a volcanic eruption (**Figure 24.3**).

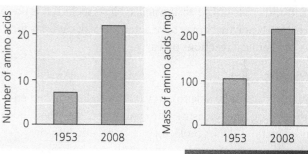

▲ **Figure 24.3 Amino acid synthesis in a simulated volcanic eruption.** In addition to his classic 1953 study, Miller also conducted an experiment simulating a volcanic eruption. In a 2008 reanalysis of those results, researchers found that far more amino acids were produced under simulated volcanic conditions than were produced in the conditions of the original 1953 experiment.

MAKE CONNECTIONS *After reviewing Concept 3.5, explain how more than 20 amino acids could have been produced in the 2008 experiment.*

Miller-Urey-type experiments show that the abiotic synthesis of organic molecules is possible under various assumptions about the composition of the early atmosphere. A second source of organic molecules may have been meteorites. For example, fragments of the Murchison meteorite, a 4.5-billion-year-old rock that fell to Australia in 1969, contain more than 80 amino acids, some in large amounts. These amino acids cannot be contaminants from Earth because they include an equal mix of two different structural forms—only one of which is typically produced or used by organisms on our planet. Recent studies have shown that the Murchison meteorite also contained other key organic molecules, including lipids, simple sugars, and nitrogenous bases such as uracil.

Abiotic Synthesis of Macromolecules

The presence of small organic molecules, such as amino acids and nitrogenous bases, is not sufficient for the emergence of life as we know it. Every cell has a vast assortment of macromolecules, including enzymes and other proteins and the nucleic acids that are essential for self-replication. Could such macromolecules have formed on early Earth? A 2009 study demonstrated that one key step, the abiotic synthesis of RNA monomers, can occur spontaneously from simple precursor molecules. In addition, by dripping solutions of amino acids or RNA nucleotides onto hot sand, clay, or rock, researchers have produced polymers of these molecules. The polymers formed spontaneously, without the help of enzymes or ribosomes. Unlike proteins, the amino acid polymers are a complex mix of linked and cross-linked amino acids. Nevertheless, it is possible that such polymers may have acted as weak catalysts for a variety of chemical reactions on early Earth.

Protocells

All organisms must be able to carry out reproduction and energy processing (metabolism). Life cannot persist without both of these functions. DNA molecules carry genetic information, including the instructions needed to replicate themselves accurately during reproduction. But the replication of DNA requires elaborate enzymatic machinery, along with an abundant supply of nucleotide building blocks that are provided by the cell's metabolism (see Chapter 13). This suggests that self-replicating molecules and a metabolism-like source of the building blocks may have appeared together in early protocells. How did that happen?

The necessary conditions may have been met in *vesicles*, fluid-filled compartments enclosed by a membrane-like structure. Recent experiments show that abiotically produced vesicles can exhibit certain properties of life, including simple reproduction and metabolism, as well as the maintenance of an internal chemical environment different from that of their surroundings.

For example, vesicles can form spontaneously when lipids or other organic molecules are added to water. When this

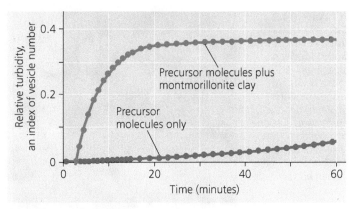

(a) **Self-assembly.** The presence of montmorillonite clay greatly increases the rate of vesicle self-assembly.

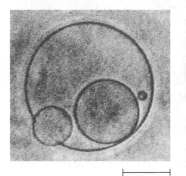

(b) **Reproduction.** Vesicles can divide on their own, as in this vesicle "giving birth" to smaller vesicles (LM).
© 2003 AAAS

(c) **Absorption of RNA.** This vesicle has incorporated montmorillonite clay particles coated with RNA (orange).

▲ **Figure 24.4 Features of abiotically produced vesicles.**

occurs, the hydrophobic molecules in the mixture organize into a bilayer similar to the lipid bilayer of a plasma membrane. Adding substances such as *montmorillonite*, a soft mineral clay produced by the weathering of volcanic ash, greatly increases the rate of vesicle self-assembly (**Figure 24.4a**). This clay, which is thought to have been common on early Earth, provides surfaces on which organic molecules become concentrated, increasing the likelihood that the molecules will react with each other and form vesicles. Abiotically produced vesicles can "reproduce" on their own (**Figure 24.4b**), and they can increase in size ("grow") without dilution of their contents. Vesicles also can absorb montmorillonite particles, including those on which RNA and other organic molecules have become attached (**Figure 24.4c**). Finally, experiments have shown that some vesicles have a selectively permeable bilayer and can perform metabolic reactions using an external source of reagents—another important prerequisite for life.

Self-Replicating RNA

The first genetic material was most likely RNA, not DNA. RNA plays a central role in protein synthesis, but it can also perform many enzyme-like catalytic functions (see Chapter 14). Such RNA catalysts are called **ribozymes**.

Some ribozymes can make complementary copies of short pieces of RNA, if they are supplied with nucleotide building blocks.

Natural selection on the molecular level has produced ribozymes capable of self-replication in the laboratory. How does this occur? Unlike double-stranded DNA, which takes the form of a uniform helix, single-stranded RNA molecules assume a variety of specific three-dimensional shapes mandated by their nucleotide sequences. In a particular environment, RNA molecules with certain nucleotide sequences replicate faster and with fewer errors than other sequences. The RNA molecule whose sequence is best suited to the surrounding environment and has the greatest ability to replicate itself will leave the most descendant molecules. Occasionally, a copying error will result in a molecule that folds into a shape that is more adept at self-replication than the ancestral sequence. Similar selection events may have occurred on early Earth. Thus, life as we know it may have been preceded by an "RNA world," in which small RNA molecules could replicate and store genetic information about the vesicles that carried them.

A vesicle with self-replicating, catalytic RNA would differ from its many neighbors that lacked such molecules. If that vesicle could grow, split, and pass its RNA molecules to its daughters, the daughters would be protocells that had some of the properties of their parent. Although the first such protocells likely carried only limited amounts of genetic information, specifying only a few properties, their inherited characteristics could have been acted on by natural selection. The most successful of the early protocells would have increased in number because they could exploit their resources effectively and pass their abilities on to subsequent generations.

Once RNA sequences that carried genetic information appeared in protocells, many additional changes would have been possible. For example, RNA could have provided the template on which DNA nucleotides were assembled. Double-stranded DNA is a more chemically stable repository for genetic information than is the more fragile RNA. DNA also can be replicated more accurately. Accurate replication was advantageous as genomes grew larger through gene duplication and other processes and as more properties of the protocells became coded in genetic information. Once DNA appeared, the stage was set for a blossoming of new forms of life—a change we see documented in the fossil record.

Fossil Evidence of Early Life

Many of the oldest known fossils are of *stromatolites*, layered rocks that form from the activities of certain prokaryotes **(Figure 24.5)**. The earliest stromatolites date to 3.5 billion years ago. For several hundred million years, all such fossils were similar in overall structure and all were from shallow marine bays; stromatolites are still found in such bays today (see Figure 23.2). By 3.1 billion years ago, stromatolites with two distinctly different morphologies had appeared, and by 2.8 billion years ago, stromatolites occurred in salty lakes as well as marine environments. Thus, early fossil stromatolites show signs of ecological and evolutionary change over time.

Ancient fossils of individual prokaryotic cells have also been discovered that are nearly as old as the oldest stromatolites. For example, a 2011 study found fossilized prokaryotic cells in 3.4-billion-year-old rocks from Australia (see Figure 24.5). In South Africa, other researchers have found 3.4-billion-year-old fossils of prokaryotes that resemble cyanobacteria, a group of photosynthetic bacteria living today. Some scientists question whether the South African fossils really were cyanobacteria, but by 2.5 billion years ago, diverse communities of cyanobacteria lived in the oceans. Cyanobacteria remained the main photosynthetic organisms for over a billion years, and they continue to be one of the most important groups of photosynthetic organisms alive today.

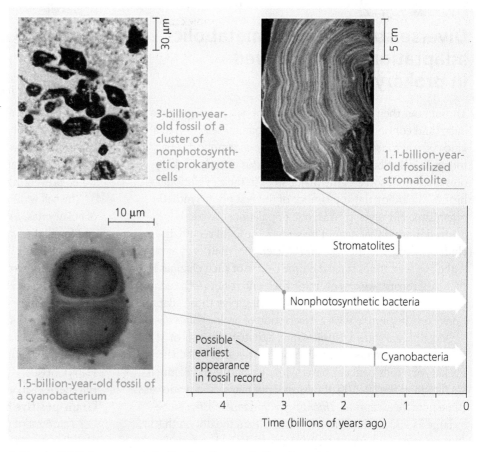

3-billion-year-old fossil of a cluster of nonphotosynthetic prokaryote cells

1.1-billion-year-old fossilized stromatolite

1.5-billion-year-old fossil of a cyanobacterium

Time (billions of years ago)

▲ **Figure 24.5 Appearance in the fossil record of early prokaryote groups.**

Early cyanobacteria began what is arguably the greatest impact organisms have ever had on our planet: the release of oxygen to Earth's atmosphere during the water-splitting step of photosynthesis. In certain of its chemical forms, oxygen attacks chemical bonds and can inhibit enzymes and damage cells. As a result, the rising concentration of atmospheric O_2 probably doomed many prokaryotic groups. Some species survived in habitats that remained anaerobic, where we find their descendants living today. As we'll see, among other survivors, diverse adaptations to the changing atmosphere evolved, including cellular respiration, which uses O_2 in the process of harvesting the energy stored in organic molecules.

CONCEPT CHECK 24.1

1. What hypothesis did Miller test in his classic experiment?
2. How would the appearance of protocells have represented a key step in the origin of life?
3. Summarize fossil evidence of early prokaryotes. Describe how these organisms altered Earth's atmosphere.
4. **MAKE CONNECTIONS** In changing from an "RNA world" to today's "DNA world," genetic information must have flowed from RNA to DNA. After reviewing Figures 14.4 and 17.7, suggest how this could have occurred. Is such a flow a common occurrence today?

For suggested answers, see Appendix A.

CONCEPT 24.2

Diverse structural and metabolic adaptations have evolved in prokaryotes

Throughout their long history, prokaryotic populations have been (and continue to be) subjected to natural selection in all kinds of environments, resulting in their enormous diversity today. As described in Concept 24.1, fossils of early prokaryotes document some of the major steps in their evolutionary history, including the appearance of the first photosynthetic organisms. However, prokaryotic populations have also evolved in ways that cannot be seen in the fossil record, including changes in the type and efficiency of their enzymes. Although we cannot trace the time course of such changes in the fossil record, we can examine their end results—the adaptations found in prokaryotes today. We'll survey those adaptations here, beginning with a description of prokaryotic cells.

Most prokaryotes are unicellular, although the cells of some species remain attached to each other after cell division. Prokaryotic cells typically have diameters of 0.5–5 μm, much smaller than the 10–100 μm diameter of many eukaryotic cells. (One notable exception, *Thiomargarita namibiensis*, can be as large as 750 μm in diameter—bigger than the dot on this i.) Prokaryotic cells have a variety of shapes (**Figure 24.6**). Finally, although they are unicellular and small, prokaryotes are well

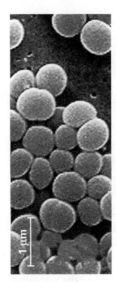 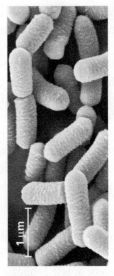 

(a) Spherical   (b) Rod-shaped   (c) Spiral

▲ **Figure 24.6 The most common shapes of prokaryotes.**
(a) Cocci (singular, *coccus*) are spherical prokaryotes. They occur singly, in pairs (diplococci), in chains of many cells (streptococci), and in clusters resembling bunches of grapes (staphylococci). **(b)** Bacilli (singular, *bacillus*) are rod-shaped prokaryotes. They are usually solitary, but in some forms the rods are arranged in chains (streptobacilli). **(c)** Spiral prokaryotes include spirilla, which range from comma-like shapes to loose coils, and spirochetes (shown here), which are corkscrew-shaped (colorized SEMs).

organized, achieving all of an organism's life functions within a single cell.

Cell-Surface Structures

A key feature of nearly all prokaryotic cells is the cell wall, which maintains cell shape, protects the cell, and prevents it from bursting in a hypotonic environment (see Concept 5.3). In a hypertonic environment, most prokaryotes lose water and shrink away from their wall (plasmolyze). Such water losses can inhibit cell reproduction. Thus, salt can be used to preserve foods because it causes food-spoiling prokaryotes to lose water, preventing them from rapidly multiplying.

The cell walls of prokaryotes differ in structure from those of eukaryotes. In eukaryotes that have cell walls, such as plants and fungi, the walls are usually made of cellulose or chitin (see Concept 3.3). In contrast, most bacterial cell walls contain **peptidoglycan**, a polymer composed of modified sugars cross-linked by short polypeptides. This molecular fabric encloses the entire bacterium and anchors other molecules that extend from its surface. Archaeal cell walls contain a variety of polysaccharides and proteins but lack peptidoglycan.

Using a staining technique developed by the Dutch scientist Hans Christian Gram, biologists can categorize many bacterial species according to cell wall composition (**Figure 24.7**). **Gram-positive** bacteria have simpler walls with a relatively large amount of peptidoglycan. **Gram-negative** bacteria have less peptidoglycan and are structurally more complex, with an outer membrane that contains lipopolysaccharides

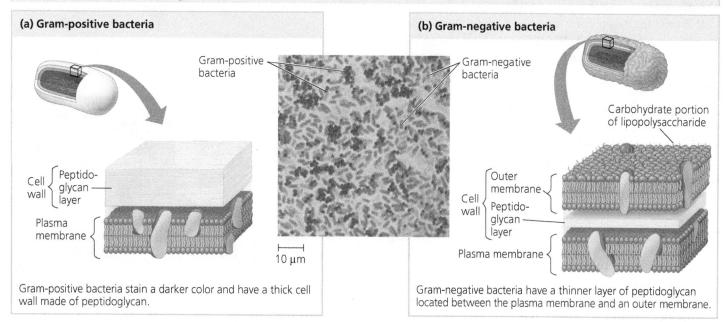

▼ **Figure 24.7 Gram staining.**

(a) Gram-positive bacteria

Gram-positive bacteria

Cell wall { Peptido-glycan layer

Plasma membrane {

10 μm

Gram-positive bacteria stain a darker color and have a thick cell wall made of peptidoglycan.

(b) Gram-negative bacteria

Gram-negative bacteria

Carbohydrate portion of lipopolysaccharide

Cell wall { Outer membrane { Peptido-glycan layer

Plasma membrane {

Gram-negative bacteria have a thinner layer of peptidoglycan located between the plasma membrane and an outer membrane.

(carbohydrates bonded to lipids). These differences in cell wall composition have medical implications. The lipid portions of the lipopolysaccharides in the walls of many gram-negative bacteria are toxic, causing fever or shock. Furthermore, the outer membrane of a gram-negative bacterium helps protect it from the body's defenses. Gram-negative bacteria also tend to be more resistant than gram-positive species to antibiotics because the outer membrane impedes entry of the drugs.

The cell wall of many prokaryotes is surrounded by a sticky layer of polysaccharide or protein. This layer is called a **capsule** if it is dense and well defined **(Figure 24.8)** or a *slime layer* if it is not as well organized. Both kinds of sticky outer layers enable prokaryotes to adhere to their substrate or to other individuals in a colony. Some capsules and slime layers protect against dehydration, and some shield pathogenic prokaryotes from attacks by their host's immune system.

Other bacteria develop resistant cells called **endospores** when they lack an essential nutrient. The original cell produces a copy of its chromosome and surrounds that copy with a tough multilayered structure, forming the endospore. Water is removed from the endospore, halting its metabolism, and the original cell then lyses, releasing the endospore. Most endospores are so durable that they can survive in boiling water; killing them requires heating lab equipment to 121°C under high pressure. In less hostile environments, endospores can remain dormant but viable for centuries, able to rehydrate and resume metabolism when their environment improves.

Finally, some prokaryotes stick to their substrate or to one another by means of hairlike appendages called **fimbriae** (singular, *fimbria*) **(Figure 24.9)**. For example, the bacterium that causes gonorrhea, *Neisseria gonorrhoeae*, uses fimbriae to fasten itself to the mucous membranes of its host. Fimbriae are usually

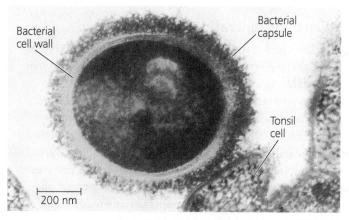

Bacterial cell wall

Bacterial capsule

Tonsil cell

200 nm

▲ **Figure 24.8 Capsule.** The polysaccharide capsule around this *Streptococcus* bacterium enables the prokaryote to attach to cells in the respiratory tract—in this colorized TEM, a tonsil cell.

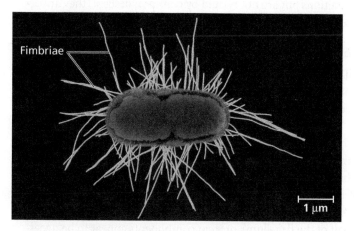

Fimbriae

1 μm

▲ **Figure 24.9 Fimbriae.** These numerous protein-containing appendages enable some prokaryotes to attach to surfaces or to other cells (colorized TEM).

shorter and more numerous than **pili** (singular, *pilus*), appendages that pull two cells together prior to DNA transfer from one cell to the other (see Figure 24.16); pili are sometimes referred to as *sex pili*.

Motility

About half of all prokaryotes are capable of **taxis**, a directed movement toward or away from a stimulus (from the Greek *taxis*, to arrange). For example, prokaryotes that exhibit *chemotaxis* change their movement pattern in response to chemicals. They may move *toward* nutrients or oxygen (positive chemotaxis) or *away from* a toxic substance (negative chemotaxis). Some species can move at velocities exceeding 50 µm/sec—up to 50 times their body length per second. For perspective, consider that a person 1.7 m tall moving that fast would be running 306 km (190 miles) per hour!

Of the various structures that enable prokaryotes to move, the most common are flagella **(Figure 24.10)**. Flagella (singular, *flagellum*) may be scattered over the entire surface of the cell or concentrated at one or both ends. Prokaryotic flagella differ greatly from eukaryotic flagella: They are one-tenth the width and typically are not covered by an extension of the plasma membrane (see Figure 4.23). The flagella of prokaryotes and eukaryotes also differ in their molecular composition and their mechanism of propulsion. Among prokaryotes, bacterial and archaeal flagella are similar in size and propulsion mechanism, but they are composed of entirely different and unrelated proteins. Overall, these structural and molecular comparisons indicate that the flagella of bacteria, archaea, and eukaryotes arose independently. Since current evidence shows that the flagella of organisms in the three domains perform similar functions but are not related by common descent, they are described as analogous, not homologous, structures.

Evolutionary Origins of Bacterial Flagella

The bacterial flagellum shown in Figure 24.10 has three main parts (the motor, hook, and filament) that are themselves composed of 42 different kinds of proteins. How could such a complex structure evolve? In fact, much evidence indicates that bacterial flagella originated as simpler structures that were modified in a stepwise fashion over time. As in the case of the human eye (see Concept 23.4), biologists asked whether a less complex version of the flagellum could still benefit its owner. Analyses of hundreds of bacterial genomes indicate that only half of the flagellum's protein components appear to be necessary for it to function; the others are inessential or not encoded in the genomes of some species. Of the 21 proteins required by

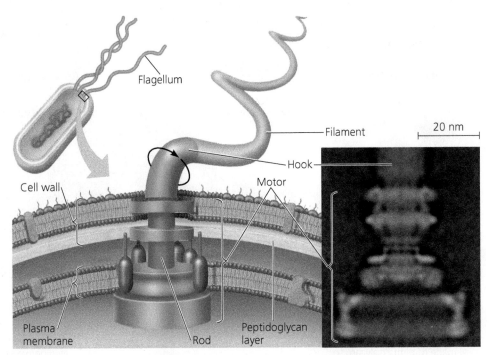

▲ **Figure 24.10 A prokaryotic flagellum.** The motor of a prokaryotic flagellum consists of a system of rings embedded in the cell wall and plasma membrane (TEM). ATP-driven pumps in the membrane transport protons out of the cell. The diffusion of protons back into the cell provides the force that turns a curved hook and thereby causes the attached filament to rotate and propel the cell. (This diagram shows flagellar structures characteristic of gram-negative bacteria.)

all species studied to date, 19 are modified versions of proteins that perform other tasks in bacteria. For example, a set of 10 proteins in the motor are homologous to 10 similar proteins in a secretory system found in bacteria. (A secretory system is a protein complex that enables a cell to secrete certain macromolecules.) Two other proteins in the motor are homologous to proteins that function in ion transport. The proteins that comprise the rod, hook, and filament are all related to each other and are descended from an ancestral protein that formed a pilus-like tube. These findings suggest that the bacterial flagellum evolved as other proteins were added to an ancestral secretory system. This is an example of *exaptation*, the process in which existing structures take on new functions through descent with modification.

Internal Organization and DNA

The cells of prokaryotes are simpler than those of eukaryotes in both their internal structure and the physical arrangement of their DNA (see Figure 4.4). Prokaryotic cells lack the complex compartmentalization associated with the membrane-enclosed organelles found in eukaryotic cells. However, some prokaryotic cells do have specialized membranes that perform metabolic functions **(Figure 24.11)**. These membranes are usually infoldings of the plasma membrane. Recent discoveries also indicate that some prokaryotes can store metabolic by-products in simple compartments that are made out of proteins (and that do not have a membrane).

The genome of a prokaryote is structurally different from a eukaryotic genome and in most cases has considerably less

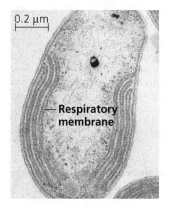

0.2 μm

Respiratory membrane

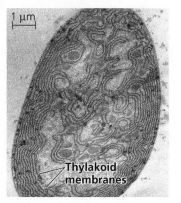

1 μm

Thylakoid membranes

(a) Aerobic prokaryote   **(b) Photosynthetic prokaryote**

▲ **Figure 24.11 Specialized membranes of prokaryotes.** **(a)** Infoldings of the plasma membrane, reminiscent of the cristae of mitochondria, function in cellular respiration in some aerobic prokaryotes (TEM). **(b)** Photosynthetic prokaryotes called cyanobacteria have thylakoid membranes, much like those in chloroplasts (TEM).

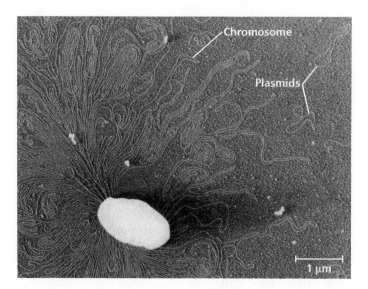

Chromosome

Plasmids

1 μm

▲ **Figure 24.12 A prokaryotic chromosome and plasmids.** The thin, tangled loops surrounding this ruptured *E. coli* cell are parts of the cell's large, circular chromosome (colorized TEM). Three of the cell's plasmids, the much smaller rings of DNA, are also shown.

DNA. Prokaryotes generally have circular chromosomes **(Figure 24.12)**, whereas eukaryotes have linear chromosomes. In addition, in prokaryotes the chromosome is associated with many fewer proteins than are the chromosomes of eukaryotes. Also unlike eukaryotes, prokaryotes lack a nucleus; their chromosome is located in the **nucleoid**, a region of cytoplasm that is not enclosed by a membrane. In addition to its single chromosome, a typical prokaryotic cell may also have much smaller rings of independently replicating DNA molecules called **plasmids** (see Figure 24.12), most carrying only a few genes.

Although DNA replication, transcription, and translation are fundamentally similar processes in prokaryotes and eukaryotes, some of the details differ between the two groups (see Chapters 13 and 14). For example, prokaryotic ribosomes are slightly smaller than eukaryotic ribosomes and differ in their protein and RNA content. These differences allow certain antibiotics, such as erythromycin and tetracycline, to bind to ribosomes and block protein synthesis in prokaryotes but not in eukaryotes. As a result, people can use these antibiotics to kill or inhibit the growth of bacteria without harming themselves.

Nutritional and Metabolic Adaptations

Like all organisms, prokaryotes can be categorized by how they obtain energy and the carbon used in building organic molecules. Every type of nutrition observed in eukaryotes is represented among prokaryotes, along with some nutritional modes unique to prokaryotes. In fact, prokaryotes have an astounding range of metabolic adaptations, much broader than that found in eukaryotes.

Organisms that obtain energy from light are called *phototrophs*, and those that obtain energy from chemicals are called *chemotrophs*. Organisms that need only CO_2 or related compounds as a carbon source are called *autotrophs*. In contrast, *heterotrophs* require at least one organic nutrient, such as glucose, to make other organic compounds. Combining possible energy sources and carbon sources results in four major modes of nutrition, summarized in **Table 24.1**.

The Role of Oxygen in Metabolism

Prokaryotic metabolism also varies with respect to oxygen (O_2). *Obligate aerobes* must use O_2 for cellular respiration (see Chapter 7) and cannot grow without it. *Obligate anaerobes*, on the other hand, are poisoned by O_2. Some obligate anaerobes live exclusively by fermentation; others extract chemical energy by **anaerobic respiration**, in which substances other than O_2, such

Table 24.1 **Major Nutritional Modes**			
Mode	**Energy Source**	**Carbon Source**	**Types of Organisms**
AUTOTROPH			
Photoautotroph	Light	CO_2, HCO_3^-, or related compound	Photosynthetic prokaryotes (for example, cyanobacteria); plants; certain protists (for example, algae)
Chemoautotroph	Inorganic chemicals (such as H_2S, NH_3, or Fe^{2+})	CO_2, HCO_3^-, or related compound	Unique to certain prokaryotes (for example, *Sulfolobus*)
HETEROTROPH			
Photoheterotroph	Light	Organic compounds	Unique to certain aquatic and salt-loving prokaryotes (for example, *Rhodobacter*, *Chloroflexus*)
Chemoheterotroph	Organic compounds	Organic compounds	Many prokaryotes (for example, *Clostridium*) and protists; fungi; animals; some plants

as nitrate ions (NO_3^-) or sulfate ions (SO_4^{2-}), accept electrons at the "downhill" end of electron transport chains. *Facultative anaerobes* use O_2 if it is present but can also carry out fermentation or anaerobic respiration in an anaerobic environment.

Nitrogen Metabolism

Nitrogen is essential for the production of amino acids and nucleic acids in all organisms. Whereas eukaryotes can obtain nitrogen from only a limited group of nitrogen compounds, prokaryotes can metabolize nitrogen in a wide variety of forms. For example, some cyanobacteria and some methanogens (a group of archaea) convert atmospheric nitrogen (N_2) to ammonia (NH_3), a process called **nitrogen fixation**. The cells can then incorporate this "fixed" nitrogen into amino acids and other organic molecules. In terms of their nutrition, nitrogen-fixing cyanobacteria are some of the most self-sufficient organisms, since they need only light, CO_2, N_2, water, and some minerals to grow.

Nitrogen fixation by prokaryotes has a large impact on other organisms. For example, it can increase the nitrogen available to plants, which cannot use atmospheric nitrogen but can use the nitrogen compounds that the prokaryotes produce from ammonia. Chapter 42 discusses this and other essential roles of prokaryotes in the nitrogen cycles of ecosystems.

Metabolic Cooperation

Cooperation between prokaryotic cells allows them to use environmental resources they could not use as individual cells. In some cases, this cooperation takes place between specialized cells of a filament. For instance, the cyanobacterium *Anabaena* has genes that encode proteins for photosynthesis and for nitrogen fixation, but a single cell cannot carry out both processes at the same time. The reason is that photosynthesis produces O_2, which inactivates the enzymes involved in nitrogen fixation. Instead of living as isolated cells, *Anabaena* forms filamentous chains **(Figure 24.13)**. Most cells in a filament carry out only photosynthesis, while a few specialized cells called **heterocysts** (sometimes called *heterocytes*) carry out only nitrogen fixation. Each heterocyst is surrounded by a thickened cell wall that restricts entry of O_2 produced by neighboring photosynthetic cells. Intercellular connections allow heterocysts to transport fixed nitrogen to neighboring cells and to receive carbohydrates.

Metabolic cooperation between different prokaryotic species often occurs in surface-coating colonies known as **biofilms**. Cells in a biofilm secrete signaling molecules that recruit nearby cells, causing the colonies to grow. The cells also produce polysaccharides and proteins that stick the cells to the substrate and to one another. Channels in the biofilm allow nutrients to reach cells in the interior and wastes to be expelled. Biofilms are common in nature, but they can cause problems by contaminating industrial products and medical equipment and contributing to tooth decay and more serious health problems. Altogether, damage caused by biofilms costs billions of dollars annually.

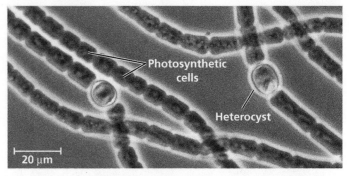

▲ **Figure 24.13 Metabolic cooperation in a prokaryote.** In the filamentous cyanobacterium *Anabaena*, cells called heterocysts fix nitrogen, while the other cells carry out photosynthesis (LM). *Anabaena* is found in many freshwater lakes.

Reproduction

Many prokaryotes can reproduce quickly in favorable environments. By *binary fission* (see Figure 9.12), a single prokaryotic cell divides into 2 cells, which then divide into 4, 8, 16, and so on. Under optimal conditions, many prokaryotes can divide every 1–3 hours; some species can produce a new generation in only 20 minutes. At this rate, a single prokaryotic cell could give rise to a colony outweighing Earth in only two days!

In reality, of course, this does not occur. The cells eventually exhaust their nutrient supply, poison themselves with metabolic wastes, face competition from other microorganisms, or are consumed by other organisms. Still, the fact that many prokaryotic species can divide after short periods of time draws attention to three key features of their biology: *They are small, they reproduce by binary fission, and they often have short generation times.* As a result, prokaryotic populations can consist of many trillions of individuals—far more than populations of multicellular eukaryotes, such as plants or animals.

Adaptations of Prokaryotes: *A Summary*

Let's step back and examine the big picture of the adaptations that have arisen in prokaryotic populations. We've described some of their key structural features, such as cell walls, endospores, fimbriae, and flagella. But prokaryotic cells are much simpler structurally than are eukaryotic cells—they do not vary as much in shape or size, and they lack the complex compartmentalization associated with the membrane-enclosed organelles of eukaryotic cells. Indeed, the ongoing success of prokaryotes is not primarily a story of structural diversification; rather, their success is an extraordinary example of physiological and metabolic diversification. As we've seen, prokaryotes thrive under a wide variety of physical and chemical conditions, and they have an astonishing range of metabolic adaptations that allow them to obtain energy and carbon in these environments.

Overall, the metabolic diversification of prokaryotes can be viewed as a first great wave of adaptive radiation in the evolutionary history of life. Bearing that broad perspective in mind, we turn now to the genetic diversity that has enabled the adaptations found in prokaryotic populations.

1. Contrast the cellular and DNA structures of prokaryotes and eukaryotes.
2. Distinguish between the four major modes of nutrition, noting which are unique to prokaryotes.
3. **MAKE CONNECTIONS** Suggest a hypothesis to explain why the thylakoid membranes of chloroplasts resemble those of cyanobacteria. Refer to Figures 4.16 and 20.20.
4. **WHAT IF?** Describe what you might eat for a typical meal if humans, like cyanobacteria, could fix nitrogen.

For suggested answers, see Appendix A.

 24.3

Rapid reproduction, mutation, and genetic recombination promote genetic diversity in prokaryotes

As we saw in Unit Three, evolution cannot occur without genetic variation. The evolutionary changes seen in the prokaryotic fossil record and the diverse adaptations found in prokaryotes living today suggest that their populations must have considerable genetic variation—and they do. In this section, we'll examine three factors that give rise to high levels of genetic diversity in prokaryotes: rapid reproduction, mutation, and genetic recombination.

Rapid Reproduction and Mutation

The generation of a novel allele by a new mutation is rare for any particular gene. Moreover, since prokaryotes do not reproduce sexually, at first glance their extensive genetic variation may seem puzzling. But in many species, this variation can result from rapid reproduction and mutation.

Consider the bacterium *Escherichia coli* as it reproduces by binary fission in a human intestine, one of its natural environments. After repeated rounds of division, most of the offspring cells are genetically identical to the original parent cell. However, if errors occur during DNA replication, some of the offspring cells may differ genetically. The probability of such a mutation occurring in a given *E. coli* gene is about one in 10 million (1×10^{-7}) per cell division. But among the 2×10^{10} new *E. coli* cells that arise each day in a person's intestine, there will be approximately $(2 \times 10^{10}) \times (1 \times 10^{-7}) =$ 2,000 bacteria that have a mutation in that gene. Thus, the total number of mutations when all 4,300 *E. coli* genes are considered is about $4,300 \times 2,000 = 9$ million per day per human host.

The key point is that new mutations, though rare on a per gene basis, can increase genetic diversity quickly in species with short generation times and large populations. This diversity, in turn, can lead to rapid evolution: Individuals that are

▼ **Figure 24.14** **Inquiry**

Can prokaryotes evolve rapidly in response to environmental change?

Experiment Vaughn Cooper and Richard Lenski tested the ability of *E. coli* populations to adapt to a new environment. They established 12 populations, each founded by a single cell from an *E. coli* strain, and followed these populations for 20,000 generations (3,000 days). To maintain a continual supply of resources, each day the researchers performed a *serial transfer*: They transferred 0.1 mL of each population to a new tube containing 9.9 mL of fresh growth medium. The growth medium used throughout the experiment provided a challenging environment that contained only low levels of glucose and other resources needed for growth.

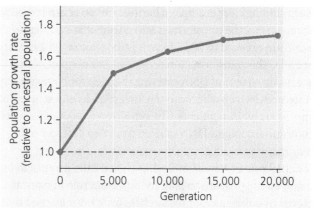

Samples were periodically removed from the 12 populations and grown in competition with the common ancestral strain in the experimental (low-glucose) environment.

Results The fitness of the experimental populations, as measured by the growth rate of each population, increased rapidly for the first 5,000 generations (2 years) and more slowly for the next 15,000 generations. The graph shows the averages for the 12 populations.

© 2000 Macmillan Publishers, Ltd.

Conclusion Populations of *E. coli* continued to accumulate beneficial mutations for 20,000 generations in their new environment, resulting in the rapid evolution of increased population growth rates.

Source V. S. Cooper and R. E. Lenski, The population genetics of ecological specialization in evolving *Escherichia coli* populations, *Nature* 407:736–739 (2000).

WHAT IF? Suggest possible functions of the genes whose sequence or expression was altered as the experimental populations evolved in the low-glucose environment.

genetically better equipped for their environment tend to survive and reproduce at higher rates than other individuals **(Figure 24.14)**. The ability of prokaryotes to adapt rapidly to new conditions highlights the point that although the structure of their cells is simpler than that of eukaryotic cells, prokaryotes are not "primitive" or "inferior" in an evolutionary sense. They are, in fact, highly evolved: For over 3.5 billion years, prokaryotic populations have responded successfully to many different types of environmental challenges.

Genetic Recombination

Although new mutations are a major source of variation in prokaryotic populations, additional diversity arises from *genetic recombination*, the combining of DNA from two sources. In eukaryotes, the sexual processes of meiosis and fertilization combine DNA from two individuals in a single zygote. But meiosis and fertilization do not occur in prokaryotes. Instead, three other mechanisms—transformation, transduction, and conjugation—can bring together prokaryotic DNA from different individuals (that is, different cells). When the individuals are members of different species, this movement of genes from one organism to another is called *horizontal gene transfer*. Although scientists have found evidence that each of these mechanisms can transfer DNA within and between species in both domain Bacteria and domain Archaea, to date most of our knowledge comes from research on bacteria.

Transformation and Transduction

In **transformation**, the genotype and possibly phenotype of a prokaryotic cell are altered by the uptake of foreign DNA from its surroundings. For example, a harmless strain of *Streptococcus pneumoniae* can be transformed into pneumonia-causing cells if the cells are exposed to DNA from a pathogenic strain (see Concept 13.1). This transformation occurs when a nonpathogenic cell takes up a piece of DNA carrying the allele for pathogenicity and replaces its own allele with the foreign allele, an exchange of homologous DNA segments. The cell is now a recombinant: Its chromosome contains DNA derived from two different cells.

For many years after transformation was discovered in laboratory cultures, most biologists thought the process to be too rare and haphazard to play an important role in natural bacterial populations. But researchers have since learned that many bacteria have cell-surface proteins that recognize DNA from closely related species and transport it into the cell. Once inside the cell, the foreign DNA can be incorporated into the genome by homologous DNA exchange.

In **transduction**, phages (from "bacteriophages," the viruses that infect bacteria) carry prokaryotic genes from one host cell to another. In most cases, transduction results from accidents that occur during the phage replicative cycle (**Figure 24.15**). A virus that carries prokaryotic DNA may not be able to replicate because it lacks some or all of its own genetic material. However, the virus can attach to another prokaryotic cell (a recipient) and inject prokaryotic DNA acquired from the first cell (the donor). If some of this DNA is then incorporated into the recipient cell's chromosome by crossing over, a recombinant cell is formed.

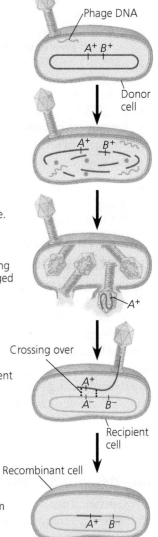

① A phage infects a bacterial cell that carries the A^+ and B^+ alleles on its chromosome (brown). This bacterium will be the "donor" cell.

② The phage DNA is replicated, and the cell makes many copies of the proteins encoded by its genes. Meanwhile, certain phage proteins halt the synthesis of proteins encoded by the host cell's DNA, and the host cell's DNA may be fragmented, as shown here.

③ As new phage particles assemble, a fragment of bacterial DNA carrying the A^+ allele happens to be packaged in a phage capsid.

④ The phage carrying the A^+ allele from the donor cell infects a recipient cell with alleles A^- and B^-. Crossing over at two sites (dotted lines) allows donor DNA (brown) to be incorporated into recipient DNA (green).

⑤ The genotype of the resulting recombinant cell (A^+B^-) differs from the genotypes of both the donor (A^+B^+) and the recipient (A^-B^-).

▲ **Figure 24.15 Transduction.** Phages may carry pieces of a bacterial chromosome from one cell (the donor) to another (the recipient). If crossing over occurs after the transfer, genes from the donor may be incorporated into the recipient's genome.

? *Under what circumstances would a transduction event result in horizontal gene transfer?*

Conjugation and Plasmids

In a process called **conjugation**, DNA is transferred between two prokaryotic cells (usually of the same species) that are temporarily joined. In bacteria, the DNA transfer is always one-way: One cell donates the DNA, and the other receives it. The best-understood mechanism is that used by *E. coli*, and we'll focus on this organism for the rest of this section.

In *E. coli*, a pilus of the donor cell attaches to the recipient (**Figure 24.16**). The pilus then retracts, pulling the two cells together, much like a grappling hook. The next step is thought to be the formation of a temporary "mating bridge" between the two cells, through which the donor may transfer DNA to the recipient. However, the mechanism by which this transfer oc-

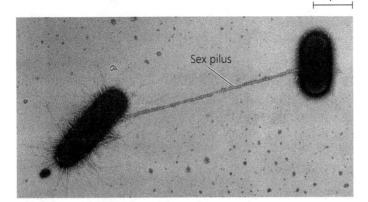

1 µm

▲ **Figure 24.16 Bacterial conjugation.** The *E. coli* donor cell (left) extends a pilus that attaches to a recipient cell, a key first step in the transfer of DNA. The pilus is a flexible tube of protein subunits (TEM).

curs is an unsettled issue; indeed, recent evidence suggests that DNA may pass directly through the pilus, which is hollow.

The F Factor However the transfer of DNA takes place, the ability to form pili and donate DNA during conjugation results from the presence of a particular piece of DNA called the **F factor** (F for fertility). The F factor of *E. coli* consists of about 25 genes, most required for the production of pili. The F factor can exist either as a plasmid or as a segment of DNA within the bacterial chromosome.

The F factor in its plasmid form is called the **F plasmid**. Cells containing the F plasmid, designated F^+ cells, function as DNA donors during conjugation. Cells lacking the F factor, designated F^-, function as DNA recipients during conjugation. The F^+ condition is transferable in the sense that an F^+ cell converts an F^- cell to F^+ if a copy of the entire F plasmid is transferred **(Figure 24.17)**. In any case, as long as some of

the F plasmid's DNA is transferred successfully to the recipient cell, that cell is now a recombinant cell.

A donor cell's F factor can also be integrated into the chromosome. In this case, chromosomal genes can be transferred to a recipient cell during conjugation. When this occurs, homologous regions of the donor and recipient chromosomes may align, allowing segments of their DNA to be exchanged. As a result, the recipient cell becomes a recombinant bacterium that has genes derived from the circular chromosomes of two different cells—a new genetic variant on which evolution can act.

R Plasmids and Antibiotic Resistance During the 1950s in Japan, physicians started noticing that some hospital patients with bacterial dysentery, which produces severe diarrhea, did not respond to antibiotics that had been effective in the past. Apparently, resistance to these antibiotics had evolved in some strains of *Shigella*, the bacterium that causes the disease.

Eventually, researchers began to identify the specific genes that confer antibiotic resistance in *Shigella* and other pathogenic bacteria. Sometimes, mutation in a chromosomal gene of the pathogen can confer resistance. For example, a mutation in one gene may make it less likely that the pathogen will transport a particular antibiotic into its cell. Mutation in a different gene may alter the intracellular target protein for an antibiotic molecule, reducing its inhibitory effect. In other cases, bacteria have "resistance genes," which code for enzymes that specifically destroy or otherwise hinder the effectiveness of certain antibiotics, such as tetracycline or ampicillin. Such resistance genes are often carried by plasmids known as **R plasmids** (R for resistance).

Exposing a bacterial population to a specific antibiotic will kill antibiotic-sensitive bacteria but not those that happen to have R plasmids with genes that counter the antibiotic. Under these circumstances, we would predict that natural selection would cause the fraction of the bacterial population carrying

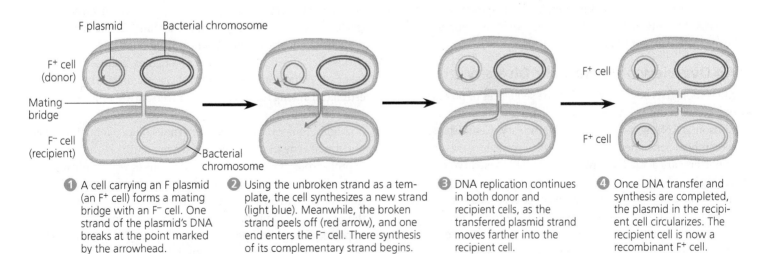

① A cell carrying an F plasmid (an F^+ cell) forms a mating bridge with an F^- cell. One strand of the plasmid's DNA breaks at the point marked by the arrowhead.

② Using the unbroken strand as a template, the cell synthesizes a new strand (light blue). Meanwhile, the broken strand peels off (red arrow), and one end enters the F^- cell. There synthesis of its complementary strand begins.

③ DNA replication continues in both donor and recipient cells, as the transferred plasmid strand moves farther into the recipient cell.

④ Once DNA transfer and synthesis are completed, the plasmid in the recipient cell circularizes. The recipient cell is now a recombinant F^+ cell.

▲ **Figure 24.17 Conjugation and transfer of an F plasmid, resulting in recombination.** The DNA replication that accompanies the transfer of an F plasmid is called *rolling circle replication*. In effect, the intact circular DNA strand from the donor cell's F plasmid "rolls" as its other strand peels off and a new complementary strand is synthesized.

genes for antibiotic resistance to increase, and that is exactly what happens. The medical consequences are also predictable: Resistant strains of pathogens are becoming more common, making the treatment of certain bacterial infections more difficult. The problem is compounded by the fact that many R plasmids, like F plasmids, have genes that encode pili and enable DNA transfer from one bacterial cell to another by conjugation. Making the problem still worse, some R plasmids carry as many as ten genes for resistance to that many antibiotics.

CONCEPT CHECK 24.3

1. Although rare on a per gene basis, new mutations can add considerable genetic variation to prokaryotic populations in each generation. Explain how this occurs.
2. Distinguish between the three mechanisms of transferring DNA from one bacterial cell to another.
3. In a rapidly changing environment, which bacterial population would likely be more successful, one that includes individuals capable of conjugation or one that does not? Explain.
4. **WHAT IF?** If a nonpathogenic bacterium were to acquire resistance to antibiotics, could this strain pose a health risk to people? Explain. In general, how does DNA transfer among bacteria affect the spread of resistance genes?

For suggested answers, see Appendix A.

CONCEPT 24.4

Prokaryotes have radiated into a diverse set of lineages

Since their origin 3.5 billion years ago, prokaryotic populations have radiated extensively as they acquired diverse structural and metabolic adaptations. Collectively, these adaptations have enabled prokaryotes to inhabit every environment known to support life; if there are organisms in a particular place, some of those organisms are prokaryotes. Yet despite their obvious success, it is only in recent decades that we have begun to uncover the full extent of prokaryotic diversity.

An Overview of Prokaryotic Diversity

Microbiologists began comparing the sequences of prokaryotic genes in the 1970s. For example, using small-subunit ribosomal RNA as a marker for evolutionary relationships, researchers concluded that many prokaryotes once classified as bacteria are actually more closely related to eukaryotes and belong in a domain of their own: Archaea. Microbiologists have since analyzed larger amounts of genetic data—including more than 1,700 entire genomes—and have concluded that a few traditional taxonomic groups, such as cyanobacteria, are monophyletic. However, other traditional groups, such as gram-negative bacteria, are scattered throughout several lineages. **Figure 24.18** shows one phylogenetic hypothesis for some of the major taxa of prokaryotes based on molecular systematics.

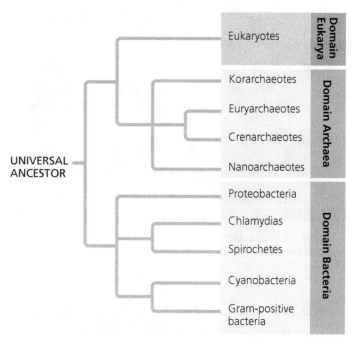

▲ **Figure 24.18 A simplified phylogeny of prokaryotes.**
This phylogenetic tree based on molecular data shows one of several debated hypotheses of the relationships between the major prokaryotic groups discussed in this chapter. Within Archaea, the placement of the korarchaeotes and nanoarchaeotes remains unclear.

? *Which domain is the sister group of Archaea?*

One lesson from studying prokaryotic phylogeny is that the genetic diversity of prokaryotes is immense. When researchers began to sequence the genes of prokaryotes, they could investigate only the small fraction of species that could be cultured in the laboratory. In the 1980s, researchers began using the polymerase chain reaction (PCR; see Figure 13.25) to analyze the genes of prokaryotes collected from the environment (such as from soil or water samples). Such "genetic prospecting" is now widely used; in fact, today entire prokaryotic genomes can be obtained from environmental samples using *metagenomics* (see Concept 18.1). Each year, these techniques add new branches to the tree of life. While only about 9,800 prokaryotic species have been assigned scientific names, a single handful of soil could contain 10,000 prokaryotic species by some estimates. Taking full stock of this diversity will require many years of research.

Another important lesson from molecular systematics is that horizontal gene transfer has played a major role in the evolution of prokaryotes. Over hundreds of millions of years, prokaryotes have acquired genes from even distantly related species, and they continue to do so today. As a result, significant portions of the genomes of many prokaryotes are actually mosaics of genes imported from other species. For example, a 2011 study of 329 sequenced bacterial genomes found that an average of 75% of the genes in each genome had been transferred horizontally at some point in their evolutionary history. As discussed in Chapter 20, such gene transfers can make it difficult to determine phylogenetic relationships. Still, it is clear that for billions of years, the prokaryotes have evolved in two separate lineages, the bacteria and the archaea (see Figure 24.18).

Bacteria

 Bacteria include the vast majority of prokaryotic species familiar to most people, from the pathogenic species that cause strep throat and tuberculosis to the beneficial species used to make Swiss cheese and yogurt. Every major mode of nutrition and metabolism is represented among bacteria, and even a small taxonomic group of bacteria may contain species exhibiting many different nutritional modes. As we'll see, the diverse nutritional and metabolic capabilities of bacteria—and archaea—are behind the great impact these organisms have on Earth and its life. **Figure 24.19**, on the next two pages, provides a closer look at several major groups of bacteria.

Archaea

 Archaea share certain traits with bacteria and other traits with eukaryotes **(Table 24.2)**. However, archaea also have many unique characteristics, as we would expect in a taxon that has followed a separate evolutionary path for so long.

The first prokaryotes assigned to domain Archaea live in environments so extreme that few other organisms can survive there. Such organisms are called **extremophiles**, meaning "lovers" of extreme conditions (from the Greek *philos*, lover), and include extreme halophiles and extreme thermophiles.

Extreme halophiles (from the Greek *halo*, salt) live in highly saline environments, such as the Great Salt Lake and the Dead Sea. Some species merely tolerate salinity, while others require an environment that is several times saltier than seawater (which has a salinity of 3.5%). For example, the proteins and cell walls of archaea in the genus *Halobacterium* have unusual features that improve function in extremely salty environments but render these organisms incapable of survival if the salinity drops below 9%.

Extreme thermophiles (from the Greek *thermos*, hot) thrive in very hot environments **(Figure 24.20)**. For example, archaea in the genus *Sulfolobus* live in sulfur-rich volcanic springs as hot as 90°C. At temperatures this high, the cells of most organisms die because their DNA does not remain in a double helix and many of their proteins denature. *Sulfolobus* and other extreme thermophiles avoid this fate because they have structural and biochemical adaptations that make their DNA and proteins stable at high temperatures. One extreme thermophile that lives near deep-sea hot springs called *hydrothermal vents* is informally known as "strain 121," since it can reproduce even at 121°C. Another extreme thermophile, *Pyrococcus furiosus*, is used in biotechnology as a source of DNA polymerase for the PCR technique.

Many other archaea live in more moderate environments. Consider the **methanogens**, archaea that release methane as

Table 24.2 **A Comparison of the Three Domains of Life**			
CHARACTERISTIC	**DOMAIN**		
	Bacteria	Archaea	Eukarya
Nuclear envelope	Absent	Absent	Present
Membrane-enclosed organelles	Absent	Absent	Present
Peptidoglycan in cell wall	Present	Absent	Absent
Membrane lipids	Unbranched hydrocarbons	Some branched hydrocarbons	Unbranched hydrocarbons
RNA polymerase	One kind	Several kinds	Several kinds
Initiator amino acid for protein synthesis	Formyl-methionine	Methionine	Methionine
Introns in genes	Very rare	Present in some genes	Present in many genes
Response to the antibiotics streptomycin and chloramphenicol	Growth usually inhibited	Growth not inhibited	Growth not inhibited
Histones associated with DNA	Absent	Present in some species	Present
Circular chromosome	Present	Present	Absent
Growth at temperatures > 100°C	No	Some species	No

▲ **Figure 24.20 Extreme thermophiles.** Orange and yellow colonies of thermophilic prokaryotes grow in the hot water of Yellowstone National Park's Grand Prismatic Spring.

MAKE CONNECTIONS *Review the discussion of enzymes in Concept 6.4. How might the enzymes of thermophiles differ from those of other organisms?*

Proteobacteria

This large and diverse clade of gram-negative bacteria includes photo-autotrophs, chemoautotrophs, and heterotrophs. Some proteobacteria are anaerobic, while others are aerobic. Molecular systematists currently recognize five subgroups of proteobacteria; the phylogenetic tree at right shows their relationships based on molecular data.

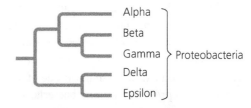

Subgroup: Alpha Proteobacteria

Many of the species in this subgroup are closely associated with eukaryotic hosts. For example, *Rhizobium* species live in nodules within the roots of legumes (plants of the pea/bean family), where the bacteria convert atmospheric N_2 to compounds the host plant can use to make proteins. Species in the genus *Agrobacterium* produce tumors in plants; genetic engineers use these bacteria to carry foreign DNA into the genomes of crop plants. Scientists hypothesize that mitochondria evolved from aerobic alpha proteobacteria through endosymbiosis.

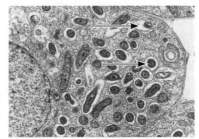

Rhizobium (arrows) inside a root cell of a legume (TEM)

Subgroup: Beta Proteobacteria

This nutritionally diverse subgroup includes *Nitrosomonas*, a genus of soil bacteria that play an important role in nitrogen recycling by oxidizing ammonium (NH_4^+), producing nitrite (NO_2^-) as a waste product.

Nitrosomonas (colorized TEM)

Subgroup: Gamma Proteobacteria

This subgroup's autotrophic members include sulfur bacteria, such as *Thiomargarita namibiensis*, which obtain energy by oxidizing H_2S, producing sulfur as a waste product (the small globules in the photograph at right). Some heterotrophic gamma proteobacteria are pathogens; for example, *Legionella* causes Legionnaires' disease, *Salmonella* is responsible for some cases of food poisoning, and *Vibrio cholerae* causes cholera. *Escherichia coli*, a common resident of the intestines of humans and other mammals, normally is not pathogenic.

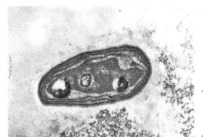

Thiomargarita namibiensis containing sulfur wastes (LM)

Subgroup: Delta Proteobacteria

This subgroup includes the slime-secreting myxobacteria. When the soil dries out or food is scarce, the cells congregate into a fruiting body that releases resistant "myxospores." These cells found new colonies in favorable environments. Another group of delta proteobacteria, the bdellovibrios, attack other bacteria, charging at up to 100 µm/sec (comparable to a human running 240 km/hr). The attack begins when a bdellovibrio attaches to specific molecules found on the outer covering of some bacterial species. The bdellovibrio then drills into its prey by using digestive enzymes and spinning at 100 revolutions per second.

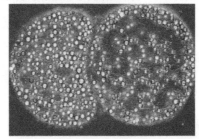

Fruiting bodies of *Chondromyces crocatus,* a myxobacterium (SEM)

Subgroup: Epsilon Proteobacteria

Most species in this subgroup are pathogenic to humans or other animals. Epsilon proteobacteria include *Campylobacter*, which causes blood poisoning and intestinal inflammation, and *Helicobacter pylori*, which causes stomach ulcers.

Helicobacter pylori (colorized TEM)

Chlamydias

These parasites can survive only within animal cells, depending on their hosts for resources as basic as ATP. The gram-negative walls of chlamydias are unusual in that they lack peptidoglycan. One species, *Chlamydia trachomatis,* is the most common cause of blindness in the world and also causes nongonococcal urethritis, the most common sexually transmitted disease in the United States.

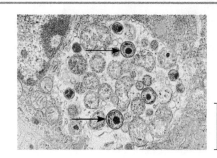

Chlamydia (arrows) inside an animal cell (colorized TEM)

2.5 μm

Spirochetes

These helical gram-negative heterotrophs spiral through their environment by means of rotating, internal, flagellum-like filaments. Many spirochetes are free-living, but others are notorious pathogenic parasites: *Treponema pallidum* causes syphilis, and *Borrelia burgdorferi* causes Lyme disease.

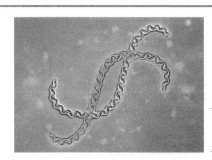

Leptospira, a spirochete (colorized TEM)

5 μm

Cyanobacteria

These gram-negative photoautotrophs are the only prokaryotes with plantlike, oxygen-generating photosynthesis. (In fact, chloroplasts likely evolved from an endosymbiotic cyanobacterium.) Both solitary and filamentous cyanobacteria are abundant components of freshwater and marine *phytoplankton*, the collection of photosynthetic organisms that drift near the water's surface. Some filaments have cells specialized for nitrogen fixation, the process that incorporates atmospheric N_2 into inorganic compounds that can be used in the synthesis of amino acids and other organic molecules.

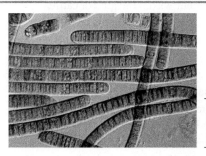

Oscillatoria, a filamentous cyanobacterium

40 μm

Gram-Positive Bacteria

Gram-positive bacteria rival the proteobacteria in diversity. Species in one subgroup, the actinomycetes (from the Greek *mykes,* fungus, for which these bacteria were once mistaken), form colonies containing branched chains of cells. Two species of actinomycetes cause tuberculosis and leprosy. However, most actinomycetes are free-living species that help decompose the organic matter in soil; their secretions are partly responsible for the "earthy" odor of rich soil. Soil-dwelling species in the genus *Streptomyces* (top) are cultured by pharmaceutical companies as a source of many antibiotics, including streptomycin.

Gram-positive bacteria include many solitary species, such as *Bacillus anthracis*, which causes anthrax, and *Clostridium botulinum*, which causes botulism. The various species of *Staphylococcus* and *Streptococcus* are also gram-positive bacteria.

Mycoplasmas (bottom) are the only bacteria known to lack cell walls. They are also the tiniest known cells, with diameters as small as 0.1 μm, only about five times as large as a ribosome. Mycoplasmas have small genomes—*Mycoplasma genitalium* has only 517 genes, for example. Many mycoplasmas are free-living soil bacteria, but others are pathogens.

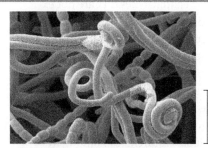

Streptomyces, the source of many antibiotics (SEM)

5 μm

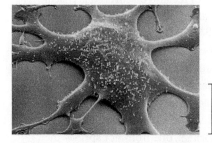

Hundreds of mycoplasmas covering a human fibroblast cell (colorized SEM)

2 μm

▲ **Figure 24.21 A highly thermophilic methanogen.** The archaean *Methanopyrus kandleri* (inset) lives in the extreme heat of "black smoker" hydrothermal vents on the ocean floor.

a by-product of their unique ways of obtaining energy. Many methanogens use CO_2 to oxidize H_2, a process that produces both energy and methane waste. Among the strictest of anaerobes, methanogens are poisoned by O_2. Although some methanogens live in extreme environments, such as around deep-sea hydrothermal vents **(Figure 24.21)**, others live in swamps where other microorganisms have consumed all the O_2. The "marsh gas" found in such environments is the methane released by these archaea. Other species of methanogens inhabit the anaerobic environment within the guts of cattle, termites, and other herbivores, playing an essential role in the nutrition of these animals. Methanogens also have an important application as decomposers in sewage treatment facilities.

Many extreme halophiles and all known methanogens are archaea in the clade Euryarchaeota (from the Greek *eurys*, broad, a reference to the habitat range of these prokaryotes). The euryarchaeotes also include some extreme thermophiles, though most thermophilic species belong to a second clade, Crenarchaeota (*cren* means "spring," such as a hydrothermal spring). Recent metagenomic studies have identified many species of euryarchaeotes and crenarchaeotes that are not extremophiles. These archaea exist in habitats ranging from farm soils to lake sediments to the surface waters of the open ocean.

New findings continue to update the picture of archaeal phylogeny. In 1996, researchers sampling a hot spring in Yellowstone National Park discovered archaea that do not appear to belong to either Euryarchaeota or Crenarchaeota. They placed these archaea in a new clade, Korarchaeota (from the Greek *koron*, young man). In 2002, researchers exploring hydrothermal vents off the coast of Iceland discovered archaeal cells only 0.4 μm in diameter attached to a much larger crenarchaeote. The genome of the smaller archaean is one of the smallest known of any organism, containing only 500,000 base pairs. Genetic analysis indicates that this prokaryote belongs to a fourth archaeal clade, Nanoarchaeota (from the Greek *nanos*, dwarf). Within a year after this clade was named, three other DNA sequences from nanoarchaeote species were isolated: one from Yellowstone's hot springs, one from hot springs in

Siberia, and one from a hydrothermal vent in the Pacific. As metagenomic prospecting continues, the tree in Figure 24.18 may well undergo further changes.

CONCEPT CHECK 24.4

1. Explain how molecular systematics has contributed to our understanding of the phylogeny and evolution of prokaryotes.
2. How has metagenomics contributed to our understanding of prokaryotic diversity and phylogeny?
3. **WHAT IF?** What would the discovery of a bacterial species that is a methanogen imply about the evolution of the methane-producing pathway?

For suggested answers, see Appendix A.

CONCEPT 24.5

Prokaryotes play crucial roles in the biosphere

If people were to disappear from the planet tomorrow, life on Earth would change for many species, but few would be driven to extinction. In contrast, prokaryotes are so important to the biosphere that if they were to disappear, the prospects of survival for many other species would be dim.

Chemical Recycling

The atoms that make up the organic molecules in all living things were at one time part of inorganic substances in the soil, air, and water. Sooner or later, those atoms will return there. Ecosystems depend on the continual recycling of chemical elements between the living and nonliving components of the environment, and prokaryotes play a major role in this process. For example, chemoheterotrophic prokaryotes function as **decomposers**, breaking down dead organisms as well as waste products and thereby unlocking supplies of carbon, nitrogen, and other elements. Without the actions of prokaryotes and other decomposers such as fungi, life as we know it would cease. (See Chapter 42 for a detailed discussion of chemical cycles.)

Prokaryotes also convert some molecules to forms that can be taken up by other organisms. Cyanobacteria and other autotrophic prokaryotes use CO_2 to make organic compounds such as sugars, which are then passed up through food chains. Cyanobacteria also produce atmospheric O_2, and a variety of prokaryotes fix atmospheric nitrogen (N_2) into forms that other organisms can use to make the building blocks of proteins and nucleic acids. Under some conditions, prokaryotes can increase the availability of nutrients that plants require for growth, such as nitrogen, phosphorus, and potassium **(Figure 24.22)**. Prokaryotes can also *decrease* the availability of key plant nutrients; this occurs when prokaryotes "immobilize" nutrients by using them to synthesize molecules that remain within their cells. Thus, prokaryotes can have complex effects on soil nutrient

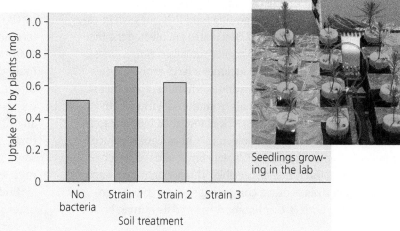

▶ **Figure 24.22 Impact of bacteria on soil nutrient availability.** Pine seedlings grown in sterile soils to which one of three strains of the bacterium *Burkholderia glathei* had been added absorbed more potassium (K⁺) than did seedlings grown in soil without any bacteria. Other results (not shown) demonstrated that strain 3 increased the amount of K⁺ released from mineral crystals to the soil.

WHAT IF? *Estimate the average uptake of K⁺ for seedlings in soils with bacteria. What would you expect this average to be if bacteria had no effect on nutrient availability?*

Seedlings growing in the lab

concentrations. In marine environments, a recent study found that an archaean from the clade Crenarchaeota can perform nitrification, a key step in the nitrogen cycle (see Figure 42.13). Crenarchaeotes dominate the oceans by numbers, comprising an estimated 10^{28} cells. Their abundance suggests that these organisms may have a large impact on the global nitrogen cycle; scientists are investigating this possibility.

Ecological Interactions

Prokaryotes play a central role in many ecological interactions. Consider **symbiosis** (from a Greek word meaning "living together"), an ecological relationship in which two species live in close contact with each other. Prokaryotes often form symbiotic associations with much larger organisms. In general, the larger organism in a symbiotic relationship is known as the **host**, and the smaller is known as the **symbiont**. There are many cases in which a prokaryote and its host participate in **mutualism**, an ecological interaction between two species in which both benefit (**Figure 24.23**). Other interactions take the form of **commensalism**, an interaction in which one species benefits while the other is not harmed or helped in any significant way. For example, more than 150 bacterial species live on the surface of your body, covering portions of your skin with up to 10 million cells per square centimeter. Some of these species are commensalists: You provide them with food, such as the oils that exude from your pores, and a place to live, while they neither harm nor benefit you. Finally, some prokaryotes engage in **parasitism**, an interaction in which a **parasite** eats the cell contents, tissues, or body fluids of its host. As a group, parasites harm but usually do not kill their host, at least not immediately (unlike a predator). Parasites that cause disease are known as **pathogens**, many of which are prokaryotic. (Chapter 41 discusses mutualism, commensalism, and parasitism in more detail.)

The very existence of an ecosystem can depend on prokaryotes. For example, consider the diverse ecological communities found at hydrothermal vents. These communities are densely populated by many different kinds of animals, including worms, clams, crabs, and fishes. But since sunlight does not penetrate to the deep ocean floor, the community does not include photosynthetic organisms. Instead, the energy that supports the community is derived from the metabolic activities of chemoautotrophic bacteria. These bacteria harvest chemical energy from compounds such as hydrogen sulfide (H_2S) that are released from the vent. An active hydrothermal vent may support hundreds of eukaryotic species, but when the vent stops releasing chemicals, the chemoautotrophic bacteria cannot survive. As a result, the entire vent community collapses.

Impact on Humans

Though the best-known prokaryotes tend to be the bacteria that cause human illness, these pathogens represent only a small fraction of prokaryotic species. Many other prokaryotes have positive interactions with people, and some play essential roles in agriculture and industry.

Mutualistic Bacteria

As is true for many other eukaryotes, human well-being can depend on mutualistic prokaryotes. For example, our intestines are home to an estimated 500–1,000 species of bacteria; their cells outnumber all human cells in the body by a factor of ten. Different species live in different portions of the intestines, and they vary in their ability to process different foods. Many of

▲ **Figure 24.23 Mutualism: bacterial "headlights."** The glowing oval below the eye of the flashlight fish (*Photoblepharon palpebratus*) is an organ harboring bioluminescent bacteria. The fish uses the light to attract prey and to signal potential mates. The bacteria receive nutrients from the fish.

these species are mutualists, digesting food that our own intestines cannot break down. In 2003, scientists published the first complete genome of one of these gut mutualists, *Bacteroides thetaiotaomicron*. The genome includes a large array of genes involved in synthesizing carbohydrates, vitamins, and other nutrients needed by humans. Signals from the bacterium activate human genes that build the network of intestinal blood vessels necessary to absorb nutrient molecules. Other signals induce human cells to produce antimicrobial compounds to which *B. thetaiotaomicron* is not susceptible. This action may reduce the population sizes of other, competing species, thus potentially benefiting both *B. thetaiotaomicron* and its human host.

Pathogenic Bacteria

All the pathogenic prokaryotes known to date are bacteria, and they deserve their negative reputation. Bacteria cause about half of all human diseases. For example, about 2 million people die each year of the lung disease tuberculosis, caused by *Mycobacterium tuberculosis*. And another 2 million people die each year from diarrheal diseases caused by various bacteria.

Some bacterial diseases are transmitted by other species, such as fleas or ticks. In the United States, the most widespread pest-carried disease is Lyme disease, which infects 15,000 to 20,000 people each year (**Figure 24.24**). Caused by a bacterium carried by ticks that live on deer and field mice, Lyme disease can result in debilitating arthritis, heart disease, nervous disorders, and death if untreated.

Pathogenic prokaryotes usually cause illness by producing poisons, which are classified as exotoxins or endotoxins. **Exotoxins** are proteins secreted by certain bacteria and other organisms. Cholera, a dangerous diarrheal disease, is caused by an exotoxin secreted by the proteobacterium *Vibrio cholerae*. The exotoxin stimulates intestinal cells to release chloride ions into the gut, and water follows by osmosis. In another example, the potentially fatal disease botulism is caused by botulinum toxin, an exotoxin secreted

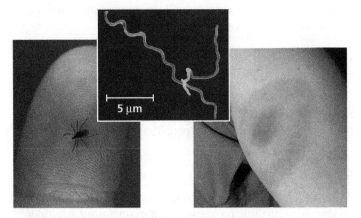

▲ **Figure 24.24 Lyme disease.** Ticks in the genus *Ixodes* spread the disease by transmitting the spirochete *Borrelia burgdorferi* (colorized SEM). A rash may develop at the site of the tick's bite; the rash may be large and ring-shaped (as shown) or much less distinctive.

by the gram-positive bacterium *Clostridium botulinum* as it ferments various foods, including improperly canned meat, seafood, and vegetables. Like other exotoxins, the botulinum toxin can produce disease even if the bacteria that manufacture it are not present. In one such case, eight people contracted botulism after eating salted fish that did not contain any *C. botulinum* bacteria, but did contain the botulinum toxin. Even though the bacterium was no longer present, at some point in the fish preparation process the bacterium must have been able to grow and secrete the toxin.

Endotoxins are lipopolysaccharide components of the outer membrane of gram-negative bacteria. In contrast to exotoxins, endotoxins are released only when the bacteria die and their cell walls break down. Endotoxin-producing bacteria include species in the genus *Salmonella*, such as *Salmonella typhi*, which causes typhoid fever. You might have heard of food poisoning caused by other *Salmonella* species that can be found in poultry and some fruits and vegetables.

Since the 19th century, improved sanitation systems in the industrialized world have greatly reduced the threat of pathogenic bacteria. Antibiotics have saved a great many lives and reduced the incidence of disease. However, resistance to antibiotics is currently evolving in many bacterial strains. As you read earlier, the rapid reproduction of bacteria enables cells carrying resistance genes to quickly give rise to large populations as a result of natural selection, and these genes can also spread to other species by horizontal gene transfer.

Horizontal gene transfer can also spread genes associated with virulence, turning normally harmless bacteria into potent pathogens. *E. coli*, for instance, is ordinarily a harmless symbiont in the human intestines, but pathogenic strains that cause bloody diarrhea have emerged. One of the most dangerous strains, O157:H7, is a global threat; in the United States alone, there are 75,000 cases of O157:H7 infection per year, often from contaminated beef or produce. In 2001, scientists sequenced the genome of O157:H7 and compared it with the genome of a harmless strain of *E. coli* called K-12. They discovered that 1,387 out of the 5,416 genes in O157:H7 have no counterpart in K-12. Many of these 1,387 genes are found in chromosomal regions that include phage DNA. This suggests that at least some of the 1,387 genes were incorporated into the genome of O157:H7 through phage-mediated horizontal gene transfer (transduction). Some of the genes found only in O157:H7 are associated with virulence, including genes that code for adhesive fimbriae that enable O157:H7 to attach itself to the intestinal wall and extract nutrients.

Prokaryotes in Research and Technology

On a positive note, we reap many benefits from the metabolic capabilities of both bacteria and archaea. For example, people have long used bacteria to convert milk to cheese and yogurt. In recent years, our greater understanding of prokaryotes has led

Making a Bar Graph and Interpreting Data

Do Soil Microorganisms Protect Against Crop Disease? The soil layer surrounding plant roots, called the *rhizosphere*, is a complex community in which archaea, bacteria, fungi, and plants interact with one another. When crop plants are attacked by fungal or bacterial pathogens, in some cases soil from the rhizosphere protects plants from future attacks. Such protective soil is called disease-suppressive soil. Plants grown in disease-suppressive soils appear to be less vulnerable to pathogen attack. In this exercise, you'll interpret data from an experiment studying whether microorganisms were responsible for the protective effects of disease-suppressive soils.

How the Experiment Was Done The researchers obtained disease-suppressive soil from 25 random sites in an agricultural field in the Netherlands in which sugar beet crops had previously been attacked by *Rhizoctonia solani*, a fungal pathogen that also afflicts potatoes and rice. The researchers collected other soil samples from the grassy margins of the field where sugar beets had not been grown. The researchers predicted that these soil samples from the margins would not offer protection against pathogens.

The researchers then planted and raised sugar beets in greenhouses, using 5 different soil treatments. Each soil treatment was applied to 4 pots, and each pot contained 8 plants. The pots were inoculated with *Rhizoctonia solani*. After 20 days, researchers determined the percentage of infected sugar beet seedlings for each soil treatment.

Data from the Experiment

Soil Treatment	Percentage of Seedlings with Fungal Disease
Disease-suppressive soil	3.0
Soil from margin of field	62
Soil from margin of field + 10% disease-suppressive soil	39
Disease-suppressive soil heated to 50°C for 1 hour	31
Disease-suppressive soil heated to 80°C for 1 hour	70

Interpret the Data

1. What hypothesis were the researchers testing in this study? What is the independent variable in this study? What is the dependent variable?
2. What is the total number of pots used in this experiment, and how many plants received each soil treatment? Explain why multiple pots and plants were used for each treatment.
3. Use the data in the table to create a bar graph. Then in words, describe and compare the results for the five soil treatments.
4. The researchers stated, "Collectively, these results indicated that disease suppressiveness [of soil] toward *Rhizoctonia solani* was microbiological in nature." Is this statement supported by the results shown in the graph? Explain.

Data from R. Mendes, et al. Deciphering the rhizosphere for disease-suppressive bacteria, *Science* 332: 1097–1100 (2011).

(MB) A version of this Scientific Skills Exercise can be assigned in MasteringBiology.

to an explosion of new applications in biotechnology; two examples are the use of *E. coli* in gene cloning (see Figure 13.22) and the use of *Agrobacterium tumefaciens* in producing transgenic plants. Naturally occurring soil bacteria may have potential for combating diseases that affect crop plants; in the **Scientific Skills Exercise**, you can interpret data from an experiment studying the effect of these bacteria.

Bacteria may soon figure prominently in another major industry: plastics. Globally, each year about 350 billion pounds of plastic are produced from petroleum and used to make toys, storage containers, soft drink bottles, and many other items. These products degrade slowly, creating environmental problems. Bacteria can now be used to make natural plastics **(Figure 24.25a)**. For example, some bacteria synthesize a type of polymer known as PHA (polyhydroxyalkanoate), which they use to store chemical energy. The PHA they produce can be extracted, formed into pellets, and used to make durable, yet biodegradable plastics. Through genetic engineering, we can now modify bacteria to produce vitamins, antibiotics, hormones, and other products (see Concept 13.4). Researchers are seeking to reduce fossil fuel use by engineering bacteria that can produce ethanol from various forms of biomass, including agricultural waste, switchgrass, municipal waste (such as paper products that are not recycled), and corn **(Figure 24.25b)**.

Another way to harness prokaryotes is in **bioremediation**, the use of organisms to remove pollutants from soil, air, or water. For example, anaerobic bacteria and archaea decompose the organic matter in sewage, converting it to material that can be used as landfill or fertilizer after chemical sterilization. Other bioremediation applications include cleaning up oil

▲ **Figure 24.25 Products from prokaryotes. (a)** These bacteria synthesize and store PHA, which can be extracted and used to make biodegradable plastic products. **(b)** Current research seeks to develop bacteria that produce ethanol (E-85) fuel efficiently from renewable plant products.

▲ **Figure 24.26 Bioremediation of an oil spill.** Spraying fertilizers on an oil-soaked area stimulates growth of native bacteria that metabolize the oil. This can speed up the natural breakdown process by a factor of five.

spills **(Figure 24.26)** and precipitating radioactive material (such as uranium) out of groundwater.

The usefulness of prokaryotes largely derives from their diverse forms of nutrition and metabolism. All this metabolic versatility evolved prior to the appearance of the structural novelties that heralded the evolution of eukaryotic organisms, to which we devote the remainder of this unit.

CONCEPT CHECK 24.5

1. Explain how prokaryotes, though small, can be considered giants in their collective impact on Earth and its life.
2. A pathogenic bacterium's toxin causes symptoms that increase the bacterium's chance of spreading from host to host. Does this information indicate whether the poison is an exotoxin or endotoxin? Explain.
3. **MAKE CONNECTIONS** Review photosynthesis in Figure 8.5. Then summarize the main steps by which cyanobacteria produce O_2 and use CO_2 to make organic compounds.
4. **WHAT IF?** How might a sudden and dramatic change in your diet affect the diversity of prokaryotic species that live in your digestive tract?

For suggested answers, see Appendix A.

24 Chapter Review

SUMMARY OF KEY CONCEPTS

CONCEPT 24.1

Conditions on early Earth made the origin of life possible (pp. 459–462)

- Experiments simulating possible early atmospheres have produced organic molecules from inorganic precursors. Amino acids, lipids, sugars, and nitrogenous bases have also been found in meteorites.
- Amino acids and RNA nucleotides polymerize when dripped onto hot sand, clay, or rock. Organic compounds can spontaneously assemble into **protocells**, membrane-enclosed droplets that have some properties of cells.
- The first genetic material may have been short pieces of RNA capable of guiding polypeptide synthesis and self-replication. Early protocells containing such RNA would have increased through natural selection.
- Fossil evidence of early prokaryotes dates to 3.5 billion years ago. By 2.8 billion years ago, prokaryotes included stromatolites that differed in morphology and habitat. Early prokaryotes also included cyanobacteria that released oxygen as a by-product of photosynthesis, thereby changing Earth's atmosphere and altering the course of evolution.

? *Describe the roles that montmorillonite clay and vesicles may have played in the origin of life.*

CONCEPT 24.2

Diverse structural and metabolic adaptations have evolved in prokaryotes (pp. 462–467)

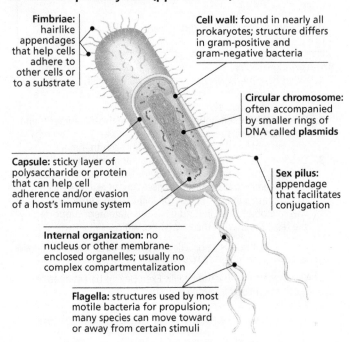

Fimbriae: hairlike appendages that help cells adhere to other cells or to a substrate

Cell wall: found in nearly all prokaryotes; structure differs in gram-positive and gram-negative bacteria

Circular chromosome: often accompanied by smaller rings of DNA called **plasmids**

Capsule: sticky layer of polysaccharide or protein that can help cell adherence and/or evasion of a host's immune system

Sex pilus: appendage that facilitates conjugation

Internal organization: no nucleus or other membrane-enclosed organelles; usually no complex compartmentalization

Flagella: structures used by most motile bacteria for propulsion; many species can move toward or away from certain stimuli

- Nutritional diversity is much greater in prokaryotes than in eukaryotes. As a group, prokaryotes perform all four modes of nutrition: photoautotrophy, chemoautotrophy, photoheterotrophy, and chemoheterotrophy.
- Among prokaryotes, obligate aerobes require O_2, obligate anaerobes are poisoned by O_2, and facultative anaerobes can survive with or without O_2.
- Unlike eukaryotes, prokaryotes can metabolize nitrogen in many different forms. Some can convert atmospheric nitrogen to ammonia, a process called **nitrogen fixation**.
- Prokaryotic cells and even species may cooperate metabolically. In *Anabaena*, photosynthetic cells and nitrogen-fixing cells exchange metabolic products. Metabolic cooperation also occurs in surface-coating **biofilms** that include different species.
- Prokaryotes can reproduce quickly by binary fission.

? *Describe features of prokaryotes that enable them to thrive in a wide range of different environments.*

CONCEPT 24.3

Rapid reproduction, mutation, and genetic recombination promote genetic diversity in prokaryotes (pp. 467–470)

- Because prokaryotes can often proliferate rapidly, mutations can quickly increase a population's genetic variation. As a result, prokaryotic populations often can evolve in short periods of time in response to changing conditions.
- Genetic diversity in prokaryotes also can arise by recombination of the DNA from two different cells (via **transformation**, **transduction**, or **conjugation**). By transferring advantageous alleles, such as ones for antibiotic resistance, genetic recombination can promote adaptive evolution in prokaryotic populations.

? *Although prokaryotes reproduce asexually, their populations can have high genetic diversity. Explain how this can occur.*

CONCEPT 24.4

Prokaryotes have radiated into a diverse set of lineages (pp. 470–474)

- Molecular systematics is leading to a phylogenetic classification of prokaryotes, allowing systematists to identify major new clades.
- Some archaea, such as **extreme thermophiles** and **extreme halophiles**, live in extreme environments. Other archaea live in moderate environments, such as soils and lakes.
- Diverse nutritional types are scattered among the major groups of bacteria. The two largest groups are the proteobacteria and gram-positive bacteria.

? *What impact have molecular data had on constructing prokaryotic phylogeny?*

CONCEPT 24.5

Prokaryotes play crucial roles in the biosphere (pp. 474–478)

- Decomposition by heterotrophic prokaryotes and the synthetic activities of autotrophic and nitrogen-fixing prokaryotes contribute to the recycling of elements in ecosystems.
- Many prokaryotes have a symbiotic relationship with a host; the relationships between prokaryotes and their hosts range from mutualism to commensalism to parasitism.

- People depend on mutualistic prokaryotes, including hundreds of species that live in our intestines and help digest food.
- Pathogenic bacteria typically cause disease by releasing **exotoxins** or **endotoxins**. Horizontal gene transfer can spread genes associated with virulence to previously harmless species or strains.
- Experiments with bacteria such as *E. coli* have led to important advances in DNA technology. Prokaryotes can be used in bioremediation and in the synthesis of vitamins, antibiotics, and other products.

? *In what ways are prokaryotes key to the survival of many species?*

TEST YOUR UNDERSTANDING

Level 1: Knowledge/Comprehension

1. Which of the following steps has *not* yet been accomplished by scientists studying the origin of life?
   a. synthesis of small RNA polymers by ribozymes
   b. abiotic synthesis of polypeptides
   c. formation of molecular aggregates with selectively permeable membranes
   d. formation of protocells that use DNA to direct the polymerization of amino acids
   e. abiotic synthesis of organic molecules

2. Fossilized stromatolites
   a. more than 2.8 billion years old have not been discovered.
   b. formed around deep-sea vents.
   c. resemble structures formed by bacterial communities that are found today in some shallow marine bays.
   d. provide evidence that plants moved onto land in the company of fungi around 500 million years ago.
   e. contain the first undisputed fossils of eukaryotes and date from 1.8 billion years ago.

3. Genetic variation in bacterial populations cannot result from
   a. transduction.
   b. transformation.
   c. conjugation.
   d. mutation.
   e. meiosis.

4. Photoautotrophs use
   a. light as an energy source and methane as a carbon source.
   b. light as an energy source and CO_2 as a carbon source.
   c. N_2 as an energy source and CO_2 as a carbon source.
   d. CO_2 as both an energy source and a carbon source.
   e. H_2S as an energy source and CO_2 as a carbon source.

5. Which of the following statements is *not* true?
   a. Archaea and bacteria have different membrane lipids.
   b. Both archaea and bacteria generally lack membrane-enclosed organelles.
   c. The cell walls of archaea lack peptidoglycan.
   d. Only bacteria have histones associated with DNA.
   e. Only some archaea use CO_2 to oxidize H_2, releasing methane.

6. Bacteria perform the following ecological roles. Which role typically does *not* involve symbiosis?
   a. skin commensalist
   b. pathogen
   c. bioluminescent bacteria in fish
   d. gut mutualist
   e. decomposer

7. Plantlike photosynthesis that releases O_2 occurs in
  a. cyanobacteria.
  b. chlamydias.
  c. archaea.
  d. actinomycetes.
  e. chemoautotrophic bacteria.

Level 2: Application/Analysis

8. SCIENTIFIC INQUIRY

  DRAW IT The nitrogen-fixing bacterium *Rhizobium* infects the roots of some plant species, forming a mutualism in which the bacterium provides nitrogen and the plant provides carbohydrates. Scientists measured the 12-week growth of one such plant species (*Acacia irrorata*) when infected by six different *Rhizobium* strains. (a) Graph the data. (b) Interpret your graph.

Rhizobium strain	1	2	3	4	5	6
Plant mass (g)	0.91	0.06	1.56	1.72	0.14	1.03

Source J. J. Burdon et al., Variation in the effectiveness of symbiotic associations between native rhizobia and temperate Australian *Acacia*: Within-species interactions, *Journal of Applied Ecology* 36:398–408 (1999).

Note: Without *Rhizobium*, after 12 weeks, *Acacia* plants have a mass of about 0.1 g.

Level 3: Synthesis/Evaluation

9. FOCUS ON EVOLUTION
  In patients infected with nonresistant strains of the tuberculosis bacterium, antibiotics can relieve symptoms in a few weeks. However, it takes much longer to halt the infection, and patients may discontinue treatment while bacteria are still present. How might this result in the evolution of drug-resistant pathogens?

10. FOCUS ON ENERGY AND MATTER
  In a short essay (about 100–150 words), discuss how prokaryotes and other members of hydrothermal vent communities transfer and transform energy.

For selected answers, see Appendix A.

MasteringBiology®

Students Go to **MasteringBiology** for assignments, the eText, and the Study Area with practice tests, animations, and activities.

Instructors Go to **MasteringBiology** for automatically graded tutorials and questions that you can assign to your students, plus Instructor Resources.

25

The Origin and Diversification of Eukaryotes

OVERVIEW

Shape Changers

The organisms in **Figure 25.1** are ciliates, a diverse group of single-celled eukaryotes named after the small appendages—cilia—that cover much of their bodies and enable them to move. The ciliate on the left, *Didinium*, has begun a seemingly impossible task: it will completely engulf the *Paramecium* (right), even though the *Paramecium* is as large as it is.

Reflect for a moment on the magnitude of this feat. If we humans could do this, in a single swallow we could ingest more food than we would typically eat in a month. Like us, even the prokaryotes discussed in Chapter 24 cannot engulf food items their own size—although prokaryotes can metabolize an astonishing range of compounds, they can only absorb small particles of food. What enables *Didinium* to tackle food items that could easily evade a hungry prokaryote?

One key to *Didinium*'s success lies within its cells—it has a complex set of cytoskeletal proteins that enable the cell to change in shape dramatically as it feeds. *Didinium* also has small structures similar to miniature harpoons that it can eject to help ensnare its prey. These two features illustrate the structural complexity that characterizes the cells of *Didinium* and the other diverse, mostly unicellular groups of eukaryotes informally known as **protists**.

As we'll see, some protists change their form as they creep along using blob-like appendages, others are shaped like tiny trumpets, and still others resemble miniature jewelry. In this chapter, we'll explore how these shape-changing, structurally complex eukaryotic cells arose from their morphologically simpler prokaryotic ancestors. We'll also examine another major step in the evolutionary history of life: the origin of multicellular eukaryotes such as plants, fungi, and animals. Finally, we'll consider how single-celled eukaryotes affect ecosystems and human health.

CONCEPT 25.1

Eukaryotes arose by endosymbiosis more than 1.8 billion years ago

As we discussed in Chapter 24, all organisms were unicellular early in the history of life. The evolution of eukaryotes did not immediately change this, but it did involve fundamental changes in the structure of these individual cells. For

▼ **Figure 25.1** What enables the cell on the left to engulf its prey?

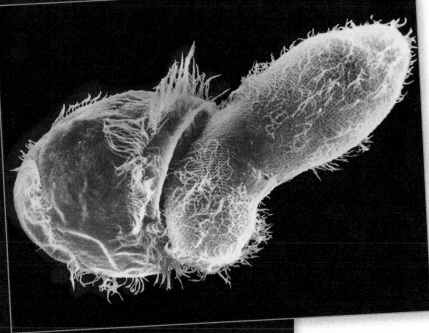

example, unlike the cells of prokaryotes, the cells of all eukaryotes have a nucleus and other membrane-enclosed organelles, such as mitochondria and the Golgi apparatus. Such organelles provide specific locations where particular cellular functions are accomplished, making the structure and organization of eukaryotic cells more complex than that of prokaryotic cells.

Another key eukaryote characteristic is a well-developed cytoskeleton that extends throughout the cell (see Figure 4.20). The cytoskeleton provides structural support that enables

eukaryotic cells to have asymmetric (irregular) forms, as well as to change shape as they feed, move, or grow. Although some prokaryotes have proteins related to eukaryotic cytoskeletal proteins, their rigid cell walls and lack of a well-developed cytoskeleton limit the extent to which their cells can maintain asymmetric forms or change shape over time.

The fossil record indicates that prokaryotes were inhabiting Earth at least 3.5 billion years ago (see Chapter 24). At what

▼ **Figure 25.2** **Exploring the Early Evolution of Eukaryotes**

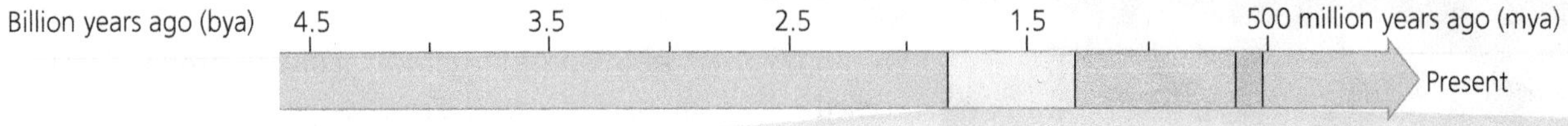

Billion years ago (bya)   4.5   3.5   2.5   1.5   500 million years ago (mya)   Present

1.8 bya   1.5 bya   1.3 bya   1.2 bya

A structure protruding from the cell surface

20 μm

Other fossils show that at a later stage of development, these cells will divide, producing reproductive cells (spores).

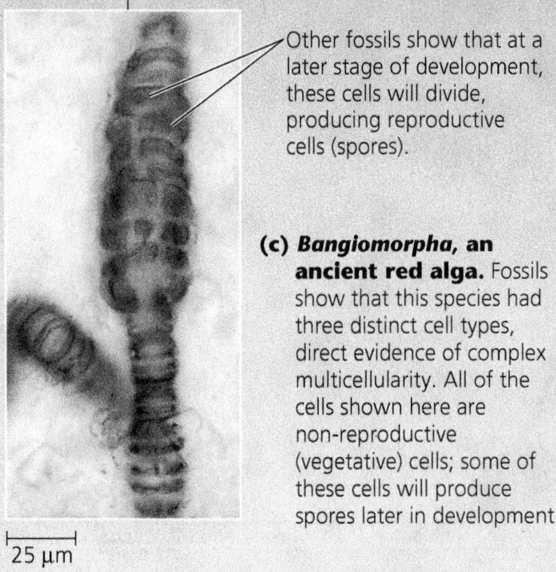

(c) *Bangiomorpha,* **an ancient red alga.** Fossils show that this species had three distinct cell types, direct evidence of complex multicellularity. All of the cells shown here are non-reproductive (vegetative) cells; some of these cells will produce spores later in development.

(a) A 1.8-billion-year-old fossil eukaryote. This ancient organism had a cell wall structure similar to that of some living algae, but different from that of prokaryotes—indicating this fossil organism was an early eukaryote.

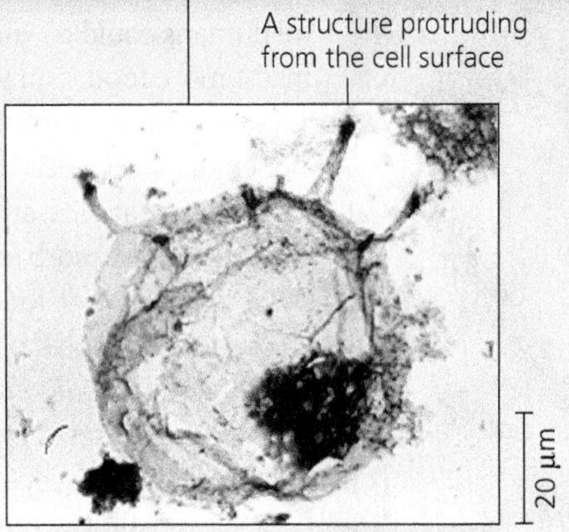

(b) *Tappania,* **a 1.5-billion-year-old fossil that may represent an early alga or fungus.** Many fossils of this organism have been found; the number, size, and location of the structures protruding from the cell's outer surface vary from one individual to another.

25 μm

Initial Diversification

The fossil record shows that a moderate diversity of single-celled eukaryotes was already present 1.8 billion years ago, including the fossil specimen in **(a)**. Researchers have discovered other fossil eukaryotes of the same age that vary in size and had shapes ranging from spherical to elliptical (some that are spindle-shaped, or tapering at each end). This variety suggests that the eukaryotes may have originated much earlier in time.

Early members of domain Eukarya had a nucleus, a flexible membrane, and a cytoskeleton capable of supporting an irregular cell shape, like that seen in **(b)**. Other fossils from this time period include several different types of simple filaments thought to be of small, multicellular eukaryotes. Although fossil eukaryotes from this time range are moderately diverse, none of these organisms can be assigned with confidence to an extant group of eukaryotes.

(*Time line not to scale.*)

Appearance of Novel Features

The oldest known eukaryotic fossils that can be resolved taxonomically are of small red algae that lived 1.2 billion years ago **(c)**; note that **algae** is a general term that includes all groups of photosynthetic protists. Other fossils from this period include green algae **(d)** and certain types of amoebas that lived within vase-shaped structures **(e)**, as well as a variety of colonial and multicellular protists of unknown taxonomic affinity.

The taxonomic diversification seen in these fossils was accompanied by a suite of novel biological features, including the origins of complex multicellularity (a term that applies to multicellular organisms with differentiated cell types), sexual life cycles, and eukaryotic photosynthesis. Some of these features can be point did irregular forms and other novel features of eukaryotes appear, signifying the origin of the group? Fossils and molecular data provide clues to when and how eukaryotes may have arisen from their prokaryotic ancestors.

The Fossil Record of Early Eukaryotes

Complex lipids that are synthesized by eukaryotes (but not by prokaryotes) have been found in rocks dated to 2.7 billion years ago. Although such chemical evidence is consistent with

eukaryotes having lived at that time, the oldest widely accepted fossils of eukaryotic organisms are 1.8 billion years old. Over time, the descendants of these organisms gave rise to the rich diversity of protists and other eukaryotes alive today.

Figure 25.2 surveys how that diversity arose, focusing on three stages documented by the fossil record: an initial diversification (1.8–1.3 billion years ago), the origin of multicellularity and other novel features (1.3 billion–635 million years ago), and the emergence of large eukaryotes (635–535 million years ago).

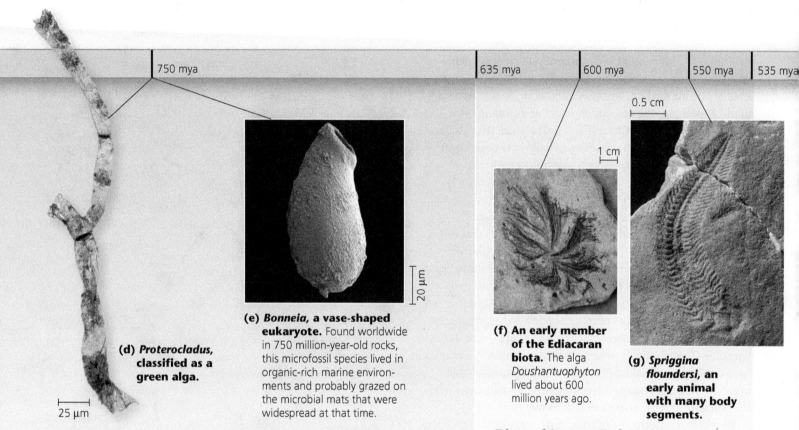

750 mya   635 mya   600 mya   550 mya   535 mya

(d) *Proterocladus*, classified as a green alga.

25 μm

(e) *Bonneia*, a vase-shaped eukaryote. Found worldwide in 750 million-year-old rocks, this microfossil species lived in organic-rich marine environments and probably grazed on the microbial mats that were widespread at that time.

20 μm

(f) An early member of the Ediacaran biota. The alga *Doushantuophyton* lived about 600 million years ago.

1 cm

0.5 cm

(g) *Spriggina floundersi*, an early animal with many body segments.

observed directly, while others are inferred from living members of the group to which a fossil belongs. For example, *Bangiomorpha* (c) had "holdfasts" similar to those that anchor living red algae to their substrate; it also had a pattern of cell division that is only known to occur in a particular group of extant red algae. Hence, *Bangiomorpha* is classified as a member of this group of red algae. Living members of this group have sexual life cycles and are photosynthetic, so it is likely that *Bangiomoprha* also had these features.

A range of other fossils show that by 800–750 million years ago, increasingly complex communities of eukaryotes had emerged, with algae at the bottom of the food chain and species that ate algae (or each other) above. These organisms remained small, however, and the entire community began to decline with the onset of a series of severe ice ages and other environmental changes.

Rise of Large Eukaryotes

For nearly 3 billion years, life on Earth was a world of microscopic forms. Larger multicellular eukaryotes do not appear in the fossil record until the Ediacaran period, 635-542 million years ago **(f, g)**. These fossils, referred to as the **Ediacaran biota**, were of soft-bodied organisms, some over 1 m long.

More generally, the fossil record from 635-535 million years ago documents changes in the history of life: maximum body size, taxonomic diversity, and the extent of morphological differences all increased dramatically. In addition, the average time that species persisted in the fossil record dropped considerably. Indeed, the entire Ediacaran biota declined 535 million years ago with the onset of another great wave of evolutionary diversification—the so-called "Cambrian explosion."

As discussed in Figure 25.2, large, multicellular eukaryotes did not appear until about 600 million years ago. Prior to that time, Earth was a microbial world: Its only inhabitants were single-celled prokaryotes and eukaryotes, along with an assortment of microscopic, multicellular eukaryotes. We'll return to the rise of large, multicellular eukaryotes in Chapters 26 and 27.

Endosymbiosis in Eukaryotic Evolution

The fossil record documents when early eukaryotes lived and when key eukaryotic traits, such as a well-developed cytoskeleton and sexual life cycles, first appeared. Additional insights into the origin of eukaryotes have come from molecular studies. In particular, DNA sequence data suggest that eukaryotes are "combination" organisms, with some of their genes and cellular characteristics being derived from archaea, and others from bacteria **(Table 25.1)**.

How did eukaryotes come to have both archaeal and bacterial features? This mixture of features may be a consequence of **endosymbiosis**, a symbiotic relationship in which one organism lives inside the body or cell of another organism. According to this hypothesis, the defining moment in the origin of eukaryotes occurred when an archaeal cell (or a cell with archaeal ancestors) engulfed a bacterium that would later become an organelle found in all eukaryotes—the mitochondrion.

Origin of Mitochondria and Plastids

The idea that eukaryotes are "combination" organisms is related to the **endosymbiont theory**, which holds that mitochondria and plastids (a general term for chloroplasts and related organelles) were formerly small prokaryotes that began living within larger cells **(Figure 25.3)**. The term *endosymbiont* refers to a cell that lives within another cell, called the *host cell*. The prokaryotic ancestors of mitochondria and plastids probably gained entry to the host cell as undigested prey or internal parasites. Though such a process may seem unlikely, scientists have directly observed cases in which endosymbionts that began as prey or parasites came to have a mutually beneficial relationship with the host in as little as five years.

By whatever means the relationship began, we can hypothesize how the symbiosis could have become mutually beneficial.

Table 25.1 Inferred Origins of Key Eukaryotic Features

Feature	Original Source
DNA replication enzymes	Archaeal
Transcription enzymes	Archaeal
Translation enzymes	Mostly archaeal
Cell division apparatus	Mostly archaeal
Endoplasmic reticulum	Archaeal and bacterial
Mitochondrion	Bacterial
Metabolic genes	Mostly bacterial

For example, in a world that was gradually becoming more aerobic, a host that was itself an anaerobe would have benefited from endosymbionts that could make use of the oxygen. Over time, the host and endosymbionts would have become a single organism, its parts inseparable. Although all eukaryotes have mitochondria or remnants of these organelles, they do not all have plastids. Thus, the **serial endosymbiosis** hypothesis

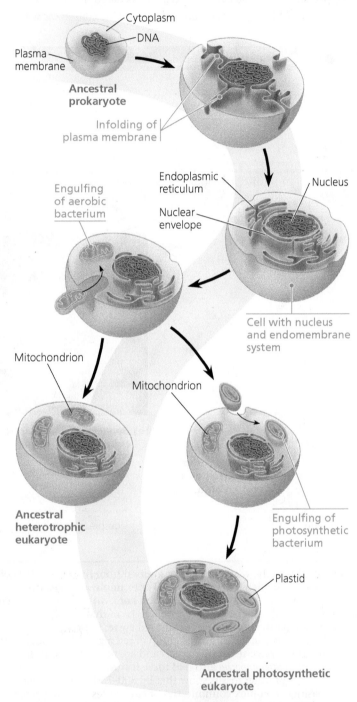

▲ **Figure 25.3 A hypothesis for the origin of eukaryotes through endosymbiosis.** The proposed host was an archaean or a cell descended from archaeal ancestors. The proposed ancestors of mitochondria were aerobic, heterotrophic prokaryotes, whereas those of plastids were photosynthetic prokaryotes. In this figure, the arrows represent change over evolutionary time.

supposes that mitochondria evolved before plastids through a sequence of endosymbiotic events (see Figure 25.3).

A great deal of evidence supports the endosymbiotic origin of mitochondria and plastids:

- The inner membranes of both organelles have enzymes and transport systems that are homologous to those found in the plasma membranes of living prokaryotes.
- Mitochondria and plastids replicate by a splitting process that is similar to that of certain prokaryotes. Mitochondria and plastids both contain circular DNA molecules that, like the chromosomes of bacteria, are not associated with histones or large amounts of other proteins.
- As might be expected of organelles descended from free-living organisms, mitochondria and plastids also have the cellular machinery (including ribosomes) needed to transcribe and translate their DNA into proteins.

- Finally, in terms of size, RNA sequences, and sensitivity to certain antibiotics, the ribosomes of mitochondria and plastids are more similar to prokaryotic ribosomes than they are to the cytoplasmic ribosomes of eukaryotic cells.

Which prokaryotic lineages gave rise to mitochondria? To answer this question, researchers have compared the DNA sequences of mitochondrial genes (mtDNA) with those found in major clades of bacteria and archaea. In the **Scientific Skills Exercise**, you will interpret one such set of DNA sequence comparisons. Collectively, such studies indicate that mitochondria arose from an alpha proteobacterium (see Figure 24.19). Researchers have also compared genome sequences of various alpha proteobacteria with the entire mtDNA sequences of animals, plants, fungi, and protists. Such studies indicate that eukaryotic mitochondria descended from a single common ancestor, suggesting that mitochondria arose only

Scientific Skills Exercise

Interpreting Comparisons of Genetic Sequences

Which Prokaryotes Are Most Closely Related to Mitochondria? The first eukaryotes acquired mitochondria by endosymbiosis: A host cell engulfed an aerobic prokaryote that persisted within the cytoplasm to the mutual benefit of both cells. In studying which living prokaryotes might be most closely related to mitochondria, researchers compared ribosomal RNA (rRNA) sequences. Because most cells contain thousands of ribosomes, rRNA is the most abundant form of RNA in living cells and is suitable for comparing even distantly related species. In this exercise, you'll interpret some of their results to draw conclusions about the phylogeny of mitochondria.

How the Research Was Done Researchers isolated and cloned nucleotide sequences from the gene that codes for the small-subunit rRNA molecule for six organisms: wheat (a plant) and five bacterial species.

- Wheat, used as the source of mitochondrial rRNA genes
- *Agrobacterium tumefaciens*, an alpha proteobacterium that lives within plant tissue and produces tumors in the host
- *Comamonas testosteroni*, a beta proteobacterium
- *Escherichia coli*, a well-studied gamma proteobacterium that inhabits human intestines
- *Mycoplasma capricolum*, a gram-positive mycoplasma, which is the only group of bacteria lacking cell walls
- *Anacystis nidulans*, a cyanobacterium

Data from the Research Cloned rRNA gene sequences for the six organisms were aligned and compared. The data table below, called a

comparison matrix, summarizes the comparison of 617 nucleotide positions from the gene sequences. Each value in the table is the percentage of the 617 nucleotide positions for which the pair of organisms have the same composition. Any positions that were identical across the rRNA genes of all six organisms were omitted from this comparison matrix.

Interpret the Data

1. First, make sure you understand how to read the comparison matrix. Find the cell that represents the comparison of *C. testosteroni* and *E. coli*. What value is given in this cell? What does that value signify about the comparable rRNA gene sequences in those two organisms? Explain why some cells have a dash rather than a value. Why are some cells shaded gray, with no value?

2. Why did the researchers choose one plant mitochondrion and five bacterial species to include in the comparison matrix?

3. Which species of bacterium has an rRNA gene that is most similar to that of the wheat mitochondrion? What is the significance of this similarity?

Data from D. Yang, et al., Mitochondrial origins, *Proceedings of the National Academy of Sciences USA* 82:4443–4447 (1985).

(MB) A version of this Scientific Skills Exercise can be assigned in MasteringBiology.

	Wheat mitochondrion	A. tumefaciens	C. testosteroni	E. coli	M. capricolum	A. nidulans
Wheat mitochondrion	–	48	38	35	34	34
A. tumefaciens		–	55	57	52	53
C. testosteroni			–	61	52	52
E. coli				–	48	52
M. capricolum					–	50
A. nidulans						–

once over the course of evolution. Similar analyses indicate that plastids arose once from an engulfed cyanobacterium.

While the lineages that gave rise to mitochondria and plastids have been identified, questions remain about the identity of the host cell that engulfed an alpha proteobacterium. According to recent genomic studies, the host came from an archaeal lineage, but which lineage remains undetermined. Alternatively, the host could have been a member of a lineage that was related to, but had diverged from, its archaeal ancestors. In this case, the host may have been a "protoeukaryote" in which certain features of eukaryotic cells had evolved, such as an endomembrane system and a cytoskeleton that enabled it to change shape (and thereby engulf the alpha proteobacterium).

Plastid Evolution: A Closer Look

As you've seen, current evidence indicates that mitochondria are descended from a bacterium that was engulfed by a cell from an archaeal lineage. This event gave rise to the eukaryotes. There is also much evidence that later in eukaryotic history, a lineage of heterotrophic eukaryotes acquired an additional endosymbiont—a photosynthetic cyanobacterium—that then evolved into plastids. According to the hypothesis illustrated in **Figure 25.4**, this plastid-bearing lineage gave rise to two lineages of photosynthetic protists, red algae and green algae.

Let's examine some of the steps shown in Figure 25.4 in more detail. First, recall that cyanobacteria are gram-negative and that gram-negative bacteria have two cell membranes, an inner plasma membrane and an outer membrane that is part of the cell wall (see Figure 24.7). Plastids in red algae and green algae are also surrounded by two membranes. Transport proteins in these membranes are homologous to proteins in the inner and outer membranes of cyanobacteria, providing further support for the hypothesis that plastids originated from a cyanobacterial endosymbiont.

On several occasions during eukaryotic evolution, red algae and green algae underwent **secondary endosymbiosis**: They were ingested in the food vacuoles of heterotrophic eukaryotes and became endosymbionts themselves. For example, as shown in Figure 25.4, protists known as chlorarachniophytes likely evolved when a heterotrophic eukaryote engulfed a green alga. Evidence for this process can be found within the engulfed cell, which contains a tiny vestigial nucleus, called a *nucleomorph*. Genes from the nucleomorph are still transcribed, and their DNA sequences indicate that the engulfed cell was a green alga. Also consistent with the hypothesis that chlorarachniophytes evolved from a eukaryote that engulfed another eukaryote, their plastids are surrounded by *four* membranes. The two inner membranes originated as the inner and

▼ **Figure 25.4 Diversity of plastids produced by endosymbiosis.** Studies of plastid-bearing eukaryotes suggest that plastids evolved from a cyanobacterium that was engulfed by an ancestral heterotrophic eukaryote (primary endosymbiosis). That ancestor then diversified into red algae and green algae, some of which were subsequently engulfed by other eukaryotes (secondary endosymbiosis).

MAKE CONNECTIONS *How many distinct genomes does a chlorarachniophyte cell contain? Explain. (See Figure 4.16.)*

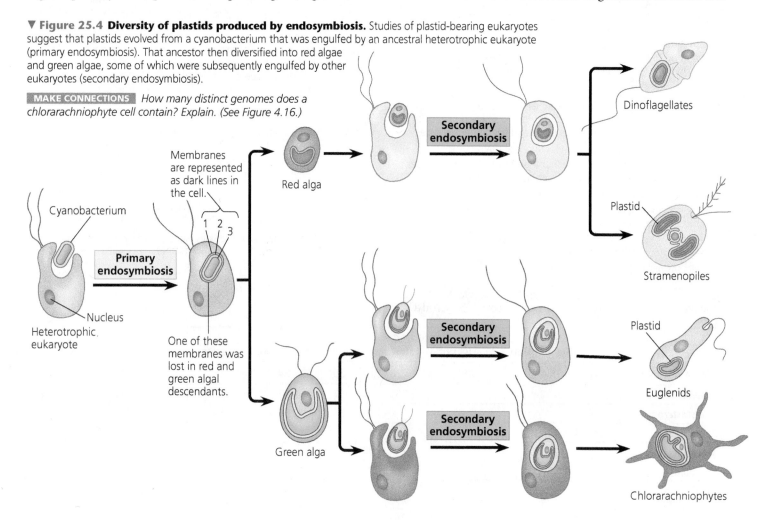

outer membranes of the ancient cyanobacterium; the third membrane is derived from the engulfed alga's plasma membrane; and the outermost membrane is derived from the heterotrophic eukaryote's food vacuole.

CONCEPT CHECK 25.1

1. Describe major events in the evolution of early eukaryotes that are documented in the fossil record.
2. Explain why eukaryotes are said to be "combination" organisms, and summarize the role of endosymbiosis in eukaryotic evolution.
3. **WHAT IF?** Suppose the photosynthetic organelle of a protist is discovered to be most closely related to a different cyanobacterium than the one that gave rise to plastids. What would this result suggest about the origin of eukaryotic photosynthesis?

For suggested answers, see Appendix A.

CONCEPT 25.2

Multicellularity has originated several times in eukaryotes

An orchestra can play a greater variety of musical compositions than a violin soloist can; the increased complexity of the orchestra makes more variations possible. Likewise, the origin of structurally complex eukaryotic cells sparked the evolution of greater morphological diversity than was possible for the simpler prokaryotic cells. This burst of evolutionary change resulted in the immense variety of unicellular protists that continue to flourish today. Another wave of diversification also occurred: Some single-celled eukaryotes gave rise to multicellular forms, whose descendants include a variety of algae, plants, fungi, and animals.

Multicellular Colonies

The first multicellular forms were *colonies*, collections of cells that are connected to one another but show little or no cellular differentiation. Multicellular colonies consisting of simple filaments, balls, or cell sheets occur early and often in the eukaryotic fossil record, and they remain common today (Figure 25.5). Such simple colonies are often found in eukaryotic lineages whose members have rigid cell walls. In such organisms, a colony may take shape as the cells divide and remain attached to one another by their shared cell walls. Simple colonies are also found in eukaryotes that lack rigid cell walls, but in this

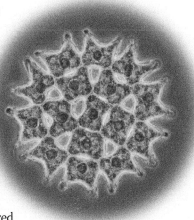

▲ **Figure 25.5** *Pediastrum.* This photosynthetic eukaryote forms flat colonies (LM).

case a colony may form when dividing cells are held together by proteins that physically connect adjacent cells to one another.

Some simple colonies have features that are intermediate between those of single-celled eukaryotes and those of more complex multicellular forms, such as plants, fungi, and animals. As you'll see in the following sections, such differences between unicellular, colonial, and multicellular eukaryotes can reveal clues to the origin of multicellularity.

Independent Origins of Complex Multicellularity

Although they occur in fewer lineages than do simple colonies, multicellular organisms with differentiated cells originated multiple times over the course of eukaryotic evolution. Examples include lineages of red, green, and brown algae, as well as plants, fungi, and animals. Genetic and morphological data indicate that these different lineages of complex multicellular eukaryotes arose independently of one another. For example, although both fungi and animals arose from single-celled ancestors, they arose from *different* single-celled ancestors.

The fact that complex multicellularity has originated multiple times allows us to examine the similarities and differences in how these independent groups arose. We'll begin with *Volvox*, a multicellular green alga with two types of differentiated cells (Figure 25.6). (It is because of these differentiated cells that most researchers refer to *Volvox* as "multicellular," as opposed to "colonial.") DNA evidence indicates that this

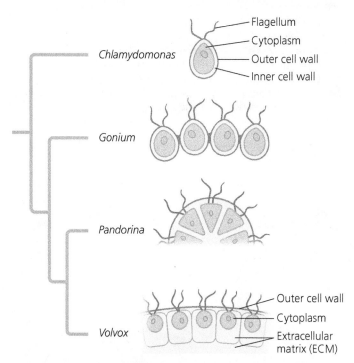

▲ **Figure 25.6 Morphological change in the *Volvox* lineage.** *Chlamydomonas* cell wall has both an outer wall (gray) and an inner wall (yellow). *Gonium* cells resemble a *Chlamydomonas* cell, and the structures that attach *Gonium* cells to one another contain proteins homologous to those in the *Chlamydomonas* cell wall. In *Pandorina* and *Volvox*, the cells are embedded in an extracellular matrix containing proteins homologous to those found in the *Chlamydomonas* inner wall.

species forms a monophyletic group with a single-celled alga (*Chlamydomonas*) and several colonial species. *Volvox* cells are embedded in an extracellular matrix composed of proteins homologous to those in the *Chlamydomonas* cell wall; the same is true for the colonial species that branch between *Chlamydomonas* and *Volvox*. This suggests that multicellularity in *Volvox* may have originated as descendants of a single-celled common ancestor gave rise to a series of larger and more complex colonial forms.

A 2010 comparison of the *Chlamydomonas* and *Volvox* genomes yielded a further surprising result: *Volvox* has few novel genes that could account for the differences in morphology seen between these species. This suggests that the transition to multicellularity may not require the origin of many new genes. Instead, this transition may result from changes in how existing genes are used—a conclusion that is also supported by recent studies on the origin of multicellularity in animals.

Steps in the Origin of Multicellular Animals

Although the origin of animals was a pivotal moment in the history of life, until recently little was known about the genetic toolkit that facilitated the emergence of multicellular animals from their single-celled ancestors. One way to gather information about this toolkit is to identify protist groups that are closely related to animals. As shown in **Figure 25.7**, a combination of morphological and molecular evidence points to choanoflagellates as the closest living relatives of animals. Based on such evidence, researchers have hypothesized that the common ancestor of

choanoflagellates and living animals may have been a unicellular suspension feeder that resembled present-day choanoflagellates.

Note that the origin of multicellularity in animals required the evolution of new ways for cells to adhere (attach) and signal (communicate) to each other. In an effort to learn more about such mechanisms, a recent study compared the genome of the unicellular choanoflagellate *Monosiga brevicollis* with those of representative animals.

This analysis uncovered 78 protein domains in *M. brevicollis* that were otherwise only known to occur in animals. (A *domain* is a key structural or functional region of a protein.) In animals, many of these shared protein domains function in cell adherence or cell signaling. To give just two examples, *M. brevicollis* has genes that encode domains of certain proteins (known as cadherins) that play key roles in how animal cells attach to one another, as well as genes that encode protein domains that animals (and only animals) use in cell-signaling pathways.

New research has also enabled us to take a closer look at specific proteins that played important roles in the origin of multicellularity in animals. Were these proteins composed mostly of domains found in ancestral choanoflagellate proteins? Or did they have a more novel structure? Consider the cadherin attachment proteins mentioned earlier. DNA sequence analyses show that animal cadherin proteins are composed primarily of domains that are also found in a cadherin-like protein of choanoflagellates (**Figure 25.8**). However, animal cadherin proteins that attach cells to one another also contain a highly conserved region not found in

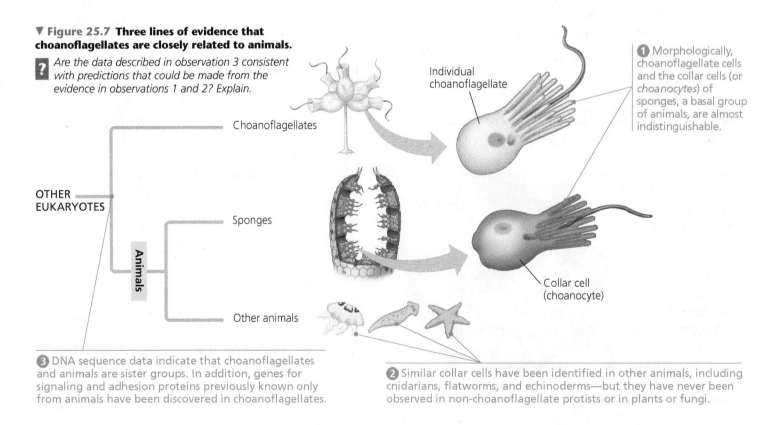

▼ **Figure 25.7 Three lines of evidence that choanoflagellates are closely related to animals.**

? *Are the data described in observation 3 consistent with predictions that could be made from the evidence in observations 1 and 2? Explain.*

Choanoflagellates

OTHER EUKARYOTES

Animals

Sponges

Other animals

Individual choanoflagellate

1 Morphologically, choanoflagellate cells and the collar cells (or *choanocytes*) of sponges, a basal group of animals, are almost indistinguishable.

Collar cell (choanocyte)

3 DNA sequence data indicate that choanoflagellates and animals are sister groups. In addition, genes for signaling and adhesion proteins previously known only from animals have been discovered in choanoflagellates.

2 Similar collar cells have been identified in other animals, including cnidarians, flatworms, and echinoderms—but they have never been observed in non-choanoflagellate protists or in plants or fungi.

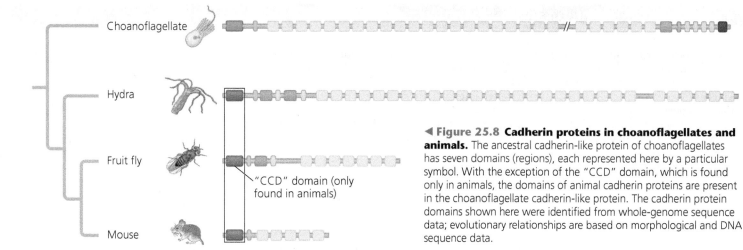

Choanoflagellate

Hydra

Fruit fly

"CCD" domain (only found in animals)

Mouse

◀ **Figure 25.8 Cadherin proteins in choanoflagellates and animals.** The ancestral cadherin-like protein of choanoflagellates has seven domains (regions), each represented here by a particular symbol. With the exception of the "CCD" domain, which is found only in animals, the domains of animal cadherin proteins are present in the choanoflagellate cadherin-like protein. The cadherin protein domains shown here were identified from whole-genome sequence data; evolutionary relationships are based on morphological and DNA sequence data.

the choanoflagellate protein (the "CCD" domain shown in Figure 25.8). These results suggest that the origin of the cadherin attachment protein occurred by the rearrangement of protein domains found in choanoflagellates—along with the incorporation of a novel domain, the conserved CCD region.

Overall, comparisons of choanoflagellate and animal genome sequences tell us that key steps in the transition to multicellularity in animals involved new ways of using proteins or parts of proteins that were encoded by genes found in choanoflagellates. Thus, as we also saw for the origin of multicellularity in *Volvox*, the origin of multicellularity in animals may have resulted mostly from the co-opting of genes used for other purposes in choanoflagellates—not from the evolution of a genetic toolkit composed of many novel genes.

CONCEPT CHECK 25.2

1. Summarize the evidence that choanoflagellates are the sister group of animals.
2. **MAKE CONNECTIONS** Describe how the origin of multicellularity in animals illustrates Darwin's concept of descent with modification (see Concept 19.2).
3. **WHAT IF?** Cells in *Volvox*, plants, and fungi are similar in being bounded by a cell wall. Predict whether the cell-to-cell attachments of these organisms form using similar or different molecules. Explain.

For suggested answers, see Appendix A.

CONCEPT 25.3

Four "supergroups" of eukaryotes have been proposed based on morphological and molecular data

How have events described so far in this chapter influenced the diversity of eukaryotes living today? First, by their very nature, eukaryotes are "combination" organisms. Having originated

by endosymbiosis, they had archaeal and bacterial genes and they possessed endosymbionts with novel metabolic capabilities. These features promoted the diversification of unicellular protists seen in the fossil record and still evident today in a drop of pond water. The independent origins of complex multicellularity in several eukaryotic lineages also had a major influence. Each of these independent groups evolved different solutions to the various challenges that all organisms face, thus contributing to the rich diversity of eukaryotes alive today. We'll survey that diversity here, beginning with an overview of the big picture: the four eukaryotic "supergroups."

Four Supergroups of Eukaryotes

Our understanding of the evolutionary history of eukaryotes has been in a state of flux in recent years. Genetic and morphological studies have shown that some protists are more closely related to plants, fungi, or animals than they are to other protists. As a result, the kingdom in which all protists once were classified, Protista, has been abandoned, and various lineages of protists are now recognized as kingdoms in their own right. Other hypotheses have been discarded as well. For example, in the early 1990s, many biologists thought that the oldest lineage of living eukaryotes consisted of the *amitochondriate protists*, organisms without conventional mitochondria. But recent structural and DNA data have undermined this hypothesis. Many of the so-called amitochondriate protists have been shown to have mitochondria—though reduced ones—and some of these organisms are now classified in distantly related groups.

The ongoing changes in our understanding of the phylogeny of eukaryotes pose challenges to students and instructors alike. Hypotheses about these relationships are a focus of scientific activity, changing rapidly as new data cause previous ideas to be modified or discarded. We'll focus here on one current hypothesis: the four supergroups of eukaryotes shown in **Figure 25.9**. Because the root of the eukaryotic tree is not

The tree below represents a phylogenetic hypothesis for the relationships among eukaryotes on Earth today. The eukaryotic groups at the branch tips are related in larger "supergroups," labeled vertically at the far right of the tree. Groups that were formerly classified in the kingdom Protista are highlighted in yellow. Dotted lines indicate evolutionary relationships that are uncertain and proposed clades that are under active debate. For clarity, this tree only includes representative clades from each supergroup. In addition, the recent discoveries of many new groups of eukaryotes indicate that eukaryotic diversity is actually much greater than shown here.

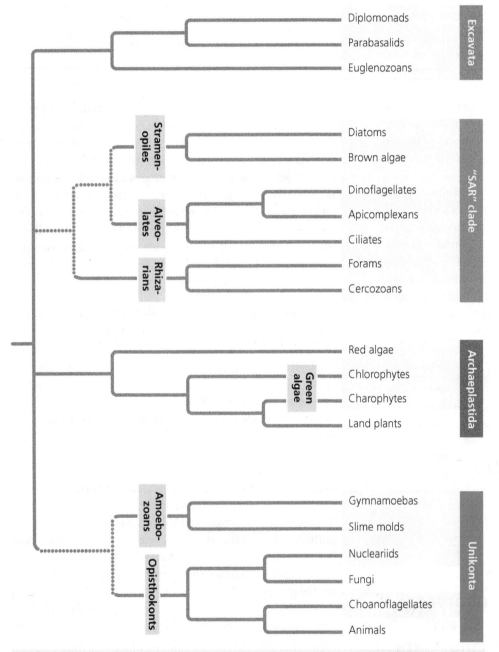

■ **Excavata**

Some members of this supergroup have an "excavated" groove on one side of the cell body. Two major clades (the parabasalids and diplomonads) have modified mitochondria; members of a third clade (the euglenozoans) have flagella that differ in structure from those of other organisms. Excavates include parasites such as *Giardia*, as well as many predatory and photosynthetic species.

5 μm

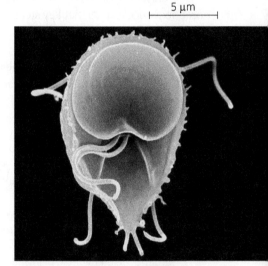

***Giardia intestinalis*, a diplomonad parasite.** This diplomonad (colorized SEM), which lacks the characteristic surface groove of the Excavata, inhabits the intestines of mammals. It can infect people when they drink water contaminated with feces containing *Giardia* cysts. Drinking such water—even from a seemingly pristine stream—can cause severe diarrhea. Boiling the water kills the parasite.

? *Based on the fossil record of early eukaryotes and the tree shown here, by what date had the supergroups begun to diverge from one another? Explain.*

■ "SAR" Clade

This supergroup contains (and is named after) three large and very diverse clades: Stramenopila, Alveolata, and Rhizaria. Stramenopiles include some of the most important photosynthetic organisms on Earth, such as the diatoms shown here. Alveolates also include photosynthetic species, as well as important pathogens, such as *Plasmodium*, which causes malaria. Many of the key groups of photosynthetic stramenopiles and alveolates are thought to have arisen by secondary endosymbiosis.

50 µm

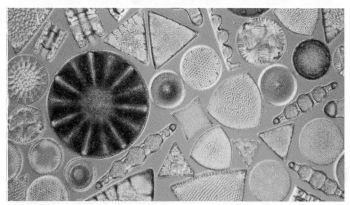

Diatom diversity. These beautiful single-celled protists are important photosynthetic organisms in aquatic communities (LM).

The rhizarian subgroup of the SAR clade includes many species of amoebas, most of which have pseudopodia that are threadlike in shape. Pseudopodia are extensions that can bulge from any portion of the cell; they are used in movement and in the capture of prey.

100 µm

***Globigerina*, a rhizarian in the SAR supergroup.** This species is a foram, a group whose members have threadlike pseudopodia that extend through pores in the shell, or test (LM). The inset shows a foram test, which is hardened by calcium carbonate.

■ Archaeplastida

This supergroup of eukaryotes includes red algae and green algae, along with land plants. Red algae and green algae include unicellular species, colonial species, and multicellular species (including the green alga *Volvox*). Many of the large algae known informally as "seaweeds" are multicellular red or green algae. Protists in Archaeplastida include key photosynthetic species that form the base of the food web in many aquatic communities.

20 µm   50 µm

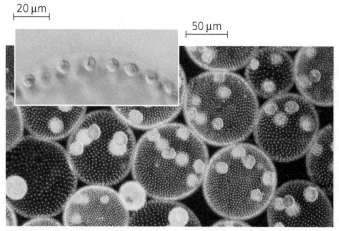

***Volvox*, a multicellular freshwater green alga.** This alga resembles a hollow ball whose wall is composed of hundreds of biflagellated cells (see inset LM) embedded in a gelatinous matrix. The cells in the wall are usually connected by cytoplasmic strands; if isolated, these cells cannot reproduce. However, the alga also contains cells that are specialized for either sexual or asexual reproduction. The large algae shown here will eventually release the small "daughter" algae that can be seen within them (LM).

■ Unikonta

This supergroup of eukaryotes includes amoebas that have lobe- or tube-shaped pseudopodia, as well as animals, fungi, and non-amoeba protists that are closely related to animals or fungi. According to one current hypothesis, the unikonts may have been the first group of eukaryotes to diverge from other eukaryotes; however, this hypothesis has yet to be widely accepted.

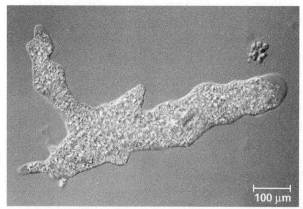

100 µm

A unikont amoeba. This amoeba, the gymnamoeba *Amoeba proteus,* is using its pseudopodia to move.

known, all four supergroups are shown as diverging simultaneously from a common ancestor. We know that this is not correct, but we do not know which organisms were the first to diverge from the others. In addition, while some of the groups in Figure 25.9 are well supported by morphological and DNA data, others are more controversial.

We'll now examine some representative members of the four supergroups. As you read about these groups, it may be helpful to focus less on the specific names of their members and more on why these organisms are important and how ongoing research is elucidating their evolutionary relationships.

Excavates

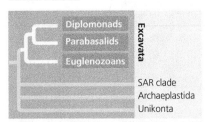

The clade **Excavata** (the excavates) was originally proposed based on morphological studies of the cytoskeleton. The name derives from the fact that some members of this diverse group feature an "excavated" feeding groove on one side of the cell body. The excavates include the diplomonads, the parabasalids, and the euglenozoans. Molecular data indicate that each of these three groups is monophyletic, and recent genomic studies have supported the monophyly of the excavate supergroup.

Diplomonads and Parabasalids

The protists in these two groups lack plastids and have highly modified mitochondria (until recently, they were thought to lack mitochondria altogether). Most diplomonads and parabasalids are found in anaerobic environments.

Diplomonads have reduced mitochondria called *mitosomes*. These organelles lack functional electron transport chains and hence cannot use oxygen to help extract energy from carbohydrates and other organic molecules. Instead, diplomonads get the energy they need from anaerobic biochemical pathways. Many diplomonads are parasites, including the infamous *Giardia intestinalis* (see Figure 25.9). These parasites propel themselves within a host using multiple flagella.

Parabasalids also have reduced mitochondria; called *hydrogenosomes*, these organelles generate some energy anaerobically, releasing hydrogen gas as a by-product. The best-known parabasalid is *Trichomonas vaginalis*, a sexually transmitted parasite that infects some 5 million people each year. *T. vaginalis* travels along the mucus-coated lining of the human reproductive and urinary tracts by moving its flagella and by undulating part of its plasma membrane **(Figure 25.10)**.

Euglenozoans

Protists called **euglenozoans** belong to a diverse clade that includes predatory heterotrophs, photosynthetic autotrophs, and parasites. The main morphological feature that

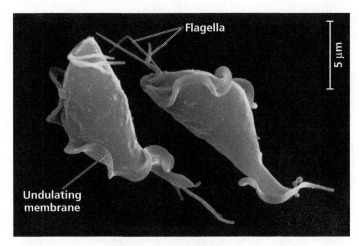

▲ **Figure 25.10 The parabasalid parasite, *Trichomonas vaginalis* (colorized SEM).**

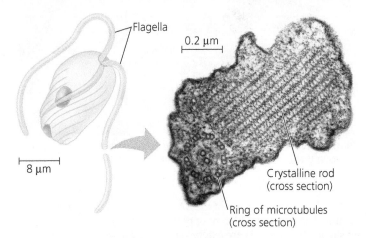

▲ **Figure 25.11 Euglenozoan flagellum.** Most euglenozoans have a crystalline rod inside one of their flagella (the TEM is a flagellum shown in cross section).

distinguishes protists in this clade is the presence of a rod with either a spiral or a crystalline structure inside each of their flagella **(Figure 25.11)**. The two best-studied groups of euglenozoans are the euglenids and the kinetoplastids.

A *euglenid* has a pocket at one end of the cell from which one or two flagella emerge (see the drawing in Figure 25.11). Some euglenids perform photosynthesis when sunlight is available; when sunlight is not available, they can become heterotrophic, absorbing organic nutrients from their environment. Many other euglenids engulf prey by phagocytosis.

A *kinetoplastid* has a single, large mitochondrion that contains an organized mass of DNA called a kinetoplast. These protists include species that feed on prokaryotes in aquatic ecosystems, as well as species that parasitize animals, plants, and other protists. For example, kinetoplastids in the genus *Trypanosoma* infect humans and cause sleeping sickness, a neurological disease that is invariably fatal if not treated **(Figure 25.12)**.

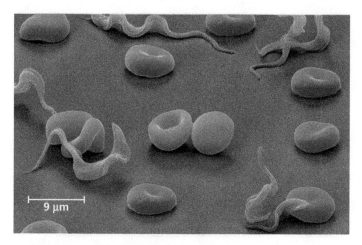

9 μm

▲ **Figure 25.12** *Trypanosoma*, **the kinetoplastid that causes sleeping sickness.** The purple, ribbon-shaped cells among these red blood cells are the trypanosomes (colorized SEM).

The "SAR" Clade

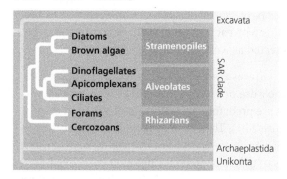

Recent genomic studies have led researchers to propose that three major clades of protists—the stramenopiles, alveolates, and rhizarians—form a monophyletic supergroup referred to as the **"SAR" clade**, after the first letters of its member clades.

Stramenopiles

One major subgroup of the SAR clade, the **stramenopiles**, arose by secondary endosymbiosis (see Figure 25.4) and include some of the most important photosynthetic organisms on the planet. Here we'll focus on two clades of stramenopiles: diatoms and brown algae.

Diatoms A key group of photosynthetic protists, **diatoms** are unicellular algae that have a unique glass-like wall made of silicon dioxide embedded in an organic matrix **(Figure 25.13)**. The wall consists of two parts that overlap like a shoe box and its lid. These walls provide effective protection from the crushing jaws of predators: Live diatoms can withstand pressures as great as 1.4 million kg/m^2, equal to the pressure under each leg of a table supporting an elephant!

With an estimated 100,000 living species, diatoms are a highly diverse group of protists. They are among the most abundant photosynthetic organisms both in the ocean and in lakes: One bucket of water scooped from the surface of the sea may contain millions of these microscopic algae. As we'll

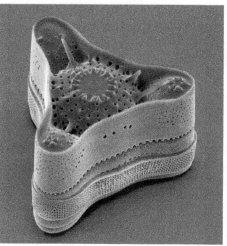

◀ **Figure 25.13** **The diatom** *Triceratium morlandii* **(colorized SEM).**

40 μm

discuss later in the chapter, the photosynthetic activity of these widespread and abundant algae can affect global carbon dioxide levels.

Brown Algae The largest and most complex algae are **brown algae**. All are multicellular, and most are marine. Brown algae are especially common along temperate coasts, where the water is cool. They owe their characteristic brown or olive color to the carotenoids in their plastids.

Many of the species commonly called "seaweeds" are brown algae. Some brown algal seaweeds have specialized tissues and organs that resemble those in plants, such as a rootlike **holdfast**, which anchors the alga, and a stemlike **stipe**, which supports the leaflike **blades (Figure 25.14)**. However, morphological and DNA evidence show that these

Blade

Stipe

Holdfast

▲ **Figure 25.14** **Seaweeds: adapted to life at the ocean's margins.** The sea palm (*Postelsia*) lives on rocks along the coast of the northwestern United States and western Canada. The body of this brown alga is well adapted to maintaining a firm foothold despite the crashing surf.

similarities evolved independently in the algal and plant lineages and are thus analogous, not homologous. In addition, while plants have adaptations (such as rigid stems) that provide support against gravity, brown algae have adaptations that enable their main photosynthetic surfaces (the leaflike blades) to be near the water surface. Some brown algae accomplish this task with gas-filled, bubble-shaped floats. Giant brown algae known as kelps that live in deep waters use a different means: Their blades are attached to stipes that can rise as much as 60 m from the seafloor, more than half the length of a football field.

Alveolates

Members of the next subgroup of the SAR clade, the **alveolates**, have membrane-enclosed sacs (alveoli) just under the plasma membrane **(Figure 25.15)**. Alveolates are abundant in many habitats and include a wide range of photosynthetic and heterotrophic protists. We'll discuss two alveolate clades here, a group of flagellates (the dinoflagellates) and a group of protists that move using cilia (the ciliates); we'll discuss a third clade (the apicomplexans) that parasitizes animals in Concept 25.4.

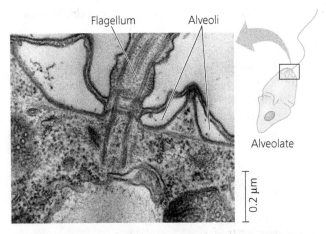

▲ **Figure 25.15 Alveoli.** These sacs under the plasma membrane are a characteristic that distinguishes alveolates from other eukaryotes (TEM).

Dinoflagellates The cells of many **dinoflagellates** are reinforced by cellulose plates. Two flagella located in grooves in this "armor" make dinoflagellates (from the Greek *dinos*, whirling) spin as they move through the waters of their marine and freshwater communities **(Figure 25.16)**. Although the group originated by secondary endosymbiosis (see Figure 25.4), roughly half of all dinoflagellates are now purely heterotrophic. Others are important photosynthetic species, while still others are **mixotrophs**, organisms that combine photosynthesis *and* heterotrophic nutrition.

Episodes of explosive population growth, or *blooms*, in dinoflagellates sometimes cause a phenomenon called "red tide." The blooms make coastal waters appear brownish red or pink because of the presence of carotenoids, the most common pigments in dinoflagellate plastids. Toxins produced by certain

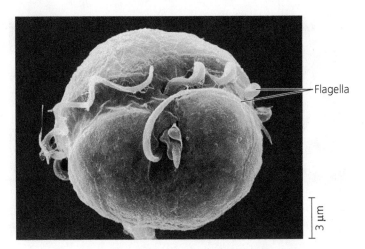

▲ **Figure 25.16 *Pfiesteria shumwayae*, a dinoflagellate.** Beating of the spiral flagellum, which lies in a groove that encircles the cell, makes this alveolate spin (colorized SEM).

dinoflagellates have caused massive kills of invertebrates and fishes. Humans who eat molluscs that have accumulated the toxins are affected as well, sometimes fatally.

Ciliates The **ciliates** are a large and varied group of protists named for their use of cilia to move and feed **(Figure 25.17)**. Most ciliates are predators, typically of bacteria or small protists (see Figure 25.1). The cilia may completely cover the cell surface or may be clustered in a few rows or tufts. In certain species, rows of tightly packed cilia function collectively in locomotion. Other ciliates scurry about on leg-like structures constructed from many cilia bonded together.

Rhizarians

Our next subgroup of the SAR clade is the **rhizarians**. Many species in this group are **amoebas**, protists that move and feed by means of **pseudopodia**, extensions that may bulge from almost anywhere on the cell surface. An amoeba moves by extending a pseudopodium and anchoring the tip; more cytoplasm then streams into the pseudopodium. Amoebas do not constitute a monophyletic group; instead, they are dispersed across many distantly related eukaryotic taxa. Most amoebas that are rhizarians differ morphologically from other amoebas by having threadlike pseudopodia. Rhizarians also include flagellated (non-amoeboid) protists that feed using threadlike pseudopodia.

We'll examine two groups of rhizarians here: forams and cercozoans.

Forams The protists called **foraminiferans** (from the Latin *foramen*, little hole, and *ferre*, to bear), or **forams**, are named for their porous shells, called **tests** (see Figure 25.9). Foram tests consist of a single piece of organic material that is hardened with calcium carbonate in most species. The pseudopodia that extend through the pores function in swimming, test formation, and feeding. Many forams also derive nourishment from the photosynthesis of symbiotic algae that live within

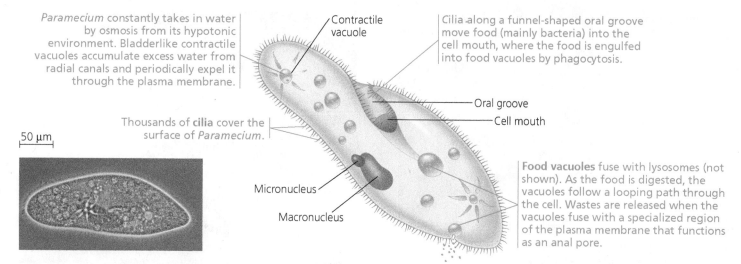

Paramecium constantly takes in water by osmosis from its hypotonic environment. Bladderlike contractile vacuoles accumulate excess water from radial canals and periodically expel it through the plasma membrane.

Contractile vacuole

Cilia along a funnel-shaped oral groove move food (mainly bacteria) into the cell mouth, where the food is engulfed into food vacuoles by phagocytosis.

Oral groove

Cell mouth

Thousands of **cilia** cover the surface of *Paramecium*.

50 µm

Micronucleus

Macronucleus

Food vacuoles fuse with lysosomes (not shown). As the food is digested, the vacuoles follow a looping path through the cell. Wastes are released when the vacuoles fuse with a specialized region of the plasma membrane that functions as an anal pore.

▲ **Figure 25.17 Structure and function in the ciliate *Paramecium caudatum*.**

the tests. Found in both lakes and oceans, most forams live in sand or attach themselves to rocks or algae, but some drift in currents near the water's surface. The largest forams, though single-celled, have tests with a diameter of several centimeters.

Cercozoans First identified in molecular phylogenies, the **cercozoans** are a large group of amoeboid and flagellated protists that feed with threadlike pseudopodia. Common in marine, freshwater, and soil ecosystems, many cercozoans are parasites of plants, animals, or other protists; many others are predators that feed on bacteria, fungi, and other protists. One small group of cercozoans, the chlorarachniophytes (mentioned earlier in the discussion of secondary endosymbiosis), are mixotrophic: These organisms ingest smaller protists and bacteria as well as perform photosynthesis. At least one other cercozoan, *Paulinella chromatophora*, is an autotroph, deriving its energy from light and its carbon from carbon dioxide. As described in **Figure 25.18**,

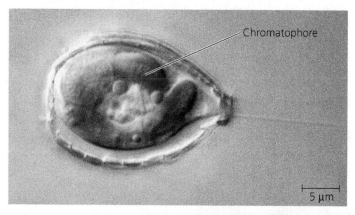

Chromatophore

5 µm

▲ **Figure 25.18 A second case of primary endosymbiosis?** The cercozoan *Paulinella* conducts photosynthesis in a unique sausage-shaped structure called a chromatophore (LM). Chromatophores are surrounded by a membrane with a peptidoglycan layer, suggesting that they are derived from a bacterium. DNA evidence indicates that chromatophores are derived from a different cyanobacterium than that from which other plastids are derived.

Paulinella appears to represent an intriguing additional evolutionary example of a eukaryotic lineage that obtained its photosynthetic apparatus directly from a cyanobacterium.

Archaeplastids

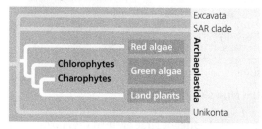

As described earlier, morphological and molecular evidence indicates that plastids arose when a heterotrophic protist acquired a cyanobacterial endosymbiont. Later, photosynthetic descendants of this ancient protist evolved into red algae and green algae (see Figure 25.4), and the lineage that produced green algae then gave rise to land plants. Together, red algae, green algae, and land plants make up our third eukaryotic supergroup, which is called **Archaeplastida**. We will examine plants and the colonization of land in Chapter 26; here we will look at the diversity of their closest algal relatives, red algae and green algae.

Red Algae

Many of the 6,000 known species of **red algae** (rhodophytes, from the Greek *rhodos*, red) are reddish, owing to a photosynthetic pigment called phycoerythrin, which masks the green of chlorophyll. However, other species (those adapted to more shallow water) have less phycoerythrin. As a result, red algal species may be greenish red in very shallow water, bright red at moderate depths, and almost black in deep water. Some species lack pigmentation altogether and function heterotrophically as parasites on other red algae.

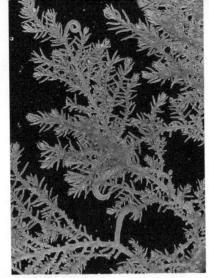

► *Bonnemaisonia hamifera.* This red alga has a filamentous form.

▼ **Nori.** The red alga *Porphyra* has a leafy form and is the source of a traditional Japanese food.

8 mm

The seaweed is grown on nets in shallow coastal waters.

After being dried, the paper-thin, glossy sheets of nori make a mineral-rich wrap for rice, seafood, and vegetables in sushi.

▲ **Figure 25.19 Red algae.**

Red algae are the most abundant large algae in the warm coastal waters of tropical oceans. Some of their photosynthetic pigments, including phycoerythrin, allow them to absorb blue and green light, which penetrate relatively far into the water—one species of red alga has been discovered near the Bahamas at a depth of more than 260 m. Most red algae are multicellular, and they grow in a variety of forms **(Figure 25.19).** Although none are as big as the giant brown kelps, the largest multicellular red algae are included in the informal designation "seaweeds." You may have eaten one of these multicellular red algae, *Porphyra* (Japanese "nori"), as crispy sheets or as a wrap for sushi. Red algae reproduce sexually. However, unlike other algae, red algae do not have flagellated gametes, so they depend on water currents to bring gametes together for fertilization.

Green Algae

The grass-green chloroplasts of **green algae** have a structure and pigment composition much like the chloroplasts of land plants. Molecular systematics and cellular morphology leave little doubt that green algae and land plants are closely related. In fact, some systematists now advocate including green algae in an expanded "plant" kingdom, Viridiplantae (from the Latin *viridis*, green). Phylogenetically, this change makes sense, since otherwise the green algae are a paraphyletic group.

(a) *Ulva,* **or sea lettuce.** This edible chlorophyte has leaflike blades and a holdfast that anchors the alga.

2 cm

(b) *Caulerpa,* **an intertidal chlorophyte.** The filaments lack cross-walls and thus are multinucleate. In effect, the algal body is one huge "supercell."

▲ **Figure 25.20 Multicellular chlorophytes.**

Green algae are divided into two main groups, the charophytes and the chlorophytes. The charophytes are the algae most closely related to land plants, and we will discuss them along with plants in Chapter 26.

The second group, the chlorophytes (from the Greek *chloros*, green), includes more than 7,000 species. Most live in fresh water, but there are also many marine and some terrestrial species. Nearly all species of chlorophytes reproduce sexually by means of biflagellated gametes that have cup-shaped chloroplasts. The simplest chlorophytes are unicellular species such as *Chlamydomonas* (see Figure 25.6), which resemble gametes of more complex chlorophytes. Some unicellular chlorophytes live independently in aquatic habitats while others live symbiotically within other eukaryotes, contributing part of their photosynthetic output to the food supply of their hosts. Larger size and greater complexity are found in various multicellular chlorophytes, including *Volvox* (see Figure 25.9) and *Ulva* **(Figure 25.20).**

Unikonts

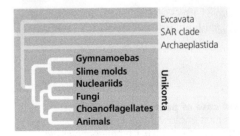

The fourth supergroup, **Unikonta,** is an extremely diverse group that includes animals, fungi, and some protists. There are two major clades of unikonts, the amoebozoans (gymnamoebas and slime molds) and the opisthokonts (animals, fungi, and closely related protist groups). Each of these two major clades is strongly supported by molecular systematics. The close relationship between amoebozoans and opisthokonts is more controversial. Support for this close relationship is provided by comparisons of myosin proteins and by some (but not all) studies based on hundreds of genes or whole genomes.

Another controversy involving the unikonts concerns the root of the eukaryotic tree. Recall that the root of a phylogenetic tree anchors the tree in time: Branch points close to the root are the oldest. At present, the root of the eukaryotic tree is uncertain; hence, we do not know which group of eukaryotes was the first to diverge from other eukaryotes. Some hypotheses, such as the amitochondriate hypothesis described earlier, have been abandoned, but researchers have yet to agree on an alternative. If the root of the eukaryotic tree were known, scientists could infer characteristics of the common ancestor of all eukaryotes.

In trying to determine the root of the eukaryotic tree, researchers have based their phylogenies on different sets of genes, some of which have produced conflicting results. Researchers have also tried a different approach based on tracing the occurrence of a rare evolutionary event (Figure 25.21). Results from this "rare event" approach suggest that the unikonts were the first eukaryotes to diverge from other eukaryotes. If this hypothesis is correct, animals and fungi belong to an early-diverging group of eukaryotes, while protists that lack typical mitochondria (such as the diplomonads and parabasalids) diverged much later in the history of life. This idea remains controversial and will require more supporting evidence to be widely accepted.

Amoebozoans

The **amoebozoan** clade includes many species of amoebas that have lobe- or tube-shaped pseudopodia, rather than the thread-like pseudopodia found in rhizarians. Although some amoebozoans are parasites, most are free-living. The gymnamoebas, for example, are a group of free-living, unicellular predators and scavengers that are ubiquitous in soil and in aquatic environments (see Figure 25.9). Free-living amoebozoans also include the slime molds, a group of multicellular amoebozoans.

Slime molds were once thought to be fungi because, like fungi, they produce fruiting bodies that aid in spore dispersal. However, the resemblance between slime molds and fungi appears to be another case of evolutionary convergence. DNA sequence analyses indicate that slime molds descended from unicellular amoebozoan ancestors, making them another example of the independent evolution of multicellularity in eukaryotes (see Concept 25.2).

The life cycle of some slime molds can prompt us to question what it means to be an individual organism. Consider the cellular slime mold *Dictyostelium*. The feeding stage of this organism consists of solitary cells that function individually; but when food is depleted, the cells form an aggregate

▼ **Figure 25.21** Inquiry

Where is the root of the eukaryotic tree?

Experiment Responding to the difficulty in determining the root of the eukaryotic phylogenetic tree, Alexandra Stechmann and Thomas Cavalier-Smith proposed a new approach. They studied two genes, one coding for the enzyme dihydrofolate reductase (DHFR), the other for the enzyme thymidylate synthase (TS). Their approach took advantage of a rare evolutionary event: In some organisms, the genes for DHFR and TS have fused, leading to the production of a single protein with both enzyme activities. Stechmann and Cavalier-Smith amplified (using PCR; see Figure 13.25) and sequenced the genes for DHFR and TS in nine species (one choanoflagellate; two amoebozoans; one euglenozoan; one stramenopile; one alveolate; and three rhizarians). They combined their data with previously published data for species of bacteria, animals, plants, and fungi.

Results The bacteria studied all have separate genes coding for DHFR and TS, suggesting that this is the ancestral condition (red dot on the tree below). Other taxa with separate genes are denoted by red type. Fused genes are a derived character, found in certain members (blue type) of the supergroups Excavata, the SAR clade, and Archaeplastida:

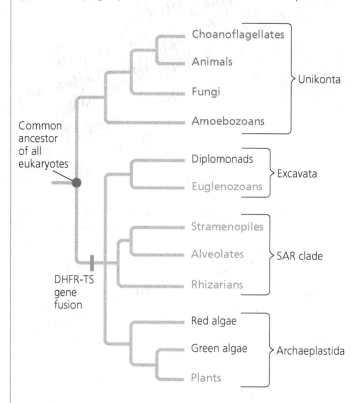

Conclusion These results support the hypothesis that the root of the tree is located between the unikonts and all other eukaryotes, suggesting that the unikonts were the first group of eukaryotes to diverge. Because support for this hypothesis is based on only one trait—the fusion of the genes for DHFR and TS—more data are needed to evaluate its validity.

Source A. Stechmann and T. Cavalier-Smith, Rooting the eukaryote tree by using a derived gene fusion, *Science* 297:89–91 (2002).

WHAT IF? Stechmann and Cavalier-Smith wrote that their conclusions are "valid only if the genes fused just once and were never secondarily split." Why is this assumption critical to their approach?

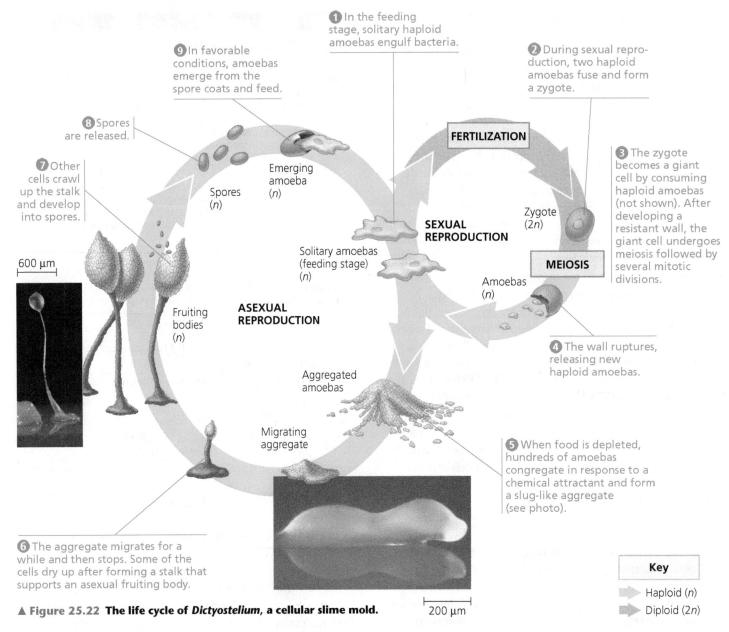

① In the feeding stage, solitary haploid amoebas engulf bacteria.

② During sexual reproduction, two haploid amoebas fuse and form a zygote.

⑨ In favorable conditions, amoebas emerge from the spore coats and feed.

FERTILIZATION

⑧ Spores are released.

③ The zygote becomes a giant cell by consuming haploid amoebas (not shown). After developing a resistant wall, the giant cell undergoes meiosis followed by several mitotic divisions.

⑦ Other cells crawl up the stalk and develop into spores.

Emerging amoeba (*n*)

Spores (*n*)

Zygote (2*n*)

SEXUAL REPRODUCTION

600 μm

Solitary amoebas (feeding stage) (*n*)

MEIOSIS

Amoebas (*n*)

Fruiting bodies (*n*)

ASEXUAL REPRODUCTION

④ The wall ruptures, releasing new haploid amoebas.

Aggregated amoebas

Migrating aggregate

⑤ When food is depleted, hundreds of amoebas congregate in response to a chemical attractant and form a slug-like aggregate (see photo).

⑥ The aggregate migrates for a while and then stops. Some of the cells dry up after forming a stalk that supports an asexual fruiting body.

Key

Haploid (*n*)

Diploid (2*n*)

▲ **Figure 25.22** **The life cycle of *Dictyostelium*, a cellular slime mold.**

200 μm

that functions as a unit **(Figure 25.22)**. These aggregated cells eventually form the slime mold's fruiting body stage. During this stage, the cells that form the stalk die as they dry out, while the spore cells at the top survive and have the potential to disperse and later reproduce.

Opisthokonts

Opisthokonts are an extremely diverse group of eukaryotes that includes animals, fungi, and several groups of protists. We will discuss the colonization of land and the evolutionary history of fungi and animals in Chapters 26 and 27. Of the opisthokont protists, we will discuss the nucleariids in Chapter 26 because they are more closely related to fungi than they are to other protists. And as we discussed earlier in this chapter, the choanoflagellates are more closely related to animals than they are to other protists. The nucleariids and choanoflagellates illustrate why scientists have abandoned the former kingdom

Protista: A monophyletic group that includes these single-celled eukaryotes would also have to include the multicellular animals and fungi that are closely related to them.

CONCEPT CHECK 25.3

1. Briefly describe the organisms found in each of the four eukaryotic supergroups.
2. **MAKE CONNECTIONS** Review Figures 7.2 and 8.5. Summarize how CO_2 and O_2 are both used and produced by aerobic algae.
3. **WHAT IF?** DNA sequence data for a diplomonad, a euglenozoan, a plant, and an unidentified protist suggest that the unidentified species is most closely related to the diplomonad. Further studies reveal that the unknown species has fully functional mitochondria. Based on these data, at what point on the phylogenetic tree in Figure 25.9 did the mystery protist's lineage probably diverge from other eukaryotic lineages? Explain.

For suggested answers, see Appendix A.

Single-celled eukaryotes play key roles in ecological communities and affect human health

As our survey of the four eukaryotic supergroups suggests, the large, multicellular organisms that we know best—the plants, animals, and fungi—are the tips of just a few branches on the eukaryotic tree of life. All the other branches are lineages of protists, and these protists exhibit an impressive range of structural and functional diversity, as we'll discuss. We'll then examine the effects of protists on ecological communities and human societies. (We focus on protists here, but we'll address similar topics for plants, fungi, and animals in Chapters 26 and 27.)

Structural and Functional Diversity in Protists

Most protists are unicellular, although there are some colonial and multicellular species. Single-celled protists are justifiably considered the simplest eukaryotes, but at the cellular level, many protists are very complex—the most elaborate of all cells. In multicellular organisms, essential biological functions are carried out by organs. Unicellular protists carry out the same functions, but they do so using subcellular organelles, not multicellular organs: the nucleus, endoplasmic reticulum, Golgi apparatus, and lysosomes.

Most protists are aquatic, and they are found almost anywhere there is water, including moist terrestrial habitats such as damp soil and leaf litter. In oceans and lakes, many protists attach to the bottom or creep through the sand and silt, while others float near the water's surface. The protists living in these varied habitats also show a wide range of nutritional diversity. As we've seen, many protists are photoautotrophs and contain chloroplasts. Many others are heterotrophs, absorbing organic molecules or ingesting larger food particles; such heterotrophic protists include important mutualistic and parasitic species. Still other protists are mixotrophs that combine photosynthesis *and* heterotrophic nutrition. Photoautotrophy, heterotrophy, and mixotrophy have all arisen independently in many different protist lineages. In part as a result of this nutritional and taxonomic diversity, protist producers and symbionts are abundant in natural communities and have large ecological effects.

Photosynthetic Protists

Many protists are important **producers**, organisms that use energy from light (or inorganic chemicals) to convert carbon dioxide to organic compounds. Producers form the base of ecological food webs. In aquatic communities, the main producers are photosynthetic protists and prokaryotes. All other organisms in the community depend on them for food, either directly (by eating them) or indirectly (by eating an organism that ate a producer; **Figure 25.23**). Scientists estimate that roughly 30% of the world's photosynthesis is performed by

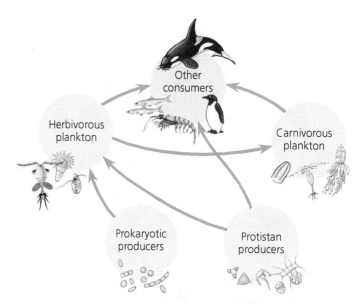

▲ **Figure 25.23 Protists: key producers in aquatic communities.** Arrows in this simplified food web lead from food sources to the organisms that eat them.

diatoms, dinoflagellates, multicellular algae, and other aquatic protists. Photosynthetic prokaryotes contribute another 20%, and land plants are responsible for the remaining 50%.

Because producers form the foundation of food webs, factors that affect producers can affect their entire community. In aquatic environments, photosynthetic protists are often held in check by low concentrations of nitrogen, phosphorus, or iron. Various human actions can increase the concentrations of these elements in aquatic communities. For example, some of the fertilizer applied to a field may be washed by rain into a river that drains into a lake or ocean. When people add nutrients to aquatic communities in this or other ways, the abundance of photosynthetic protists can increase spectacularly.

Such increases can have major ecological consequences. For example, earlier in the chapter we mentioned that diatoms can affect global carbon dioxide levels. This effect can result from a chain of events that occurs when ample nutrients produce a rapid increase (a bloom) in diatom abundance. Typically, diatoms are eaten by a variety of protists and invertebrates, but during a bloom, many escape this fate. When these uneaten diatoms die, their bodies sink to the ocean floor. Diatoms that sink to the ocean floor are not very likely to be broken down by bacteria and other decomposers. Hence, the carbon in their bodies remains there, rather than being released as carbon dioxide as the decomposers respire. The overall effect of these events is that carbon dioxide absorbed by diatoms during photosynthesis is transported, or "pumped," to the ocean floor. With an eye toward reducing global warming by lowering atmospheric carbon dioxide levels, some scientists advocate promoting diatom blooms by fertilizing the ocean with essential nutrients such as iron. Other scientists question this strategy, noting that small-scale tests of this idea have yielded mixed results and that it is difficult to predict the effects of large-scale manipulations of ecological communities.

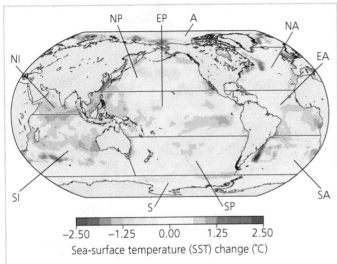

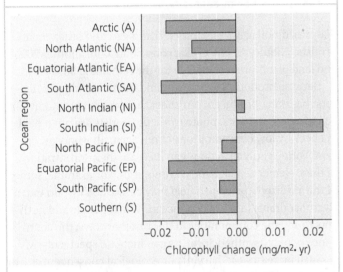

(a) Researchers studied 10 ocean regions, identified with letters on the map (see (b) for the corresponding names). SSTs have increased since 1950 in most areas of these regions.

(b) The concentration of chlorophyll, an index for the biomass and growth of marine producers, has decreased over the same time period in most ocean regions.

▲ **Figure 25.24 Effects of climate change on marine producers.**

A related and pressing question is how global warming will affect photosynthetic protists and other producers. Satellite data and historical observations show that the growth of photosynthetic protists and prokaryotes has declined in many ocean regions as sea surface temperatures have increased **(Figure 25.24)**. By what mechanism do rising sea surface temperatures reduce the growth of marine producers? One hypothesis relates to the rise, or upwelling, of cold, nutrient-rich waters from below. Many marine producers rely on nutrients brought to the surface in this way. However, rising sea surface temperatures can cause the formation of a layer of light, warm water that acts as a barrier to nutrient upwelling—thus reducing the growth of marine producers. If sustained, these changes would likely have far-reaching effects on marine ecosystems, fishery yields, and the global carbon cycle (see Chapter 42).

▶ **Figure 25.25 A symbiotic protist.** This organism is a hypermastigote, a member of a group of parabasalids that live in the gut of termites and certain cockroaches and enable the hosts to digest wood (SEM).

Symbiotic Protists

Many protists form symbiotic associations with other species. For example, photosynthetic dinoflagellates are food-providing symbiotic partners of the coral polyps that build coral reefs. Coral reefs are highly diverse ecological communities. That diversity ultimately depends on corals—and on the mutualistic protist symbionts that nourish them. Corals support reef diversity by providing food to some species and habitat to many others.

Another example is the wood-digesting protists that inhabit the gut of many termite species **(Figure 25.25)**. Unaided, termites cannot digest wood, and they rely on protistan or prokaryotic symbionts to do so. Termites cause over $3.5 billion in damage annually to wooden homes in the United States.

Symbiotic protists also include parasites that feed on the tissues of plants or animals. Among the species that parasitize plants, the stramenopile *Phytophthora ramorum* has emerged as a major new forest pathogen. This species causes sudden oak death (SOD), a disease that has killed millions of oaks and other trees in California and Oregon (see Chapter 41). A closely related species, *P. infestans*, causes potato late blight, which turns the stalk and stem of potato plants to black slime. Late blight contributed to the devastating Irish famine of the 19th century, in which a million people died and at least that many were forced to leave Ireland. The disease remains a major problem today, destroying as much as 70% of the crop in some areas.

We'll close the chapter by taking a closer look at the parasitic protists that cause disease in humans.

Effects on Human Health

Our bodies are home to many symbiotic species, including some protists that can cause disease. While bacteria and viruses may be the pathogens that most readily come to mind, protists that cause infectious disease can pose major challenges, both to our immune systems and to public health.

Consider *Trypanosoma*, the excavate that causes sleeping sickness (see Figure 25.12). This disease is fatal if not treated.

Trypanosomes evade immune responses with an effective "bait-and-switch" defense. The surface of a trypanosome is coated with millions of copies of a single protein. However, before the host's immune system can recognize the protein and mount an attack, new generations of the parasite switch to another surface protein with a different molecular structure. Frequent changes in the surface protein prevent the host from developing immunity. About a third of *Trypanosoma*'s genome is dedicated to producing these surface proteins.

A group of alveolates, the **apicomplexans**, includes protists that cause serious human diseases such as malaria. Nearly all apicomplexans are parasites of animals—and virtually all animal species examined so far are attacked by these parasites. Although apicomplexans are not photosynthetic, they retain a modified plastid (*apicoplast*), most likely of red algal origin

(see Figure 25.4). Apicomplexans typically have intricate life cycles with both sexual and asexual stages. Those life cycles often require two or more host species for completion. For example, *Plasmodium*, the parasite that causes malaria, lives in both mosquitoes and humans (**Figure 25.26**).

Historically, malaria has rivaled tuberculosis (which is caused by a bacterium) as the leading cause of human death by infectious disease. The incidence of malaria was diminished in the 1960s by insecticides that reduced carrier populations of *Anopheles* mosquitoes and by drugs that killed *Plasmodium* in humans. But the emergence of resistant varieties of both *Anopheles* and *Plasmodium* has led to a resurgence of malaria. About 250 million people in the tropics are currently infected, and 900,000 die each year. Efforts are under way to develop new methods of treatment, including drugs that target the

▼ **Figure 25.26 The two-host life cycle of *Plasmodium*, the apicomplexan that causes malaria.** The parasite enters its human host as tiny infectious cells called sporozoites.

? *In 2011, researchers discovered that the merozoite apicoplast has only one essential function: It synthesizes a chemical that the parasite requires for survival and cannot otherwise make. Explain why drugs that target the metabolic pathway by which this chemical is made would probably not harm humans.*

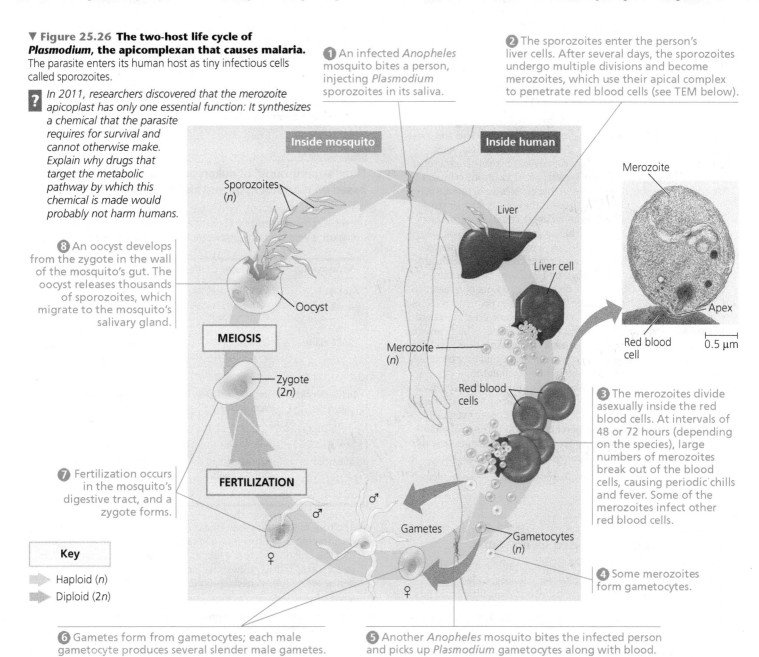

❶ An infected *Anopheles* mosquito bites a person, injecting *Plasmodium* sporozoites in its saliva.

❷ The sporozoites enter the person's liver cells. After several days, the sporozoites undergo multiple divisions and become merozoites, which use their apical complex to penetrate red blood cells (see TEM below).

❽ An oocyst develops from the zygote in the wall of the mosquito's gut. The oocyst releases thousands of sporozoites, which migrate to the mosquito's salivary gland.

❼ Fertilization occurs in the mosquito's digestive tract, and a zygote forms.

❸ The merozoites divide asexually inside the red blood cells. At intervals of 48 or 72 hours (depending on the species), large numbers of merozoites break out of the blood cells, causing periodic chills and fever. Some of the merozoites infect other red blood cells.

❹ Some merozoites form gametocytes.

❻ Gametes form from gametocytes; each male gametocyte produces several slender male gametes.

❺ Another *Anopheles* mosquito bites the infected person and picks up *Plasmodium* gametocytes along with blood.

Inside mosquito

Inside human

Sporozoites (*n*)

Oocyst

MEIOSIS

Zygote (2*n*)

FERTILIZATION

Gametes

Gametocytes (*n*)

Liver

Liver cell

Merozoite (*n*)

Red blood cells

Merozoite

Apex

Red blood cell

0.5 μm

Key

Haploid (*n*)

Diploid (2*n*)

apicoplast. This approach may be effective because the apicoplast, derived by secondary endosymbiosis from a prokaryote, has metabolic pathways different from those in humans.

As we've seen in this chapter, the origin of eukaryotes had an enormous impact on the history of life, leading to a great increase in the structural diversity of cells and ultimately to the rise of large, multicellular organisms. These changes set the stage for the events we'll describe in the next two chapters: the colonization of land by plants and fungi (Chapter 26) and the ecological and evolutionary effects resulting from the origin of animals (Chapter 27).

CONCEPT CHECK 25.4

1. Justify the claim that photosynthetic protists are among the biosphere's most important organisms.
2. Describe three symbioses that include protists.
3. **WHAT IF?** High water temperatures and pollution can cause corals to expel their dinoflagellate symbionts. Predict how such "coral bleaching" would affect corals and other species in the community.

For suggested answers, see Appendix A.

25 Chapter Review

SUMMARY OF KEY CONCEPTS

CONCEPT 25.1

Eukaryotes arose by endosymbiosis more than 1.8 billion years ago (pp. 481–487)

- Domain Eukarya contains many groups of **protists**, along with plants, animals, and fungi. Eukaryotic cells have a nucleus and other membrane-enclosed organelles, unlike the cells of prokaryotes. These membrane-enclosed organelles make the cells of eukaryotes more complex than the cells of prokaryotes. Eukaryotic cells also have a well-developed cytoskeleton that enables them to have asymmetric forms and to change in shape as they move, feed, or grow.
- The oldest fossils of eukaryotes are of single-celled organisms that lived 1.8 billion years ago. By 1.5 billion years ago, some fossil eukaryotes had asymmetric forms, indicating a well-developed cytoskeleton. Other biological innovations, such as complex multicellularity and sexual life cycles, were in place by 1.2 billion years ago. Larger eukaryotes appeared in the fossil record about 600 million years ago.
- DNA sequence analyses indicate that eukaryotes contain a mixture of archaeal and bacterial genes and cellular characteristics. According to **endosymbiont theory,** this mixture of features likely resulted because eukaryotes originated when an archaeal host (or a host with archaeal ancestors) engulfed a bacterium that would later become an organelle found in all eukaryotes, the mitochondrion.
- In addition to mitochondria, plastids are also thought to be descendants of bacteria that were engulfed by an early eukaryote and became endosymbionts. The plastid-bearing lineage eventually evolved into **red algae** and **green algae**. Other groups of photosynthetic protists evolved from secondary endosymbiosis events in which red algae or green algae were themselves engulfed.

? *What evidence indicates that mitochondria arose before plastids in eukaryotic evolution?*

CONCEPT 25.2

Multicellularity has originated several times in eukaryotes (pp. 487–489)

- The first multicellular eukaryotes were colonies, collections of cells that are connected to one another but show little or no cellular differentiation.
- Complex multicellular eukaryotes—those with differentiated cell types—arose independently in a variety of eukaryotic groups, including plants, fungi, animals, and several lineages of algae.

- Genomic analyses suggest that a transition to multicellularity from unicellular ancestors does not require the origin of large numbers of novel genes; instead, such transitions can result primarily from changes in how existing genes are used.

? *Describe an example that illustrates the role of co-opting genes in the origin of complex multicellular eukaryotes from their unicellular ancestors.*

CONCEPT 25.3

Four "supergroups" of eukaryotes have been proposed based on morphological and molecular data (pp. 489–498)

- In one hypothesis, eukaryotes are grouped into four supergroups, each a monophyletic clade. Each eukaryotic supergroup contains a great diversity of organisms, most of which are unicellular.

Supergroup	Major Clades	Specific Example
Excavata	Diplomonads, parabasalids, euglenozoans	*Euglena*
"SAR" clade	Stramenopiles, alveolates, rhizarians	*Plasmodium*
Archaeplastida	Red algae, green algae, land plants	*Chlamydomonas*
Unikonta	Amoebozoans, opisthokonts	*Amoeba*

- The root of the eukaryotic tree is not known. An approach based on a tracing the occurrence of a rare evolutionary event suggests that the unikonts were the first eukaryotes to diverge from other eukaryotes. This hypothesis will require more supporting evidence before it is widely accepted.

? *Summarize recent changes in our understanding of the evolutionary history of eukaryotes, beginning with an explanation for why kingdom Protista has been abandoned.*

CONCEPT 25.4

Single-celled eukaryotes play key roles in ecological communities and affect human health (pp. 499–506)

- The most elaborate of all cells, unicellular protists use subcellular organelles to accomplish the essential biological functions that multicellular organisms perform with organs. Protists live in a wide range of habitats and include many different lineages of photoautotrophic, heterotrophic, and mixotrophic species.
- Photosynthetic protists are among the most important **producers** in aquatic communities. Because they are at the base of the food web, factors that affect photosynthetic protists affect many other species in the community.
- Protists form a wide range of mutualistic and parasitic relationships that affect their symbiotic partners and many other members of the community. Some protists, such as the malaria parasite *Plasmodium*, pose major challenges to human health.

? *Describe several protists that are ecologically important.*

TEST YOUR UNDERSTANDING

Level 1: Knowledge/Comprehension

1. The oldest fossil eukaryote that can be resolved taxonomically is of
   a. a red alga that lived 1.2 billion years ago.
   b. a red alga that lived 635 million years ago.
   c. a fungus that lived 2 billion years ago.
   d. a fungus that lived 550 million years ago.
   e. an Ediacaran that lived 550 million years ago.

2. The evolution of complex multicellularity in eukaryotes
   a. occurred only once, in the common ancestor of all eukaryotes.
   b. occurred only once, in the common ancestor of all multicellular eukaryotes.
   c. occurred only once, in the animal lineage.
   d. is not documented by the fossil record.
   e. occurred independently in several different eukaryotic lineages.

3. Plastids that are surrounded by more than two membranes are evidence of
   a. evolution from mitochondria.
   b. fusion of plastids.
   c. origin of the plastids from archaea.
   d. secondary endosymbiosis.
   e. budding of the plastids from the nuclear envelope.

4. Biologists think that endosymbiosis gave rise to mitochondria before plastids partly because
   a. the products of photosynthesis could not be metabolized without mitochondrial enzymes.
   b. all eukaryotes have mitochondria (or their remnants), whereas many eukaryotes do not have plastids.
   c. mitochondrial DNA is less similar to prokaryotic DNA than is plastid DNA.
   d. without mitochondrial CO_2 production, photosynthesis could not occur.
   e. mitochondrial proteins are synthesized on cytosolic ribosomes, whereas plastids utilize their own ribosomes.

5. Which group is *incorrectly* paired with its description?
   a. rhizarians—morphologically diverse group that includes amoebas with threadlike pseudopodia
   b. diatoms—important producers in aquatic communities
   c. red algae—acquired plastids by secondary endosymbiosis
   d. apicomplexans—parasites with intricate life cycles
   e. diplomonads—protists with modified mitochondria

Level 2: Application/Analysis

6. Based on the phylogenetic tree in Figure 25.9, which of the following statements is correct?
   a. The most recent common ancestor of Excavata is older than that of the SAR clade.
   b. The most recent common ancestor of the SAR clade is older than that of Unikonta.
   c. The most recent common ancestor of red algae and land plants is older than that of nucleariids and fungi.
   d. The most basal (first to diverge) eukaryotic supergroup cannot be determined.
   e. Excavata is the most basal eukaryotic supergroup.

Level 3: Synthesis/Evaluation

7. **MAKE CONNECTIONS** The bacterium *Wolbachia* is a symbiont that lives in mosquito cells and spreads rapidly through mosquito populations. *Wolbachia* can make mosquitoes resistant to infection by *Plasmodium*; researchers are seeking a strain that confers resistance and does not harm mosquitoes. Compare evolutionary changes that could occur if malaria control is attempted using such a *Wolbachia* strain versus using insecticides to kill mosquitoes. (Review Figure 25.26 and Concept 21.3.)

8. **SCIENTIFIC INQUIRY**
   Applying the "If … then" logic of science (see Chapter 1), what are a few of the predictions that arise from the hypothesis that plants evolved from green algae? Put another way, how could you test this hypothesis?

9. **FOCUS ON EVOLUTION**
   DRAW IT Medical researchers seek to develop drugs that can kill or restrict the growth of human pathogens yet have few harmful effects on patients. These drugs often work by disrupting the metabolism of the pathogen or by targeting its structural features.
   Draw and label a phylogenetic tree that includes an ancestral prokaryote and the following groups of organisms: Excavata, the SAR clade, Archaeplastida, Unikonta, and, within Unikonta, amoebozoans, animals, choanoflagellates, fungi, and nucleariids. Based on this tree, hypothesize whether it would be most difficult to develop drugs to combat human pathogens that are prokaryotes, protists, animals, or fungi. (You do not need to consider the evolution of drug resistance by the pathogen.)

10. **FOCUS ON INTERACTIONS**
    Organisms interact with each other and the physical environment. In a short essay (100–150 words), explain how the response of diatom populations to a drop in nutrient availability can affect both other organisms and aspects of the physical environment (such as carbon dioxide concentrations).

For selected answers, see Appendix A.

MasteringBiology®

Students Go to **MasteringBiology** for assignments, the eText, and the Study Area with practice tests, animations, and activities.

Instructors Go to **MasteringBiology** for automatically graded tutorials and questions that you can assign to your students, plus Instructor Resources.

26

The Colonization of Land by Plants and Fungi

▼ **Figure 26.1** How have plants and fungi changed the world?

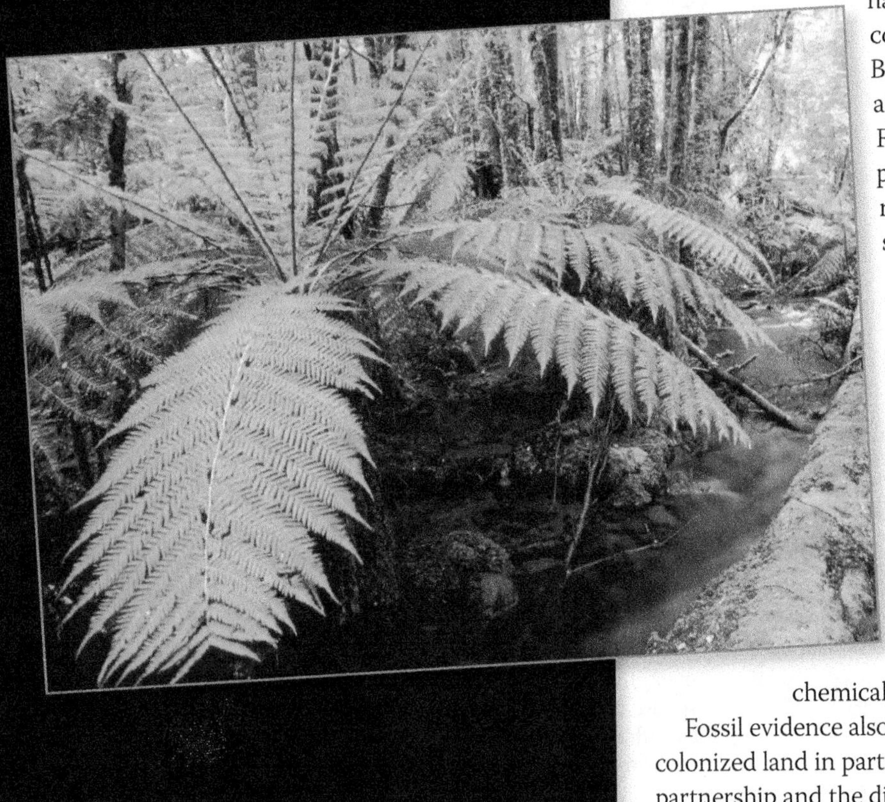

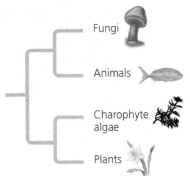

OVERVIEW

The Greening of Earth

Looking at a lush landscape, such as the forest scene in **Figure 26.1**, it is difficult to imagine the terrestrial environment without plants* or other organisms. Yet for more than 2 billion years of Earth's history, the land surface was largely lifeless. Geochemical and fossil evidence suggest that this had changed by 1.2 billion years ago, by which time thin coatings of cyanobacteria and protists existed on land. But it was only within the last 500 million years that fungi as well as small plants and animals joined them ashore. Finally, by about 385 million years ago, some plants appeared that could grow much taller, leading to the formation of the first forests (though with a very different set of species than those in Figure 26.1).

In this chapter, we'll examine the colonization of land by plants and fungi; we'll turn to animals in Chapter 27. Although plants and fungi are not closely related **(Figure 26.2)**, we discuss them together in this chapter in part because fossil evidence suggests that they both arrived on land before animals, which depend on them to survive. Plants supply oxygen and ultimately most of the food eaten by terrestrial animals. Also, plant roots create habitats for animals and other organisms by stabilizing the soil in many terrestrial environments. Fungi break down organic material and recycle nutrients, allowing other organisms to assimilate essential chemical elements.

Fossil evidence also suggests that plants colonized land in partnership with fungi. This partnership and the diversification of plants and fungi that occurred in terrestrial environments fundamentally changed biotic interactions and chemical cycling. We'll begin this story with the origin of plants, an event that occurred over millions of years as the algal ancestors of early plants adapted to life in a new environment—land.

---

*Although a few plant species returned to aquatic habitats during their evolution, most present-day plants live on land. In this chapter, we often refer to all plants as *land* plants, even those that are now aquatic, to distinguish them from algae, which are photosynthetic protists.

Fungi

Animals

Charophyte algae

Plants

▲ **Figure 26.2 Relationships among multicellular eukaryotes.** As shown in this phylogenetic tree, fungi and animals are more closely related than either group is to plants or charophytes (or other algae).

504

Fossils show that plants colonized land more than 470 million years ago

Evidence in the form of fossils documents key steps in the origin of plants from their algal ancestors. As you read in Chapter 25, researchers have identified green algae called charophytes as the closest living relatives of land plants (see Figure 26.2). After discussing evidence for this relationship, we'll describe the terrestrial adaptations and fossil record of early land plants.

Evidence of Algal Ancestry

Many key traits of land plants also appear in some algae. For example, plants are multicellular, eukaryotic, photosynthetic autotrophs, as are brown, red, and certain green algae. Plants have cell walls made of cellulose, and so do green algae, dinoflagellates, and brown algae. And chloroplasts with chlorophylls a and b are present in green algae, euglenids, and a few dinoflagellates, as well as in plants.

However, the charophytes are the only present-day algae that share certain distinctive traits with land plants, suggesting that they are the closest living relatives of plants. For example, the cells of both land plants and charophytes have distinctive circular rings of proteins in the plasma membrane (Figure 26.3); these protein rings synthesize the cellulose found in the cell wall. In contrast, noncharophyte algae have linear sets of proteins that synthesize cellulose. Likewise, in species of land plants that have flagellated sperm, the structure of the sperm closely resembles that of charophyte sperm.

Biochemical studies and analyses of nuclear and chloroplast genes from a wide range of plants and algae also indicate that charophytes—particularly *Chara* and *Coleochaete*—are the closest living relatives of land plants (Figure 26.4). Note that this does not mean that plants are descended from these living algae; however, present-day charophytes may tell us something about what the algal ancestors of plants were like.

Adaptations Enabling the Move to Land

Many species of charophyte algae inhabit shallow waters around the edges of ponds and lakes, where they are subject to occasional drying. In such environments, natural selection favors individual algae that can survive periods when they are

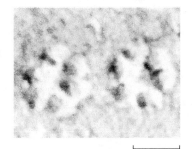

▶ Figure 26.3 **Rings of cellulose-synthesizing proteins.** These circular sets of proteins embedded in the plasma membrane are found only in land plants and charophyte algae (SEM).

30 nm

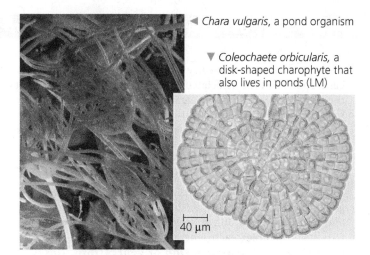

◀ *Chara vulgaris*, a pond organism

▼ *Coleochaete orbicularis,* a disk-shaped charophyte that also lives in ponds (LM)

40 µm

▲ Figure 26.4 **Examples of charophytes, the closest algal relatives of land plants.**

not submerged in water. In charophytes, a layer of a durable polymer called **sporopollenin** prevents exposed zygotes from drying out. A similar chemical adaptation is found in the tough sporopollenin walls that encase the spores of plants.

The accumulation of such traits by at least one population of charophyte ancestors probably enabled their descendants—the first land plants—to live permanently above the waterline. This ability opened a new frontier: a terrestrial habitat that offered enormous benefits. The bright sunlight was unfiltered by water and plankton; the atmosphere offered more plentiful carbon dioxide than did water; and the soil by the water's edge was rich in some mineral nutrients. But these benefits were accompanied by challenges: a relative scarcity of water and a lack of structural support against gravity. (To appreciate why such support is important, picture how the soft body of a jellyfish sags when taken out of water.) Land plants diversified as adaptations evolved that enabled plants to thrive despite these challenges.

Today, what adaptations are unique to plants? The answer depends on where you draw the boundary dividing plants from algae (Figure 26.5). Since the placement of this boundary is the

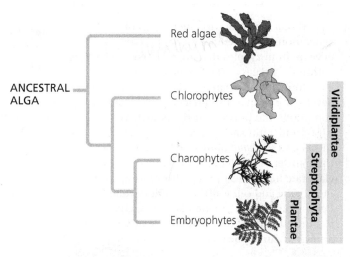

ANCESTRAL ALGA

Red algae

Chlorophytes

Charophytes

Embryophytes

Viridiplantae

Streptophyta

Plantae

▲ Figure 26.5 **Three possible "plant" kingdoms.**

Charophyte algae lack the key traits of land plants described in this figure: alternation of generations and the associated trait of multicellular, dependent embryos. As described on the facing page, charophyte algae also lack walled spores produced in sporangia and apical meristems. This suggests that these four traits were absent in the ancestor common to land plants and charophytes but instead evolved as derived traits of land plants.

Alternation of Generations

The life cycles of all land plants alternate between two generations of distinct multicellular organisms: gametophytes and sporophytes. As shown in the diagram below (using a fern as an example), each generation gives rise to the other, a process that is called **alternation of generations**. This type of reproductive cycle evolved in various groups of algae but does not occur in the charophytes, the algae most closely related to land plants. Take care not to confuse the alternation of generations in plants with the haploid and diploid stages in the life cycles of other sexually reproducing organisms (see Figure 10.6). Alternation of generations is distinguished by the fact that the life cycle

Alternation of generations: five generalized steps

includes both multicellular haploid organisms and multicellular diploid organisms. The multicellular haploid **gametophyte** ("gamete-producing plant") is named for its production by mitosis of haploid gametes—eggs and sperm—that fuse during fertilization, forming diploid zygotes. Mitotic division of the zygote produces a multicellular diploid **sporophyte** ("spore-producing plant"). Meiosis in a mature sporophyte produces haploid **spores**, reproductive cells that can develop into a new haploid organism without fusing with another cell. Mitotic division of the spore cell produces a new multicellular gametophyte, and the cycle begins again.

1 The gametophyte produces haploid gametes by mitosis.

Gametophyte (n)

Gamete from another plant

Mitosis

Mitosis

n

n

n

n — Spore

Gamete

2 Two gametes unite (fertilization) and form a diploid zygote.

5 The spores develop into multicellular haploid gametophytes.

MEIOSIS

FERTILIZATION

4 The sporophyte produces unicellar haploid spores by meiosis.

Zygote

$2n$

3 The zygote develops into a multicellular diploid sporophyte.

Sporophyte ($2n$)

Mitosis

Key	
➡	Haploid (n)
➡	Diploid ($2n$)

Multicellular, Dependent Embryos

As part of a life cycle with alternation of generations, multicellular plant embryos develop from zygotes that are retained within the tissues of the female parent (a gametophyte). The parental tissues protect the developing embryo from harsh environmental conditions and provide nutrients such as sugars and amino acids. The embryo has specialized *placental transfer cells* that enhance the transfer of nutrients to the embryo through elaborate ingrowths of the wall surface (plasma membrane and cell wall). The multicellular, dependent embryo of land plants is such a significant derived trait that land plants are also known as **embryophytes**.

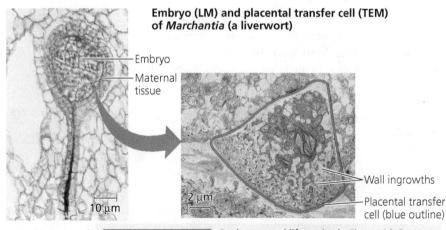

Embryo (LM) and placental transfer cell (TEM) of *Marchantia* (a liverwort)

Embryo

Maternal tissue

Wall ingrowths

Placental transfer cell (blue outline)

10 μm

2 μm

MAKE CONNECTIONS *Review sexual life cycles in Figure 10.6. Identify which type of sexual life cycle has alternation of generations, and summarize how it differs from other life cycles.*

subject of ongoing debate, this text uses a traditional definition that equates the kingdom Plantae with embryophytes (plants with embryos). In this context, let's now examine the derived traits that separate land plants from their closest algal relatives.

Derived Traits of Plants

A series of adaptations that facilitate survival and reproduction on dry land emerged after land plants diverged from their algal relatives. Examples of such traits that are found in land plants but not in the charophyte algae include the following:

- **Alternation of generations.** This type of life cycle, consisting of multicellular forms that give rise to each other in turn, is described in **Figure 26.6**, on the preceding page.
- **Walled spores produced in sporangia.** The sporophyte stage of the plant life cycle has multicellular organs called **sporangia** (singular, *sporangium*) that produce spores **(Figure 26.7)**. The polymer sporopollenin makes the walls of these spores resistant to harsh environments, enabling plant spores to be dispersed through dry air without harm.
- **Apical meristems.** Land plants also differ from their algal ancestors in having **apical meristems**, localized regions of cell division at the tips of roots and shoots (see Figure 28.16). Apical meristem cells can divide throughout the plant's life, enabling its roots and shoots to elongate, thus increasing the plant's exposure to environmental resources.

Additional derived traits that relate to terrestrial life have evolved in many plant species. For example, the epidermis in many species has a covering, the **cuticle**, that consists of wax and other polymers. Permanently exposed to the air, land plants run a far greater risk of desiccation (drying out) than their algal ancestors. The cuticle acts as waterproofing, helping prevent excessive water loss from the aboveground plant organs, while also providing some protection from microbial attack. Most plants also have specialized pores called

stomata (singular, *stoma*), which support photosynthesis by allowing the exchange of CO_2 and O_2 between the outside air and the plant (see Figure 8.3). Stomata are also the main avenues by which water evaporates from the plant; in hot, dry conditions, the stomata close, minimizing water loss. As we describe in the next section, fossil evidence documents the appearance of stomata and other novel traits in early land plants.

Early Land Plants

The algae from which land plants evolved include many unicellular and small, colonial species. Since their ancestors were small, the search for the earliest fossils of land plants has focused on the microscopic world. As mentioned earlier, microorganisms colonized land as early as 1.2 billion years ago. But the microscopic fossils documenting life on land changed dramatically 470 million years ago with the appearance of spores from early land plants.

What distinguishes these spores from those of algae or fungi? One clue comes from their chemical composition, which matches that found in plant spores but differs from that in the spores of other organisms. In addition, the structure of the walls of these ancient spores shows features found only in the spores of certain land plants (liverworts). And in rocks dating to 450 million years ago, researchers have discovered similar spores embedded in plant cuticle material that resembles spore-bearing tissue in living plants **(Figure 26.8)**.

It is not surprising that spores provide the earliest fossil evidence of land plants. For one thing, plants produce large numbers of widely dispersed spores. In addition, recall that plant spores contain sporopollenin, a durable compound that allows the spores to be well represented in the fossil record. Larger plant structures, such as the spore-producing structure

(a) Fossilized spores. The chemical composition and physical structure of these 450 million-year-old spores match those found in land plants.

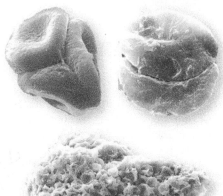

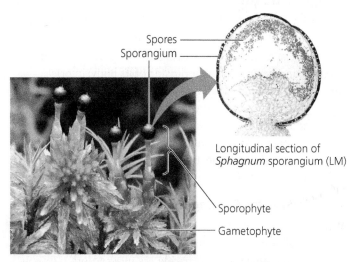

Spores
Sporangium

Longitudinal section of *Sphagnum* sporangium (LM)

Sporophyte
Gametophyte

▲ **Figure 26.7 Sporophytes and sporangia of a moss (*Sphagnum*).** Each of the many spores produced by a sporangium is encased by a durable, sporopollenin-enriched wall.

(b) Fossilized sporophyte tissue. The spores in (a) were embedded in tissue that appears to be from plants.

▲ **Figure 26.8 Ancient plant spores and tissue** (colorized SEMs).

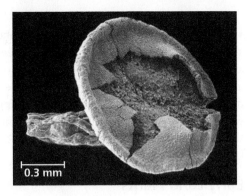

▶ **Cooksonia sporangium fossil (425 million years old).**

0.3 mm

(sporangium) from *Cooksonia* shown above, first appear in the fossil record dating to 425 million years ago. By 400 million years ago, a diverse assemblage of plants lived on land. Some of these early plants had key traits not found in their algal ancestors, including specialized tissues for water transport, stomata, and branched sporophytes **(Figure 26.9)**. Although these early plants were less than 20 cm tall, their branching enabled their bodies to become more complex. As plant bodies became increasingly complex, competition for space and sunlight probably increased. That competition may have stimulated still more evolution in later plant lineages—eventually leading to the formation of the first forests.

Overall, the fossil record shows that by 400 million years ago, early land plants differed greatly from their algal ancestors. As they adapted to life on land, plants evolved a suite of novel features, including sporopollenin-containing spores, cuticles, stomata, transport systems, and branched sporophytes. In

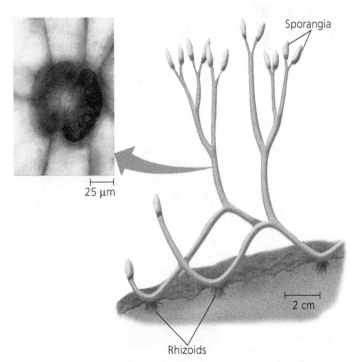

Sporangia

25 μm

2 cm

Rhizoids

▲ **Figure 26.9 *Aglaophyton major*, an early land plant.** This reconstruction from 405-million-year-old fossils exhibits dichotomous (Y-shaped) branching with sporangia at the ends of the branches. *Aglaophyton* had rhizoids that anchored it to the ground. The inset shows a fossilized stoma of *A. major* (colorized LM).

addition, early land plants formed a key symbiotic association with the group we turn to next, the fungi.

CONCEPT CHECK 26.1

1. Why do researchers identify charophytes rather than another group as the closest relatives of land plants?
2. Identify three derived traits that distinguish plants from charophytes *and* facilitate life on land.
3. Describe fossil evidence of early land plants.
4. **WHAT IF?** What would the human life cycle be like if we had alternation of generations? Assume that the multicellular diploid stage would be similar in form to an adult human.

For suggested answers, see Appendix A.

CONCEPT 26.2

Fungi played an essential role in the colonization of land

The earliest land plants lacked true roots and leaves. Without roots, how did these plants absorb nutrients from the soil? Fossil evidence reveals an adaptation that may have aided their uptake of nutrients: They formed symbiotic associations with fungi. We'll describe these associations, called *mycorrhizae*, a little later in the chapter. For now, the main point is that mycorrhizal fungi form extensive networks of filaments through the soil and transfer nutrients to their symbiotic plant partners. This benefit may have helped plants without roots to colonize land.

Fungi may, in fact, have colonized land before plants. Once on land, fungi diversified into a wide range of living species. To help us interpret the role fungi played in the colonization of land, we'll begin by examining some of their key features, including how they feed and reproduce.

Fungal Nutrition

Like animals, fungi are heterotrophs: They cannot make their own food as plants and algae can. But unlike animals, fungi do not ingest (eat) their food. Instead, a fungus absorbs nutrients from the environment outside of its body; in brief, fungi are heterotrophs that feed by absorption. Many fungi accomplish this task by secreting hydrolytic enzymes into their surroundings. These enzymes break down complex molecules to smaller organic compounds that the fungi can absorb into their bodies and use. Collectively, fungi can digest compounds from a wide range of sources, living or dead.

Adaptations for Feeding by Absorption

What fungal traits facilitate feeding by absorption? One such trait is a cell wall strengthened by **chitin**, a strong but flexible nitrogen-containing polysaccharide. As fungi absorb nutrients from their environment, the concentration of those nutrients in their cells increases; that, in turn, causes water to move into

▶ **Figure 26.10 Structure of a multicellular fungus.** The top photograph shows the sexual structures, in this case called mushrooms, of the penny bun fungus (*Boletus edulis*). The bottom photograph shows a mycelium growing on fallen conifer needles. The inset SEM shows hyphae.

❓ *Although the mushrooms in the top photograph appear to be different individuals, could their DNA be identical? Explain.*

Reproductive structure. Tiny haploid cells called spores are produced inside the mushroom.

Hyphae. The mushroom and its subterranean mycelium are a continuous network of hyphae.

Spore-producing structures

60 μm

Mycelium

fungal cells by osmosis. The movement of water into fungal cells creates pressure that would cause their cells to burst if they were not surrounded by a rigid cell wall.

Many fungi also have a structure that increases the efficiency of nutrient absorption. The most common fungal body structures are multicellular filaments and single cells (**yeasts**). Many fungal species can grow as both filaments and yeasts, but even more grow only as filaments; relatively few species grow only as yeasts. Yeasts often inhabit moist environments, including plant sap and animal tissues, where there is a ready supply of soluble nutrients, such as sugars and amino acids.

The morphology of multicellular fungi enhances their ability to grow into and absorb nutrients from their surroundings (**Figure 26.10**). The bodies of these fungi typically form a network of tiny filaments called **hyphae** (singular, *hypha*). Hyphae consist of tubular (chitin-rich) cell walls surrounding the plasma membrane and cytoplasm of the cells. Fungal hyphae form an interwoven mass called a **mycelium** (plural, *mycelia*) that infiltrates the material on which the fungus feeds. The structure of a mycelium maximizes its surface-to-volume ratio, making feeding very efficient. Just 1 cm³ of rich soil may contain as much as 1 km of hyphae with a total surface area of 300 cm² in contact with the soil.

Specialized Hyphae in Mycorrhizal Fungi

Some fungi have specialized hyphae called **haustoria** (**Figure 26.11**), which the fungi use to extract nutrients from, or exchange nutrients with, their plant hosts. Mutually beneficial relationships between such fungi and plant roots are called **mycorrhizae** (the term means "fungus roots").

Mycorrhizal fungi (fungi that form mycorrhizae) can improve delivery of phosphate ions and other minerals to plants

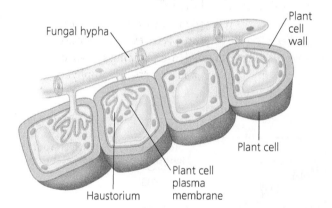

Fungal hypha — Plant cell wall

Plant cell

Haustorium — Plant cell plasma membrane

▲ **Figure 26.11 Haustoria of mycorrhizae.** Mutualistic mycorrhizal fungi grow specialized hyphae called haustoria that can exchange nutrients with living plant cells. Haustoria remain separated from a plant cell's cytoplasm by the plasma membrane of the plant cell (orange).

because the vast mycelial networks of the fungi are more efficient than the plants' roots at acquiring these minerals from the soil. In exchange, the plants supply the fungi with organic nutrients such as carbohydrates.

There are two main types of mycorrhizal fungi. **Ectomycorrhizal fungi** (from the Greek *ektos*, out) form sheaths of hyphae over the surface of a root and typically grow into the extracellular spaces of the root cortex (see Figure 29.13a). **Arbuscular mycorrhizal fungi** (from the Latin *arbor*, tree) extend branching hyphae through the root cell wall and into tubes formed by invagination (pushing inward) of the root cell plasma membrane (see Figure 29.13b). In the **Scientific Skills Exercise**, you'll interpret data from an experiment studying how mycorrhizae affect plants.

Synthesizing Information from Multiple Data Sets

Can Mycorrhizae Help Plants Cope with High-Temperature Soils? The branching hyphae of arbuscular mycorrhizal (AM) fungi extend through the cell walls of host plants, bringing water and inorganic nutrients into the plant roots in exchange for sugars. Researchers wondered whether AM fungi also can help plants grow in high-temperature (thermal) soils. To study this question, they investigated the role of AM fungi in the growth of *Dichanthelium lanuginosum*, a grass species that grows only in thermal soils.

How the Study Was Done The researchers collected *D. lanuginosum* seeds from geothermally heated soils in Yellowstone National Park. After the seeds germinated, 27 seedlings were transferred to a greenhouse, where they were grown separately in heated pots. Temperatures in the pots ranged from 30°C at the soil surface to 50°C at the base of the pot, comparable to conditions in thermal soils.

Each pot received one of three treatments: nine pots were not inoculated with AM fungi, nine pots were inoculated with nonthermal AM fungi collected from grassland soil in a nongeothermal area, and nine pots were inoculated with thermal AM fungi collected from high-temperature geothermal areas of Yellowstone. All seedlings received the same amount of light and water. After 80 days, all plants were harvested.

Data from the Study

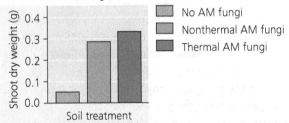

	Total root length (cm)	Mean root diameter (mm)
No AM fungi	1,800	0.19
Nonthermal AM fungi	4,800	0.23
Thermal AM fungi	4,300	0.22

Interpret the Data

1. Compare the mean dry weight of shoots, total root length, and mean root diameter of *D. lanuginosum* grown in pots with and without inoculation by AM fungi. How do AM fungi appear to affect *D. lanuginosum* plants grown at high temperatures?

2. Compare the mean dry weight of shoots, total root length, and mean root diameter of *D. lanuginosum* in pots inoculated with thermal and nonthermal AM fungi. Do *D. lanuginosum* plants grow equally well when the soil is inoculated with thermal and nonthermal AM fungi? What does this suggest about the thermal tolerances of AM fungi from geothermal and grassland soils?

3. The researchers also measured the length of *D. lanuginosum* roots and the hyphal length of AM fungi in geothermal soils of different temperatures. The curves below, which were estimated from a statistical best fit to the data, show how the average root or hyphal length (per gram of soil) varies with soil temperature. Use these curves to estimate average root and hyphal lengths in soils of 25°C and soils of 35°C.

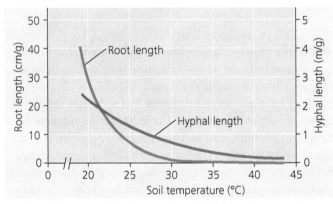

4. What do the curves in the graph suggest about the relative heat tolerances of *D. lanuginosum* roots and fungal hyphae? How might these results explain the differences in growth of *D. lanuginosum* plants grown in soils with and without AM fungi?

Data from R. Bunn et al., Arbuscular mycorrhizal fungi ameliorate temperature stress in thermophilic plants, *Ecology* 90: 1378–1388 (2009).

(MB) A version of this Scientific Skills Exercise can be assigned in MasteringBiology.

Sexual and Asexual Reproduction

Most fungi propagate themselves by producing vast numbers of spores, either sexually or asexually. Spores can be carried long distances by wind or water. If they land in a moist place where there is food, they germinate, producing new mycelia. **Figure 26.12** generalizes the many different life cycles that can produce fungal spores.

As shown in this figure, the sexual portion of a fungal life cycle typically occurs in two stages. First, the cytoplasms of two parent mycelia fuse, an event known as **plasmogamy**. Hours, days, or (in some fungi) even centuries may pass between plasmogamy and the next stage in the sexual cycle, **karyogamy**. During karyogamy, the haploid nuclei contributed by the two

parents fuse, producing diploid cells. Zygotes and other structures formed during karyogamy are the only diploid stage in most fungi. Meiosis then restores the haploid condition. Many fungi then reproduce asexually by growing as filamentous fungi that produce (haploid) spores by mitosis; such species are informally referred to as *molds* if they form visible mycelia. Other species reproduce asexually as single-celled yeasts that divide to produce genetically identical daughter cells.

The Origin of Fungi

Although fungi were once thought to be closely related to plants, molecular data show that fungi and animals are more closely related to each other than either group is to plants

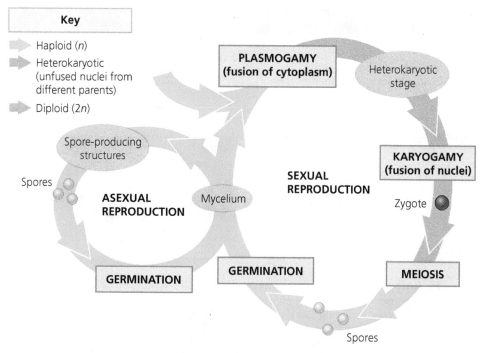

Key

→ Haploid (n)

→ Heterokaryotic (unfused nuclei from different parents)

→ Diploid ($2n$)

PLASMOGAMY (fusion of cytoplasm)

Heterokaryotic stage

KARYOGAMY (fusion of nuclei)

SEXUAL REPRODUCTION

Zygote

Spore-producing structures

Spores

Mycelium

ASEXUAL REPRODUCTION

GERMINATION

GERMINATION

MEIOSIS

Spores

▲ **Figure 26.12 Generalized life cycle of fungi.** Many—but not all—fungi reproduce both sexually and asexually. Some reproduce only sexually, others only asexually.

or most other eukaryotes (see Figure 25.9). DNA sequence data also indicate that fungi are more closely related to several groups of single-celled protists than they are to animals, suggesting that the ancestor of fungi was unicellular. One such group of unicellular protists, the **nucleariids**, consists of amoebas that feed on algae and bacteria. As we discussed in Chapter 25, animals are more closely related to a *different* group of protists (the choanoflagellates) than they are to either fungi or nucleariids. Together, these results suggest that multicellularity must have evolved in animals and fungi independently, from different single-celled ancestors.

Based on molecular clock analyses (see Chapter 20), scientists have estimated that the ancestors of animals and fungi diverged into separate lineages 1–1.5 billion years ago. Fossils of certain unicellular, marine eukaryotes that lived as early as 1.5 billion years ago have been interpreted as fungi, but those claims remain controversial. Furthermore, although most biologists think that fungi originated in aquatic environments, the oldest fossils that are widely accepted as fungi are of terrestrial species that lived about 460 million years ago **(Figure 26.13)**. Overall, additional fossil discoveries will be needed to clarify when fungi originated and what features were present in their earliest lineages.

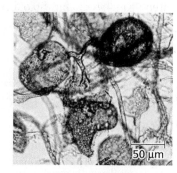

▲ **Figure 26.13 Fossil fungal hyphae and spores from the Ordovician period (about 460 million years ago)** (LM).

The Move to Land

As we mentioned earlier, fungi may have colonized land before plants. Indeed, some researchers have described life on land before the arrival of plants as a "green slime" that consisted of cyanobacteria, algae, and a variety of small, heterotrophic species, including fungi. With their rigid cell walls and extracellular digestion, fungi would have been well suited for feeding on other early terrestrial organisms (or their remains).

Once on land, some fungi formed symbiotic associations with early land plants. For example, 405-million-year-old fossils of the early land plant *Aglaophyton* (see Figure 26.9) contain evidence of mycorrhizal relationships between plants and fungi. This evidence includes fossils of hyphae that have penetrated within plant cells and formed structures that resemble the haustoria of arbuscular mycorrhizae **(Figure 26.14)**. Similar structures have been found in a variety of other early land plants, suggesting that plants probably existed in beneficial relationships with fungi from the earliest periods of colonization of land.

Support for the antiquity of mycorrhizal associations has also come from recent molecular studies. For a mycorrhizal fungus and its plant partner to establish a symbiotic relationship,

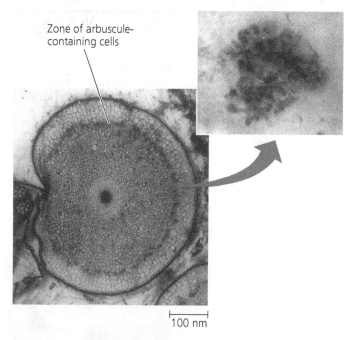

Zone of arbuscule-containing cells

100 nm

▲ **Figure 26.14 An ancient symbiosis.** This 405-million-year-old fossil stem (cross section) documents arbuscular mycorrhizae in the early land plant *Aglaophyton major*. The inset shows an enlarged view of a cell containing an arbuscule that has branched extensively; the fossil arbuscule resembles those seen today (see Figure 29.13b).

The phylogeny of fungi is currently the subject of much research. Most mycologists recognize five major groups of fungi, although the chytrids and zygomycetes are probably paraphyletic (as indicated by the parallel lines).

Chytrids (1,000 species)

In chytrids such as *Chytridium*, the globular fruiting body forms multicellular, branched hyphae (LM); other species are single-celled. Ubiquitous in lakes and soil, chytrids have flagellated spores and are thought to include some of the earliest fungal groups to diverge from other fungi.

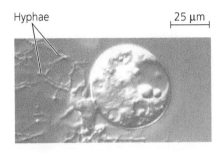

Hyphae   25 µm

Zygomycetes (1,000 species)

The hyphae of some zygomycetes, including this mold in the genus *Mucor* (LM), grow rapidly in foods such as fruits and bread. As such, the fungi may act as decomposers (if the food is not alive) or parasites; other species live as neutral (commensal) symbionts.

Glomeromycetes (160 species)

The glomeromycetes form arbuscular mycorrhizae with plant roots, supplying minerals and other nutrients to the roots; about 80% of all plant species have such mutualistic partnerships with glomeromycetes. This SEM shows the branched hyphae—an arbuscule—of *Glomus mosseae* bulging into a plant root cell (the root has been treated to remove the cytoplasm).

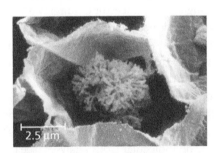

2.5 µm

Ascomycetes (65,000 species)

Also called sac fungi, members of this diverse group are common to many marine, freshwater, and terrestrial habitats. The cup-shaped ascocarp (fruiting body) of the ascomycete shown here (*Aleuria aurantia*) gives this species its common name: orange peel fungus.

Basidiomycetes (30,000 species)

Often important as decomposers and ectomycorrhizal fungi, basidiomycetes, or club fungi, are unusual in having a long-lived, heterokaryotic stage in which each cell has two nuclei (one from each parent). The fruiting bodies—commonly called mushrooms—of this fly agaric (*Amanita muscaria*) are a familiar sight in coniferous forests of the Northern Hemisphere.

certain genes must be expressed by the fungus and other genes must be expressed by the plant. Researchers focused on three plant genes (called *sym* genes) whose expression is required for the formation of mycorrhizae in flowering plants. They found that these genes were present in all major plant lineages, including basal lineages such as liverworts (see Figure 26.16). Furthermore, after they transferred a liverwort *sym* gene to a flowering plant mutant that could not form mycorrhizae, the mutant recovered its ability to form mycorrhizae. These results suggest that mycorrhizal *sym* genes were present in the land plant common ancestor—and that the function of these genes has been conserved for hundreds of millions of years as plants continued to adapt to life on land.

Diversification of Fungi

In the past decade, molecular analyses have helped clarify the evolutionary relationships between fungal groups, although there are still areas of uncertainty. **Figure 26.15** presents a simplified version of one current hypothesis.

The groups shown in Figure 26.15 may represent only a small fraction of the diversity of extant fungi. While there are roughly 100,000 known species of fungi, there may actually be close to 1.5 million species. Two metagenomic studies published in 2011 support such higher estimates: Entirely new groups of unicellular fungi were discovered, and the genetic variation in some of these groups is as large as that across all of the groups in Figure 26.15.

As these phylogenetic data suggest, fungi diversified extensively after they colonized land. So, too, did the land plants that fungi helped ashore, as we'll discuss next.

CONCEPT CHECK 26.2

1. Compare and contrast the nutritional mode of a fungus with your own nutritional mode.
2. Describe the importance of mycorrhizae, both today and in the colonization of land. What evidence supports the antiquity of mycorrhizal associations?
3. **MAKE CONNECTIONS** Review Figures 8.3 and 8.5. If a plant has mycorrhizae, where might carbon that enters the plant's stomata as CO_2 eventually be deposited: in the plant, in the mycorrhizal fungus, or in both? Explain.

For suggested answers, see Appendix A.

CONCEPT 26.3

Early land plants radiated into a diverse set of lineages

As early land plants adapted to terrestrial environments, they gave rise to the vast diversity of living plants. An overview of that diversity is provided by **Figure 26.16**, which summarizes the evolutionary history of extant plant groups. (Extant lineages are those that have surviving members.)

One way to distinguish plant groups is whether they have an extensive system of **vascular tissue**, cells joined into tubes that transport water and nutrients throughout the plant body. Most present-day plants have a complex vascular tissue system and are therefore called **vascular plants**. We'll return to

▼ **Figure 26.16 Highlights of plant evolution.** The phylogeny shown here illustrates a leading hypothesis about the relationships between plant groups.

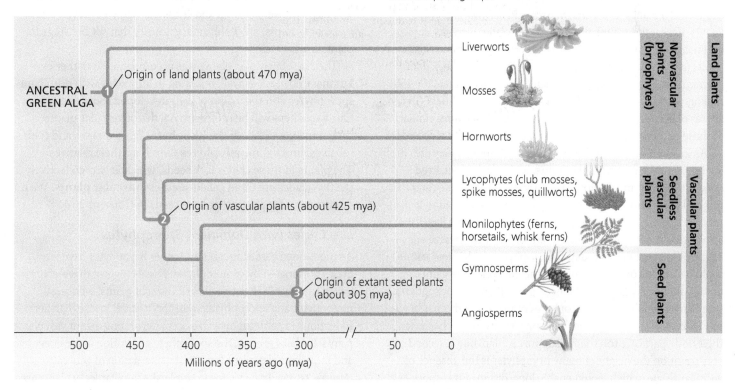

(a) *Plagiochila deltoidea,* a liverwort. This group's name refers to the shape of its gametophytes. In medieval times, their shape was thought to be a sign that the plants could help treat liver diseases.

(b) *Polytrichum commune,* a moss. Moss gametophytes are less than 15 cm tall in most species but can reach up to 2 m. The familiar carpet of moss you observe consists mainly of gametophytes.

(c) *Anthoceros* sp., a hornwort. This group's name refers to the long, tapered shape of the sporophyte, which can grow to about 5 cm high.

▲ **Figure 26.17 Bryophytes (nonvascular plants).** Molecular and morphological data indicate that bryophytes are paraphyletic; they do not form a single clade.

vascular plants later in this section, but first we'll discuss the nonvascular plants, or **bryophytes** (from the Greek *bryon,* moss, and *phyton,* plant), an informal name for plants that lack an extensive transport system.

Bryophytes: A Collection of Early-Diverging Plant Lineages

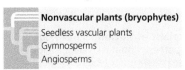

The nonvascular plants (bryophytes) are represented today by three clades of small herbaceous (nonwoody) plants: *liverworts, mosses,* and *hornworts* (**Figure 26.17**). Researchers think that these three clades were the earliest lineages to have diverged from the common ancestor of land plants (see Figure 26.16). Fossil evidence provides some support for this idea: The earliest spores of land plants (dating to 470–450 million years ago) have structural features found only in the spores of liverworts, and by 430 million years ago, spores similar to those of mosses and hornworts also occur in the fossil record.

As in some early land plants, the bryophytes of today are anchored to the ground by **rhizoids**, which lack specialized conducting cells and do not play a primary role in water and mineral absorption. Living bryophytes are typically found in moist habitats—as you might expect, since they have flagellated sperm that must swim through a film of water to fertilize an egg. Unlike most plants today, in bryophytes the haploid gametophytes are the dominant stage of the life cycle: The gametophytes are usually larger and longer-living than the sporophytes (see Figure 26.17). The gametophytes of mosses and other bryophytes typically form ground-hugging carpets, partly because their body parts are too thin to support a tall plant. A second constraint on the height of many bryophytes is the absence of vascular tissue, which would enable long-distance transport

of water and nutrients. These constraints were removed in the group we turn to next, the vascular plants.

Seedless Vascular Plants: The First Plants to Grow Tall

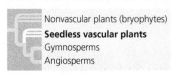

During the first 100 million years of plant evolution, bryophytes were prominent members of the vegetation. But it is vascular plants that dominate most landscapes today. The earliest fossils of vascular plants date to 425–420 million years ago. These plants lacked seeds but had well-developed vascular systems, an evolutionary novelty that set the stage for plants to grow tall.

The rise of vascular plants was accompanied by other evolutionary changes as well, resulting in life cycles with dominant sporophytes and the origin of well-developed roots and leaves. Our focus here will be on the two clades of vascular plants shown in **Figure 26.18**, the **lycophytes** (club mosses and their relatives) and the **monilophytes** (ferns and their relatives). The plants in these clades lack seeds, which is why collectively the two clades are often called **seedless vascular plants**. We'll discuss vascular plants that have seeds in Concept 26.4.

Life Cycles with Dominant Sporophytes

As mentioned earlier, mosses and other bryophytes have life cycles dominated by gametophytes. Fossils suggest that a change began to occur in the ancestors of vascular plants, whose gametophytes and sporophytes were about equal in size. Further reductions in gametophyte size occurred among extant vascular plants; in these groups, the sporophyte generation is the larger and more complex plant form in the alternation of generations (**Figure 26.19**). In ferns, for example, the familiar leafy plants are

► **Figure 26.18 Lycophytes and monilophytes (seedless vascular plants).** Although lycophytes and monilophytes each form a monophyletic group, seedless vascular plants are paraphyletic.

Strobili (conelike structures in which spores are produced)

2.5 cm

2.5 cm

(a) *Diphasiastrum tristachyum*, **a lycophyte.** The spores of lycophytes such as this club moss are released in clouds and are so rich in oil that magicians and photographers once ignited them to create smoke or flashes of light.

(b) *Athyrium filix-femina*, **a monilophyte.** The sporophytes of ferns typically have horizontal stems that give rise to large leaves called fronds, which grow as their coiled tips unfurl.

	PLANT GROUP		
	Mosses and other nonvascular plants	**Ferns and other seedless vascular plants**	**Seed plants (gymnosperms and angiosperms)**
Gametophyte	Dominant	Reduced, independent (photosynthetic and free-living)	Reduced (usually microscopic), dependent on surrounding sporophyte tissue for nutrition
Sporophyte	Reduced, dependent on gametophyte for nutrition	Dominant	Dominant
Example	Sporophyte ($2n$) Gametophyte (n)	Sporophyte ($2n$) Gametophyte (n)	**Gymnosperm** Microscopic female gametophytes (n) inside ovulate cone Microscopic male gametophytes (n) inside pollen cone Sporophyte ($2n$) **Angiosperm** Microscopic female gametophytes (n) inside these parts of flowers Microscopic male gametophytes (n) inside these parts of flowers Sporophyte ($2n$)

▲ **Figure 26.19 Gametophyte-sporophyte relationships in different plant groups.**

the sporophytes. You would have to get down on your hands and knees and search the ground carefully to find fern gametophytes, which are tiny structures that often grow on or just below the soil surface. However, as in nonvascular plants, the sperm of ferns and all other seedless vascular plants are flagellated and must swim through a film of water to reach eggs.

Transport in Xylem and Phloem

Vascular plants have two types of vascular tissue: xylem and phloem. **Xylem** conducts most of the water and minerals. The xylem of most vascular plants includes **tracheids**, tube-shaped cells that carry water and minerals up from the roots (see Figure 28.9). The water-conducting cells in vascular plants are *lignified*; that is, their cell walls are strengthened by the polymer **lignin**. The tissue called **phloem** has cells arranged into tubes that distribute sugars, amino acids, and other organic products (see Figure 28.9).

Lignified vascular tissue helped enable vascular plants to grow tall. Their stems became strong enough to provide support against gravity, and they could transport water and mineral nutrients high above the ground. Tall plants could also outcompete short plants for access to the sunlight needed for photosynthesis. In addition, the spores of tall plants could disperse farther than those of short plants, enabling tall species to colonize new environments rapidly. Overall, the ability to grow tall gave vascular plants a competitive edge over nonvascular plants, which rarely grow above 20 cm in height. Competition among vascular plants also increased, and taller growth forms were favored by natural selection—such as the trees that formed the first forests about 385 million years ago.

Evolution of Roots and Leaves

Vascular tissue also provides benefits below ground. In contrast to the rhizoids of bryophytes, roots with vascular tissue evolved in the sporophytes of almost all vascular plants. **Roots** are organs that absorb water and nutrients from the soil; roots also anchor vascular plants.

Leaves increase the surface area of the plant body and serve as the primary photosynthetic organ of vascular plants. In terms of size and complexity, leaves can be classified as either microphylls or megaphylls. All of the lycophytes (the oldest lineage of extant vascular plants)—and only the lycophytes—have **microphylls**, small, usually spine-shaped leaves supported by a single strand of vascular tissue. Almost all other vascular plants have **megaphylls**, leaves with a highly branched vascular system; a few species have reduced leaves that appear to have evolved from megaphylls. Megaphylls are typically larger and support greater photosynthetic productivity than microphylls. Microphylls first appear in the fossil record 410 million years ago, but megaphylls do not emerge until about 370 million years ago.

Seedless vascular plants were abundant in the swampy forests and other moist ecosystems of the Carboniferous period (359–299 million years ago). Growing along with these seedless

plants were early seed plants. Though seed plants were not dominant at that time, they rose to prominence after the climate became drier at the end of the Carboniferous period. In Concept 26.4, we'll trace the origin and diversification of seed plants, continuing the story of adaptation to life on land.

CONCEPT CHECK 26.3

1. How do the main similarities and differences between seedless vascular plants and nonvascular plants influence function in these plants?
2. **MAKE CONNECTIONS** Figure 26.16 identifies lineages as land plants, nonvascular plants, vascular plants, seedless vascular plants, and seed plants. Which of these categories are monophyletic, and which are paraphyletic (see Figure 20.10)? Explain.
3. **MAKE CONNECTIONS** Monilophytes and seed plants both have megaphylls, as well as other traits not found in lycophytes. Explain this observation using Figure 26.16 and the concept of descent with modification (see Concept 19.2).

For suggested answers, see Appendix A.

CONCEPT 26.4

Seeds and pollen grains are key adaptations for life on land

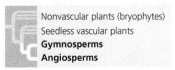

Nonvascular plants (bryophytes)
Seedless vascular plants
Gymnosperms
Angiosperms

Seed plants originated about 360 million years ago. As this new group of plants became established, they expanded into a broad range of terrestrial environments, dramatically altering the course of plant evolution. This large impact was due in part to the innovation for which this group of plants is named: the seed. A **seed** consists of an embryo and its food supply, surrounded by a protective coat. When mature, seeds are dispersed from their parent by wind or other means.

Extant seed plants can be divided into two major clades, gymnosperms (pines and their relatives) and angiosperms (flowering plants). **Gymnosperms** (from the Greek *gymnos*, naked, and *sperm*, seed) are grouped together as "naked seed" plants because their seeds are not enclosed in chambers. In contrast, the seeds of **angiosperms** (from the Greek *angion*, container) develop inside chambers called ovaries. We'll begin our discussion of seed plants with an overview of their adaptations for life on land. Then we'll turn to their origin and evolutionary history.

Terrestrial Adaptations in Seed Plants

In addition to seeds, all seed plants have reduced gametophytes, ovules, and pollen. These adaptations provided new ways for seed plants to cope with terrestrial conditions such as drought and exposure to the ultraviolet (UV) radiation in sunlight. These adaptations also freed seed plants from requiring water for fertilization, enabling reproduction to occur under a broader range of conditions than in seedless plants.

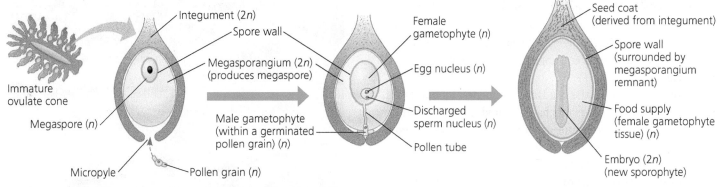

(a) Unfertilized ovule. In this longitudinal section through the ovule of a pine (a gymnosperm), a fleshy megasporangium is surrounded by a protective layer of tissue called an integument. The micropyle, the only opening through the integument, allows entry of a pollen grain.

(b) Fertilized ovule. A megaspore develops into a female gametophyte, which produces an egg. The pollen grain, which had entered through the micropyle, contains a male gametophyte. The male gametophyte develops a pollen tube that discharges sperm, thereby fertilizing the egg.

(c) Gymnosperm seed. Fertilization initiates the transformation of the ovule into a seed, which consists of a sporophyte embryo, a food supply, and a protective seed coat derived from the integument. The megasporangium dries out and collapses.

▲ **Figure 26.20 From ovule to seed in a gymnosperm.**

? *A gymnosperm seed contains cells from how many different plant generations? Identify the cells and whether each is haploid or diploid.*

Reduced Gametophytes

Unlike mosses and other bryophytes, ferns and other seedless vascular plants have sporophyte-dominated life cycles. The evolutionary trend of gametophyte reduction continued further in the vascular plant lineage that led to seed plants. While the gametophytes of seedless vascular plants are visible to the naked eye, the gametophytes of most seed plants are microscopic (see Figure 26.19).

This miniaturization allowed for an important evolutionary innovation in seed plants: Their tiny gametophytes can develop from spores retained within the sporangia of the parental sporophyte. The moist reproductive tissues of the sporophyte shield the gametophytes from UV radiation and protect them from drying out. This relationship also enables the dependent gametophytes to obtain nutrients from the sporophyte. In contrast, the free-living gametophytes of seedless vascular plants must fend for themselves.

Ovules and Pollen

Seed plants are unique in retaining the structures that develop into a female gametophyte within the parent sporophyte. Early in this process, a layer of sporophyte tissue called **integument** envelops and protects the tissues that will eventually give rise to the female gametophyte. The integument and the tissues it encloses together make up an **ovule** (**Figure 26.20a**). Inside each ovule, an egg-producing female gametophyte develops from a haploid spore. Spores that produce female gametophytes are called *megaspores* because they are larger than spores that produce male gametophytes (*microspores*).

A microspore develops into a **pollen grain** that consists of a male gametophyte enclosed within the pollen wall. The pollen wall, which contains sporopollenin, protects the gametophyte as it is transported from the parent plant by wind or by

hitchhiking on the body of an animal. The transfer of pollen to the part of a seed plant that contains the ovules is called **pollination**. If a pollen grain germinates (begins growing), it gives rise to a pollen tube that discharges sperm into the female gametophyte within the ovule, as shown in **Figure 26.20b**.

Recall that in nonvascular plants and seedless vascular plants such as ferns, free-living gametophytes release flagellated sperm that swim through a film of water to reach eggs; given this requirement, it is not surprising that many of these species are found in moist habitats. But in seed plants, a sperm-producing male gametophyte inside a pollen grain can be carried long distances by wind or animals, eliminating the dependence on water for sperm transport. The ability of seed plants to transfer sperm without water likely contributed to their successful colonization of dry habitats.

The Evolutionary Advantage of Seeds

If a sperm fertilizes an egg of a seed plant, the zygote grows into a sporophyte embryo. As shown in **Figure 26.20c**, the whole ovule develops into a seed: the embryo, along with a food supply, packaged within a protective coat derived from the integument.

Until the advent of seeds, the spore was the only protective stage in any plant life cycle. What advantages do seeds provide over spores? Spores are usually single-celled, whereas seeds are multicellular, consisting of an embryo protected by a layer of tissue, the seed coat. A seed can remain dormant for days, months, or even years after being released from the parent plant, whereas most spores have shorter lifetimes. Also, unlike spores, seeds have a supply of stored food. Under favorable conditions, the seed can emerge from dormancy and germinate, with its stored food providing critical support for growth as the sporophyte embryo emerges as a seedling.

Early Seed Plants and the Rise of Gymnosperms

Recall from Figure 26.16 that extant seed plants form two sister clades: gymnosperms and angiosperms. How did these two groups arise?

Fossils reveal that by the late Devonian period (about 380 million years ago), some plants had acquired features found in seed plants, such as the megaspores and microspores mentioned earlier. But these plants did not bear seeds and hence are not classified as seed plants. The first seed plants to appear in the fossil record date from around 360 million years ago, 55 million years before the first fossils of extant gymnosperms and more than 200 million years before the first angiosperm fossils. These early seed plants became extinct, and it remains uncertain which of these extinct lineages ultimately gave rise to the gymnosperms.

The earliest fossils of extant gymnosperms are about 305 million years old. These early gymnosperms lived in moist Carboniferous ecosystems still dominated by lycophytes, ferns, and other seedless vascular plants. As the Carboniferous period gave way to the Permian (299 million years ago), the climate became much drier. As a result, the lycophytes and ferns that dominated moist Carboniferous swamps were largely replaced by gymnosperms, which were better suited to the drier climate.

Gymnosperms thrived as the climate dried in part because they have the key terrestrial adaptations found in all seed plants, such as seeds and pollen. In addition, some gymnosperms were particularly well suited to arid conditions because of the thick cuticles and relatively small surface areas of their needle-shaped leaves. Today, gymnosperms remain an important part of Earth's flora (**Figure 26.21**). For example, vast regions in northern latitudes are covered by forests of cone-bearing gymnosperms called **conifers**, which include spruce, pine, fir, and redwood. Yet despite the ongoing importance of gymnosperms, most terrestrial ecosystems are now dominated by the group we turn to next, the angiosperms.

The Origin and Diversification of Angiosperms

Commonly known as flowering plants, angiosperms are seed plants that produce the reproductive structures called flowers and fruits. Today, angiosperms are the most diverse and widespread of all plants, with more than 250,000 species (about 90% of all plant species). Before considering the evolution of angiosperms, we'll examine their two key adaptations—flowers and fruits.

Flowers and Fruits

The **flower** is a unique angiosperm structure specialized for sexual reproduction. In many angiosperm species, insects or other animals transfer pollen from one flower to the sex organs on another flower, which makes pollination more directed than the wind-dependent pollination of most gymnosperms.

(a) Sago palm (*Cycas revolute*). This "palm" is actually a cycad, the next largest group of gymnosperms after the conifers (true palms are flowering plants). Cycads have large cones and palmlike leaves.

(b) Douglas fir (*Pseudotsuga menziesii*). This conifer dominates large forested regions and provides more timber than any other North American tree species.

(c) Creeping juniper (*Juniperus horizontalis*). The "berries" of this low-growing conifer are actually ovule-producing cones consisting of fleshy sporophylls.

▲ **Figure 26.21 Examples of gymnosperms.**

A flower is a specialized shoot that can have up to four types of modified leaves called floral organs: sepals, petals, stamens, and carpels (**Figure 26.22**). Starting at the base of the flower are the **sepals**, which are usually green and enclose the flower before it opens (think of a rosebud). Interior to the sepals are the **petals**, which are brightly colored in most flowers and aid

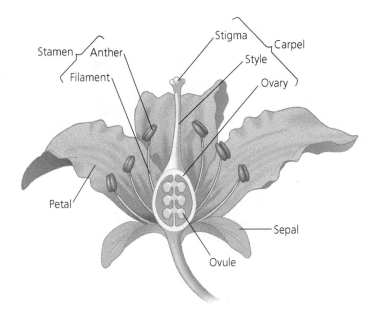

▲ **Figure 26.22 The structure of an idealized flower.**

in attracting pollinators. Flowers that are wind-pollinated, however, generally lack brightly colored parts. In all angiosperms, the sepals and petals are sterile floral organs, meaning that they do not produce sperm or eggs. Within the petals are two whorls of fertile floral organs, the stamens and carpels. **Stamens** produce pollen grains containing male gametophytes. A stamen consists of a stalk called the filament and a terminal sac, the anther, where pollen is produced. **Carpels** make ovules, which, as in gymnosperms, contain female gametophytes. At the tip of the carpel is a sticky stigma that receives pollen. A style leads from the stigma to a structure at the base of the carpel, the **ovary**; the ovary contains one or more ovules. If fertilized, an ovule develops into a seed.

As seeds develop from ovules after fertilization, the ovary wall thickens and the ovary matures into a **fruit**. A pea pod is an example of a fruit, with seeds (mature ovules, the peas) encased in the ripened ovary (the pod). Fruits protect seeds and aid in their dispersal (see Figure 30.12). For example, the seeds of some flowering plants, such as dandelions and maples, are contained within fruits that function like parachutes or propellers, adaptations that enhance dispersal by wind. Many other angiosperms rely on animals to carry seeds. Some of these plants have fruits modified as burrs that cling to animal fur (or the clothes of humans). Other angiosperms produce edible fruits, which are usually nutritious, sweet tasting, and vividly colored, advertising their ripeness. When an animal eats the fruit, it digests the fruit's fleshy part, but the tough seeds usually pass unharmed through the

animal's digestive tract. When the animal defecates, it may deposit the seeds, along with a supply of natural fertilizer, many kilometers from where the fruit was eaten.

Angiosperm Evolution

Charles Darwin once referred to the origin of angiosperms as an "abominable mystery." He was particularly troubled by the relatively sudden and geographically widespread appearance of angiosperms in the fossil record. Fossil evidence and phylogenetic analyses have led to progress in solving Darwin's mystery, but we still do not fully understand how angiosperms arose from earlier seed plants.

Fossil Evidence Angiosperms are thought to have originated in the early Cretaceous period, about 140 million years ago. By the mid-Cretaceous (100 million years ago), angiosperms began to dominate some terrestrial ecosystems. Landscapes changed dramatically as conifers and other gymnosperms gave way to flowering plants in many parts of the world. The Cretaceous ended 65 million years ago with mass extinctions of dinosaurs and many other animal groups and with further increases in the diversity and importance of angiosperms.

What evidence suggests that angiosperms arose 140 million years ago? First, although pollen grains are common in rocks from the Jurassic period (200–145 million years ago), none of these pollen fossils have features diagnostic of angiosperms, suggesting that angiosperms may have originated after the Jurassic. Indeed, the earliest fossils with distinctive angiosperm features are 130-million-year-old pollen grains discovered in China, Israel, and England. Early fossils of larger flowering plant structures include those of *Archaefructus* **(Figure 26.23)** and

(a) *Archaefructus sinensis*, **a 125-million-year-old fossil.** This species may represent the sister group to all other angiosperms, or it may belong to the water lily group. Researchers are testing these two hypotheses with phylogenetic analyses.

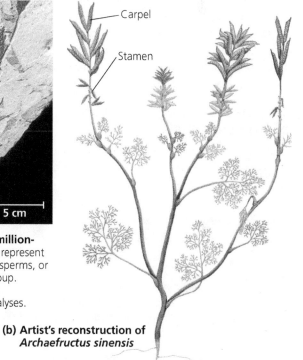

(b) Artist's reconstruction of *Archaefructus sinensis*

▲ **Figure 26.23 An early flowering plant.**

Leefructus, both of which were discovered in China in rocks that are about 125 million years old. Overall, early angiosperm fossils indicate that the group arose and began to diversify over a 20- to 30-million-year period—a less sudden event than was suggested by the fossils known during Darwin's lifetime.

Can we infer traits of the angiosperm common ancestor from traits found in early fossil angiosperms? *Archaefructus*, for example, was herbaceous and had bulbous structures that may have served as floats, suggesting it was aquatic. But investigating whether the common ancestor of angiosperms was herbaceous and aquatic also requires examining fossils of other seed plants thought to have been closely related to angiosperms. All of those plants were woody, indicating that the common ancestor was probably woody. As we'll see, this conclusion has been supported by recent phylogenetic analyses.

Angiosperm Phylogeny Molecular and morphological evidence suggests that living gymnosperm lineages diverged from the ancestors of angiosperms about 305 million years ago. Indeed, extant angiosperms may be more closely related to several extinct lineages of woody seed plants than they are to living gymnosperms. One such lineage is the Bennettitales, a group with flowerlike structures that may have been pollinated by insects **(Figure 26.24)**.

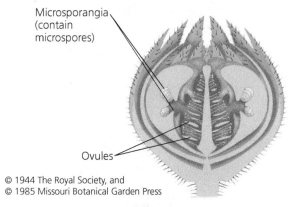

Microsporangia (contain microspores)

Ovules

© 1944 The Royal Society, and
© 1985 Missouri Botanical Garden Press

▲ **Figure 26.24 A close relative of the angiosperms?** This reconstruction shows a longitudinal section through the flowerlike structures found in Bennettitales, an extinct group of seed plants hypothesized to be more closely related to extant angiosperms than to living gymnosperms.

MAKE CONNECTIONS *Suppose the Bennettitales and extant angiosperms are sister taxa. Draw a phylogenetic tree that includes Bennettitales, angiosperms, gymnosperms, monilophytes, extant lycophytes. Identify the common ancestor and circle the basal taxon (see Figure 20.5).*

Making sense of the origin of angiosperms also depends on working out the order in which angiosperm clades diverged from one another. Here, dramatic progress has been made in

▼ **Figure 26.25** **Exploring Angiosperm Phylogeny**

The phylogenetic tree below represents one current hypothesis of angiosperm evolutionary relationships, based on morphological and molecular evidence.

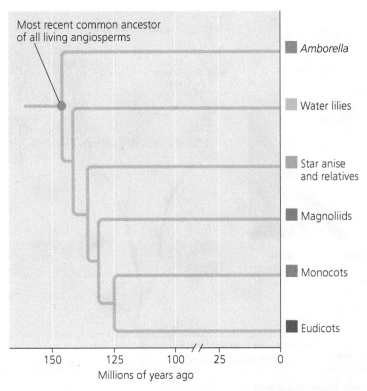

Most recent common ancestor of all living angiosperms

Amborella

Water lilies

Star anise and relatives

Magnoliids

Monocots

Eudicots

150   125   100   25   0

Millions of years ago

Amborella. This small shrub (*Amborella trichopoda*), found only on the South Pacific island of New Caledonia, may be the sole survivor of a branch at the base of the angiosperm tree. *Amborella* lacks vessels, efficient water-conducting cells found in angiosperms in later-diverging lineages.

Water lilies. Species of water lilies (genus *Nymphaea*) are found in aquatic habitats throughout the world. Water lilies are living members of a clade that may be predated only by the *Amborella* lineage.

recent years. Molecular and morphological evidence suggests that a small South Pacific shrub called *Amborella trichopoda* and water lilies are living representatives of two of the most ancient angiosperm lineages **(Figure 26.25)**. *Amborella* is woody, supporting the conclusion mentioned earlier that the angiosperm common ancestor was likely woody. Among the other lineages shown in Figure 26.25, the monocots and eudicots in particular have radiated extensively: There are now 70,000 species of monocots and 170,000 species of eudicots.

From their humble beginnings in the Cretaceous, angiosperms have diversified into more than 250,000 species, making them by far the largest group of living plants. This large group, along with fungi and nonflowering plants, has enormous ecological and evolutionary effects on other species.

CONCEPT CHECK 26.4

1. What features not present in seedless plants have contributed to the enormous success of seed plants on land?
2. Explain why Darwin called the origin of angiosperms an "abominable mystery," and describe what has been learned from fossil evidence and phylogenetic analyses.
3. **MAKE CONNECTIONS** Does the hypothesis that living gymnosperms and angiosperms are sister clades imply that they originated at the same time (see Figure 20.5)?

For suggested answers, see Appendix A.

Land plants and fungi fundamentally changed chemical cycling and biotic interactions

Throughout Unit Four, we are highlighting major steps in the evolutionary history of life. We have focused on great waves of adaptive radiation, such as the metabolic diversification of prokaryotes (Chapter 24) and the rise in structural diversity that followed the origin of eukaryotes (Chapter 25). In this chapter, we've examined another major step in the history of life: the colonization of land by plants and fungi. Let's now explore how the colonization of land has altered the physical environment and the organisms that live there.

Physical Environment and Chemical Cycling

Fungi and plants have profound effects on the physical environment. Consider a **lichen**, a symbiotic association between a fungus and a photosynthetic microorganism. Lichens are important pioneers on cleared rock and soil surfaces, such as volcanic flows and burned forests. They break down the surface by physically penetrating and chemically altering it,

Star anise. Some of the shrubs and small trees in this genus (*Illicium*) are native to southeast Asia, others to the southeastern United States. Living species in the genus probably descended from ancestors whose populations were separated by continental drift.

Magnoliids. This clade consists of about 8,000 woody and herbaceous species, including such familiar and economically important plants as magnolias, laurels, avocado, cinnamon, and black pepper. The variety of southern magnolia shown here (*Magnolia grandiflora*, also called "Goliath"), has flowers that can measure up to about a foot across.

Monocots. Over 25% of extant angiosperms are monocots. This large clade includes the most important crop plants in the world today: grains such as maize, rice, and wheat. Other monocots are widely used as ornamental plants, such as the pygmy date palm (*Phoenix roebelenii*) shown at left. The monocots also include plants such as orchids, grasses, irises, and onions.

Eudicots. Nearly 70% of living flowering plants are eudicots. One example, zucchini, a subspecies of *Cucurbita pepo*, is an important crop, as are acorn squash, pumpkin, and other *C. pepo* subspecies. The eudicots also include sunflowers, roses, cacti, clovers, oaks, and a wide range of other species.

and they trap windblown soil. These processes affect the formation of soil and make it possible for plants to grow. **Figure 26.26** shows two examples of the diverse forms of lichens along with the structure of a lichen composed of a fungus and a green alga. Fossils show that lichens were on land 420 million years ago. These early lichens may have modified rocks and soil much as they do today, helping pave the way for plants.

The colonization of land by plants resulted in great changes to the physical environment. Like lichens, plants affect the formation of soil: Their roots hold the soil in place, and leaf litter and other decaying plant parts add nutrients to the soil. Plants also have altered the composition of Earth's atmosphere, perhaps most importantly by releasing oxygen to the air as a by-product of photosynthesis.

Plants and fungi also have profound effects on the cycling of chemicals in ecosystems (see Figure 1.9). This process begins when plants absorb nutrients from the physical environment. Next, those nutrients pass to organisms that eat plants. Decomposers then break down the bodies of dead organisms, thereby returning nutrients to the physical environment and completing the cycle. Fungi are well adapted as decomposers of organic material. In fact, almost any carbon-containing substrate—even jet fuel and house paint—can be consumed by at least some fungi. (The same is true of bacteria.) As a result, fungi and bacteria play a central role in keeping ecosystems stocked with the inorganic nutrients essential for plant growth. Without these decomposers, carbon, nitrogen, and other elements would remain tied up in organic matter; if that were to happen, life as we know it would cease.

Let's take a closer look at how plants affect carbon recycling. Carbon forms the basis of the organic compounds that are essential for life. During photosynthesis, plants remove large quantities of CO_2 from the atmosphere—an action that can influence the global climate. A dramatic example occurred when seedless vascular plants first grew tall, forming the first forests about 385 million years ago **(Figure 26.27)**. With the evolution of vascular tissue, roots, and leaves, these plants accelerated their rate of photosynthesis, greatly increasing the removal of CO_2 from the atmosphere. Scientists estimate that CO_2 levels dropped by up to a factor of five during the Carboniferous (359–299 million years ago), causing global cooling that resulted in widespread glacier formation. Today, plants continue to influence carbon cycling and thereby both the global climate and the extent of global climate change (see Chapters 42 and 43).

▼ Crustose
(encrusting) lichens

▼ A foliose
(leaflike) lichen

(a) Two common lichen growth forms

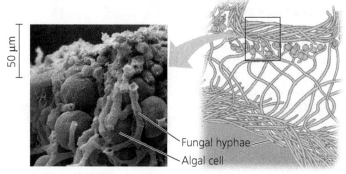

Fungal hyphae
Algal cell

50 μm

(b) Anatomy of a lichen involving an ascomycete fungus and an alga

▲ **Figure 26.26 Lichens.** Often found growing on rocks or rotting logs, lichens are a symbiotic association between a fungus and a photosynthetic microorganism (a green alga or a cyanobacterium).

Fern   Lycophyte trees   Horsetail   Tree trunk covered   Lycophyte tree
                                                with small leaves   reproductive structures

▲ **Figure 26.27 Artist's conception of a Carboniferous forest based on fossil evidence.** In addition to plants, animals, including giant dragonflies like the one in the foreground, also thrived in Carboniferous forests.

Biotic Interactions

The colonization of land by plants and fungi also had a dramatic effect on interactions between members of different species. Such biotic interactions include those in which both species benefit (mutualism) and those in which one species benefits while the other is harmed (as when a parasite feeds on its host).

Plants and fungi had such large effects on biotic interactions because their presence on land increased the availability of energy and nutrients for other organisms. For example, during photosynthesis, plants convert light energy to the chemical energy of food. That chemical energy supports all life on land, either directly (as when an insect eats a plant leaf) or indirectly (as when a bird eats an insect that ate a plant). Likewise, nitrogen and other nutrients are first absorbed by plants and then passed to organisms that eat plants; ultimately, these nutrients are returned to the environment by the actions of fungi and other decomposers. If plants and fungi had not colonized land, biotic interactions would still result in the transfer of energy and nutrients, but those transfers would likely occur on a much

smaller scale, such as that of the "green slime" mentioned earlier in the chapter.

The previous paragraphs describe the big picture of how plants and fungi have affected biotic interactions. We'll close the chapter with several specific examples.

Fungi as Mutualists and Pathogens

The different enzymes found in various fungal species can digest compounds from a wide range of sources, living or dead. This diversity of food sources corresponds to the varied roles of fungi in ecological communities, with different species living as decomposers, mutualists, or parasites. Having already described the importance of fungi as decomposers, we'll focus here on mutualism and parasitism.

Mutualistic fungi absorb nutrients from a host organism, but they reciprocate with actions that benefit the host—as we already saw for the enormously important mycorrhizal associations that fungi form with most vascular plants. In addition, all plant species studied to date appear to harbor symbiotic **endophytes**, fungi that live inside leaves or other plant parts without causing harm. Endophytes have been shown to benefit certain grasses by making toxins that deter herbivores or by increasing host plant tolerance of heat, drought, or heavy metals. Seeking to discover how endophytes affect a woody plant, researchers tested whether leaf endophytes benefit seedlings of the cacao tree, *Theobroma cacao* (**Figure 26.28**). Their findings show that the endophytes of woody flowering plants can play an important role in defending against pathogens.

Parasitic fungi also absorb nutrients from the cells of living hosts, but they provide no benefits in return (**Figure 26.29**).

▼ **Figure 26.28** Inquiry

Do endophytes benefit a woody plant?

Experiment Endophytes are symbiotic fungi found within the bodies of all plants examined to date. Researchers tested whether endophytes benefit the cacao tree (*Theobroma cacao*). This tree, whose name means "food of the gods" in Greek, is the source of the beans used to make chocolate, and it is cultivated throughout the tropics. Endophytes were added to the leaves of some cacao seedlings, but not others. (In cacao, endophytes colonize leaves after the seedling germinates.) The seedlings were then inoculated with a virulent pathogen, the protist *Phytophthora*.

Results Fewer leaves were killed by the pathogen in seedlings with endophytes than in seedlings without endophytes. Among leaves that survived, pathogens damaged less of the leaf surface area in seedlings with endophytes than in seedlings without endophytes.

Endophyte not present; pathogen present (E−P+)
Both endophyte and pathogen present (E+P+)

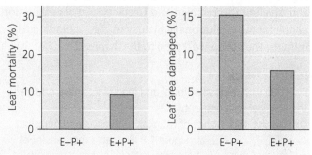

Conclusion Endophytes appear to benefit cacao trees by reducing the leaf mortality and damage caused by *Phytophthora*.

Source A. E. Arnold et al., Fungal endophytes limit pathogen damage in a tropical tree, *Proceedings of the National Academy of Sciences* 100:15649–15654 (2003).

WHAT IF? The researchers also performed control treatments. Suggest two controls they might have used, and explain how each would be helpful in interpreting the results described here.

(a) Corn smut on corn

(b) Tar spot fungus on maple leaves

(c) Ergots on rye

▲ **Figure 26.29 Examples of fungal diseases of plants.** About 30% of the 100,000 known species of fungi make a living as parasites or pathogens, mostly of plants.

Some parasitic fungi are pathogenic, including many species that cause diseases in plants. For example, *Cryphonectria parasitica*, the ascomycete fungus that causes chestnut blight, dramatically changed the landscape of the northeastern United States. Accidentally introduced on trees imported from Asia in the early 1900s, spores of the fungus enter cracks in the bark of American chestnut trees and produce hyphae, killing the tree. The once-common chestnuts now survive mainly as sprouts from the stumps of former trees.

Plant-Animal Interactions

Plants and animals have interacted for hundreds of millions of years, and those interactions have led to evolutionary change. For example, herbivores can reduce a plant's reproductive success by eating its roots, leaves, or seeds. As a result, if an effective defense against herbivores originates in a group of plants, those plants may be favored by natural selection—as will any herbivores that can overcome this new defense.

Interactions between plants and animals also may have affected the rates at which new species form. Consider the impact of flower shape, which can be symmetric in one direction only (*bilateral symmetry*) or symmetric in all directions (*radial symmetry*). On a flower with bilateral symmetry, an insect pollinator may only be able to enter the flower from a certain direction. This constraint can make it more likely that as an insect moves from flower to flower, pollen is placed on a part of the insect's body that will come into contact with the stigma of a flower of the same species.

Bilateral symmetry

Radial symmetry

Such specificity of pollen transfer tends to reduce gene flow between diverging populations and hence could lead to increased rates of plant speciation in plants with bilateral symmetry. This hypothesis can be tested using the approach illustrated in this diagram:

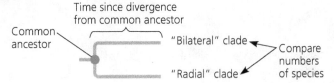

A key step is to identify cases in which a clade with bilaterally symmetric flowers shares an immediate common ancestor with a clade whose members have radially symmetric flowers. One recent study identified 19 such pairs of closely related "bilateral" and "radial" clades. On average, the clade with bilaterally symmetric flowers had nearly 2,400 more species than did its closely related clade with radially symmetric flowers. This result suggests that flower shape can affect the rate at which new species form—perhaps because of how flower shape affects the behavior of insect pollinators. Overall, the effects of plant-pollinator interactions are thought to have contributed

(a) A satellite image from 2000 shows clear-cut areas in Brazil (brown) surrounded by dense tropical forest (green).

(b) By 2009, much more of this same tropical forest had been cut down.

4 km

▲ **Figure 26.30 Clear-cutting of tropical forests.** Over the past several hundred years, nearly half of Earth's tropical forests have been cut down and converted to farmland and other uses.

to the diversification and increasing dominance of flowering plants in the Cretaceous period.

While angiosperms continue to dominate the communities of today, they and other plant groups are being threatened by the exploding human population and its demand for space and resources. The problem is especially severe in the tropics, where more than two-thirds of the human population live and where population growth is fastest. About 55,000 km^2 (14 million acres) of tropical rain forest are cleared each year **(Figure 26.30)**, a rate that would completely eliminate the remaining 11 million km^2 of tropical forests in 200 years. As forests disappear, so do large numbers of plant species. Of course, once a species becomes extinct, it can never return.

The loss of plant species is often accompanied by the loss of insects and other rain forest animals. Scientists estimate that if current rates of loss in the tropics and elsewhere continue, 50% or more of Earth's species will become extinct within the next few centuries. Such losses would constitute a global mass extinction, rivaling the Permian and Cretaceous mass extinctions and changing the evolutionary history of life—including that of the animals, the group we'll turn to in Chapter 27.

CONCEPT CHECK 26.5

1. Describe how terrestrial fungi and land plants have affected the physical environment.
2. Discuss the importance of fungi as mutualists and parasites.
3. **MAKE CONNECTIONS** Figure 1.9 illustrates the transfer of energy and matter in ecosystems. Draw a simple diagram of energy flow and chemical cycling in a terrestrial ecosystem; circle the steps that were affected by the colonization of land by plants and fungi.
4. **WHAT IF?** Explain why researchers testing whether flower shape (bilateral versus radial) affected speciation rates only analyzed cases in which a bilateral clade shared an immediate common ancestor with a radial clade.

For suggested answers, see Appendix A.

26 Chapter Review

SUMMARY OF KEY CONCEPTS

CONCEPT 26.1

Fossils show that plants colonized land more than 470 million years ago (pp. 505–508)

- Morphological and biochemical traits, as well as similarities in nuclear and chloroplast gene sequences, indicate that land plants arose from charophyte green algae.
- A protective layer of **sporopollenin** and other traits allow charophytes to tolerate occasional drying along the edges of ponds and lakes. Such traits may have enabled the algal ancestors of plants to survive in terrestrial conditions, opening the way to the colonization of dry land.
- Derived traits that distinguish land plants from charophytes, their closest algal relatives, include **apical meristems**, **cuticles**, **stomata**, and the two shown here:

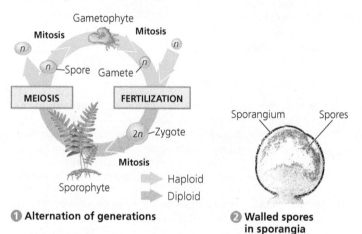

1 Alternation of generations

2 Walled spores in sporangia

- Fossil evidence indicates that plants were inhabiting land by 470 million years ago. By 400 million years ago, a diverse assemblage of fossil plant species lived on land, some of which had specialized tissues for water transport, stomata, and branched sporophytes.

? *The oldest fossil representing a large structure from a plant is 425 million years old, yet scientists think that plants colonized land 470 million years ago. What evidence supports this idea?*

CONCEPT 26.2

Fungi played an essential role in the colonization of land (pp. 508–513)

- All **fungi** are heterotrophs that acquire nutrients by absorption. Many fungi secrete enzymes that break down complex molecules to smaller molecules that can be absorbed.
- The cell walls of fungi are strengthened by **chitin**, a strong but flexible polysaccharide; these strong cell walls enable the cell to absorb nutrients and water without bursting.
- Most fungi grow as thin, multicellular filaments called **hyphae**; relatively few species grow only as single-celled **yeasts**. In their multicellular form, fungi consist of **mycelia**, networks of branched hyphae adapted for absorption. Mycorrhizal fungi have specialized hyphae that enable them to form a mutually beneficial relationship with plants.

- Fungi typically propagate themselves by producing **spores**, either sexually or asexually. Spores can be transported by wind or water; if they are deposited in a moist place that has food, they germinate, producing new mycelia.
- Although fungi likely colonized land before plants, the earliest fossils of fungi date to 460 million years ago. Once on land, some fungi formed mycorrhizal associations with early plants—a symbiosis that probably helped plants without roots to colonize land.
- Molecular data show that fungi arose from a single-celled protist and are more closely related to animals than to plants or most other eukaryotes. Since colonizing land, fungi have radiated into a diverse set of lineages.

? *Explain how the morphology of multicellular fungi affects the efficiency of nutrient absorption and may have played a role in the colonization of land by plants.*

CONCEPT 26.3

Early land plants radiated into a diverse set of lineages (pp. 513–516)

- The three extant phyla of nonvascular plants, or **bryophytes**—liverworts, mosses, and hornworts—are the earliest-diverging plant lineages.
- In bryophytes, the dominant generation consists of haploid **gametophytes**, such as those that make up a carpet of moss. The flagellated sperm require a film of water to travel to the eggs.
- Fossils of the forerunners of today's vascular plants date back 425–420 million years and show that these small plants lacked seeds but had independent, branching sporophytes and a well-developed vascular system.
- Over time, other derived traits of living vascular plants arose, such as a life cycle with dominant sporophytes; lignified vascular tissue; and well-developed roots and leaves.
- Seedless vascular plants formed the first forests about 385 million years ago. Today, seedless vascular plants include the **lycophytes** (club mosses and their relatives) and the **monilophytes** (ferns and their relatives).

? *What trait(s) allowed vascular plants to grow tall, and why might increased height have been advantageous?*

CONCEPT 26.4

Seeds and pollen grains are key adaptations for life on land (pp. 516–521)

- Derived traits of seed plants include **seeds** (which survive better than spores), highly reduced gametophytes (which are nourished and protected by the sporophyte), **ovules** (which house female gametophytes), and pollen (which eliminates dependency on water for fertilization).
- Seed plants originated 360 million years ago. Living seed plants can be divided into two monophyletic groups: **gymnosperms** and **angiosperms**. Gymnosperms appear early in the seed plant fossil record and dominated many terrestrial ecosystems until angiosperms (flowering plants) began to replace them 100 million years ago.
- **Flowers** typically have four whorls of modified leaves: **sepals, petals, stamens**, and **carpels**. Ovaries ripen into **fruits**, which often carry seeds by wind, water, or animals to new locations.

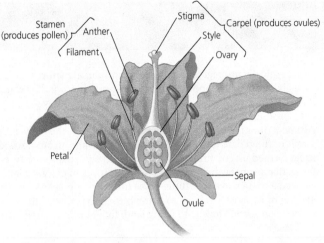

Flower anatomy

- Angiosperms arose and diversified greatly during the Cretaceous period. Fossils and phylogenetic analyses offer insights into the origin of flowering plants, which today are by far the largest group of extant land plants. The two most diverse angiosperm clades are monocots and eudicots.

> **?** *Summarize fossil and phylogenetic evidence that suggests that the angiosperm common ancestor was likely woody.*

CONCEPT 26.5

Land plants and fungi fundamentally changed chemical cycling and biotic interactions (pp. 521–524)

- **Lichens** and plants affect soil formation. Plants also alter the composition of Earth's atmosphere by releasing oxygen to the air as a by-product of photosynthesis.
- Plants play a central role in chemical cycling by absorbing nutrients from the physical environment; those nutrients then pass to organisms that eat plants. Fungal decomposers break down the bodies of dead organisms; this returns nutrients to the physical environment, completing the cycle.
- Since colonizing land, the activities of plants and fungi have altered biotic interactions by increasing the availability of energy and nutrients for other organisms.
- Fungi play key ecological roles as decomposers, mutualists (such as **endophytes** that help protect plants from herbivores and pathogens), and parasites.
- Interactions between plants and animals have led to natural selection in plant and animal populations and may have affected speciation rates. Destruction of habitat threatens the extinction of many plant species and the animal species they support.

> **?** *Summarize how plants and fungi have increased the availability of energy and nutrients for other organisms, and explain how this affects biotic interactions.*

TEST YOUR UNDERSTANDING

Level 1: Knowledge/Comprehension

1. *All* fungi are
   a. symbiotic
   b. heterotrophic
   c. flagellated
   d. pathogenic
   e. decomposers

2. Which of the following characteristics of plants is absent in their closest relatives, the charophyte algae?
   a. chlorophyll *b*
   b. cellulose in cell walls
   c. multicellularity
   d. sexual reproduction
   e. alternation of generations

3. Identify each of the following structures as haploid or diploid.
   a. sporophyte
   b. spore
   c. gametophyte
   d. zygote
   e. sperm

4. A fruit is usually
   a. a mature ovary.
   b. a thickened style.
   c. an enlarged ovule.
   d. a modified root.
   e. a mature female gametophyte.

5. Among the organisms listed here, which are thought to be the closest relatives of fungi?
   a. slime molds
   b. vascular plants
   c. animals
   d. brown algae
   e. mosses

Level 2: Application/Analysis

6. The adaptive advantage associated with the filamentous nature of fungal mycelia is primarily related to
   a. the ability to form haustoria and parasitize other organisms.
   b. avoiding sexual reproduction until the environment changes.
   c. the potential to inhabit almost all terrestrial habitats.
   d. the increased probability of contact between different mating types.
   e. an extensive surface area well suited for invasive growth and absorptive nutrition.

7. **DRAW IT** Use the letters a–d to label where on the phylogenetic tree each of the following derived characters appears.
   a. flowers
   b. embryos
   c. seeds
   d. vascular tissue

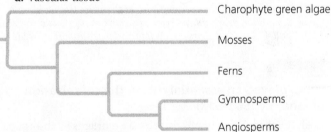

8. **SCIENTIFIC INQUIRY**
   DRAW IT The grass *Dichanthelium languinosum* lives in hot soils and houses fungi of the genus *Curvularia* as endophytes. Researchers performed field experiments to test the impact of *Curvularia* on the heat tolerance of this grass. They grew plants without (E−) and with (E+) *Curvularia* endophytes in soils of different temperatures and measured plant mass and the number of new shoots the plants produced. Draw a bar graph of the results for plant mass versus temperature and interpret it.

Soil Temp.	*Curvularia* Presence	Plant Mass (g)	Number of New Shoots
30°C	E−	16.2	32
	E+	22.8	60
35°C	E−	21.7	43
	E+	28.4	60
40°C	E−	8.8	10
	E+	22.2	37
45°C	E−	0	0
	E+	15.1	24

Source R. S. Redman et al., *Science* 298:1581 (2002).

Level 3: Synthesis/Evaluation

9. FOCUS ON EVOLUTION

The history of life has been punctuated by several mass extinctions. For example, the impact of a meteorite may have wiped out most of the dinosaurs and many forms of marine life at the end of the Cretaceous period (see Chapter 23). Fossils indicate that plants were less severely affected by this mass extinction. What adaptations may have enabled plants to withstand this disaster better than animals?

10. FOCUS ON INTERACTIONS

Giant lycophyte trees of Earth's early forests (see Figure 26.27) had microphylls, whereas ferns and seed plants have megaphylls. Write a short essay (100–150 words) describing how a forest of lycophyte trees may have differed from a forest of large ferns or seed plants. In your answer, consider how the type of forest in which they grew may have affected interactions among small plants growing beneath the tall ones.

For selected answers, see Appendix A.

MasteringBiology®

Students Go to **MasteringBiology** for assignments, the eText, and the Study Area with practice tests, animations, and activities.

Instructors Go to **MasteringBiology** for automatically graded tutorials and questions that you can assign to your students, plus Instructor Resources.

27

The Rise of Animal Diversity

KEY CONCEPTS

27.1 Animals originated more than 700 million years ago

27.2 The diversity of large animals increased dramatically during the "Cambrian explosion"

27.3 Diverse animal groups radiated in aquatic environments

27.4 Several animal groups had features that facilitated their colonization of land

27.5 Animals have transformed ecosystems and altered the course of evolution

OVERVIEW

Life Becomes Dangerous

Although slow moving on its feet, the chameleon in **Figure 27.1** can wield its long, sticky tongue with blinding speed to capture unsuspecting prey. Other animals overwhelm their prey using their strength, speed, or toxins, while still others build traps or blend into their surroundings, enabling them to capture unwary prey. And hunting animals are not the only ones that pose a threat to other organisms. Herbivorous animals can strip the plants they eat bare of leaves or seeds, while parasitic animals weaken their hosts by consuming their tissues or body fluids.

As these examples suggest, animals can make life dangerous for the organisms around them. Most animals are mobile and can detect, capture, and eat other organisms—including those that are mobile themselves and can flee from attack. Indeed, all but the simplest animals have specialized muscle and nerve cells that allow them to move and respond rapidly to changing environmental conditions. Most animals also have a complete digestive tract, an efficient digestive system that has a mouth at one end and an anus at the other. Together, their mobility, nervous system, and digestive tract, accompanied by often complex behaviors, make animals highly effective eating machines.

Animals are so integral to our lives today that it is difficult to imagine what Earth would be like without animals. The fossil record, however, paints an intriguing picture. Large eukaryotes were once soft-bodied and lived in a relatively safe world—until the appearance of animals changed everything. In this chapter, we'll examine how animals have evolved over time and influenced the world around them.

▼ **Figure 27.1 What adaptations make a chameleon a fearsome predator?**

CONCEPT 27.1

Animals originated more than 700 million years ago

Current evidence indicates that animals evolved from single-celled eukaryotes similar to present-day choanoflagellates (see Chapter 25). These early animals have given rise to a vast diversity of living animal species: To date, biologists have named more than 1.3 million species, and estimates of the actual number

(a) *Dickinsonia costata* (taxonomic affiliation unknown)

2.5 cm

▲ **Figure 27.2 Ediacaran fossils.** Fossils dating to about 560 million years ago include the earliest macroscopic fossils of animals, including these two species. Earlier members of the Ediacaran biota include the alga *Doushantuophyton* (see Figure 25.2).

(b) The fossil mollusc *Kimberella*

1 cm

run far higher—nearly 8 million species according to one recent study. When did this diverse group originate?

Fossil and Molecular Evidence

Researchers have unearthed 710-million-year-old sediments containing the fossilized remains of steroids that today are primarily produced by a particular group of sponges. Hence, these fossil steroids suggest that animals had arisen by 710 million years ago.

DNA analyses generally agree with this fossil biochemical evidence; for example, one recent molecular clock study

estimated that sponges originated about 700 million years ago. These findings are also consistent with molecular analyses suggesting that the common ancestor of all extant (living) animal species lived about 770 million years ago.

Despite the data from molecular clocks and fossil steroids indicating an earlier origin, the first generally accepted macroscopic fossils of animals date from about 560 million years ago **(Figure 27.2)**. These fossils are members of an early group of soft-bodied multicellular eukaryotes known collectively as the **Ediacaran biota**. The name comes from the Ediacara Hills of Australia, where fossils of these organisms were first discovered. Similar fossils have since been found on other continents. Among the Ediacaran fossils that resemble animals, some may be sponges, while others may be related to living cnidarians (sea anemones and their relatives) and molluscs (snails and their relatives). Still others are difficult to classify, as they do not seem to be closely related to any living animals or algae.

Early-Diverging Animal Groups

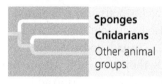

Sponges
Cnidarians
Other animal groups

As the first animals evolved over time, their descendants gave rise to several early-diverging groups, two of which we'll discuss here: sponges and cnidarians.

Sponges

Animals in the phylum Porifera are known informally as sponges **(Figure 27.3)**. (Recent molecular studies indicate that sponges are monophyletic, and that is the phylogeny we present

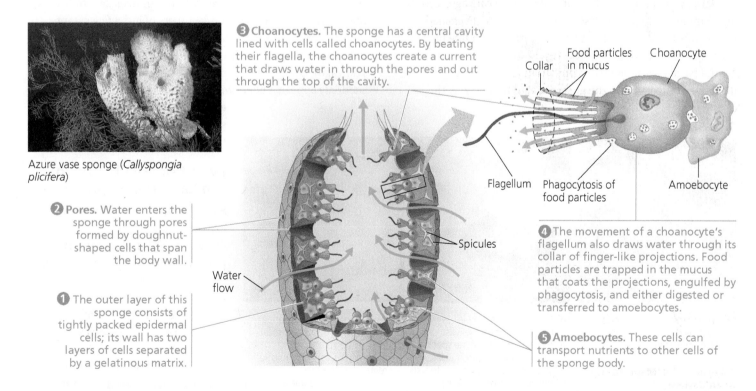

Azure vase sponge (*Callyspongia plicifera*)

❸ **Choanocytes.** The sponge has a central cavity lined with cells called choanocytes. By beating their flagella, the choanocytes create a current that draws water in through the pores and out through the top of the cavity.

Collar — Food particles in mucus — Choanocyte

Flagellum — Phagocytosis of food particles — Amoebocyte

❷ **Pores.** Water enters the sponge through pores formed by doughnut-shaped cells that span the body wall.

Spicules

Water flow

❶ The outer layer of this sponge consists of tightly packed epidermal cells; its wall has two layers of cells separated by a gelatinous matrix.

❹ The movement of a choanocyte's flagellum also draws water through its collar of finger-like projections. Food particles are trapped in the mucus that coats the projections, engulfed by phagocytosis, and either digested or transferred to amoebocytes.

❺ **Amoebocytes.** These cells can transport nutrients to other cells of the sponge body.

▲ **Figure 27.3 Anatomy of a sponge.**

here; this remains under debate, however, as some studies suggest that sponges are paraphyletic.) Among the simplest of animals, sponges are sedentary and were mistaken for plants by the ancient Greeks. Most species are marine, and they range in size from a few millimeters to a few meters. Sponges are **filter feeders**: They filter out food particles suspended in the water as they draw it through their body (see Figure 27.3).

Sponges represent a lineage that originates near the root of the phylogenetic tree of animals; thus, they are said to be *basal animals*. Unlike nearly all other animals, sponges lack **tissues**, groups of similar cells that act as a functional unit. However, the sponge body does contain several different cell types. For example, the interior of the body is lined with flagellated **choanocytes**, or collar cells (named for the finger-like projections that form a "collar" around the flagellum). These cells engulf bacteria and other food particles by phagocytosis. Choanocytes resemble the cells of choanoflagellates, a finding that is consistent with the similarities between the DNA sequences of sponges and those of choanoflagellates. Together, these results suggest that animals evolved from a choanoflagellate-like ancestor (see Figure 25.7). Sponges also have mobile cells called **amoebocytes**, named for their use of pseudopodia. As these cells move through the sponge body, they take up food from the surrounding water and from choanocytes, digest it, and carry nutrients to other cells.

Cnidarians

All animals except sponges and a few other groups are *eumetazoans* ("true animals"), members of a clade of animals that have tissues. One of the oldest lineages in this clade is the phylum Cnidaria, which originated about 680 million years ago according to molecular clock analyses. Cnidarians have diversified into a wide range of sessile and motile forms, including hydrozoans, jellies, and sea anemones **(Figure 27.4)**.

The basic morphology of a cnidarian is a sac with a central digestive compartment, the **gastrovascular cavity**. A single

opening to this cavity functions as both mouth and anus. Cnidarians are carnivores that often use tentacles arranged in a ring around their mouth to capture prey and pass the food into their gastrovascular cavity. Enzymes are then secreted into the cavity, breaking down the prey into a nutrient-rich broth. Cells lining the cavity then absorb these nutrients and complete the digestive process; any undigested remains are expelled through the cnidarian's mouth/anus.

Muscles and nerves occur in their simplest forms in cnidarians. Movements are coordinated by a noncentralized nerve net. Cnidarians have no brain, and the nerve net is associated with sensory structures distributed around the body. Thus, the animal can detect and respond to stimuli from all directions.

CONCEPT CHECK 27.1

1. Summarize fossil and DNA evidence documenting the origin and early diversification of animals.
2. **WHAT IF?** Suppose the most recent common ancestor of choanoflagellates and animals lived 900 million years ago. If extant choanoflagellates arose 890 million years ago, would extant animals also have been alive at that time? Explain.

   For suggested answers, see Appendix A.

CONCEPT 27.2

The diversity of large animals increased dramatically during the "Cambrian explosion"

As we've seen, the oldest fossils of large animals date to 560 million years ago and include members of just a few extant groups—sponges, cnidarians, and molluscs. In fossils formed in the early Cambrian period (between 535 and 525 million years ago), large forms of many other present-day animal phyla suddenly appear, a phenomenon referred to as the **Cambrian explosion**. What factors may have spurred this rapid (in geologic terms) diversification?

Evolutionary Change in the Cambrian Explosion

Strata formed during the Cambrian explosion contain the oldest fossils of about half of all extant animal phyla, including the first arthropods, chordates, and echinoderms **(Figure 27.5)**. Many of these fossils, which include the first animals with hard, mineralized skeletons, look very different from most living animals **(Figure 27.6)**. Even so, paleontologists have established that these

(a) Hydrozoa. Some species, such as this one, live as colonial polyps.

▲ **Figure 27.4 Major groups of cnidarians.**

(b) Scyphozoa. Many jellies (commonly called jellyfish) are bioluminescent. Some species stun their prey with specialized stinging cells called nematocysts located on their tentacles.

(c) Anthozoa. Sea anemones and other anthozoans exist only as polyps. Many anthozoans form symbiotic relationships with photosynthetic algae.

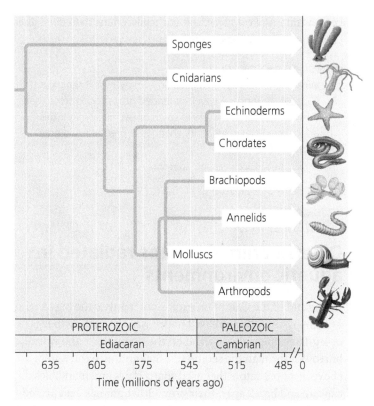

▲ **Figure 27.5 Appearance of selected animal groups.** The white bars indicate earliest appearances of these animal groups in the fossil record.

DRAW IT *Circle the branch point that represents the most recent common ancestor of chordates and annelids. What is a minimum estimate of that ancestor's age?*

Cambrian fossils are members of extant animal phyla, or at least are close relatives. In particular, most of the fossils from the Cambrian explosion are of **bilaterians**, an enormous clade whose members (unlike sponges and cnidarians) have a complete digestive tract and a two-sided—bilaterally symmetric—form. As we'll discuss later in the chapter, bilaterians include molluscs, arthropods, chordates, and most other living animal phyla.

Entirely new sorts of animals made their debut during the Cambrian explosion. Previously, virtually all large animals were soft-bodied. In addition, the fossils of large pre-Cambrian animals reveal little evidence of predation. Instead, these animals seem to have been grazers (feeding on mats of algae and bacteria), filter feeders, or scavengers, not hunters. In a relatively short period of time (10 million years), predators over 1 m in length emerged that had claws and other features for capturing prey; simultaneously, new defensive adaptations, such as sharp spines

and heavy body armor, appeared in their prey (see Figure 27.6). These and other changes set the stage for many of the key events in the history of life over the last 500 million years.

The increase in the diversity of large animals during the Cambrian explosion was accompanied by a decline in the diversity of Ediacaran life-forms. What caused these trends? Fossil evidence suggests that during the Cambrian period, predators acquired novel adaptations, such as forms of locomotion that helped them catch prey, while prey species acquired new defenses, such as protective shells. As new predator-prey relationships emerged, natural selection may have led to the decline of the soft-bodied Ediacaran species and the rise of various bilaterian phyla. Another hypothesis focuses on an increase in atmospheric oxygen that preceded the Cambrian explosion. More plentiful oxygen would have enabled animals with higher metabolic rates and larger body sizes to thrive, while potentially harming other species. A third hypothesis proposes that the origin of *Hox* genes (see Concept 23.3) and other genetic changes affecting the regulation of developmental genes facilitated the evolution of new body forms. These hypotheses are not mutually exclusive, however; predator-prey relationships, atmospheric changes, and changes in the regulation of development may each have played a role.

Dating the Origin of Bilaterians

Although the radiation of bilaterians during the Cambrian explosion had an enormous impact on life on Earth, it is possible that many animal phyla originated long before that time. As we've seen, molecular clock analyses suggest that two early-diverging groups, sponges and cnidarians, had evolved by

Hallucigenia fossil (530 mya)

▲ **Figure 27.6 A Cambrian seascape.** This artist's reconstruction depicts a diverse array of organisms found in fossils from the Burgess Shale site in British Columbia, Canada. The animals include *Pikaia* (eel-like chordate at top left), *Marella* (arthropod swimming at left), *Anomalocaris* (large animal with anterior grasping limbs and a circular mouth), and *Hallucigenia* (animals with toothpick-like spikes on the seafloor and in inset).

700–680 million years ago. Molecular estimates also suggest that bilaterians had evolved by 670 million years ago—135 million years *before* the Cambrian explosion.

Turning to the fossil record, fossil steroids corroborate the molecular dates for the origin of sponges. However, no fossil bilaterians are close in age to the molecular clock estimates for when this group originated. The oldest fossil bilaterian is the mollusc *Kimberella* (see Figure 27.2), which lived 560 million years ago. Thus, the fossil evidence differs from molecular clock estimates by more than 100 million years.

Seeking to resolve this discrepancy, researchers have taken a closer look at the fossil record from the Ediacaran period (635–542 million years ago). Prior to the Ediacaran, eukaryotes were microscopic and smooth-walled, and such forms appeared in the fossil record for hundreds of millions of years **(Figure 27.7a)**. Then eukaryotic life changed dramatically. Some eukaryotic lineages gave rise to large organisms, such as the 600-million-year-old alga shown in Figure 25.2. Organisms in other eukaryotic lineages remained relatively small, but defensive structures such as spines began to appear on their outer surfaces **(Figure 27.7b)**. Additional fossil evidence shows that such well-defended eukaryotes originated more rapidly and persisted in the fossil record for shorter periods of time than did their smooth-walled, pre-Ediacaran counterparts.

What triggered these dramatic changes? Recall from the chapter opening that living animals are dangerous feeding machines because of their mobility, nervous system, and efficient digestive tract. Most bilaterians have these features, and early bilaterians may have decimated populations of the small, soft-bodied organisms on which they fed. Thus, the feeding activities of early bilaterians may have resulted in natural selection for increased size or new defensive structures in the organisms that they ate—exactly the change seen in the fossil record during the Ediacaran period.

Overall, the fossil record and molecular clock results suggest that bilaterians arose sometime between 670 and 635 million years ago. Possibly aided by a later rise in the atmospheric concentration of oxygen, these early bilaterians then diversified explosively during the Cambrian and beyond.

CONCEPT CHECK 27.2
1. What is the "Cambrian explosion," and why is it significant?
2. **WHAT IF?** Suppose a well-defended prey species arose that was difficult for predators to catch or eat. How might this affect ongoing evolutionary changes in predator and prey populations?

For suggested answers, see Appendix A.

CONCEPT 27.3

Diverse animal groups radiated in aquatic environments

By the end of the Cambrian explosion, many of the big steps in animal evolution were well under way. Animals with legs or leg-like appendages walked on the ocean floor, and worms burrowed through the sediments. Swimming in the waters above were predators that used sharp claws and mandibles to capture and break apart their prey. Other animals had protective spikes or armor, as well as modified mouthparts that enabled their bearers to filter food from the water.

As these examples suggest, the animals in early Cambrian oceans were very diverse in morphology, way of life, and taxonomic affiliation. We'll examine that diversity here, beginning with an overview of how to categorize the morphological variation found in different animal groups.

Animal Body Plans

The diversity in form of the animals that emerged from the Cambrian explosion consists of a relatively small number of major "body plans." A **body plan** is a particular set of morphological and developmental traits, integrated into a functional whole—the living animal. Note that the term *plan* here does not imply that animal forms are the result of conscious planning or invention. But body plans do provide a succinct way to compare and contrast key animal features. We'll focus on three aspects of animal body plans: symmetry, tissues, and body cavities.

Symmetry

A basic feature of animal bodies is their type of symmetry—or absence of symmetry. (Many sponges, for example, lack symmetry altogether.) Some animals exhibit **radial symmetry**, the type of symmetry found in a flowerpot **(Figure 27.8a)**. Sea anemones, for example, have a top side (where the mouth is located) and a bottom side. But they have no front and back ends and no left and right sides.

By contrast, the two-sided symmetry of a shovel is an example of **bilateral symmetry (Figure 27.8b)**. A bilateral animal has two axes of orientation: front to back and top to bottom. Such animals have a **dorsal** (top) side and a **ventral** (bottom)

(a) *Valeria* (800 mya): roughly spherical, no structural defenses, soft-bodied

(b) Spiny acritarch (575 mya): about five times larger than *Valeria* and covered in hard spines

▲ **Figure 27.7 Indirect evidence of the appearance of bilaterians?** The rise in the fossil record of larger, well-defended eukaryotes during the Ediacaran period (635-542 million years ago) suggests that bilaterian animals with a complete digestive tract may have originated by that time.

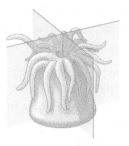

(a) Radial symmetry. A radial animal, such as a sea anemone (phylum Cnidaria), does not have a left side and a right side. Any imaginary slice through the central axis divides the animal into mirror images.

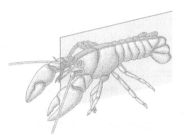

(b) Bilateral symmetry. A bilateral animal, such as a lobster (phylum Arthropoda), has a left side and a right side. Only one imaginary cut divides the animal into mirror-image halves.

▲ Figure 27.8 Body symmetry. The flowerpot and shovel are included to help you remember the radial-bilateral distinction.

side, a left side and a right side, and an **anterior** (front) end and a **posterior** (back) end. Many animals with a bilaterally symmetric body plan (such as arthropods and mammals) have sensory equipment concentrated at their anterior end, including a central nervous system ("brain") in the head.

The symmetry of an animal generally fits its lifestyle. Many radial animals are sessile (living attached to a substrate) or planktonic (drifting or weakly swimming, such as jellies). Their symmetry equips them to meet the environment equally well from all sides. In contrast, bilateral animals typically move actively from place to place. Most bilateral animals have a central nervous system that enables them to coordinate the complex movements involved in crawling, burrowing, flying, or swimming.

Tissues

Animal body plans also vary with regard to tissue organization. Recall that tissues are collections of specialized cells that act as a functional unit; in animals, true tissues are isolated from other tissues by membranous layers. Sponges and a few other groups lack true tissues. In all other animals, the embryo becomes layered during development; these layers, called *germ layers*, form the various tissues and organs of the body **(Figure 27.9)**. **Ectoderm**, the germ layer covering the surface of the embryo, gives rise to the outer covering of the animal and, in some phyla, to the central nervous system. **Endoderm**, the innermost germ layer, gives rise to the lining of the digestive tract (or cavity) and organs such as the liver and lungs of vertebrates.

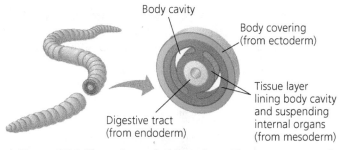

▲ Figure 27.9 **Tissue layers in bilaterians.** The organ systems of a bilaterally symmetric animal develop from the three germ layers that form in the embryo. Blue represents tissue derived from ectoderm, red from mesoderm, and yellow from endoderm. The internal organs of most bilaterians are suspended in a "body cavity," a fluid- or air-filled space that helps protect the organs from injury.

Cnidarians and a few other animal groups have only these two germ layers. In contrast, all bilaterally symmetric animals have a third germ layer, called the **mesoderm**, which fills much of the space between the ectoderm and endoderm. In bilaterally symmetric animals, the mesoderm forms the muscles and most other organs between the digestive tract and the outer covering of the animal.

Body Cavities

Most bilaterians have a **body cavity**, a fluid- or air-filled space located between the digestive tract and the outer body wall (see Figure 27.9). This body cavity is also called a *coelom*. The inner and outer layers of tissue that surround the cavity connect and form structures that suspend the internal organs.

A body cavity has many functions. Its fluid cushions the suspended organs, helping to prevent internal injury. In soft-bodied bilaterians, such as earthworms, the coelom contains noncompressible fluid that acts like a skeleton against which muscles can work. The cavity also enables the internal organs to grow and move independently of the outer body wall. If it were not for your coelom, every beat of your heart or ripple of your intestine would warp your body's surface.

The Diversification of Animals

As animals radiated in the early Cambrian, some lineages arose, thrived for a period of time, and then became extinct, leaving no descendants. However, by 500 million years ago, most animal phyla with members alive today were established.

Evolutionary relationships among living animals provide a helpful framework for studying the rise of animals. These relationships have been estimated using ribosomal RNA (rRNA) genes, *Hox* genes, and dozens of protein-coding nuclear genes, as well as mitochondrial genes and morphological traits. Zoologists currently recognize about three dozen animal phyla, 14 of which are shown in **Figure 27.10**. Notice how the following points are reflected in this phylogeny.

1. **All animals share a common ancestor.** Current evidence indicates that animals are monophyletic, forming

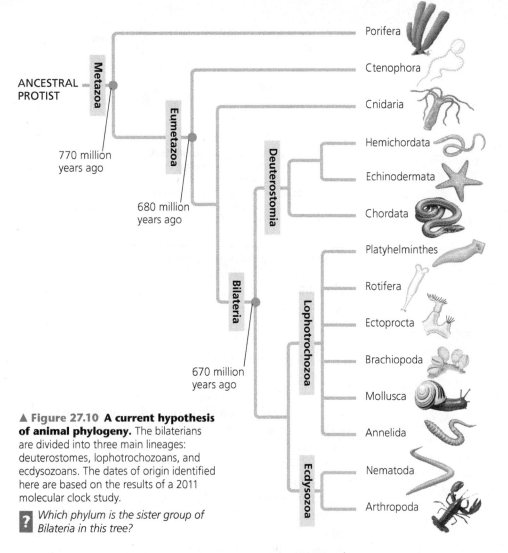

ANCESTRAL PROTIST

Metazoa

770 million years ago

Eumetazoa

680 million years ago

Bilateria

670 million years ago

Deuterostomia

Lophotrochozoa

Ecdysozoa

Porifera

Ctenophora

Cnidaria

Hemichordata

Echinodermata

Chordata

Platyhelminthes

Rotifera

Ectoprocta

Brachiopoda

Mollusca

Annelida

Nematoda

Arthropoda

▲ **Figure 27.10 A current hypothesis of animal phylogeny.** The bilaterians are divided into three main lineages: deuterostomes, lophotrochozoans, and ecdysozoans. The dates of origin identified here are based on the results of a 2011 molecular clock study.

? *Which phylum is the sister group of Bilateria in this tree?*

backbone. Only one animal phylum, Chordata, includes **vertebrates**, animals with a backbone.

With the phylogeny in Figure 27.10 providing the overall context for the rise of animals, let's examine the bilaterian radiation in more detail; we'll begin with invertebrates.

Bilaterian Radiation I: Diverse Invertebrates

As shown in Figure 27.10, bilaterian animals have diversified into three major clades: Lophotrochozoa, Ecdysozoa, and Deuterostomia. The species in these clades dominated life in the Cambrian oceans—and initially, at least, all of these species were invertebrates.

An Overview of Invertebrate Diversity

Bilaterian invertebrates account for 95% of known animal species. They occupy almost every habitat on Earth, from the scalding water released by deep-sea hydrothermal vents to the frozen ground of Antarctica. Evolution in these varied environments has produced an immense diversity of forms, ranging from tiny worms with a flat body shape to species with features such as silk-spinning glands, pivoting spines, and tentacles covered with suction cups. Bilaterian invertebrates also show enormous variation in size, from microscopic organisms to organisms that can grow to 18 m long (1.5 times the length of a school bus).

The morphological diversity found in invertebrate animals is mirrored by their taxonomic diversity: There are literally millions of species of invertebrates. The vast majority of these species are members of two of the bilaterian clades that emerged from the Cambrian explosion: Lophotrochozoa and Ecdysozoa **(Figure 27.11)**. The third major bilaterian clade, Deuterostomia, also includes some invertebrates.

The seven phyla shown in Figure 27.11 serve as representatives of the great diversity of invertebrate bilaterians. Next, we'll examine the origin of one of these phyla, Arthropoda, the most species-rich (by far) of all animal groups. We focus on this group because its members were among the first animals to colonize land (see Concept 27.4).

Arthropod Origins

Zoologists estimate that there are about a billion billion (10^{18}) arthropods living on Earth. More than 1 million arthropod

a clade called Metazoa: All extant and extinct animal lineages have descended from a common ancestor.

2. **Sponges are basal animals.** Among the extant taxa, sponges (phylum Porifera) branch from the base of the animal tree.

3. **Eumetazoa is a clade of animals with true tissues.** All animals except for sponges and a few others belong to a clade of **eumetazoans** ("true animals"). True tissues evolved in the common ancestor of living eumetazoans. Basal eumetazoans, such as ctenophores and cnidarians, have two germ layers and generally have radial symmetry.

4. **Most animal phyla belong to the clade Bilateria.** Bilateral symmetry and the presence of three germ layers are shared derived characters that help define the clade Bilateria. This clade contains the majority of animal phyla, and its members are known as **bilaterians**. The Cambrian explosion was primarily a rapid diversification of bilaterians.

5. **Most animals are invertebrates.** The members of most animal phyla are **invertebrates**, animals that lack a

The overwhelming majority of the 1.3 million known animal species are bilaterians, and most bilaterians are invertebrates. This figure highlights just a few of the invertebrate groups within the three major clades of bilaterians: Lophotrochozoa, Ecdysozoa, and Deuterostomia.

Lophotrochozoa

Ectoprocts

Ectoprocta (4,500 species) Ectoprocts (also known as bryozoans) live as sessile colonies. Most species have a hard exoskeleton studded with pores; ciliated tentacles extend through the pores and trap food particles from the surrounding water.

An octopus

Mollusca (93,000 species) Molluscs (including snails, clams, squids, and octopuses) have a soft body that in many species is protected by a hard shell.

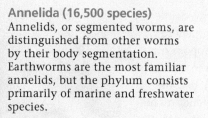

Annelida (16,500 species) Annelids, or segmented worms, are distinguished from other worms by their body segmentation. Earthworms are the most familiar annelids, but the phylum consists primarily of marine and freshwater species.

A fireworm, a marine annelid

Ecdysozoa

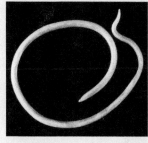

A roundworm

Nematoda (25,000 species) Also called roundworms, nematodes are enormously abundant and diverse in the soil and in aquatic habitats; many species parasitize plants and animals. Their most distinctive feature is a tough cuticle that coats the body.

Arthropoda (1,000,000 species) The vast majority of known animal species, including insects, millipedes, crabs, and arachnids, are arthropods. All arthropods have a segmented exoskeleton and jointed appendages.

A web-building spider (an arachnid)

Deuterostomia

An acorn worm

Hemichordata (85 species) Hemichordates share some traits with chordates, such as gill slits and a dorsal nerve cord. The largest group of hemichordates are the acorn worms, marine animals that may grow to more than 2 m in length.

Echinodemata (7,000 species) Echinoderms, such as sea stars, sea urchins, and sand dollars, are marine animals that are bilaterally symmetric as larvae but not as adults. They move and feed using unique "tube feet" whose gripping action results from the secretion of adhesive chemicals.

Sea urchins and a sea star

species have been described, most of which are insects. In fact, two out of every three known species are arthropods, and members of this group can be found in nearly all habitats of the biosphere. By the criteria of species diversity, distribution, and sheer numbers, arthropods must be regarded as the most successful of all animal phyla.

Biologists hypothesize that the diversity and success of **arthropods** are related to their body plan—their segmented body, hard exoskeleton, and jointed appendages (*arthropod* means "jointed feet"). The earliest fossils with this body plan are from the Cambrian explosion (535–525 million years ago), indicating that the arthropods are at least that old.

Along with arthropods, the fossil record of the Cambrian explosion contains many species of *lobopods*, a group from which arthropods may have evolved. Lobopods such as *Hallucigenia* (see Figure 27.6) had segmented bodies, but most of their body segments were identical to one another. Early arthropods, such as the trilobites, also showed little variation from segment to segment. As arthropods continued to evolve, the segments tended to fuse and become fewer, and the appendages became specialized for a variety of functions. These evolutionary changes resulted not only in great diversification but also in an efficient body plan that permits the division of labor among different body regions.

▲ **A fossil trilobite**

What genetic changes led to the increasing complexity of the arthropod body plan? Arthropods today have two unusual *Hox* genes, both of which influence segmentation. To test whether these genes could have driven the evolution of increased body segment diversity in arthropods, researchers studied *Hox* genes in onychophorans, close relatives of arthropods (**Figure 27.12**). Their results indicate that the diversity of arthropod body plans did *not* arise from the acquisition of new *Hox* genes. Instead, the evolution of body segment diversity in arthropods may have been driven by changes in the sequence or regulation of existing *Hox* genes (see Concept 23.3).

Bilaterian Radiation II: Aquatic Vertebrates

The appearance of large predatory animals about 530 million years ago and the accompanying explosive radiation of bilaterian invertebrates radically altered life in the oceans. In the face of these tumultuous events, it would have been easy to overlook certain slender, 3-cm-long creatures gliding through the water: *Myllokunmingia fengjiaoa* (**Figure 27.13**). Although lacking armor and appendages, this ancient species was closely related to one of the most successful groups of animals ever to

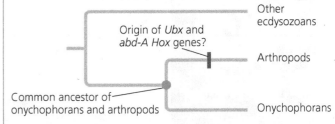

▼ **Figure 27.12** Inquiry

Did the arthropod body plan result from new *Hox* genes?

Experiment One hypothesis suggests that the arthropod body plan resulted from the origin (by a gene duplication event) of two unusual *Hox* genes found in arthropods: *Ultrabithorax* (*Ubx*) and *abdominal-A* (*abd-A*). Researchers tested this hypothesis using onychophorans, a group of invertebrates closely related to arthropods. Unlike many living arthropods, onychophorans have a body plan in which most body segments are identical to one another. If the origin of the *Ubx* and *abd-A Hox* genes drove the evolution of body segment diversity in arthropods, these genes probably arose on the arthropod branch of the evolutionary tree:

According to this hypothesis, *Ubx* and *abd-A* would not have been present in the common ancestor of arthropods and onychophorans; hence, onychophorans should not have these genes. The researchers examined the *Hox* genes of the onychophoran *Acanthokara kaputensis*.

Results The onychophoran *A. kaputensis* has all arthropod *Hox* genes, including *Ubx* and *abd-A*.

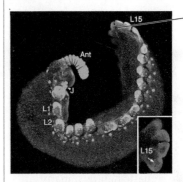

Red indicates the body regions of this onychophoran embryo in which *Ubx* or *abd-A* genes were expressed. (The inset shows this area enlarged.)

Ant = antenna
J = jaws
L1–L15 = body segments

Conclusion Since *A. kaputensis*, an onychophoran, has the arthropod *Hox* genes, the evolution of increased body segment diversity in arthropods must not have been related to the origin of new *Hox* genes.

Source J. K. Grenier et al., Evolution of the entire arthropod *Hox* gene set predated the origin and radiation of the onychophoran/arthropod clade, *Current Biology* 7:547–553 (1997).

WHAT IF? If the researchers had found that *A. kaputensis* did *not* have the *Ubx* and *abd-A Hox* genes, how would their conclusion have been affected? Explain.

swim, walk, slither, or fly: the vertebrates, which derive their name from vertebrae, the series of bones that make up the backbone.

Vertebrates are members of the phylum Chordata. As seen in Figure 27.10, **chordates** are bilaterian animals, and within Bilateria, they belong to the animal clade Deuterostomia.

▲ Figure 27.13 *Myllokunmingia fengjiaoa*, a 530-million-year-old chordate.

Among the deuterostomes that radiated during the Cambrian, we will focus on the chordates.

Early Chordate Evolution

All chordates share a set of derived characters, though many species possess some of these traits only during embryonic development. **Figure 27.14** illustrates four key characters of chordates: a **notochord**; a dorsal, hollow nerve cord; **pharyngeal slits** (or **pharyngeal clefts**); and a muscular, post-anal tail.

Among extant chordates, a group of blade-shaped animals called *lancelets* **(Figure 27.15a)** closely resemble the idealized chordate shown in Figure 27.14. Lancelets branch at the base of the chordate phylogenetic tree. *Tunicates* **(Figure 27.15b)**, another early diverging chordate group, also display key chordate traits, but only as larvae (adult tunicates have a highly modified body plan). These findings suggest that the ancestral chordate may have looked something like a lancelet—that is, it

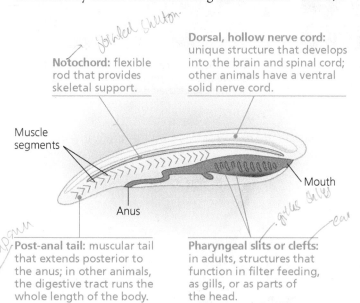

Notochord: flexible rod that provides skeletal support.

Dorsal, hollow nerve cord: unique structure that develops into the brain and spinal cord; other animals have a ventral solid nerve cord.

Muscle segments

Anus

Mouth

Post-anal tail: muscular tail that extends posterior to the anus; in other animals, the digestive tract runs the whole length of the body.

Pharyngeal slits or clefts: in adults, structures that function in filter feeding, as gills, or as parts of the head.

▲ **Figure 27.14 Chordate characteristics.** All chordates possess the four highlighted structural trademarks at some point during their development.

(a) Lancelet

(b) Tunicate

▲ **Figure 27.15 Present-day basal groups of chordates.**

had an anterior end with a mouth; a notochord; a dorsal, hollow nerve cord; pharyngeal slits; and a post-anal tail.

After the evolution of the basic chordate body plan, another major step in early chordate evolution was the origin of vertebrates. Unlike lancelets and tunicates, vertebrates not only have a backbone, they also have a well-defined head with a brain, eyes and other sensory organs, and a skull.

Some of the fossils that formed during the Cambrian explosion 530 million years ago appear to straddle the transition to vertebrates. Some of these fossil chordates resembled lancelets, yet (unlike lancelets) they had a brain and eyes. *Myllokunmingia*, for example, not only had a brain and eyes; it also had parts of a skull surrounding its eyes and ears, making it one of the earliest chordates with a well-defined head. (The earliest "ears" were organs for maintaining balance, a function still performed by the ears of humans and other living vertebrates.)

The Rise of Vertebrates

Vertebrates originated about 500 million years ago. With a more complex nervous system and a more elaborate skeleton than those of their ancestors, vertebrates became more efficient at two essential tasks: capturing food and avoiding being eaten.

Some of the earliest fossil vertebrates are of *conodonts*, soft-bodied, jawless vertebrates that hunted by impaling prey on a set of barbed hooks in their mouth. Other early vertebrates had paired fins and an inner ear with two semicircular canals that provided a sense of balance. Like conodonts, these vertebrates lacked jaws, but they had a muscular pharynx, which they may have used to suck in bottom-dwelling organisms or detritus. They were also armored with mineralized bone, which covered varying amounts of their body and may have offered protection from predators.

Only two lineages of jawless vertebrates survive today, the *hagfishes* and *lampreys* **(Figure 27.16)**. Living jawless vertebrates are far outnumbered by jawed vertebrates, known as **gnathostomes**. Gnathostomes appeared in the fossil record about 450 million years ago and steadily became more diverse. Their success probably resulted from a combination of anatomical features: Their paired fins and tail allowed them to

This phylogenetic hypothesis shows the relationships among major clades of vertebrates. Derived characters are listed for some clades; for example, only gnathostomes have a jaw. In some lineages, derived traits have been lost over time or occur in reduced form; for example, hagfishes and lampreys are vertebrates with highly reduced vertebrae.

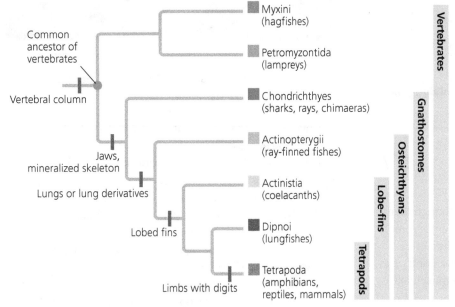

Myxini. Hagfishes (30 species) are scavengers that live and feed on the seafloor. They have slime-secreting glands that function in defense.

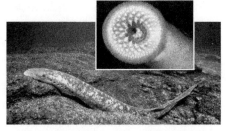

Petromyzontida. Most of the 35 species of lampreys are parasites that use their mouth (inset) and tongue to bore a hole in the side of a fish. The lamprey then ingests the blood and other tissues of its host.

Chondrichthyes. Chondrichthyans (1,000 species) such as this black-tipped reef shark have skeletons made primarily of cartilage; the group also includes rays and chimaeras (ratfishes).

Actinopterygii. There are over 27,000 species of ray-finned fishes, including this tropical lionfish that can inject venom through its spines.

Actinistia. Coelacanths (1–2 species) were thought to have become extinct 75 million years ago until they were rediscovered in the Indian Ocean in 1938.

Dipnoi. Lungfishes (6 species) have both gills and lungs and can gulp air into their lungs.

Tetrapoda. Tetrapods (over 29,000 species) have limbs with digits; this group includes a diverse collection of amphibians, reptiles, and mammals (such as this giraffe).

swim efficiently after prey, and their jaws enabled them to grab prey or simply bite off chunks of flesh (Figure 27.17).

By 420 million years ago, gnathostomes had diverged into the three lineages of jawed vertebrates that survive today: chondrichthyans, ray-finned fishes, and lobe-fins. (Despite its name, this last group includes humans and other terrestrial animals with legs.)

Chondrichthyans Sharks, rays, and their relatives include some of the biggest and most successful vertebrate predators in the oceans today (see Figure 27.16). They belong to the clade Chondrichthyes, which means "cartilage fish." As their name indicates, the **chondrichthyans** have a skeleton composed predominantly of cartilage, though often impregnated with calcium. There are about 1,000 species of living chondrichthyans, many of which are threatened by overfishing.

Ray-Finned Fishes The vast majority of vertebrates belong to the clade of gnathostomes called Osteichthyes. Unlike sharks and their relatives, living **osteichthyans** typically have an ossified (bony) endoskeleton; they also have lungs or lung derivatives. Nearly all the aquatic osteichthyans familiar to us are among the **ray-finned fishes** (see Figure 27.16), named for the bony rays that support their fins. Today, there are more than 27,000 species of ray-finned fishes—almost as many species as in all other vertebrate groups combined.

Lobe-Fins Along with the ray-finned fishes, the other major lineage of osteichthyans is the **lobe-fins** (see Figure 27.16). A key derived character of lobe-fins is the presence of rod-shaped bones surrounded by a thick layer of muscle in their pectoral and pelvic fins. During the Devonian (416–359 million years ago), many lobe-fins lived in brackish waters, such

0.5 m

▲ **Figure 27.17 Fossil of an early gnathostome.** A formidable predator, *Dunkleosteus* grew up to 10 m in length. An analysis of its jaw structure concluded that *Dunkleosteus* could exert a force of 560 kg/cm^2 (8,000 pounds per square inch) at the tip of its jaws.

as in coastal wetlands. There they may have used their lobed fins to swim and "walk" underwater across the substrate (as do some living lobe-fins).

Today, only three lineages of lobe-fins survive. Two of these lineages are the coelacanths and the lungfishes (see Figure 27.16), but the third surviving lineage of lobe-fins is far more diverse. As you'll see in the next section, these organisms adapted to life on land and gave rise to the **tetrapods**, vertebrates with limbs and digits.

CONCEPT CHECK 27.3

1. Explain what is meant by "body plan" and describe three key features of animal body plans.
2. Describe the major steps in animal evolution shown in Figure 27.10 and evaluate this statement: "The Cambrian explosion actually consists of three explosions, not one."
3. **MAKE CONNECTIONS** The bilaterian diversification in marine environments from 535 to 400 million years ago demonstrates that evolution is not goal oriented—it is not, for example, directed toward the origin of terrestrial vertebrates. Explain. (Review Concept 23.4.)

For suggested answers, see Appendix A.

CONCEPT 27.4

Several animal groups had features facilitating their colonization of land

Following the Cambrian explosion and its transformation of marine communities, some bilaterian animals colonized land, leading to profound changes there as well.

Early Land Animals

In contrast to plants, whose ancestors appear to have colonized land only once (see Chapter 26), members of many animal groups made the transition to terrestrial life. Arthropods, for example, invaded land multiple times, including a relatively recent event (4 million years ago) in which a crab lineage colonized the island of Jamaica. The same is true of other animal groups, such as marine snails that have given rise to terrestrial species repeatedly over the course of evolution.

Fossil evidence suggests that arthropods were among the first animals to colonize land, roughly 450 million years ago. This evidence includes fragments of arthropod remains, as well as possible millipede burrows. By 410 million years ago, well-preserved arthropod fossils from several continents indicate that millipedes, centipedes, spiders, and a variety of wingless insects all had colonized land. Vertebrates colonized land 365 million years ago, by which time early forests had also formed. By the end of the Devonian period, 360 million years ago, terrestrial animal communities were broadly similar to those of today and included predators, detritivores (animals that feed on decaying organic matter, such as plant debris), and herbivores.

		GREEN ALGA	MARINE CRUSTACEAN	AQUATIC LOBE-FIN
AQUATIC ANCESTOR				
CHARACTER	**Anchoring structure**	Derived (roots)	N/A	N/A
	Support structure	Derived (lignin/stems)	Ancestral	Ancestral (skeletal system) Derived (limbs)
	Internal transport	Derived (vascular system)	Ancestral	Ancestral
	Muscle/nerve cells	N/A	Ancestral	Ancestral
	Protection against desiccation	Derived (cuticle)	Ancestral	Derived (amniotic egg/scales)
	Gas exchange	Derived (stomata)	Derived (tracheal system)	Ancestral
TERRESTRIAL ORGANISM		LAND PLANTS	INSECTS	TERRESTRIAL VERTEBRATES

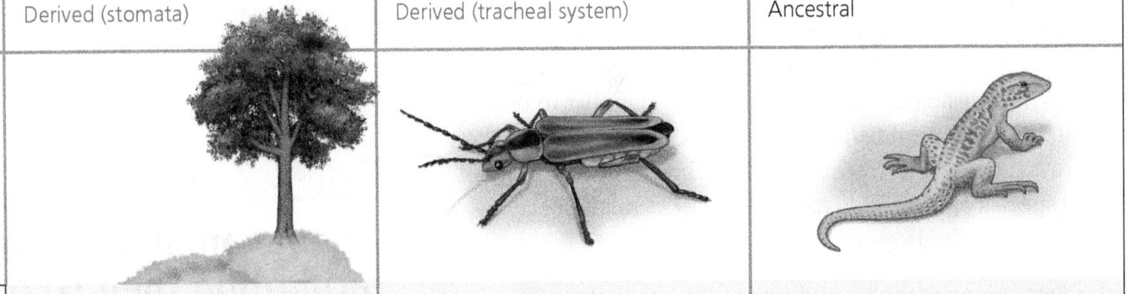

▲ **Figure 27.18 Descent with modification during the colonization of land.** This chart identifies some key characteristics that enable three major groups of terrestrial organisms—land plants, insects, and terrestrial vertebrates—to live on land. Red type indicates adaptations that have evolved since the lineages diverged from their aquatic ancestors. In land plants, most terrestrial adaptations evolved after the split. In contrast, two large clades of terrestrial animals—the insects and the vertebrates—display many ancestral characteristics that facilitated their transition to life on land.

Land animals often bear a striking resemblance to their aquatic ancestors **(Figure 27.18)**. In some cases, the resemblance is so strong that it appears as if the land animals simply walked or crawled ashore, as in terrestrial crabs and snails. In other cases, more extensive changes took place, as in the vertebrate colonization of land that we'll describe shortly. But even in vertebrates, the evolutionary changes involved in the transition to terrestrial life were less extensive in animals than in plants. For example, the animals that colonized land already had well-developed skeletal, muscular, digestive, and nervous systems. Plants, in contrast, arose from a small green alga whose structure bore little resemblance to those of its descendants—the land plants that now cover Earth.

Colonization of Land by Arthropods

As mentioned earlier, terrestrial lineages have arisen in several different arthropod groups, including millipedes, spiders and their relatives, crabs, and insects. After describing general features of arthropods, we'll focus on their largest clade, the insects.

General Characteristics of Arthropods

Over the course of evolution, the appendages of some arthropods have become modified, specializing in functions such as walking, feeding, sensory reception, reproduction, and defense. Like the appendages from which they were derived, these modified structures are jointed and come in pairs. **Figure 27.19** illustrates the diverse appendages and other arthropod characteristics of a lobster.

The body of an arthropod is completely covered by the **cuticle**, an exoskeleton constructed from layers of protein and the polysaccharide chitin. As you know if you've ever eaten a crab or lobster, the cuticle can be thick and hard over some parts of the body and thin and flexible over others, such as the joints. The rigid exoskeleton protects the animal and provides points of attachment for the muscles that move the

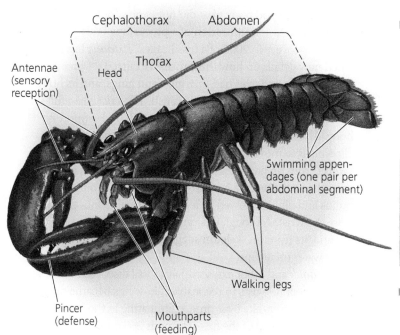

Antennae (sensory reception)

Cephalothorax — Abdomen

Head — Thorax

Swimming appendages (one pair per abdominal segment)

Walking legs

Pincer (defense)

Mouthparts (feeding)

▲ **Figure 27.19 External anatomy of an arthropod.** Many of the distinctive features of arthropods are apparent in this dorsal view of a lobster. The body is segmented, but this characteristic is obvious only in the abdomen. The appendages (including antennae, pincers, mouthparts, walking legs, and swimming appendages) are jointed. The head bears a pair of compound (multilens) eyes, each situated on a movable stalk. The whole body, including appendages, is covered by an exoskeleton.

appendages. Later, the exoskeleton enabled some arthropods to live on land. The exoskeleton's relative impermeability to water helped prevent desiccation, and its strength provided support when arthropods left the buoyancy of water.

A variety of specialized gas exchange organs have evolved in arthropods. Most aquatic species have gills with thin, feathery extensions that place an extensive surface area in contact with the surrounding water. Terrestrial arthropods generally have internal surfaces specialized for gas exchange. Most insects, for instance, have tracheal systems, branched air ducts leading into the interior from pores in the cuticle. These ducts infiltrate the body, carrying oxygen directly to cells.

Insects

One of the arthropod groups that colonized land, the insects and their relatives, is more species-rich than all other eukaryotic groups combined (Figure 27.20). Insects live in almost every terrestrial habitat and in fresh water, and flying insects fill the air. Insects are rare, though not absent, in marine habitats.

The oldest insect fossils date to about 416 million years ago. Later, an explosion in insect diversity took place when insect flight evolved during the Carboniferous and Permian periods (359–251 million years ago). An animal that can fly can escape predators, find food and mates, and disperse to new habitats more effectively than an animal that must crawl about on the ground. Many insects have one or two pairs

► **Lepidopterans**—moths and butterflies—undergo complete metamorphosis: The larval stage (called a caterpillar), which is specialized for eating and growing, looks completely different from the adult stage, which is specialized for dispersal and reproduction.

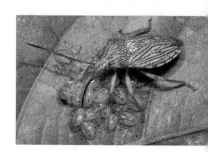

◄ **Hymenopterans** include ants, bees, and wasps. They undergo complete metamorphosis and most are highly social insects.

► **Hemipterans** include stink bugs, bed bugs, and other so-called "true bugs." They have piercing mouthparts and undergo incomplete metamorphosis: The young (nymphs) resemble the adults but are smaller and lack wings.

▲ **Figure 27.20 Insect diversity.**

of wings that emerge from the dorsal side of the thorax (Figure 27.21). Because the wings are extensions of the cuticle, insects can fly without sacrificing any walking legs. By contrast, the flying vertebrates—birds and bats—have one of their two pairs of walking legs modified into wings, making some of these species clumsy on the ground.

Insects also radiated in response to the origin of new plant species, which provided new sources of food. As you read in Chapter 22, an insect population feeding on a new plant species can diverge from other populations, eventually forming a new species of insect. A fossil record of diverse insect mouthparts, for example, suggests that specialized modes of feeding on gymnosperms and other Carboniferous plants contributed to early adaptive radiations of insects. Later, a major increase in insect diversity appears to have been stimulated by the evolutionary expansion of flowering plants during the

◄ **Figure 27.21 Ladybird beetle in flight.**

mid-Cretaceous period (about 90 million years ago). Although insect and plant diversity decreased during the Cretaceous mass extinction, both groups rebounded over the past 65 million years.

Terrestrial Vertebrates

Another key event in the colonization of land by animals took place 365 million years ago, when the fins of a lineage of lobe-fins evolved into the limbs and feet of tetrapods. Until then, all vertebrates had shared the same basic fishlike anatomy. After tetrapods moved onto land, they developed many new forms, from leaping frogs to flying eagles to bipedal humans.

The most significant character of tetrapods gives the group its name, which means "four feet" in Greek. In place of pectoral and pelvic fins, tetrapods have limbs with digits. Limbs support a tetrapod's weight on land, while feet with digits efficiently transmit muscle-generated forces to the ground when the tetrapod walks.

The Origin of Tetrapods

The Devonian coastal wetlands were home to a wide range of lobe-fins. Those that entered shallow, oxygen-poor water could use their lungs to breathe air. Some species probably used their stout fins to help them move across logs or the muddy bottom.

Thus, the tetrapod body plan did not evolve "out of nowhere" but was simply a modification of a preexisting body plan.

The discovery in 2006 of a fossil called *Tiktaalik* has provided new details on how this process occurred (**Figure 27.22**). Like a fish, this species had fins, gills, and lungs, and its body was covered in scales. But unlike a fish, *Tiktaalik* had a full set of ribs that would have helped it breathe air and support its body. Also unlike a fish, *Tiktaalik* had a neck and shoulders, allowing it to move its head about. Finally, the bones of *Tiktaalik*'s front fin had the same basic pattern found in all limbed animals: one bone (the humerus), followed by two bones (the radius and ulna), followed by a group of small bones that comprise the wrist. Although it is unlikely that *Tiktaalik* could walk on land, its front fin skeleton suggests that it could prop itself up in water on its fins.

Tiktaalik and other extraordinary fossil discoveries have allowed paleontologists to reconstruct how fins became progressively more limb-like over time, culminating in the appearance in the fossil record of the first tetrapods 365 million years ago (**Figure 27.23**). Over the next 60 million years, a great diversity of tetrapods arose. Judging from the morphology and locations of their fossils, most of these early tetrapods probably remained tied to water, a characteristic they share with some members of the most basal group of living tetrapods, the amphibians.

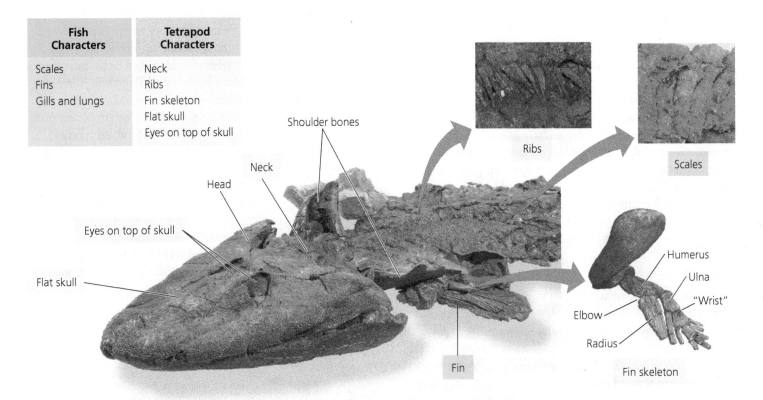

Fish Characters	Tetrapod Characters
Scales	Neck
Fins	Ribs
Gills and lungs	Fin skeleton
	Flat skull
	Eyes on top of skull

▲ **Figure 27.22 Discovery of a "fishapod":** *Tiktaalik.* Paleontologists were on the hunt for fossils that could shed light on the evolutionary origin of tetrapods. Based on the ages of previously discovered fossils, researchers were looking for a dig site with rocks about 365–385 million years old. Ellesmere Island, in the Canadian Arctic, was one of the few such sites that was also likely to contain fossils, because it was once a river. The search at this site was rewarded by the discovery of fossils of a 375-million-year-old lobe-fin, named *Tiktaalik*. As shown in the chart and photographs, *Tiktaalik* exhibits both fish and tetrapod characters.

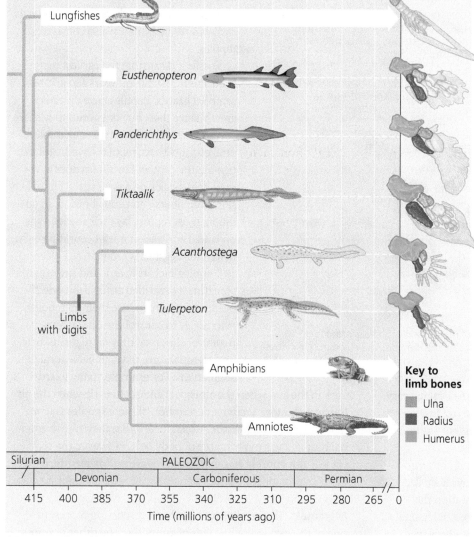

© 2006 Macmillan Publishers, Ltd.

▲ **Figure 27.23 Steps in the origin of limbs with digits.** The white bars on the branches of this diagram place known fossils in time; arrowheads indicate lineages that extend to today. The drawings of extinct organisms are based on fossilized skeletons, but the colors are fanciful.

WHAT IF? *If the most recent common ancestor of* Tulerpeton *and living tetrapods originated 380 million years ago, what range of dates would include the origin of amphibians?*

▲ Salamanders retain their tails as adults.

▲ Cecilians have no legs and are mainly burrowing animals.

◀ Frogs and toads lack tails as adults.

▲ **Figure 27.24 Amphibian diversity.**

Amphibians

The **amphibians** are represented today by about 6,150 species of salamanders, frogs, and caecilians (**Figure 27.24**). Some salamanders are entirely aquatic, but others live on land as adults or throughout life. Most salamanders that live on land walk with a side-to-side bending of the body, a trait also found in early terrestrial tetrapods.

Frogs are better suited than salamanders for moving on land. Adult frogs use their powerful hind legs to hop along the terrain. Although often distinctive in appearance, the animals known as "toads" are simply frogs that have leathery skin or other adaptations for life on land.

Finally, the caecilians are legless and nearly blind. Their lack of legs is a secondary adaptation, as they evolved from a legged ancestor. Caecilians inhabit tropical areas, where most species burrow in moist forest soil.

Most amphibians are found in damp habitats such as swamps and rain forests. Even those adapted to drier habitats spend much of their time in burrows or under moist leaves, where humidity is high.

Over the past 30 years, zoologists have documented a rapid and alarming decline in amphibian populations in locations throughout the world. There appear to be several causes, including the spread of a disease-causing chytrid fungus, habitat loss, climate change, and pollution. These and other factors have not only reduced populations, but also led to extinctions.

Terrestrial Adaptations in Amniotes

Compared to the amphibians, a more extensive colonization of dry habitats occurred in the **amniotes**, a group of tetrapods whose extant members are the reptiles (including birds, as we'll discuss shortly) and mammals. Amniotes are named for the major derived character of the clade, the **amniotic egg**, which contains four specialized membranes: the amnion, the chorion, the yolk sac, and the

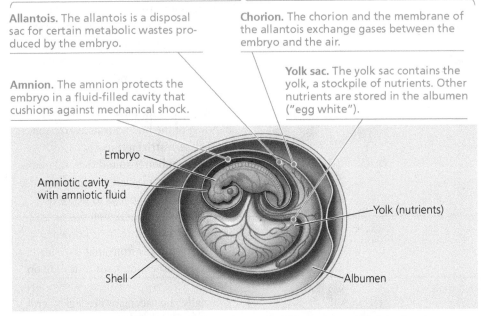

Extraembryonic membranes

Allantois. The allantois is a disposal sac for certain metabolic wastes produced by the embryo.

Chorion. The chorion and the membrane of the allantois exchange gases between the embryo and the air.

Amnion. The amnion protects the embryo in a fluid-filled cavity that cushions against mechanical shock.

Yolk sac. The yolk sac contains the yolk, a stockpile of nutrients. Other nutrients are stored in the albumen ("egg white").

Embryo

Amniotic cavity with amniotic fluid

Yolk (nutrients)

Shell

Albumen

▲ **Figure 27.25 The amniotic egg.** The embryos of reptiles and mammals form four extraembryonic membranes: the amnion, chorion, yolk sac, and allantois. This diagram shows these membranes in the shelled egg of a reptile.

allantois **(Figure 27.25)**. The amniotic egg was a key evolutionary innovation for terrestrial life: It allowed the embryo to develop on land in its own private "pond," reducing the dependence of tetrapods on an aqueous environment for reproduction.

In contrast to the shell-less eggs of amphibians, the amniotic eggs of most reptiles and some mammals have a shell. A shell slows dehydration of the egg in air, an adaptation that helped amniotes to occupy a wider range of terrestrial habitats than amphibians, their closest living relatives. (Seeds played a similar role in the evolution of land plants; see Chapter 26.) Most mammals have dispensed with the eggshell over the course of their evolution, and the embryo avoids desiccation by developing within the amnion inside the mother's body.

The Origin and Radiation of Amniotes

The most recent common ancestor of living amphibians and amniotes lived about 350 million years ago. Based on where their fossils have been found, the earliest amniotes appear to have lived in warm, moist environments, as did the first tetrapods. Over time, however, early amniotes expanded into a wide range of new environments, including dry and high-latitude regions. The earliest amniotes resembled a small lizard with sharp teeth, a sign that they were predators.

Amniotes today include two large clades of terrestrial vertebrates, reptiles and mammals.

Reptiles Living members of the **reptile** clade include tuataras, lizards and snakes, turtles, crocodilians, and birds **(Figure 27.26)**. There are about 18,300 species of reptiles, the majority of which are squamates (lizards and snakes; 7,900 species) or birds (10,000 species). Notice in Figure 27.26 that dinosaurs are reptiles and

that birds originated from saurischian dinosaurs (a group that includes *Tyrannosaurus rex*); as a result, birds are also considered reptiles.

Fossils indicate that the earliest reptiles lived about 310 million years ago and resembled lizards. Reptiles have diverged greatly since then, but as a group they share several derived characters. For example, unlike amphibians, reptiles have scales that contain the protein keratin (as does a human nail). Scales help protect the animal's skin from desiccation and abrasion. In addition, most reptiles lay their shelled eggs on land. Fertilization must occur internally, before the eggshell is secreted.

Reptiles such as lizards and snakes are sometimes described as "cold-blooded" because they do not use their metabolism extensively to control their body temperature. However, they do regulate their body temperature through behavioral adaptations. For example, many lizards bask in the sun when the air is cool and seek shade when the air is warm. A more accurate description of these reptiles is to say that they are **ectothermic**, which means that they absorb external heat as their main source of body heat. However, the reptile clade is not entirely ectothermic; birds are **endothermic**, capable of maintaining body temperature through metabolic activity.

Mammals The reptiles we have been discussing represent one of the two living lineages of amniotes. The other amniote lineage is our own, the **mammals**, named for their distinctive mammary glands, which produce milk for offspring. Hair, another mammalian characteristic, and a fat layer under the skin help the body retain heat. Like birds, mammals are endothermic, and most have a high metabolic rate. In addition, whereas the teeth of reptiles are generally uniform in size and shape, the jaws of mammals bear a variety of teeth with sizes and shapes adapted for chewing many kinds of foods. Humans, like most mammals, have teeth modified for shearing (incisors and canine teeth) and for crushing and grinding (premolars and molars; see Figure 33.14).

Mammals originated from a group of amniotes called **synapsids**. Early nonmammalian synapsids lacked hair, had a sprawling gait, and laid eggs. Over the course of 120 million years, these ancestors gave rise to a series of increasingly mammal-like synapsids (see Figure 23.4). Finally, about 180 million years ago, the first true mammals arose. A diverse set of mammals coexisted with dinosaurs from 180 to 65 million years ago, but these species were not abundant and most measured less than 1 m. One possible explanation for their small size is that dinosaurs already occupied ecological niches of large-bodied animals.

▼ **Figure 27.26** **Exploring Reptilian Diversity**

The reptile clade consists of five groups with living members, shown below, along with extinct groups such as the plesiosaurs, pterosaurs, and nonflying dinosaurs. The dotted line indicates the uncertain relationship of turtles to other reptiles.

? *Are plesiosaurs dinosaurs? Are birds? Explain.*

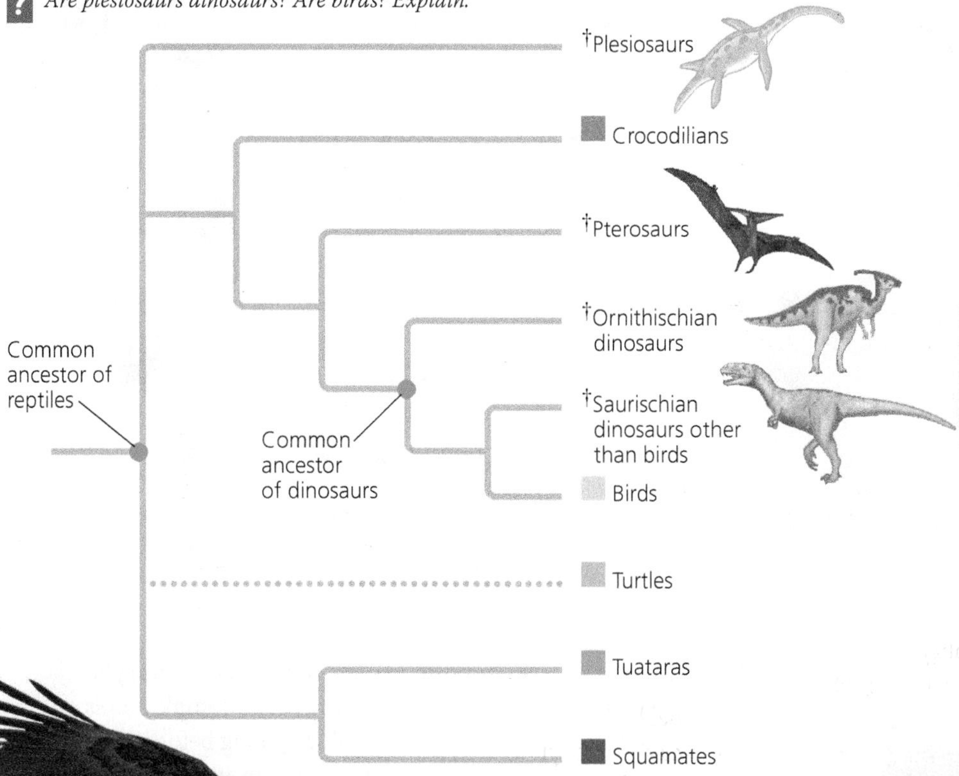

Phylogenetic tree showing:
- †Plesiosaurs
- Crocodilians
- †Pterosaurs
- †Ornithischian dinosaurs
- †Saurischian dinosaurs other than birds
- Birds
- Turtles
- Tuataras
- Squamates

Common ancestor of reptiles

Common ancestor of dinosaurs

Crocodilians. Crocodiles and alligators (23 species, collectively called crocodilians) belong to an ancient lineage whose earliest members lived on land more than 200 million years ago. Later, some species adapted to life in water, breathing air through their upturned nostrils.

Birds. The anatomy of birds (10,000 species) includes many adaptations that facilitate flight, such as the lightweight "honeycombed" structure of their bones and stiff feathers that contribute to the aerodynamic shapes of their wings.

Turtles. The 307 species in this group have a boxlike shell fused to their skeletons. Some turtles live on land, while others live in freshwater or marine habitats, but all are air-breathing.

Tuataras. Although their ancestors were widespread during the Cretaceous period, today the two living species of tuataras are found only on 30 islands off the coast of New Zealand.

Squamates. Snakes, together with lizards, make up the squamate lineage of reptiles (7,910 species). Snakes are carnivorous, and despite their lack of legs, have adaptations that make them effective predators, including the ability of various species to detect heat, chemicals, or vibrations that signal the presence of prey.

▼ **Figure 27.27 The major mammalian lineages.**

Monotremes

Found only in Australia and New Guinea, there are five extant species of monotremes (the platypus and four species of spiny anteaters). Monotremes have hair and produce milk, but they lack nipples. They are the only mammals that lay eggs (inset).

Marsupials

Kangaroos, opossums, and koalas are examples of marsupials (324 species). Like eutherians, they have nipples that provide milk and they give birth to live young. Offspring are born early in development; they finish their growth while nursing from a nipple (in their mother's pouch in most species).

Eutherians

Most mammals are eutherians, a clade that include primates, whales, rodents, and many other mammal groups (5,010 species). Eutherians have a longer pregnancy than marsupials, and they have a more complex **placenta** (a structure in which nutrients diffuse into the embryo from the mother's blood).

? *Monotremes are basal mammals. Draw a phylogenetic tree showing evolutionary relationships among the three lineages.*

By 140 million years ago, the three major lineages of mammals had emerged: those leading to **monotremes** (egg-laying mammals), **marsupials** (mammals with a pouch), and **eutherians** (placental mammals) **(Figure 27.27)**. After the extinction of terrestrial dinosaurs (65 million years ago), mammals continued to diversify, ultimately resulting in the more than 5,300 species living today.

Human Evolution

Humans (*Homo sapiens*) are primates, nested with a group informally called apes **(Figure 27.28)**. Unlike other apes, humans stand upright and are bipedal (walk on two legs). Humans

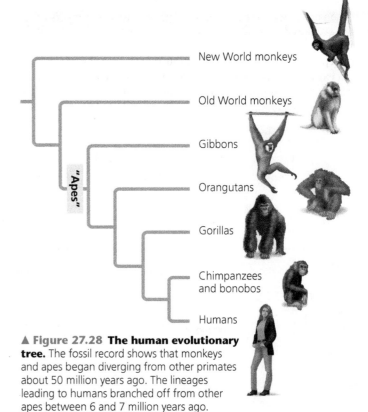

▲ **Figure 27.28 The human evolutionary tree.** The fossil record shows that monkeys and apes began diverging from other primates about 50 million years ago. The lineages leading to humans branched off from other apes between 6 and 7 million years ago.

also have a larger brain and are capable of language, symbolic thought, artistic expression, and the use of complex tools.

Early human ancestors were bipedal long before their brains increased in size. Consider the 4.4-million-year-old *Ardipithecus ramidus*. This species showed signs of bipedalism, yet its brain (325 cm^3 in volume) was much smaller than that of *H. sapiens* ($1,300 \text{ cm}^3$). By 2.5 million years ago, fossils show that human ancestors walked upright and used tools—yet they still had a brain the size of a softball.

The earliest fossils placed in our genus, *Homo*, include those of *Homo habilis*, which lived 2.4 to 1.6 million years ago. Compared to earlier human ancestors, *H. habilis* had a shorter jaw and a larger brain volume, about 675 cm^3. Brain size, body size, and tool use continued to increase over time in various fossil *Homo* species, some of which lived as recently as 28,000 years ago. Our own species, *H. sapiens*, appears to have originated in Africa about 200,000 years ago and spread from there around the world **(Figure 27.29)**.

▲ **Figure 27.29 Early fossils of *Homo sapiens*.** These fossilized remains of an adult and a child, discovered in a cave in Israel, are thought to be around 92,000 years old.

We turn now to the ecological and evolutionary effects of animals—including humans.

CONCEPT CHECK 27.4

1. Describe two adaptations that have enabled insects to thrive on land.
2. **MAKE CONNECTIONS** Compare and contrast how the colonization of land by plants and by vertebrates exemplifies descent with modification. (Review Concepts 19.2 and 26.1.)
3. **WHAT IF?** Which came first, the chicken or the egg? Explain, basing your answer on evolutionary principles.

For suggested answers, see Appendix A.

CONCEPT 27.5

Animals have transformed ecosystems and altered the course of evolution

The rise of animals coincided with one of the most monumental changes in the history of life: the transformation of a microbe-only world to a world filled with large producers, predators, and prey. This change affected all aspects of ecological communities, in the sea and on land.

Ecological Effects of Animals

As we saw in Chapter 25, until 600 million years ago, life in the oceans was almost entirely microscopic. Among other differences from life today, there were no large filter feeders in early marine communities. As a result, researchers think that ocean waters were cloudy, thick with microorganisms and suspended organic matter **(Figure 27.30a)**. Geologic and fossil evidence suggests that these turbid waters also had low oxygen levels and were dominated by cyanobacteria. Marine ecosystems remained in this condition for over a billion years, despite the fact that algae and a variety of heterotrophic eukaryotes were present for most of that time. What changes did the rise of animals bring?

Marine Ecosystems

Fossil biochemical evidence suggests that the abundance of cyanobacteria decreased in the early Cambrian. This decrease may have been caused by the activities of crustaceans and other animals with filter-feeding mouthparts. Such filter feeders can process an enormous amount of water: Every 20 days, animals filter an estimated volume of ocean water equal to that in which most organisms live (the top 500 m). As early filter-feeding animals removed cyanobacteria and other suspended matter from the water, the ocean waters would have become clearer. As a result, algae, which require more light for photosynthesis than do cyanobacteria, increased in abundance and moved to deeper waters **(Figure 27.30b)**.

Along with changes in water clarity and a shift to algae as the dominant producers, a different set of feeding relationships also emerged. A host of small animals evolved that ate marine

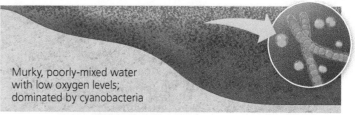

Murky, poorly-mixed water with low oxygen levels; dominated by cyanobacteria

(a) Ocean conditions before 600 mya

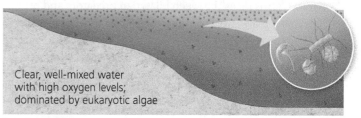

Clear, well-mixed water with high oxygen levels; dominated by eukaryotic algae

(b) Changes to ocean conditions by 530 mya

▲ **Figure 27.30 A sea change for Earth's oceans.**

producers and detritus. Those small animals, in turn, were eaten by larger animals—which were themselves eaten by still larger animals. Overall, the explosion of animal diversity in the early Cambrian marked the end of the microbial world and the beginning of ocean life as we know it today—a world filled with predators, filter feeders, and scavengers of all shapes and sizes.

Terrestrial Ecosystems

Before animals joined plants and fungi onshore, terrestrial ecosystems had a simple structure: Producers (early land plants) harnessed energy from the sun and drew essential nutrients from the soil, while decomposers returned nutrients to the soil. By 410 million years ago, animals had transformed these ecosystems. Plants and decomposers continued to be important, of course, but new biotic interactions were also in place: Plants were being consumed by herbivorous animals, and they, in turn, were being eaten by predators. Still other animals (detritivores) consumed organic debris, making for a complex network of ecological interactions—much of it driven by animals.

The lesser snow goose (*Chen caerulescens*), a migratory bird that breeds in marsh lands bordering Canada's Hudson Bay, illustrates the impact of animals on terrestrial communities. These birds feed on grasses and other marsh plants. At low population numbers, lesser snow geese improve the growth of marsh plants. This positive effect may be due to the fact that the birds defecate every few minutes as they feed, thereby adding nitrogen (which plants need to grow) to the soil. At high population numbers, however, the feeding activities of the birds can destroy a marsh, converting it to a mudflat **(Figure 27.31)**.

▶ **Figure 27.31 Effects of herbivory.** The area inside the fence, which the geese could not access, shows the original state of the marsh.

Evolutionary Effects of Animals

The rise of animals also set in motion a series of profound evolutionary changes. As we've seen, many of these changes resulted from the fact that animals can make life dangerous: The origin of mobile, heterotrophic animals with a complete digestive tract drove some species to extinction and initiated ongoing "arms races" between bilaterian predators and prey.

In this section, we'll consider the related topic of whether increases in animal diversity have led to other evolutionary radiations. Then we'll examine the ongoing evolutionary effects of one particular animal species—humans.

Evolutionary Radiations

Two species that interact can exert selective pressures on one another. A plant (or any other species) that interacts with an animal may evolve in response to selection imposed by the animal—and the animal, in turn, may evolve in response to evolutionary changes in the plant **(Figure 27.32)**. In the **Scientific Skills Exercise**, you can interpret data from a study of selection occurring in a predator-prey interaction over time. Such reciprocal selective pressures also occur when the origin of new species in one group of organisms stimulates further radiations in other organisms, especially those that can eat, escape from, or compete effectively with the new group.

As animal groups have diversified, they have often had this effect. For example, the origin of a new group of animals provides new sources of food for *parasites*, organisms that feed on

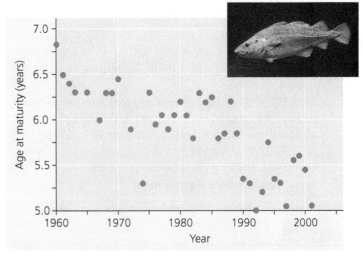

▲ **Figure 27.33 Reproducing at a younger age.** Age at sexual maturity has dropped over time in heavily fished populations of northern cod (*Gadus morhua*). Size at maturity has also dropped (not shown).

? *Fish that reproduce when they are younger and smaller typically have fewer offspring than fish that reproduce when they are older and larger. Predict how evolution in response to fishing will affect the ability of cod populations to recover from overfishing.*

the tissues of another organism (the *host*). Many parasites feed on a single host species. As a result, the ongoing diversification of animals has led to evolutionary radiations in many groups of parasites—the animals, fungi, protists, and bacteria that can feed on newly evolved animal hosts.

Human Impacts on Evolution

As can be seen from satellite photographs or the window of an airplane, humans have dramatically altered the environment. By making large changes to the environment, we have altered the selective pressures faced by many species. This suggests that we are likely causing evolutionary change—and we are. For example, by using antibiotics to kill bacteria, we have (inadvertently) caused the evolution of resistance in bacterial populations (see Concept 19.3). We have also caused evolutionary change in species that we hunt for sport or food. For example, in cod and other fishes harvested for food, commercial fisheries target older and larger fish. This has led to a reduction in the age and size at which individuals reach sexual maturity **(Figure 27.33)**. Natural selection has favored fish that mature at a younger age and smaller size because such individuals are more likely to reproduce before they are caught than are individuals that mature when they are older and larger.

In addition to causing evolution by natural selection, our actions may cause a mass extinction, thereby greatly altering the future course of evolution. Species extinction rates have increased greatly in the last 400 years, raising concern that unless dramatic preventative measures are taken, a sixth, human-caused mass extinction may occur (see Chapter 23). Among the many taxa under threat, molluscs have the dubious distinction of being the animal group with the

▼ **Figure 27.32 Results of reciprocal selection.** The Madagascar orchid *Angraecum sesquipedale* secretes a sugary nectar solution to the base of its unusually long floral tube. Based on the tube's length, Charles Darwin predicted the existence of a pollinating moth with a 28-cm-long proboscis—long enough to reach the bottom of the tube. Such a moth (*Xanthopan morganii*, shown here) was discovered two decades after Darwin's death.

Understanding Experimental Design and Interpreting Data

Is There Evidence of Selection for Defensive Adaptations in Mollusc Populations Exposed to Predators? The course of animal evolution has been shaped by the interactions of predator and prey species. The fossil record provides evidence that historically, increased risk to prey species from predators is often accompanied by increased incidence and expression of prey defenses.

A team of researchers studied the possible selective pressure exerted by a predator, the European green crab (*Carcinus maenas*), on its prey, the flat periwinkle (*Littorina obtusata*), a mollusc, in the Gulf of Maine. Periwinkles from southern sites in the Gulf have experienced predation by European green crabs for over 100 generations, at about one generation per year. Periwinkles from northern sites in the Gulf have been interacting with the invasive green crabs for relatively few generations, as the invasive crabs spread to the northern Gulf comparatively recently.

Previous research shows that (1) flat periwinkle shells recently collected from the Gulf are thicker than those collected in the late 1800s, and (2) periwinkle populations from southern sites in the Gulf have thicker shells than periwinkle populations from northern sites. In this exercise, you'll interpret the design and results of the researchers' experiment studying the rates of predation by European green crabs on periwinkles from northern and southern populations.

How the Experiment Was Done The researchers collected periwinkles and crabs from sites in the northern and southern Gulf of Maine, separated by 450 km of coastline.

A single crab was placed in a cage with eight periwinkles of different sizes. After three days, researchers assessed the fate of the eight periwinkles. Four different treatments were set up, with crabs from northern or southern populations offered periwinkles from northern and southern populations. All crabs were of similar size and included equal numbers of males and females. Each experimental treatment was tested 12 to 14 times.

In a second part of the experiment, the bodies of periwinkles from northern and southern populations were removed from their shells and presented to crabs from northern and southern populations.

Data from the Experiment

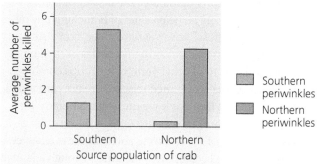

When the researchers presented the crabs with unshelled periwinkles, all the unshelled periwinkles were consumed in less than an hour.

Interpret the Data

1. What hypothesis were the researchers testing in this study? What are the independent variables in this study? What are the dependent variables in this study?

2. Why did the research team set up four different treatments?

3. Why did researchers present unshelled periwinkles to the crabs? Explain the significance of the results of this part of the experiment.

4. Summarize the results of the experiment in words. Do these results support the hypothesis you identified in question 1? Explain.

5. Suggest how natural selection may have affected populations of flat periwinkles in the southern Gulf of Maine over the last 100 years.

Data from R. Rochette, S. P. Doyle, and T. C. Edgell, Interaction between an invasive decapod and a native gastropod: Predator foraging tactics and prey architectural defenses, *Marine Ecology Progress Series* 330:179–188 (2007).

(MB) A version of this Scientific Skills Exercise can be assigned in MasteringBiology.

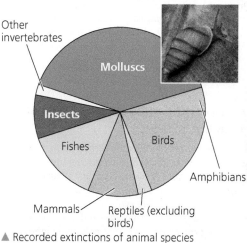

▲ Recorded extinctions of animal species
© 2004 American Institute of Biology Sciences

◀ An endangered Pacific island land snail, *Partula suturalis*

▲ Workers on a mound of pearl mussels killed to make buttons (ca. 1919)

▲ **Figure 27.34 The silent extinction.** Molluscs account for a largely unheralded but sobering 40% of all documented extinctions of animal species. These extinctions have resulted from habitat loss, pollution, introduced species, overharvesting, and other human actions. Many pearl mussel populations, for example, were driven to extinction by overharvesting for their shells, which were used to make buttons and other goods. Land snails such as the species pictured above are highly vulnerable to the same threats; like pearl mussels, they are among the world's most imperiled animal groups.

largest number of documented extinctions (**Figure 27.34**). Pearl mussels, a group of freshwater molluscs that can make natural pearls, are among the world's most endangered animals. Thirty of the pearl mussel species that once lived in North America have become extinct in the last 100 years, and nearly 200 of the 270 that remain are threatened by extinction.

Threats faced by pearl mussels and other molluscs include habitat loss, pollution, and competition or predation by non-native species introduced by people. Is it too late to protect these molluscs? In some locations, reducing water pollution and changing how water is released from dams have led to dramatic rebounds in pearl mussel populations. Such results provide hope that with corrective measures, other endangered species can be revived.

Our discussion of how humans affect evolution brings this unit on the history of life to an end. But this organization isn't meant to imply that life consists of a ladder leading from lowly microorganisms to lofty humanity. The history of life shows that biological diversity is the product of branching phylogeny, not ladderlike "progress," however we choose to measure it. The fact that there are almost as many species of ray-finned fishes alive today as in all other vertebrate groups combined is a clear indication that our finned relatives are not outmoded underachievers that failed to leave the water. Similarly, the ubiquity of diverse prokaryotes throughout the biosphere today is a reminder of the enduring ability of these relatively simple organisms to keep up with the times through adaptive evolution. Biology exalts life's diversity, past and present.

27 Chapter Review

SUMMARY OF KEY CONCEPTS

CONCEPT 27.1

Animals originated more than 700 million years ago (pp. 528–530)

- The earliest evidence of animal life comes from fossil steroids indicative of sponges that date to 710 million years ago.
- The first fossils of large animals date to 560 million years ago and include sponges as well as fossil organisms that resemble living cnidarians and molluscs.
- Sponges are basal animals that, unlike nearly all other animals, lack true tissues. Cnidarians are one of the oldest lineages of **eumetazoans**, an animal clade whose members have tissues.

> **?** *What features are shared by sponges and choanoflagellates? Interpret these observations.*

CONCEPT 27.2

The diversity of large animals increased dramatically during the "Cambrian explosion" (pp. 530–532)

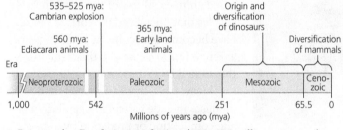

- Prior to the **Cambrian explosion** (535–525 million years ago), virtually all large animals were soft-bodied and poorly defended.
- Fossils dating to the Cambrian explosion include the oldest known members of many living animal phyla, some of which had features for capturing prey while others had defensive adaptations such as spines and body armor.
- Fossil and molecular evidence suggests that **bilaterians** had emerged by 635 million years ago.

> **?** *What caused the Cambrian explosion? Describe current hypotheses.*

CONCEPT 27.3

Diverse animal groups radiated in aquatic environments (pp. 532–539)

- The diverse animals that emerged from the Cambrian explosion can be categorized by their **body plan**, the morphological and developmental traits that are integrated into a functional whole, the living animal.
- Most living animals are bilaterians, bilaterally symmetric animals with three tissue layers and a complete digestive tract.
- Bilaterally symmetric animals have diverged into three major clades: Lophotrochozoa, Ecdysozoa, and Deuterostomia.
- By 420 million years ago, aquatic bilaterians had radiated into a diverse set of **invertebrate** clades, along with three major clades of **vertebrates**: chondrichthyans, ray-finned fishes, and lobe-fins.

> **?** **DRAW IT** *Draw a phylogenetic tree showing relationships among Lophotrochozoa, Cnidaria, Ecdysozoa, Ctenophora, Porifera, and Deuterostomia. On the tree, mark the animal common ancestor as well as the origin of three germ layers, true tissues, and bilateral symmetry.*

CONCEPT 27.4

Several animal groups had features facilitating their colonization of land (pp. 539–547)

- Unlike plants, whose ancestors colonized land only once, many animal groups have made the transition to terrestrial life.
- Animals that colonized land were "pre-adapted" for their new environment in that they already had a complete digestive tract and well-developed skeletal, muscle, and nervous systems.
- Arthropods were the first animals to colonize land, about 450 million years ago. Among the arthropods that colonized land, the insects radiated explosively and now contain more known species than all other eukaryotic groups combined.
- Vertebrates colonized land 365 million years ago when early tetrapods arose from aquatic lobe-fins. Amphibians, an early-diverging group of tetrapods, are more dependent on water than are amniotes, a diverse group whose living members include reptiles and mammals.

> **?** *Describe the amniotic egg and evaluate its significance.*

CONCEPT 27.5

Animals have transformed ecosystems and altered the course of evolution (pp. 547–550)

- The rise of animals coincided with the change from a microbe-only world to a world filled with large producers, scavengers, predators, and prey.
- The origin of animals with filter-feeding mouthparts may have caused sweeping changes in early oceans, such as an increase in water clarity and a shift from cyanobacteria to algae as the dominant producers.
- The diversification of bilaterians in the sea and on land has changed biotic interactions and stimulated evolutionary radiations in other groups of organisms.
- Human actions have caused evolution by natural selection and have the potential to cause a mass extinction.

? *Explain how the activities of animals (including humans) can lead to evolutionary change, and provide an example.*

TEST YOUR UNDERSTANDING

Level 1: Knowledge/Comprehension

1. Which of the following clades contains the greatest number of animal species?
   a. the vertebrates
   b. the bilaterians
   c. the sponges
   d. the deuterostomes
   e. the insects

2. Fossil steroid and molecular clock evidence suggests that animals originated
   a. between 770 and 710 million years ago.
   b. more than 100 million years before the oldest known fossils of large animals.
   c. during the Cambrian explosion.
   d. after sponges diverged from other metazoans.
   e. both a and b

3. Which of the following was probably the *least* important factor in bringing about the Cambrian explosion?
   a. the emergence of predator-prey relationships among animals
   b. the accumulation of diverse adaptations, such as shells and different modes of locomotion
   c. the origin of *Hox* genes and other genetic changes affecting the regulation of developmental genes
   d. the movement of animals onto land
   e. the accumulation of sufficient atmospheric oxygen to support the more active metabolism of mobile animals

4. Which of the following could be considered the most recent common ancestor of living tetrapods?
   a. a sturdy-finned, shallow-water lobe-fin whose appendages had skeletal supports similar to those of terrestrial vertebrates
   b. an armored gnathostome with two pairs of appendages
   c. an early ray-finned fish that developed bony skeletal supports in its paired fins
   d. a salamander that had legs supported by a bony skeleton but moved with the side-to-side bending typical of fishes
   e. an early terrestrial caecilian whose legless condition had evolved secondarily

Level 2: Application/Analysis

5. Which clade does *not* include humans?
   a. synapsids
   b. lobe-fins
   c. lophotrochozoans
   d. tetrapods
   e. osteichthyans

6. In Figure 27.10, the Deuterostomia clade is most closely related to which two main clades?
   a. Ctenophora and Cnidaria
   b. Lophotrochozoa and Ecdysozoa
   c. Cnidaria and Bilateria
   d. Platyhelminthes and Rotifera
   e. Echinodermata and Hemichordata

Level 3: Synthesis/Evaluation

7. **SCIENTIFIC INQUIRY**

   DRAW IT As a consequence of size alone, organisms that are large tend to have larger brains than organisms that are small. However, some organisms have brains that are considerably larger than expected for an animal of their size. There are high energy costs associated with the development and maintenance of brains that are large relative to body size.

   (a) The fossil record documents trends in which brains that are large relative to body size evolved in certain lineages, including ancestors of humans. In such lineages, what can you infer about the relative costs and benefits of large brains?

   (b) Hypothesize how natural selection might favor the evolution of large brains despite their high maintenance costs.

   (c) Data for 14 bird species are listed below. Graph the data, placing deviation from expected brain size on the x-axis and mortality rate on the y-axis. What can you conclude about the relationship between brain size and mortality?

Deviation from Expected Brain Size*	–2.4	–2.1	2.0	–1.8	–1.0	0.0	0.3	0.7	1.2	1.3	2.0	2.3	3.0	3.2
Mortality Rate	0.9	0.7	0.5	0.9	0.4	0.7	0.8	0.4	0.8	0.3	0.6	0.6	0.3	0.6

   D. Sol et al., Big-brained birds survive better in nature, *Proceedings of the Royal Society B* 274:763–769 (2007).

   *Values <0 indicate brain sizes smaller than expected; values >0 indicate sizes larger than expected.

8. **FOCUS ON EVOLUTION**
   In Figure 27.26, circle the monophyletic group that includes dinosaurs. Explain your answer and list the taxa that are in this clade. Knowing that birds are endothermic and crocodiles are ectothermic, can phylogenetic bracketing be used to predict whether dinosaurs other than birds are ectothermic or endothermic?

9. **FOCUS ON ORGANIZATION**
   Early tetrapods had a sprawling gait (like that of a lizard): As the right front foot moved forward, the body twisted to the left and the left rib cage and lung were compressed; the reverse occurred with the next step. Normal breathing, in which both lungs expand equally with each breath, was hindered during walking and prevented during running. In a short essay (100–150 words), explain how the origin of organisms such as dinosaurs, whose gait allowed them to move without compressing their lungs, could have led to emergent properties in biological communities.

For selected answers, see Appendix A.

MasteringBiology®

Students Go to **MasteringBiology** for assignments, the eText, and the Study Area with practice tests, animations, and activities.

Instructors Go to **MasteringBiology** for automatically graded tutorials and questions that you can assign to your students, plus Instructor Resources.

Chapter 16

Figure Questions

Figure 16.4 Even if the mutant MyoD protein couldn't activate the *myoD* gene, it could still turn on genes for the other proteins in the pathway (other transcription factors, which would turn on the genes for muscle-specific proteins, for example). Therefore, some differentiation would occur. But unless there were other activators that could compensate for the loss of the MyoD protein's activation of the *myoD* gene, the cell would not be able to maintain its differentiated state.   **Figure 16.10** Normal Bicoid protein would be made in the anterior end and compensate for the presence of mutant *bicoid* mRNA put into the egg by the mother. Development should be normal, with a head present. (This is what was observed.)   **Figure 16.11** None of the eggs with the transplanted nuclei from the four-cell embryo at the upper left would have developed into a tadpole. Also, the resulting samples might include only some of the tissues of a tadpole. The tissues that develop might differ from treatment to treatment, depending on which of the four nuclei was transplanted. (This assumes that there was some way to tell the four cells apart, as one can in some frog species.)

Concept Check 16.1

1. Cells undergo differentiation during embryonic development, becoming different from each other. Therefore, in the adult organism, there are many highly specialized cell types. **2.** By binding to a receptor on the receiving cell's surface and triggering a signal transduction pathway involving intracellular molecules such as second messengers and transcription factors that affect gene expression **3.** Because their products, made and deposited into the egg by the mother, determine the head and tail ends, as well as the back and belly, of the embryo (and eventually the adult fly)

Concept Check 16.2

1. The state of chromatin modification in the nucleus from the intestinal cell was undoubtedly less similar to that of a nucleus from a fertilized egg, explaining why many fewer of these nuclei were able to be reprogrammed. In contrast, the chromatin in a nucleus from a cell at the four-cell stage would have been much more like that of a nucleus in a fertilized egg and therefore much more easily programmed to direct development. **2.** No, primarily because of subtle (and perhaps not so subtle) differences in their environments **3.** A technique would have to be worked out for turning a human iPS cell into a pancreatic cell (probably by inducing expression of pancreas-specific regulatory genes in the cell).

Concept Check 16.3

1. Apoptosis is signaled by p53 protein when a cell has extensive DNA damage, so apoptosis plays a protective role in eliminating a cell that might contribute to cancer. If mutations in the genes in the apoptotic pathway blocked apoptosis, a cell with such damage could continue to divide and might lead to tumor formation. **2.** When an individual has inherited an oncogene or a mutant allele of a tumor-suppressor gene **3.** A cancer-causing mutation in a proto-oncogene usually makes the gene product overactive, whereas a cancer-causing mutation in a tumor-suppressor gene usually makes the gene product nonfunctional.

Summary of Key Concepts Questions

16.1 The first process involves cytoplasmic determinants, including mRNAs and proteins, placed into specific locations in the egg by the mother. The cells that are formed from different regions in the egg during early cell divisions will have different proteins in them, which will direct different programs of gene expression. The second process involves how the cells respond to signaling molecules secreted by neighboring cells. The signaling pathways in the responding cells lead to different patterns of gene expression. The coordination of these two processes results in each cell following a unique pathway in the developing embryo. **16.2** Cloning a mouse involves transplanting a nucleus from a differentiated mouse cell into a mouse egg cell that has had its own nucleus removed. Activating the egg cell and promoting its development into an embryo in a surrogate mother results in a mouse that is genetically identical to the mouse that donated the nucleus. In this case, the differentiated nucleus has been reprogrammed by factors in the egg cytoplasm. Mouse ES cells are generated from inner cells in mouse blastocysts, so in this case the cells are "naturally" reprogrammed by the process of reproduction and development. (Cloned mouse embryos can also be used as a source of ES cells.) iPS cells can be generated without the use of embryos from a differentiated adult mouse cell by adding certain transcription factors into the cell. In this case, the transcription factors are reprogramming the cells to become pluripotent. **16.3** The protein product of a proto-oncogene is usually involved in a pathway that stimulates cell division. The protein product of a tumor-suppressor gene is usually involved in a pathway that inhibits cell division.

Test Your Understanding

1. a **2.** a **3.** d **4.** c **5.** b

Chapter 18

Figure Questions

Figure 18.2 In stage 2 of this figure, the order of the fragments relative to each other is not known and will be determined later by computer. The unordered nature of the fragments is reflected by their scattered arrangement in the diagram. **Figure 18.7** The transposon would be cut out of the DNA at the original site rather than copied, so the figure would show the original stretch of DNA without the transposon after the mobile transposon had been cut out. **Figure 18.9** The RNA transcripts extending from the DNA in each transcription unit are shorter on the left and longer on the right. This means that RNA polymerase must be starting on the left end of the unit and moving toward the right.
Figure 18.12

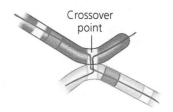

Crossover point

Figure 18.13 Pseudogenes are nonfunctional. They could have arisen by any mutations in the second copy that made the gene product unable to function. Examples would be base changes that introduce stop codons in the sequence, alter amino acids, or change a region of the gene promoter so that the gene can no longer be expressed. **Figure 18.14** Let's say a transposable element (TE) existed in the intron to the left of the indicated EGF exon in the EGF gene, and the same TE was present in the intron to the right of the indicated F exon in the fibronectin gene. During meiotic recombination, these TEs could cause nonsister chromatids on homologous chromosomes to pair up incorrectly, as seen in Figure 18.12. One gene might end up with an F exon next to an EGF exon. Further mistakes in pairing over many generations might result in these two exons being separated from the rest of the gene and placed next to a single or duplicated K exon. In general, the presence of repeated sequences in introns and between genes facilitates these processes because it allows incorrect pairing of nonsister chromatids, leading to novel exon combinations.

Concept Check 18.1

1. In the whole-genome shotgun approach, short fragments generated by multiple restriction enzymes are cloned and sequenced and then ordered by computer programs that identify overlapping regions. In this way, a composite sequence is obtained.

Concept Check 18.2

1. The Internet allows centralization of databases such as GenBank and software resources such as BLAST, making them freely accessible. Having all the data in a central database, easily accessible on the Internet, minimizes the possibility of errors and of researchers working with different data. It streamlines the process of science, since all researchers are able to use the same software programs, rather than each having to obtain their own, possibly different, software. It speeds up dissemination of data and ensures as much as possible that errors are corrected in a timely fashion. These are just a few answers; you can probably think of more. **2.** Cancer is a disease caused by multiple factors. To focus on a single gene or a single defect would ignore other factors that may influence the cancer and even the behavior of the single gene being studied. The systems approach, because it takes into account many factors at the same time, is more likely to lead to an understanding of the causes and most useful treatments for cancer. **3.** Some of the transcribed region is accounted for by introns. The rest is transcribed into noncoding RNAs, including small RNAs, such as microRNAs (miRNAs). These RNAs help regulate gene expression by blocking translation, causing degradation of mRNA, binding to the promoter and repressing transcription, or causing remodeling of chromatin structure. The functions of the remainder are not yet known.

Concept Check 18.3

1. Alternative splicing of RNA transcripts from a gene and post-translational processing of polypeptides **2.** The total number of completed genomes is found by clicking on "Complete Projects" under "Isolate Genomes"; the numbers of completed genomes for each domain are at the top of this page. The number of genomes "in progress" is visible if you click on "Incomplete Projects" under "Isolate Genomes" on the home page; the number is broken down by domains and also by the status of the project. (*Note:* Back at the home page, you can click on "Phylogenetic" under "Genome Distribution" to see how the numbers of sequenced genomes are distributed among phylogenetic groups at the phylum level. Note the number of Chordate genomes near the bottom of the table.) **3.** Prokaryotes are generally smaller cells than eukaryotic cells, and they reproduce by binary fission. The evolutionary process involved is natural selection for more quickly reproducing cells: The faster they can replicate their DNA and divide, the more likely they will be able to dominate a population of prokaryotes. The less DNA they have to replicate, then, the faster they will reproduce.

Concept Check 18.4

1. The number of genes is higher in mammals, and the amount of noncoding DNA is greater. Also, the presence of introns in mammalian genes makes them larger, on average, than prokaryotic genes. **2.** The copy-and-paste transposon mechanism and retrotransposition **3.** In the rRNA gene family, identical transcription units for the three different RNA products are present in long, tandemly repeated arrays. The large number of copies of the rRNA genes enables organisms to produce the rRNA for enough ribosomes to carry out active protein synthesis, and the single transcription unit ensures that the relative amounts of the different rRNA molecules produced are correct. Each globin gene family consists of a relatively small number of nonidentical genes. The differences in the globin proteins encoded by these genes result in production of hemoglobin molecules adapted to particular developmental stages of the organism.

Concept Check 18.5

1. If meiosis is faulty, two copies of the entire genome can end up in a single cell. Errors in crossing over during meiosis can lead to one segment being duplicated while another is deleted. During DNA replication, slippage backward along the template strand can result in segment duplication. **2.** For either gene, a mistake in crossing over during meiosis could have occurred between the two copies of that gene, such that one ended up with a duplicated exon. This could have happened several times, resulting in the multiple copies of a particular exon in each gene. **3.** Homologous transposable elements scattered throughout the genome provide sites where recombination can occur between different chromosomes. Movement of these elements into coding or regulatory sequences may change expression of genes. Transposable elements also can carry genes with them, leading to dispersion of genes and in some cases different patterns of expression. Transport of an exon during transposition and its insertion into a gene may add a new functional domain to the originally encoded protein, a type of exon shuffling. (For any of these changes to be heritable, they must happen in germ cells, cells that will give rise to gametes.)

Concept Check 18.6

1. Because both humans and macaques are primates, their genomes are expected to be more similar than the macaque and mouse genomes are. The mouse lineage diverged from the primate lineage before the human and macaque lineages diverged. **2.** Homeotic genes differ in their *non*homeobox sequences, which determine the interactions of homeotic gene products with other transcription factors and hence which genes are regulated by the homeotic genes. These nonhomeobox sequences differ in the two organisms, as do the expression patterns of the homeobox genes.

Summary of Key Concepts Questions

18.1 One focus of the Human Genome Project was to improve sequencing technology in order to speed up the process. During the project, many advances in sequencing technology allowed faster reactions, which were therefore less expensive. **18.2** The most significant finding was that more than 90% of the human genomic region studied was transcribed, which suggested that the transcribed RNA (and thus the DNA from which it was produced) was performing some unknown functions. The project has been expanded to include other species because to determine the functions of these transcribed DNA elements, it is necessary to carry out this type of analysis on the genomes of species that can be used in laboratory experiments. **18.3** (a) In general, bacteria and archaea have smaller genomes, lower numbers of genes, and higher gene density than eukaryotes. (b) Among eukaryotes, there is no apparent systematic relationship between genome size and phenotype. The number of genes is often lower than would be expected from the size of the genome—in other words, the gene density is often lower in larger genomes. (Humans are an example.) **18.4** Transposable elements can move from place to place in the genome, and some of these sequences make a new copy of themselves when they do so. Thus, it is not surprising that they make up a significant percentage of the genome, and this percentage might be expected to increase over evolutionary time. **18.5** Chromosomal rearrangements within a species lead to some individuals having different chromosomal arrangements. Each of these individuals could still undergo meiosis and produce gametes, and fertilization involving gametes with different chromosomal arrangements could result in viable offspring. However, during meiosis in the offspring, the maternal and paternal chromosomes might not be able to pair up, causing gametes with incomplete sets of chromosomes to form. Most often, when zygotes are produced from such gametes, they do not survive. Ultimately, a new species could form if two different chromosomal arrangements became prevalent within a population and individuals could mate successfully only with other individuals having the same arrangement. **18.6** Comparing the genomes of closely related species can reveal information about more recent evolutionary events, perhaps events that resulted in the distinguishing characteristics of the species. Comparing the genomes of very distantly related species can tell us about evolutionary events that occurred a very long time ago. For example, genes that are shared between distantly related species must have arisen before those species diverged.

Test Your Understanding

1. c **2.** a **3.** a **4.** c **5.** b

6. 1. ATETI...PKSSD...TSSTT...NARRD

2. ATETI...PKSSE...TSSTT...NARRD

3. ATETI...PKSSD...TSSTT...NARRD

4. ATETI...PKSSD...TSSNT...SARRD

5. ATETI...PKSSD...TSSTT...NARRD

6. VTETI...PKSSD...TSSTT...NARRD

(a) Lines 1, 3, and 5 are the C, G, R species. (b) See the underlined amino acids in Line 4. (Line 4 is the human sequence.) (c) Line 6 is the orangutan sequence. (d) There is one amino acid difference between the mouse (the E on line 2) and the C, G, R species (which have a D in that position). There are three amino acid differences between the mouse and the human. (The E, T, and N in the mouse sequence are instead D, N, and S, respectively, in the human sequence.) (e) Because only one amino acid difference arose during the 60–100 million years since the mouse and C, G, R species diverged, it is somewhat surprising that two additional amino acid differences resulted during the 6 million years since chimpanzees and humans diverged. This indicates that the *FOXP2* gene has been evolving faster in the human lineage than in the lineages of other primates.

Chapter 19

Figure Questions

Figure 19.6 The cactus-eater is more closely related to the seed-eater; Figure 1.16 shows that they share a more recent common ancestor (a seed-eater) than the cactus-eater shares with the insect-eater. **Figure 19.9** The common ancestor lived more than 5.5 million years ago. **Figure 19.13** The colors and body forms of these mantids allow them to blend into their surroundings, providing an example of how organisms are well matched to life in their environments. The mantids also share features with one another (and with all other mantids), such as six legs, grasping forelimbs, and large eyes. These shared features illustrate another key observation about life: the unity of life that results from descent from a common ancestor. Over time, as these mantids diverged from a common ancestor, they accumulated different adaptations that made them well suited for life in their different environments. Eventually, these differences became large enough that new species were formed, thus contributing to the great diversity of life. **Figure 19.14** These results show that being reared from the egg stage on one plant species or the other did not result in the adult having a beak length appropriate for that host; instead, adult beak lengths were determined primarily by the population from which the eggs were obtained. Because an egg from a balloon vine population likely had long-beaked parents, while an egg from a goldenrain tree population likely had short-beaked parents, these results indicate that beak length is an inherited trait. **Figure 19.20** Hind limb structure changed first. *Rodhocetus* lacked flukes, but its pelvic bones and hind limbs had changed substantially from how those bones were shaped and arranged in *Pakicetus*. For example, in *Rodhocetus*, the pelvis and hind limbs appear to be oriented for paddling, whereas they were oriented for walking in *Pakicetus*.

Concept Check 19.1

1. Hutton and Lyell proposed that geologic events in the past were caused by the same processes operating today, at the same gradual rate. This principle suggested that Earth must be much older than a few thousand years, the age that was widely accepted at that time. Hutton and Lyell's ideas also stimulated Darwin to reason that the slow accumulation of small changes could ultimately produce the profound changes documented in the fossil record. In this context, the age of Earth was important to Darwin, because unless Earth was very old, he could not envision how there would have been enough time for evolution to occur. **2.** By these criteria, Cuvier's explanation of the fossil record and Lamarck's hypothesis of evolution are both scientific. Cuvier thought that species did not evolve over time. He also suggested that sudden, catastrophic events caused extinctions in particular areas. These assertions can be tested against the fossil record, and his assertion that species do not evolve has been falsified. With respect to Lamarck, his principle of use and disuse can be used to make testable predictions for fossils of groups such as whale ancestors as they adapted to a new habitat. Lamarck's principle of use and disuse and his associated principle of the inheritance of acquired characteristics can also be tested directly in living organisms; these principles have been falsified.

Concept Check 19.2

1. Organisms share characteristics (the unity of life) because they share common ancestors; the great diversity of life occurs because new species have repeatedly formed when descendant organisms gradually adapted to different environments, becoming different from their ancestors. **2.** The fossil mammal species (or its ancestors) would most likely have colonized the Andes from within South America, whereas ancestors of mammals currently found in African mountains would most likely have colonized those mountains from other parts of Africa. As a result, the Andes fossil species would share a more recent common ancestor with South American mammals than with mammals in Africa. Thus, for many of its traits, the fossil mammal species would probably more closely resemble mammals that live in South American jungles than mammals that live on African mountains. It is also possible, however, that the fossil mammal species could resemble the African mountain mammals because similar environments selected for similar adaptations (even though they were only distantly related to one another). **3.** As long as the white phenotype (encoded by the genotype pp) continues to be favored by natural selection, the frequency of the p allele will likely increase over time in the population. If the proportion of white individuals increases relative to purple individuals, the frequency of the recessive p allele will also increase relative to that of the P allele, which only appears in purple individuals (some of whom also carry a p allele).

Concept Check 19.3

1. An environmental factor such as a drug does not create new traits, such as drug resistance, but rather selects for traits among those that are already present in the population. **2.** (a) Despite their different functions, the forelimbs of different mammals are structurally similar because they all represent modifications of a structure found in the common ancestor. (b) This is a case of convergent evolution. The similarities between the sugar glider and flying squirrel indicate that similar environments selected for similar adaptations despite different ancestry. **3.** At the time that dinosaurs originated, Earth's landmasses formed a single large continent, Pangaea. Because many dinosaurs were large and mobile, it is likely that early members of these groups lived on many different parts of Pangaea. When Pangaea broke apart, fossils of these organisms would have moved with the rocks in which they were deposited. As a result, we would predict that fossils of early dinosaurs would have a broad geographic distribution (this prediction has been upheld).

Summary of Key Concepts Questions

19.1 Darwin thought that descent with modification occurred as a gradual, steplike process. The age of Earth was important to him because if Earth were only a few thousand years old (as conventional wisdom suggested), there wouldn't have been sufficient time for major evolutionary change. **19.2** All species have the potential to overreproduce—that is, to produce more offspring than can be supported by the environment. This ensures that there will be what Darwin called a "struggle for existence" in which many of the offspring are eaten, starved, diseased, or unable to reproduce for a variety of other reasons. Members of a population exhibit a range of heritable variations, some of which make it likely that their bearers will leave more offspring than other individuals (for example, the bearer may escape predators more effectively or be more tolerant of the physical conditions of the environment). Over time, natural selection resulting from factors such as predators, lack of food, or the physical conditions of the environment can increase the proportion of individuals with favorable traits in a population (evolutionary adaptation). **19.3** The hypothesis that cetaceans originated from a terrestrial mammal and are closely related to even-toed ungulates is supported by several lines of evidence. For example, fossils document that early cetaceans had hind limbs, as expected for organisms that descended from a land mammal; these fossils also show that cetacean hind limbs became reduced over time. Other fossils show that early cetaceans had a type of ankle bone that is otherwise found only in even-toed ungulates, providing strong evidence that even-toed ungulates are the land mammals to which cetaceans are most closely related. DNA sequence data also indicate that even-toed ungulates are the land mammals to which cetaceans are most closely related.

Test Your Understanding
1. b **2.** d **3.** d **4.** c **5.** a
6. (a)

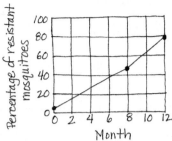

(b) The rapid rise in the percentage of mosquitoes resistant to DDT was most likely caused by natural selection in which mosquitoes resistant to DDT could survive and reproduce while other mosquitoes could not. (c) In India—where DDT resistance first appeared—natural selection would have caused the frequency of resistant mosquitoes to increase over time. If resistant mosquitoes then migrated from India (for example, transported by wind or in planes, trains, or ships) to other parts of the world, the frequency of DDT resistance would increase there as well.

Chapter 20

Figure Questions

Figure 20.5 The new version (shown below) does not alter any of the evolutionary relationships shown in Figure 20.5. For example, B and C remain sister taxa, taxon A is still as closely related to taxon B as it is to taxon C, and so on.

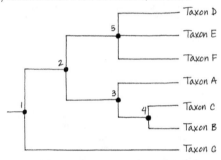

Figure 20.6 Unknown 1b (a portion of sample 1) and Unknowns 9–13 all would have to be located on the branch of the tree that currently leads to Minke (Southern Hemisphere) and Unknowns 1a and 2–8. **Figure 20.9** There are four possible bases (A, C, G, T) at each nucleotide position. If the base at each position depends on chance, not common descent, we would expect roughly one out of four (25%) of them to be the same. **Figure 20.11** You should have circled the frog, turtle, and leopard lineages, along with their most recent common ancestor. **Figure 20.12** The zebrafish lineage; of the five vertebrate lineages shown, its branch is the longest. **Figure 20.15** The lizard and snake lineage is the most basal taxon shown (closest to the root of the tree). Among the descendants of the common ancestor indicated by the blue dot, the crocodilian lineage is the most basal. **Figure 20.18** The molecular clock indicates that the divergence time is roughly 45–50 million years. **Figure 20.20** This tree indicates that the sequences of rRNA and other genes in mitochondria are most closely related to those of proteobacteria, while the sequences of chloroplast genes are most closely related to those of cyanobacteria. These gene sequence relationships are what would be predicted from the endosymbiont theory illustrated in Figure 4.16, which posits that both mitochondria and chloroplasts originated as engulfed prokaryotic cells.

Concept Check 20.1

1. We are classified the same from the domain level to the class level; both the leopard and human are mammals. Leopards belong to order Carnivora, whereas humans do not. **2.** The branching pattern of the tree indicates that the badger and the wolf share a common ancestor that is more recent than the ancestor that these two animals share with the leopard. **3.** The tree in (c) shows a different pattern of evolutionary relationships. In (c), C and B are sister taxa, whereas C and D are sister taxa in (a) and (b). **4.**

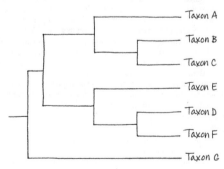

Concept Check 20.2

1. (a) Analogy, since porcupines and cacti are not closely related and since most other animals and plants do not have similar structures; (b) homology, since cats and humans are both mammals and have homologous forelimbs, of which the hand and paw are the lower part; (c) analogy, since owls and hornets are not closely related and since the structure of their wings is very different **2.** Species 2 and 3 are more likely to be closely related. Small genetic changes (as between species 2 and 3) can produce divergent physical appearances, but if many genes have diverged greatly (as in species 1 and 2), then the lineages have probably been separate for a long time.

Concept Check 20.3

1. No; hair is a shared ancestral character common to all mammals and thus is not helpful in distinguishing different mammalian subgroups. **2.** The principle of maximum parsimony states that the hypothesis about nature we investigate first should be the simplest explanation found to be consistent with the facts. Actual evolutionary relationships may differ from those inferred by parsimony owing to complicating factors such as convergent evolution. **3.** The traditional classification provides a poor match to evolutionary history, thus violating the basic principle of cladistics—that classification should be based on common descent. Both birds and mammals originated from groups traditionally designated as reptiles, making reptiles (as traditionally delineated) a paraphyletic group. These problems can be addressed by removing *Dimetrodon* and cynodonts from the reptiles and by regarding birds as a group of reptiles (specifically, as a group of dinosaurs).

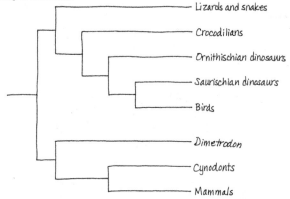

Concept Check 20.4

1. A molecular clock is a method of estimating the actual time of evolutionary events based on numbers of base changes in genes that are related by descent. It is based on the assumption that the regions of genomes being compared evolve at constant rates. **2.** There are many portions of the genome that do not code for genes; mutations that alter the sequence of bases in these regions could accumulate without affecting an organism's fitness. Even in coding regions of the genome, some mutations may not have a critical effect on genes or proteins. **3.** The gene (or genes) used for the molecular clock may have evolved more slowly in these two taxa than in the species used to calibrate the clock; as a result, the clock would underestimate the time at which the taxa diverged from each other.

Concept Check 20.5

1. The kingdom Monera included bacteria and archaea, but we now know that these organisms are in separate domains. Kingdoms are subsets of domains, so a single kingdom (like Monera) that includes taxa from different domains is not valid. **2.** Because of horizontal gene transfer, some genes in eukaryotes are more closely related to bacteria, while others are more closely related to archaea; thus, depending on which genes are used, phylogenetic trees constructed from DNA data can yield conflicting results. **3.**

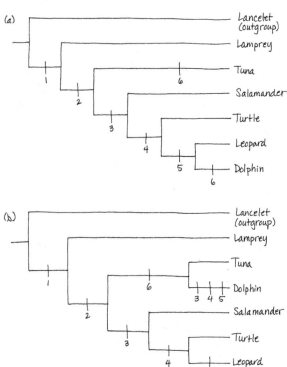

The fossil record indicates that prokaryotes originated long before eukaryotes. This suggests that the third tree, in which the eukaryotic lineage diverged first, is not accurate and hence is not likely to receive support from genetic data.

Summary of Key Concepts Questions

20.1 The fact that humans and chimpanzees are sister species indicates that we share a more recent common ancestor with chimpanzees than we do with any other living primate species. But that does not mean that humans evolved from chimpanzees, or vice versa; instead, it indicates that both humans and chimpanzees are descendants of that common ancestor. **20.2** Homologous characters result from shared ancestry. As organisms diverge over time, some of their homologous characters will also diverge. The homologous characters of organisms that diverged long ago typically differ more than do the homologous characters of organisms that diverged more recently. As a result, differences in homologous characters can be used to infer phylogeny. In contrast, analogous characters result from convergent evolution, not shared ancestry, and hence can give misleading estimates of phylogeny. **20.3** All features of organisms arose at some point in the history of life. In the group in which a new feature first arose, that feature is a shared derived character that is unique to that clade. The group in which each shared derived character first appeared can be determined, and the resulting nested

pattern can be used to infer evolutionary history. **20.4** A key assumption of molecular clocks is that nucleotide substitutions occur at fixed rates, and hence the number of nucleotide differences between two DNA sequences is proportional to the time since the sequences diverged from each other. Some limitations of molecular clocks: No gene marks time with complete precision; natural selection can favor certain DNA changes over others; nucleotide substitution rates can change over long periods of time (causing molecular-clock estimates of when events in the distant past occurred to be highly uncertain); and the same gene can evolve at different rates in different organisms. **20.5** Genetic data indicated that many prokaryotes differed as much from each other as they did from eukaryotes. This indicated that organisms should be grouped into three "super-kingdoms," or domains (Archaea, Bacteria, Eukarya). These data also indicated that the previous kingdom Monera (which had contained all the prokaryotes) did not make biological sense and should be abandoned. Later genetic and morphological data also indicated that the former kingdom Protista (which had primarily contained single-celled organisms) should be abandoned because some protists are more closely related to plants, fungi, or animals than they are to other protists.

Test Your Understanding

1. a **2.** d **3.** b **4.** d **5.** d **6.** c **7.** d
8.

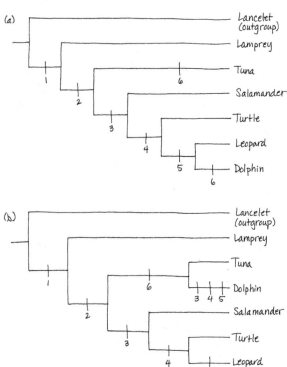

(c) The tree in (a) requires seven evolutionary changes, while the tree in (b) requires nine evolutionary changes. Thus, the tree in (a) is more parsimonious, since it requires fewer evolutionary changes.

Chapter 21

Figure Questions

Figure 21.4 The genetic code is redundant, meaning that more than one codon can specify the same amino acid. As a result, a substitution at a particular site in a coding region of the *Adh* gene might change the codon but not the translated amino acid and thus not the resulting protein encoded by the gene. One way an insertion in an exon would not affect the gene produced is if it occurs in an untranslated region of the exon. This is the case for the insertion at location 1,703. **Figure 21.8** The predicted frequencies are 36% $C^R C^R$, 48% $C^R C^W$, and 16% $C^W C^W$. **Figure 21.13** Directional selection. Goldenrain tree has smaller fruit than does the native host, balloon vine. Thus, in soapberry bug populations feeding on goldenrain tree, bugs with shorter beaks had an advantage, resulting in directional selection for shorter beak length. **Figure 21.16** Crossing a single female's eggs with both an SC and an LC male's sperm allowed the researchers to directly compare the effects of the males' contribution to the next generation, since both batches of offspring had the same maternal contribution. This isolation of the male's impact enabled researchers to draw conclusions about differences in genetic "quality" between the SC and LC males. **Figure 21.18** The researchers measured the percentage of successfully reproducing adults in the breeding population that had each phenotype. This approach of determining which phenotype was favored by selection assumes that reproduction was a sufficient indicator of relative fitness (as opposed to counting the number of eggs laid or offspring hatched, for example) and that mouth phenotype was the driving factor determining the fish's ability to reproduce.

Concept Check 21.1

1. Within a population, genetic differences among individuals provide the raw material on which natural selection and other mechanisms can act. Without such differences, allele frequencies could not change over time—and hence the population could not evolve. **2.** Many mutations occur in somatic cells, which do not produce gametes and so are lost when the organism dies. Of mutations that do occur in cell lines that produce gametes, many do not have a phenotypic effect on which natural selection can act. Others have a harmful effect and are thus unlikely to increase in frequency because they decrease the reproductive success of their bearers. **3.** Its genetic variation (whether measured at the level of the gene or at the level of nucleotide sequences) would probably drop over time. During meiosis, crossing over and the independent assortment of chromosomes produce many new combinations of alleles. In addition, a population contains a vast number of possible mating combinations, and fertilization brings together the gametes of individuals with different genetic backgrounds. Thus, via crossing over, independent assortment of chromosomes, and fertilization, sexual reproduction reshuffles alleles into fresh combinations each generation. Without sexual reproduction, the rate of forming new combinations of alleles would be vastly reduced, causing the overall amount of genetic variation to drop.

Concept Check 21.2

1. Each individual has two alleles, so the total number of alleles is 1,400. To calculate the frequency of allele A, note that each of the 85 individuals of genotype AA has two A alleles, each of the 320 individuals of genotype Aa has one A allele, and each of the 295 individuals of genotype aa has zero A alleles. Thus, the frequency (p) of allele A is

$$p = \frac{(2 \times 85) + (1 \times 320) + (0 \times 295)}{1,400} = 0.35$$

There are only two alleles (A and a) in our population, so the frequency of allele a must be $q = 1 - p = 0.65$. **2.** Because the frequency of allele a is 0.45, the frequency of allele A must be 0.55. Thus, the expected genotype frequencies are $p^2 = 0.3025$ for genotype AA, $2pq = 0.495$ for genotype Aa, and $q^2 = 0.2025$ for genotype aa. **3.** There are 120 individuals in the population, so there are 240 alleles. Of these, there are 124 V alleles—32 from the 16 VV individuals and 92 from the 92 Vv individuals. Thus, the frequency of the V allele is $p = 124/240 = 0.52$; hence, the frequency of the v allele is $q = 0.48$. Based on the Hardy-Weinberg equation, if the population were not evolving, the frequency of genotype VV should be $p^2 = 0.52 \times 0.52 = 0.27$; the frequency of genotype Vv should be $2pq = 2 \times 0.52 \times 0.48 = 0.5$; and the frequency of genotype vv should be $q^2 = 0.48 \times 0.48 = 0.23$. In a population of 120 individuals, these expected genotype frequencies lead us to predict that there would be 32 VV individuals (0.27×120), 60 Vv individuals (0.5×120), and 28 vv individuals (0.23×120). The actual numbers for the population (16 VV, 92 Vv, 12 vv) deviate from these expectations (fewer homozygotes and more heterozygotes than expected). This indicates that the population is not in Hardy-Weinberg equilibrium and hence may be evolving at this locus.

Concept Check 21.3

1. Natural selection is more "predictable" in that it alters allele frequencies in a nonrandom way: It tends to increase the frequency of alleles that increase the organism's reproductive success in its environment and decrease the frequency of alleles that decrease the organism's reproductive success. Alleles subject to genetic drift increase or decrease in frequency by chance alone, whether or not they are advantageous. **2.** Genetic drift results from chance events that cause allele frequencies to fluctuate at random from generation to generation; within a population, this process tends to decrease genetic variation over time. Gene flow is the transfer of alleles between populations, a process that can introduce new alleles to a population and hence may increase its genetic variation (albeit slightly, since rates of gene flow are often low). **3.** Selection is not important at this locus; furthermore, the populations are not small, and hence the effects of genetic drift should not be pronounced. Gene flow is occurring via the movement of pollen and seeds. Thus, allele and genotype frequencies in these populations should become more similar over time as a result of gene flow.

Concept Check 21.4

1. Zero, because fitness includes reproductive contribution to the next generation, and a sterile mule cannot produce offspring **2.** Although both gene flow and genetic drift can increase the frequency of advantageous alleles in a population, they can also decrease the frequency of advantageous alleles or increase the frequency of harmful alleles. Only natural selection *consistently* results in an increase in the frequency of alleles that enhance survival or reproduction. Thus, natural selection is the only mechanism that consistently leads to adaptive evolution. **3.** The three modes of natural selection (directional, stabilizing, and disruptive) are defined in terms of the selective advantage of different *phenotypes*, not different genotypes. Thus, the type of selection represented by heterozygote advantage depends on the phenotype of the heterozygotes. In this question, because heterozygous individuals have a more extreme phenotype than either homozygote, heterozygote advantage represents directional selection. **4.** Under prolonged low-oxygen conditions, some of the red blood cells of a heterozygote may sickle, leading to harmful effects (see Figure 3.22). This does not occur in individuals with two normal hemoglobin alleles, suggesting that there may be selection against heterozygotes in malaria-free regions (where heterozygote advantage does not occur). However, since heterozygotes are healthy under most conditions, selection against them is unlikely to be strong.

Summary of Key Concepts Questions

21.1 Much of the nucleotide variability at a genetic locus occurs within introns. Nucleotide variation at these sites typically does not affect the phenotype because introns do not code for the protein product of the gene. (Note to students: In certain circumstances, it is possible that a change in an intron could affect RNA splicing and ultimately have some phenotypic effect on the organism, but such mechanisms are not covered in this introductory text.) There are also many variable nucleotide sites within exons. However, most of the variable sites within exons reflect changes to the DNA sequence that do not change the sequence of amino acids encoded by the gene (and hence may not affect the phenotype). **21.2** No, this is not an example of circular reasoning. Calculating p and q from observed genotype frequencies does not imply

that those genotype frequencies must be in Hardy-Weinberg equilibrium. Consider a population that has 195 individuals of genotype AA, 10 of genotype Aa, and 195 of genotype aa. Calculating p and q from these values yields $p = q = 0.5$. Using the Hardy-Weinberg equation, the predicted equilibrium frequencies are $p^2 = 0.25$ for genotype AA, $2pq = 0.5$ for genotype Aa, and $q^2 = 0.25$ for genotype aa. Since there are 400 individuals in the population, these predicted genotype frequencies indicate that there should be 100 AA individuals, 200 Aa individuals, and 100 aa individuals—numbers that differ greatly from the values that we used to calculate p and q. **21.3** It is unlikely that two such populations would evolve in similar ways. Since their environments are very different, the alleles favored by natural selection would probably differ between the two populations. Although genetic drift may have important effects in each of these small populations, drift causes unpredictable changes in allele frequencies, so it is unlikely that drift would cause the populations to evolve in similar ways. Both populations are geographically isolated, suggesting that little gene flow would occur between them (again making it less likely that they would evolve in similar ways). **21.4** Compared to males, it is likely that the females of such species would be larger, more colorful, endowed with more elaborate ornamentation (for example, a large morphological feature such as the peacock's tail), and more apt to engage in behaviors intended to attract mates or prevent other members of their sex from obtaining mates.

Test Your Understanding

1. e **2.** c **3.** e **4.** b **5.** a **6.** d

7. The frequency of the lap^{94} allele increases as one moves from southwest to northeast across Long Island Sound.

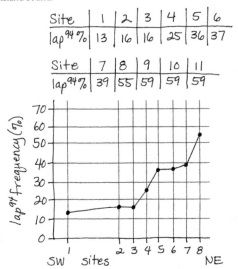

A hypothesis that explains the shape of the graph and accounts for the observations stated in the question is that the frequency of the lap^{94} allele at different sites results from an interaction between selection and gene flow. Under this hypothesis, in the southwest portion of the Sound, salinity is relatively low, and selection against the lap^{94} allele is strong. Moving toward the northeast and into the open ocean, where salinity is relatively high, selection favors a high frequency of the lap^{94} allele. However, because mussel larvae disperse long distances, gene flow prevents the lap^{94} allele from becoming fixed in the open ocean or from declining to zero in the southwestern portion of Long Island Sound.

Chapter 22

Figure Questions

Figure 22.8 If this had not been done, the strong preference of "starch flies" and "maltose flies" to mate with like-adapted flies could have occurred simply because the flies could detect (for example, by sense of smell) what their potential mates had eaten as larvae—and they preferred to mate with flies that had a similar smell to their own. **Figure 22.10** In murky waters where females distinguish colors poorly, females of each species might mate often with males of the other species. Hence, since hybrids between these species are viable and fertile, the gene pools of the two species could become more similar over time. **Figure 22.11** The graph suggests there has been gene flow of some fire-bellied toad alleles into the range of the yellow-bellied toad. Otherwise, all individuals located to the left of the hybrid zone portion of the graph would have allele frequencies very close to 1. **Figure 22.12** Because the populations had only just begun to diverge from one another at this point in the process, it is likely that any existing barriers to reproduction would weaken over time. **Figure 22.16** Over time, the chromosomes of the experimental hybrids came to resemble those of *H. anomalus*. This occurred even though conditions in the laboratory differed greatly from conditions in the field, where *H. anomalus* is found, suggesting that selection for laboratory conditions was not strong. Thus, it is unlikely that the observed rise in the fertility of the experimental hybrids was due to selection for life under laboratory conditions. **Figure 22.17** The presence of *M. cardinalis* plants that carry the *M. lewisii* *yup* allele would make it more likely that bumblebees would transfer pollen between the two monkey flower species. As a result, we would expect the number of hybrid offspring to increase.

Concept Check 22.1

1. (a) All except the biological species concept can be applied to both asexual and sexual species because they define species on the basis of characteristics other than the ability to reproduce. In contrast, the biological species concept can be applied only to sexual species. (b) The easiest species concept to apply in the field would be the morphological species concept because it is based only on the appearance of the organism. Additional information about its ecological habits, evolutionary history, and reproduction are not required. **2.** Because these birds live in fairly similar environments and can breed successfully in captivity, the reproductive barrier in nature is probably prezygotic; given the species' differences in habitat preference, this barrier could result from habitat isolation.

Concept Check 22.2

1. In allopatric speciation, a new species forms while in geographic isolation from its parent species; in sympatric speciation, a new species forms in the absence of geographic isolation. Geographic isolation greatly reduces gene flow between populations, whereas ongoing gene flow is more likely in sympatric populations. As a result, sympatric speciation is less common than allopatric speciation. **2.** Gene flow between subsets of a population that live in the same area can be reduced in a variety of ways. In some species—especially plants—changes in chromosome number can block gene flow and establish reproductive isolation in a single generation. Gene flow can also be reduced in sympatric populations by habitat differentiation (as seen in the apple maggot fly, *Rhagoletis*) and sexual selection (as seen in Lake Victoria cichlids). **3.** Allopatric speciation would be less likely to occur on a nearby island than on an isolated island of the same size. The reason we expect this result is that continued gene flow between mainland populations and those on a nearby island reduces the chance that enough genetic divergence will take place for allopatric speciation to occur. **4.** If all of the homologs failed to separate during anaphase I of meiosis, some gametes would end up with an extra set of chromosomes (and others would end up with no chromosomes). If a gamete with an extra set of chromosomes fused with a normal gamete, a triploid would result; if two gametes with an extra set of chromosomes fused with each other, a tetraploid would result.

Concept Check 22.3

1. Hybrid zones are regions in which members of different species meet and mate, producing some offspring of mixed ancestry. Such regions can be viewed as "natural laboratories" in which to study speciation because scientists can directly observe factors that cause (or fail to cause) reproductive isolation. **2.** (a) If hybrids consistently survived and reproduced poorly compared with the offspring of intraspecific matings, reinforcement could occur. If it did, natural selection could cause prezygotic barriers to reproduction between the parent species to strengthen over time, decreasing the production of unfit hybrids and leading to a completion of the speciation process. (b) If hybrid offspring survived and reproduced as well as the offspring of intraspecific matings, indiscriminate mating between the parent species would lead to the production of large numbers of hybrid offspring. As these hybrids mated with each other and with members of both parent species, the gene pools of the parent species could fuse over time, reversing the speciation process.

Concept Check 22.4

1. The time between speciation events includes (1) the length of time that it takes for populations of a newly formed species to begin diverging reproductively from one another and (2) the time it takes for speciation to be complete once this divergence begins. Although speciation can occur rapidly once populations have begun to diverge from one another, it may take millions of years for that divergence to begin. **2.** Investigators transferred alleles at the *yup* locus (which influences flower color) from each parent species to the other. *M. lewisii* plants with an *M. cardinalis yup* allele received many more visits from hummingbirds than usual; hummingbirds usually pollinate *M. cardinalis* but avoid *M. lewisii*. Similarly, *M. cardinalis* plants with an *M. lewisii yup* allele received many more visits from bumblebees than usual; bumblebees usually pollinate *M. lewisii* and avoid *M. cardinalis*. Thus, alleles at the *yup* locus can influence pollinator choice, which in these species provides the primary barrier to interspecific mating. Nevertheless, the experiment does not prove that the *yup* locus alone controls barriers to reproduction between *M. lewisii* and *M. cardinalis*; other genes might enhance the effect of the *yup* locus (by modifying flower color) or cause entirely different barriers to reproduction (for example, gametic isolation or a postzygotic barrier). **3.** Crossing over. If crossing over did not occur, each chromosome in an experimental hybrid would remain as in the F_1 generation: composed entirely of DNA from one parent species or the other.

Summary of Key Concepts Questions

22.1 According to the biological species concept, a species is a group of populations whose members interbreed and produce viable, fertile offspring; thus, gene flow occurs between populations of a species. In contrast, members of different species do not interbreed, and hence no gene flow occurs between their populations. Overall, then, in the biological species concept, species can be viewed as designated by the *absence* of gene flow—making gene flow of central importance to the biological species concept. **22.2** Sympatric speciation can be promoted by factors such as polyploidy, habitat shifts, and sexual selection, all of which can reduce gene flow between the subpopulations of a larger population. But such factors can also occur in allopatric populations and hence can also promote allopatric speciation. **22.3** If the hybrids are selected against, the hybrid zone could persist if individuals from the parent species regularly travel into the zone, where they mate to produce hybrid offspring. If hybrids are not selected against, there is no cost to the continued production of hybrids, and large numbers of hybrid offspring may be produced. Natural selection for life in different environments may keep the gene pools of the two parent species distinct, thus preventing the loss (by fusion) of the parent species and once again causing the hybrid zone to be stable over time. **22.4** As the goatsbeard plant, Bahamas mosquitofish, and apple maggot fly illustrate, speciation continues to happen today. A new species

can begin to form whenever gene flow is reduced between populations of the parent species. Such reductions in gene flow can occur in many ways: A new, geographically isolated population may be founded by a few colonists; some members of the parent species may begin to utilize a new habitat; and sexual selection may isolate formerly connected populations or subpopulations. These and many other such events are happening today.

Test Your Understanding

1. b **2.** c **3.** c **4.** a **5.** e **6.** d
7. Here is one possibility:

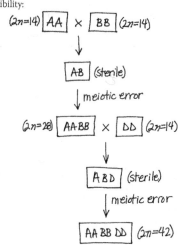

Chapter 23

Figure Questions

Figure 23.5 There are two speciation events and two extinctions in lineage A, while there are three speciation events and no extinctions in lineage B. **Figure 23.8** The Australian plate's current direction of movement is roughly similar to the northeasterly direction that the continent traveled over the past 65 million years. **Figure 23.10** The blue curve is for marine animal families. Families often contain many species, and if even one of those species survives, the family would not become extinct. Hence, we would expect the percentage of families that became extinct to be lower than the percentage of species that became extinct. **Figure 23.17** In this bat, the ratio of the length of the longest set of hand and finger bones to the length of the radius is approximately equal to 2. Although answers will vary from person to person, the corresponding ratio is typically less than 1 in humans. **Figure 23.20** The coding sequence of the *Pitx1* gene would differ between the marine and lake populations, but patterns of gene expression would not.

Concept Check 23.1

1. 22,920 years (four half-lives: 5,730 × 4) **2.** The fossil record shows that different groups of organisms dominated life on Earth at different points in time and that many organisms once alive are now extinct; specific examples can be found in Figure 23.2. The fossil record also indicates that new groups of organisms can arise via the gradual modification of previously existing organisms, as illustrated by fossils that document the origin of mammals from their cynodont ancestors. **3.** Because uranium-238 has a half-life of 4.5 billion years, the *x*-axis would be relabeled (in billions of years) as 4.5, 9, 13.5, and 18. **4.** A fossil record of life today would include many organisms with hard body parts (such as vertebrates and many marine invertebrates), but might not include some species we are very familiar with, such as those that have small geographic ranges and/or small population sizes (for example, endangered species such as the giant panda, tiger, and several rhinoceros species). **5.** The discovery of such a (hypothetical) fossil organism would indicate that aspects of our current understanding of the origin of mammals are not correct because mammals are thought to have originated much more recently (see Figure 23.4). For example, such a discovery could suggest that the dates of previous fossil discoveries are not correct or that the lineages shown in Figure 23.4 shared features with mammals but were not their direct ancestors. Such a discovery would also suggest that radical changes in multiple aspects of the skeletal structure of organisms could arise suddenly—an idea that is not supported by the known fossil record.

Concept Check 23.2

1. Continental drift alters the physical geography and climate of Earth, as well as the extent to which organisms are geographically isolated. Because these factors affect extinction and speciation rates, continental drift has a major impact on life on Earth. **2.** In each of the five mass extinctions documented in the fossil record, 50% or more of marine species became extinct, as did large numbers of terrestrial species. As a result, a mass extinction alters the course of evolution dramatically, removing many evolutionary lineages and reducing the diversity of life on Earth for millions of years. A mass extinction can also change ecological communities by changing the types of organisms that live in them. **3.** Mass extinctions; major evolutionary innovations; the diversification of another group of organisms (which can provide new sources of food); migration to new locations where few competitor species exist **4.** In theory, fossils of both common and rare species would be present right up to the time of the catastrophic event, then disappear. Reality is more complicated because the fossil record is not perfect. So the most recent fossil for a species might be a million years before the mass extinction—even though the species did not become extinct *until* the mass extinction. This complication is especially likely for rare species because so few of their fossils will form and be discovered. Hence, for many rare species, the fossil record would not document that the species was alive immediately before the extinction (even if it was).

Concept Check 23.3

1. Heterochrony can cause a variety of morphological changes. For example, if the onset of sexual maturity changes, a retention of juvenile characteristics (paedomorphosis) may result. Paedomorphosis can be caused by small genetic changes that result in large changes in morphology, as seen in the axolotl salamander. **2.** In animal embryos, *Hox* genes influence the development of structures such as limbs and feeding appendages. As a result, changes in these genes—or in the regulation of these genes—are likely to have major effects on morphology. **3.** From genetics, we know that gene regulation is altered by how well transcription factors bind to noncoding DNA sequences called control elements. Thus, if changes in morphology are often caused by changes in gene regulation, portions of noncoding DNA that contain control elements are likely to be strongly affected by natural selection.

Concept Check 23.4

1. Complex structures do not evolve all at once, but in increments, with natural selection selecting for adaptive variants of the earlier versions. **2.** Although the myxoma virus is highly lethal, initially some of the rabbits are resistant (0.2% of infected rabbits are not killed). Thus, assuming resistance is an inherited trait, we would expect the rabbit population to show a trend for increased resistance to the virus. We would also expect the virus to show an evolutionary trend toward reduced lethality. We would expect this trend because a rabbit infected with a less lethal virus would be more likely to live long enough for a mosquito to bite it and hence potentially transmit the virus to another rabbit. (A virus that kills its rabbit host before a mosquito transmits the virus to another rabbit dies with its host.)

Summary of Key Concepts Questions

23.1 One challenge is that organisms do not use radioisotopes that have long half-lives to build their bones or shells. As a result, fossils older than 75,000 years cannot be dated directly. Fossils are often found in sedimentary rock, but those rocks typically contain sediments of different ages, again posing a challenge when trying to date old fossils. To circumvent these challenges, geologists date layers of volcanic rock that surround old fossils and that contain radioisotopes with long half-lives. This approach provides minimum and maximum estimates for the ages of fossils sandwiched between two layers of volcanic rock. **23.2** The broad evolutionary changes documented by the fossil record reflect the rise and fall of major groups of organisms. In turn, the rise or fall of any particular group results from a balance between speciation and extinction rates: A group increases in size when the rate at which its members produce new species is greater than the rate at which its member species are lost to extinction, while a group shrinks in size if extinction rates are greater than speciation rates. **23.3** A change in the sequence or regulation of a developmental gene can produce major morphological changes. In some cases, such morphological changes may enable organisms to perform new functions or live in new environments—thus potentially leading to an adaptive radiation and the formation of a new group of organisms. **23.4** Evolutionary change results from interactions between organisms and their current environments. No goal is involved in this process. As environments change over time, the features of organisms favored by natural selection may also change. When this happens, what once may have seemed like a "goal" of evolution (for example, improvements in the function of a feature previously favored by natural selection) may cease to be beneficial or may even be harmful.

Test Your Understanding

1. e **2.** b **3.** d **4.** c **5.** b **6.** The synapsid clade. *Dimetrodon* and mammals share a common ancestor that was a synapsid; hence, both *Dimetrodon* and mammals are synapsids. Although mammals are also therapsids, *Dimetrodon* is not a therapsid because it diverged from the mammal evolutionary lineage before the origin of the first therapsids.

Chapter 24

Figure Questions

Figure 24.3 Proteins are almost always composed of the same 20 amino acids shown in Figure 3.17. However, many other amino acids could potentially form in this or any other experiment. For example, any molecule that had a different R group than those listed in Figure 3.17 (yet still contained an α carbon, an amino group, and a carboxyl group) would be an amino acid—yet it would not be one of the 20 amino acids commonly found in nature today. **Figure 24.14** It is likely that the expression or sequence of genes that affect glucose metabolism may have changed; genes for metabolic processes no longer needed by the cell also may have changed. **Figure 24.15** Transduction results in horizontal gene transfer when the host and recipient cells are members of different species. **Figure 24.18** Eukarya **Figure 24.20** Thermophiles live in very hot environments, so it is likely that their enzymes can continue to function normally at much higher temperatures than do the enzymes of other organisms. At low temperatures, however, the enzymes of thermophiles may not function as well as the enzymes of other organisms. **Figure 24.22** From the graph, plant uptake can be estimated as 0.7, 0.6, and 0.95 mg K^+ for strains 1, 2, and 3, respectively. These values average to 0.75 mg K^+. If bacteria had no effect, the average plant uptake of potassium for strains 1, 2, and 3 should be close to 0.5 mg K^+, the value observed for plants grown in bacteria-free soil.

Concept Check 24.1

1. The hypothesis that conditions on early Earth could have permitted the synthesis of organic molecules from inorganic ingredients **2.** In contrast to random mingling of molecules in an open solution, segregation of molecular systems by the membranes of protocells could concentrate organic molecules, assisting biochemical reactions. **3.** The earliest prokaryotic fossils are of stromatolites that lived in shallow marine environments 3.5 billion years ago. By 3.1 billion years ago, stromatolites had diversified into two different morphological types, and by 2.8 billion years ago, they had expanded to live in salty lakes as well as marine environments. Fossils of individual prokaryotic cells have also been found, the earliest dating to 3.4 billion years ago. By 2.5 billion years ago, diverse communities of photosynthetic cyanobacteria lived in the oceans. These cyanobacteria released oxygen to Earth's atmosphere during the water-splitting step of photosynthesis. As a result, the composition of the atmosphere changed and many prokaryotic groups were driven to extinction—thus altering the course of evolution. **4.** Today, genetic information usually flows from DNA to RNA, as when the DNA sequence of a gene is used as a template to synthesize the mRNA encoding a particular protein. However, the life cycle of retroviruses such as HIV shows that genetic information can flow in the reverse direction (from RNA to DNA). In these viruses, the enzyme reverse transcriptase uses RNA as a template for DNA synthesis, suggesting that a similar enzyme could have played a key role in the transition from an RNA world to a DNA world.

Concept Check 24.2

1. Prokaryotic cells lack the complex compartmentalization associated with the membrane-enclosed organelles of eukaryotic cells. Prokaryotic genomes have much less DNA than eukaryotic genomes, and most of this DNA is contained in a single ring-shaped chromosome located in the nucleoid rather than within a true membrane-enclosed nucleus. In addition, many prokaryotes also have plasmids, small ring-shaped DNA molecules containing a few genes. **2.** A phototroph derives its energy from light, while a chemotroph gets its energy from chemical sources. An autotroph derives its carbon from CO_2, HCO_3^-, or related compounds, while a heterotroph gets its carbon from organic nutrients such as glucose. Thus, there are four nutritional modes: photoautotrophic, photoheterotrophic (unique to prokaryotes), chemoautotrophic (unique to prokaryotes), and chemoheterotrophic. **3.** Plastids such as chloroplasts are thought to have evolved from an endosymbiotic photosynthetic prokaryote. More specifically, the phylogenetic tree shown in Figure 20.20 indicates that plastids are closely related to cyanobacteria. Hence, we can hypothesize that the thylakoid membranes of chloroplasts resemble those of cyanobacteria because chloroplasts evolved from an endosymbiotic cyanobacterium. **4.** If humans could fix nitrogen, we could build proteins using atmospheric N_2 and hence would not need to eat high-protein foods such as meat, fish, or soy. Our diet would, however, need to include a source of carbon, along with minerals and water. Thus, a typical meal might consist of carbohydrates as a carbon source, along with fruits and vegetables to provide essential minerals (and additional carbon).

Concept Check 24.3

1. Prokaryotes can have extremely large population sizes, in part because they often have short generation times. The large number of individuals in prokaryotic populations makes it likely that in each generation there will be many individuals that have new mutations at any particular gene, thereby adding considerable genetic diversity to the population. **2.** In transformation, naked, foreign DNA from the environment is taken up by a bacterial cell. In transduction, phages carry bacterial genes from one bacterial cell to another. In conjugation, a bacterial cell directly transfers plasmid or chromosomal DNA to another cell via a mating bridge that temporarily connects the two cells. **3.** The population that includes individuals capable of conjugation would probably be more successful, since some of its members could form recombinant cells whose new gene combinations might be advantageous in a novel environment. **4.** Yes. Genes for antibiotic resistance could be transferred (by transformation, transduction, or conjugation) from the nonpathogenic bacterium to a pathogenic bacterium; this could make the pathogen an even greater threat to human health. In general, transformation, transduction, and conjugation tend to increase the spread of resistance genes.

Concept Check 24.4

1. Molecular systematic studies indicate that organisms once classified as bacteria are more closely related to eukaryotes and belong in a domain of their own: Archaea. Such studies have also shown that horizontal gene transfer is common and plays an important role in the evolution of prokaryotes. **2.** By not requiring that organisms be cultured in the laboratory, metagenomic studies have revealed an immense diversity of previously unknown prokaryotic species. Over time, the ongoing discovery of new species by metagenomic analyses may alter our understanding of prokaryotic phylogeny greatly. **3.** At present, all known methanogens are archaea in the clade Euryarchaeota; this suggests that this unique metabolic pathway probably arose in ancestral species within Euryarchaeota. Since Bacteria and Archaea have been separate evolutionary lineages for billions of years, the discovery of a methanogen from the domain Bacteria would suggest that adaptations that enabled the use of CO_2 to oxidize H_2 may have evolved twice—once in Archaea (within Euryarchaeota) and once in Bacteria. (It is also possible that a newly discovered bacterial methanogen could have acquired the genes for this metabolic pathway by horizontal gene transfer from a methanogen in domain Archaea. However, horizontal gene transfer is not a likely explanation because of the large number of genes involved and because gene transfers between species in different domains are rare.)

Concept Check 24.5

1. Although prokaryotes are small, their large numbers and metabolic abilities enable them to play key roles in ecosystems by decomposing wastes, recycling chemicals, and affecting the concentrations of nutrients available to other organisms. Prokaryotes also play a key role in ecological interactions such as mutualism and parasitism. **2.** No. If the poison is secreted as an exotoxin, live bacteria could be transmitted to another person. But the same is true if the poison is an endotoxin—only in this case, the live bacteria that are transmitted may be descendants of the (now-dead) bacteria that produced the poison. **3.** Cyanobacteria produce oxygen when water is split in the light reactions of photosynthesis. The Calvin cycle incorporates CO_2 from the air into organic molecules, which are then converted to sugars. **4.** Some of the many different species of prokaryotes that live in the human gut compete with one another for resources (from the food that you eat). Because different prokaryotic species have different adaptations, a change in diet may alter which species can grow most rapidly, thus altering species abundance.

Summary of Key Concepts Questions

24.1 Particles of montmorillonite clay may have provided surfaces on which organic molecules became concentrated and hence were more likely to react with one another. Montmorillonite clay particles may also have facilitated the transport of key molecules, such as short strands of RNA, into vesicles. These vesicles can form spontaneously from simple precursor molecules, "reproduce" and "grow" on their own, and maintain internal concentrations of molecules that differ from those in the surrounding environment. These features of vesicles represent key steps in the emergence of protocells and (ultimately) the first living cells. **24.2** Specific structural features that enable prokaryotes to thrive in diverse environments include their cell walls (which provide shape and protection), flagella (which function in directed movement), and ability to form capsules or endospores (both of which can protect against adverse environmental conditions). Prokaryotes also have an exceptionally broad range of metabolic adaptations, enabling them to thrive in many different environments. **24.3** Many prokaryotic species can reproduce extremely rapidly, and their populations can number in the trillions. As a result, even though mutations are rare, every day many offspring are produced that have new mutations at particular gene loci. In addition, even though prokaryotes reproduce asexually and hence the vast majority of offspring are genetically identical to their parent, the genetic variation of their populations can be increased by transduction, transformation, and conjugation. Each of these (nonreproductive) processes can increase genetic variation by transferring DNA from one cell to another—even among cells that are of different species. **24.4** Molecular data have revealed that prokaryotes form two domains (Bacteria and Archaea), and they have elucidated relationships among major groups of prokaryotes. Molecular data have also allowed researchers to sample genes directly from the environment; using such genes to construct phylogenies has led to the discovery of major new groups of prokaryotes. **24.5** Prokaryotes play key roles in the chemical cycles on which life depends. For example, prokaryotes are important decomposers, breaking down corpses and waste materials, thereby releasing nutrients to the environment, where they can be used by other organisms. Prokaryotes also convert inorganic compounds to forms that other organisms can use. With respect to their ecological interactions, many prokaryotes form life-sustaining mutualisms with other species. For example, human well-being depends on our associations with mutualistic prokaryotes, such as the many species that live in our intestines and digest food that we cannot. In some cases, such as hydrothermal vent communities, the metabolic activities of prokaryotes provide an energy source on which hundreds of other species depend; in the absence of the prokaryotes, the community collapses.

Test Your Understanding

1. d **2.** c **3.** e **4.** b **5.** d **6.** e **7.** a

8. (a)

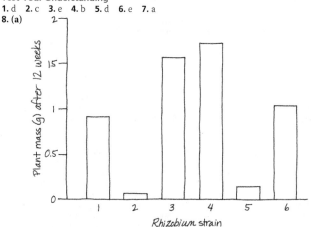

(b) Some *Rhizobium* strains are much more effective at promoting plant growth than other *Rhizobium* strains; the most ineffective strains have little positive effect (plant growth with these strains differs little from plant growth in the absence of *Rhizobium*). The ineffective strains may transfer relatively little nitrogen to their plant host, limiting plant growth.

Chapter 25

Figure Questions

Figure 25.4 Four. The first (and primary) genome is the DNA located in the chlorarachniophyte nucleus. A chlorarachniophyte also contain remnants of a green alga's nuclear DNA, located in the nucleomorph. Finally, mitochondria and chloroplasts contain DNA from the (different) bacteria from which they evolved. These two prokaryotic genomes comprise the third and fourth genomes contained within a chlorarachniophyte. **Figure 25.7** As described in observations 1 and 2, choanoflagellates and several groups of animals have collar cells. Since collar cells have never been observed in plants, fungi, or non-choanoflagellate protists, this suggests that choanoflagellates may be more closely related to animals than to other eukaryotes. If choanoflagellates are more closely related to animals than to any other group of eukaryotes, choanoflagellates and animals should share other traits that are not found in other eukaryotes. The data described in observation 3 are consistent with this prediction. **Figure 25.9** Based on the age of the oldest taxonomically resolved fossil eukaryote, a red alga that lived 1.2 billion years ago, we can conclude that the

supergroups must have begun to diverge no later than 1.2 billion years ago. **Figure 25.21** If the assumption is correct, then their results indicate that the fusion of the genes for DHFR and TS may be a derived trait shared by members of three supergroups of eukaryotes (Excavata, the SAR clade, and Archaeplastida). However, if the assumption is not correct, the presence or absence of the gene fusion may tell little about phylogenetic history. For example, if the genes fused multiple times, groups could share the trait because of convergent evolution rather than common descent. If instead the genes were secondarily split, a group with such a split could be placed (incorrectly) in Unikonta rather than its correct placement in one of the other three supergroups. **Figure 25.26** The apicoplast is a modified plastid and hence was derived from a cyanobacterium. Thus, the metabolic pathway that the apicoplast uses to synthesize this essential chemical would likely differ from pathways found in humans—and hence drugs that target this pathway would probably not harm humans.

Concept Check 25.1

1. The earliest fossil eukaryotes date to 1.8 billion years ago. By 1.3 billion years ago, the fossil record documents a moderate diversity of unicellular and simple multicellular eukaryotes, some of which had asymmetric forms indicating the presence of a well-developed cytoskeleton. Fossil organisms that lived from 1.3 billion to 635 million years ago include those with complex multicellularity, sexual life cycles, and eukaryotic photosynthesis. Large, multicellular eukaryotes first appeared about 600 million years ago. **2.** Eukaryotes are considered "combination" organisms because some of their genes and cellular characteristics are derived from archaea, while others are derived from bacteria. Strong evidence shows that eukaryotes acquired mitochondria after a host cell (either an archaean or a cell with archaeal ancestors) first engulfed and then formed an endosymbiotic association with an alpha proteobacterium. Similarly, chloroplasts in red and green algae appear to have descended from a photosynthetic cyanobacterium that was engulfed by an ancient heterotrophic eukaryote. Secondary endosymbiosis also played an important role: Various protist lineages acquired plastids by engulfing unicellular red or green algae. **3.** Photosynthetic eukaryotes are descended from the endosymbiositic event that gave rise to plastids. Thus, such a discovery would suggest that eukaryotic photosynthesis arose at least twice, in two separate endosymbiotic events in which a cyanobacterium was engulfed by a heterotrophic eukaryote.

Concept Check 25.2

1. Morphologically, choanoflagellates are almost indistinguishable from the collar cells of sponges, a basal animal lineage. Other animals also have collar cells, whereas such cells have never been observed in fungi, plants, or protists other than choanoflagellates. Finally, DNA sequence comparisons indicate that choanoflagellates are the sister group of animals. **2.** The evolution of proteins that attach animal cells to one another was a key step in the origin of multicellularity in animals. Choanoflagellates encode many of the domains found in one such group of animal attachment proteins, the cadherins. Other eukaryotes do not encode these domains; thus, animal cadherin proteins appear to have descended from proteins found in choanoflagellates. Evidence for modification is also clear: As seen in Figure 25.8, the protein domains found in animal cadherins differ in type, number, and location from those found in the ancestral choanoflagellate protein. **3.** Multicellularity originated independently in *Volvox*, plants, and fungi. Since each of these groups arose from different single-celled ancestors, it is likely that their cell-to-cell attachments form using different molecules. (Data from recent molecular studies are consistent with this prediction.)

Concept Check 25.3

1. Many members of the supergroup Excavata have unique cytoskeletal features, and some have an "excavated" feeding groove on one side of their cells; two major clades of excavates are characterized by having reduced mitochondria. The SAR supergroup contains three large clades—stramenopiles, alveolates, and rhizarians—which collectively include diatoms and other key photosynthetic species, protists that move using cilia, and amoebas with threadlike pseudopodia. The supergroup Archaeplastida contains clades that descended from a protist ancestor that engulfed a cyanobacterium, including red algae, green algae, and land plants. Finally, the supergroup Unikonta includes a large clade of amoebas that have lobe- or tube-shaped pseudopodia, as well as animals, fungi, and their close protist relatives. **2.** During photosynthesis, aerobic algae produce O_2 and use CO_2. O_2 is produced as a by-product of the light reactions, while CO_2 is used as an input to the Calvin cycle (the end products of which are sugars). Aerobic algae also perform cellular respiration, which uses O_2 as an input and produces CO_2 as a waste product. **3.** Since the unknown protist is more closely related to diplomonads than to euglenozoans, it must have originated after the diplomonads and parabasalids diverged from the euglenozoans. In addition, since the unknown species has fully functional mitochondria—yet both diplomonads and parabasalids do not—it is likely that the unknown species originated *before* the last common ancestor of the diplomonads and parabasalids.

Concept Check 25.4

1. Because photosynthetic protists constitute the base of aquatic food webs, many aquatic organisms depend on them for food, either directly or indirectly. (In addition, a substantial percentage of the oxygen produced by photosynthesis is made by photosynthetic protists.) **2.** Protists form mutualistic and parasitic associations with other organisms. Examples include photosynthetic dinoflagellates that form a mutualistic symbiosis with coral polyps; parabasalids that form a mutualistic symbiosis with termites; and the stramenopile *Phytophthora ramorum*, a parasite of oak trees. **3.** Corals depend on their dinoflagellate symbionts for nourishment, so coral bleaching would probably cause the corals to die. As the corals died, less food would be available for fishes and other species that eat coral. As a result, populations of these species might decline, and that, in turn, might cause populations of their predators to decline.

Summary of Key Concepts Questions

25.1 All eukaryotes have mitochondria or remnants of these organelles, but not all eukaryotes have plastids. **25.2** Two such examples are described in this chapter: the evolution of multicellularity in *Volvox* and the evolution of multicellularity in animals. In each case, structures or genes present in unicellular ancestors were co-opted and used

for new purposes in the multicellular lineage. In *Volvox*, cells are attached to one another using proteins that are homologous to proteins in the inner cell wall of their unicellular ancestor, *Chlamydomonas*. Likewise, in animals the cadherin proteins that function in cell attachment represent modified versions of proteins that served other purposes in their unicellular, choanoflagellate ancestors.   **25.3** Kingdom Protista has been abandoned because some protists are more closely related to plants, fungi, or animals than they are to other protists. In addition, in the early 1990s many biologists hypothesized that a collection of eukaryotes that seemed to lack mitochondria represented the oldest lineage of living eukaryotes. That hypothesis, known as the "amitochondriate hypothesis," has also been abandoned for two reasons: Species previously thought to lack mitochondria have since been shown to have reduced mitochondria, and DNA sequence data have shown that some of these organisms are not closely related to one another. Finally, morphological studies and DNA sequence analyses suggest that the vast diversity of eukaryotes alive today can be grouped into four very large clades, the eukaryotic "supergroups."
25.4 Sample response: Ecologically important protists include photosynthetic dinoflagellates that provide essential sources of energy to their symbiotic partners, the corals that build coral reefs. Other important protistan symbionts include those that enable termites to digest wood and *Plasmodium*, the pathogen that causes malaria. Photosynthetic protists such as diatoms are among the most important producers in aquatic communities; as such, many other species in aquatic environments depend on them for food.

Test Your Understanding
1. a   **2.** e   **3.** d   **4.** b   **5.** c   **6.** d
7. The two approaches differ in the evolutionary changes they may bring about. A strain of *Wolbachia* that confers resistance to infection by *Plasmodium* and does not harm mosquitoes would spread rapidly through the mosquito population. In this case, natural selection would favor any *Plasmodium* individuals that could overcome the resistance to infection conferred by *Wolbachia*. If insecticides are used, mosquitoes that are resistant to the insecticide would be favored by natural selection. Hence, use of *Wolbachia* could cause evolution in *Plasmodium* populations, while using insecticides could cause evolution in mosquito populations.
9.

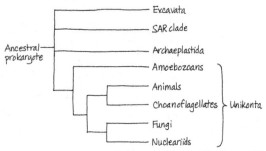

Pathogens that share a relatively recent common ancestor with humans will likely also share metabolic and structural characteristics with humans. Because drugs target the pathogen's metabolism or structure, developing drugs that harm the pathogen but not the patient should be most difficult for pathogens with which we share the most recent evolutionary history. Working backward in time, we can use the phylogenetic tree to determine the order in which humans shared a common ancestor with pathogens in different taxa. This process leads to the prediction that it should be hardest to develop drugs to combat animal pathogens, followed by choanoflagellate pathogens, fungal and nucleariid pathogens, amoebozoans, other protists, and finally prokaryotes.

Chapter 26

Figure Questions
Figure 26.6 The life cycle in Figure 10.6b has alternation of generations; the others do not. Unlike the animal life cycle (Figure 10.6a), in alternation of generations, meiosis produces spores, not gametes. These spores then divide repeatedly by mitosis, ultimately forming a multicellular haploid individual that produces gametes. There is no multicellular haploid stage in the animal life cycle. An alternation of generations life cycle also has a multicellular diploid stage, whereas the life cycle shown in Figure 10.6c does not.   **Figure 26.10** DNA from each of these mushrooms would be identical if each mushroom is part of a single hyphal network, as could well be the case.
Figure 26.20 It contains cells from three generations: (1) the current sporophyte (cells of ploidy 2*n*, found in the seed coat and in the megasporangium remnant that surrounds the spore wall); (2) the female gametophyte (cells of ploidy *n*, found in the food supply); and (3) the sporophyte of the next generation (cells of ploidy 2*n*, found in the embryo).   **Figure 26.24** All taxa in this tree are vascular plants; you should have circled the lycophytes, the earliest-diverging group of vascular plants.

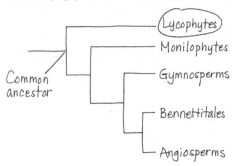

Figure 26.28 Two possible controls would be E−P− and E+P−. Results from an E−P− control could be compared with results from the E−P+ experiment, and results from an E+P− control could be compared with results from the E+P+ experiment. Together, these two comparisons would indicate whether the addition of the pathogen causes an increase in leaf mortality. Results from an E−P− experiment could also be compared with results from the second control (E+P−) to determine whether adding the endophytes has a negative effect on the plant.

Concept Check 26.1
1. Land plants share some key traits only with charophytes, including rings of cellulose-synthesizing complexes and similarity in sperm structure. Comparisons of nuclear and chloroplast genes also indicate that charophytes are the closest living relatives of land plants.   **2.** Possible answers include: spore walls toughened by sporopollenin (protects against harsh environmental conditions); multicellular, dependent embryos (provides nutrients and protection to the developing embryo); cuticle (reduces water loss); stoma (supports photosynthesis by allowing the exchange of CO_2 and O_2 between the outside air and the plant body; stoma close during dry conditions, reducing water loss)   **3.** The earliest fossil evidence of land plants comes from spores that date to 470 million years ago. These spores had a chemical composition similar to that in plant spores but different from the spores of other organisms; the walls of these spores also had structural features found only in the spore walls of certain land plants. Larger plant structures appear in the fossil record by 425 million years ago. By 400 million years ago, fossil evidence shows that a diverse assemblage of plants lived on land; collectively, these plants had key traits not found in their algal ancestors, such as specialized tissues for water transport, stomata, and branched sporophytes.   **4.** The multicellular diploid stage of the life cycle would not produce gametes. Instead, both males and females would produce haploid spores by meiosis. These spores would give rise to multicellular male and female haploid stages—a major change from the single-celled haploid stages (sperm and eggs) that we actually have. The multicellular haploid stages would produce gametes and reproduce sexually. An individual at the multicellular haploid stage of the human life cycle might look like us, or it might look completely different.

Concept Check 26.2
1. Both a fungus and a human are heterotrophs. Many fungi digest their food externally by secreting enzymes into the food and then absorbing the small molecules that result from digestion. Other fungi absorb such small molecules directly from their environment. In contrast, humans (and most other animals) ingest relatively large pieces of food and digest the food within their bodies.   **2.** Mycorrhizae form extensive networks of hyphae through the soil, enabling nutrients to be absorbed more efficiently than a plant can do on its own; this is true today, and similar associations were probably very important for the earliest land plants (which lacked roots). Evidence for the antiquity of mycorrhizal associations includes fossils showing arbuscular mycorrhizae in the early land plant *Aglaophyton* and molecular results showing that genes required for the formation of mycorrhizae are present in liverworts and other basal plant lineages.   **3.** Carbon that enters the plant through stomata is fixed into sugar through photosynthesis. Some of these sugars are absorbed by the fungus that partners with the plant to form mycorrhizae; others are transported within the plant body and used in the plant. Thus, the carbon may be deposited in either the body of the plant or the body of the fungus.

Concept Check 26.3
1. Both seedless vascular plants and bryophytes have flagellated sperm that require moisture for fertilization; this shared similarity poses challenges for these species in arid regions. With respect to key differences, seedless vascular plants have lignified, well-developed vascular tissue, a trait that enables the sporophyte to grow tall and that has transformed life on Earth (via the formation of forests). Seedless vascular plants also have true leaves and roots, which, when compared with bryophytes, provide increased surface area for photosynthesis and improve their ability to extract nutrients from soil.   **2.** Land plants, vascular plants, and seed plants are monophyletic because each of these groups includes the common ancestor of the group and all of the descendants of that common ancestor. The other two categories of plants, the nonvascular plants and the seedless vascular plants, are paraphyletic: These groups do not include all of the descendants of the group's most recent common ancestor.
3. The phylogeny in Figure 26.16 shows that while monilophytes and lycophytes are all seedless vascular plants, monilophytes share a more recent common ancestor with seed plants than with lycophytes. Therefore, we would expect key traits that arose *after* monilophytes diverged from lycophytes but *before* monilophytes diverged from seed plants should be found in the most recent common ancestor of monilophytes and seed plants. The concept of descent with modification indicates that key traits found in the common ancestor of monilophytes and seed plants would likely also be found in that ancestor's descendants, the monilophytes and the seed plants.

Concept Check 26.4
1. The reduced gametophytes of seed plants are nurtured by sporophytes and protected from stress, such as drought conditions and UV radiation. Pollen grains, with walls containing sporopollenin, provide protection during transport by wind or animals; because the sperm-producing male gametophytes are contained within pollen grains, the sperm of seed plants do not require water to reach the eggs. The ovule has a layer of tissue called integument that protects the female gametophyte as it develops from a megaspore. When mature, the ovule forms a seed, which has a thick layer of protective tissue, the seed coat. Seeds also contain a stored supply of food, which provides nourishment for growth after dormancy is broken and the embryo emerges as a seedling.
2. Darwin was troubled by the relatively sudden and geographically widespread appearance of angiosperms in the fossil record. Fossil evidence shows that angiosperms arose and began to diversify over a period of 20–30 million years, a less rapid event than was suggested by the fossils known during Darwin's lifetime. Fossil discoveries have also uncovered extinct lineages of woody seed plants that may have been closely related to angiosperms; one such group, the Bennettitales, had flowerlike structures that may have been pollinated by insects. Phylogenetic analyses have identified *Amborella* as the most basal angiosperm lineage; *Amborella* is woody, and hence its basal position supports the

conclusion (from fossils) that the angiosperm common ancestor was likely woody.
3. No. Their sister clade relationship indicates that these two groups share a more recent common ancestor with each other than they do with other plant groups—but that does not necessarily mean that they originated at the same time. Indeed, while fossil evidence indicates that gymnosperms originated at least 305 million years ago, this does not mean that angiosperms are that old—only that the most recent common ancestor of gymnosperms and angiosperms must be that old.

Concept Check 26.5
1. Lichens, symbiotic associations between fungi and photosynthetic microorganisms (algae or cyanobacteria), break down bare rock surfaces by physically penetrating and chemically altering them. This influences the formation of soil and enables a succession of plants to grow. Plants also affect the formation of soil: Their roots hold soil in place, and leaf litter and other decaying plant parts add nutrients to the soil. Plants also affect the composition of Earth's atmosphere by releasing oxygen to the air and by their impact on the atmospheric concentration of CO_2. **2.** Mutualistic fungi absorb nutrients from their host organism but reciprocate by providing benefits to the host. Important examples include mycorrhizal associations with plant roots (in which fungal hyphae increase the efficiency with which the plant can absorb nutrients such as phosphorous from the soil) and symbiotic endophytes (fungi that live within leaves or other plant parts and provide the plant with benefits such as increased resistance to disease or increased tolerance of heat, drought, or heavy metals). Parasitic fungi also absorb nutrients from host cells but provide no benefits in return. Examples include the ascomycete fungus *Cryphonectria parasitica* (which causes chestnut blight, a disease that has virtually eliminated the once-common chestnut tree from forests of the northeastern United States). **3.** You should have circled steps that represent light energy absorption, photosynthesis, consumers eating producers, uptake of nutrients by plants, and decomposition. **4.** By focusing on cases in which a radial clade shared an immediate common ancestor with a bilateral clade, the researchers could control for effects of time; that is, each radial clade had the same amount of time over which new species could form as did the bilateral clade to which it was compared. As a result, differences in the number of species between the two clades could be attributed to flower shape (rather than to differences in the length of time over which new species could form).

Summary of Key Concepts Questions
26.1 The earliest fossil evidence of land plants comes from spores that date to 470 million years ago. These spores have a chemical composition that matches that found in the spores of extant plants, yet differs from the spores of other organisms. Furthermore, the structure of the walls these spores is only found in the spores of certain land plants (liverworts). Finally, similar spores dating to 450 million years ago have been found embedded in plant cuticle material. **26.2** The body of a multicellular fungus typically consists of thin filaments called hyphae. These filaments form an interwoven mass (mycelium) that penetrates the substrate on which the fungus grows and feeds. Because the individual filaments are thin, the surface-to-volume ratio of the mycelium is maximized, making nutrient absorption highly efficient. Furthermore, fungi that form mycorrhizal associations with plant roots have specialized hyphae (called haustoria) through which they can exchange nutrients with their host plant. The high efficiency with which fungal filaments absorb nutrients, together with the ability of mycorrhizae to exchange nutrients through haustoria, may have provided early land plants (which lacked roots) with greater access to soil nutrients—thus aiding the colonization of land by plants. **26.3** Lignified vascular tissue provided the strength needed to support a tall plant against gravity, as well as a means to transport water and nutrients to plant parts located high above ground. Roots were another key trait, anchoring the plant to the ground and providing additional structural support for plants that grew tall. Tall plants could shade shorter plants, thereby outcompeting them for light. Because the spores of a tall plant disperse farther than the spores of a short plant, it is also likely that tall plants could colonize new habitats more rapidly than short plants. **26.4** The Bennettitales is one of several groups of fossil seed plants that are thought to be more closely related to extant angiosperms than to extant gymnosperms. All of the species in the Bennettitales and such fossil seed plants were woody. The earliest-diverging lineage of extant angiosperms (*Amborella*) is also woody. The fact that both the seed plant ancestors of angiosperms and the most basal taxon of extant angiosperms were woody suggests that the angiosperm common ancestor was woody. **26.5** During photosynthesis, plants convert light energy to the chemical energy of food; that chemical energy supports all life on land, either directly (as when an herbivore eats a plant) or indirectly (as when a predator eats an herbivore that ate a plant). Large animals, such as vertebrate herbivores and their predators, could not survive on land in the absence of land plants. Thus, the presence of plants on land has enabled the myriad biotic interactions that occur among large animal species today. Similarly, plants extract nutrients from the soil and capture carbon (in the form of CO_2) from the air; as a result, those nutrients become available to terrestrial animals. Fungi also play an essential role in increasing the availability of nutrients to other terrestrial organisms. As decomposers, fungi break down the bodies of dead organisms, thereby recycling chemical nutrients to the physical environment. If plants and fungi had not colonized land, photosynthesis and decomposition would still occur—but all terrestrial life would be microbial, and hence biotic interactions among terrestrial organisms would occur on a much smaller scale than they do today.

Test Your Understanding
1. b **2.** e **3.** a. diploid; b. haploid; c. haploid; d. diploid; e. haploid **4.** a **5.** c **6.** e
7.

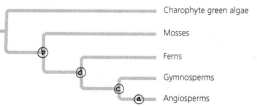

8.

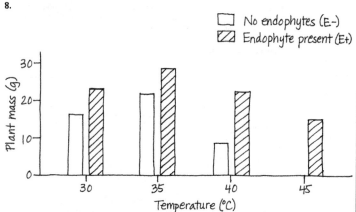

As indicated by the raw data and bar graph, grass plants with endophytes (E+) produced more new shoots and had greater biomass than did grass plants that lacked endophytes (E−). These differences were especially pronounced at the highest soil temperature, where E− grass plants produced no new shoots and had a biomass of zero (indicating they were dead).

Chapter 27

Figure Questions
Figure 27.5 You should have circled the node, shown in the tree diagram at approximately 580 million years ago (mya), that leads to the echinoderm/chordate lineage and to the lineage that gave rise to brachiopods, annelids, molluscs, and arthropods. Although the 580 mya date is estimated, this common ancestor must be at least as old as any of its descendants. Since fossil molluscs date to about 560 mya, the common ancestor represented by the circled branch point must be at least 560 million years old. **Figure 27.10** Cnidaria is the sister phylum in this figure. **Figure 27.12** Such a result would be consistent with the *Ubx* and *abd-A Hox* genes having played a major role in the evolution of increased body segment diversity in arthropods. However, by itself, such a result would simply show that the presence of the *Ubx* and *abd-A Hox* genes was *correlated with* an increase in body segment diversity in arthropods; it would not provide direct experimental evidence that the acquisition of the *Ubx* and *abd-A* genes *caused* an increase in arthropod body segment diversity. **Figure 27.23** Sometime between 380 mya and 340 mya. We can infer this because amphibians must have originated after the most recent common ancestor of *Tulerpeton* and living tetrapods (and that ancestor originated 380 mya), but no later than the date of the earliest known fossils of amphibians (shown in the figure as 340 mya). **Figure 27.26** Crocodilians. Among extant amniotes, crocodilians are the sister group of birds. Hence, it is likely that DNA sequences in birds are more similar to those in crocodilians than they are to those of more distantly related amniotes.
Figure 27.27

Monotremes

Marsupials

Eutherians

Common ancestor of mammals

Figure 27.32 Since the cod are adapting to the pressure of fishing by reproducing at younger ages, their overall number of offspring will be lower. This may cause the population to decline as time goes on, thereby further reducing the population's ability to recover.

Concept Check 27.1
1. The earliest fossil evidence of animal life comes from fossilized steroids indicative of sponges that date to 710 million years ago (mya). This fossil biochemical evidence is consistent with molecular clock results indicating that animals originated 770 mya, sponges originated 700 mya, and cnidarians originated 680 mya. The oldest fossils of large animals date to about 560 mya; these fossils are of sponges, cnidarians, and molluscs. Thus, by 560 mya at the latest, the two early-diverging animal groups, sponges and cnidarians, had diverged from other animal groups. **2.** We cannot infer whether extant animals originated before or after extant choanoflagellates. If correct, the date provided for the most recent common ancestor of choanoflagellates and animals would indicate that extant animals originated some time within the last 900 million years. Fossil biochemical evidence indicates that extant animals (in particular, sponges) originated 710 million years ago. Assuming that this evidence accurately indicates the presence of sponges, we could conclude only that extant animals originated sometime between 900 and 710 million years ago.

Concept Check 27.2
1. The "Cambrian explosion" refers to a relatively short interval of time (535–525 million years ago) during which large forms of many present-day animal phyla first appear

in the fossil record. The evolutionary changes that occurred during this time, such as the appearance of large predators and well-defended prey, were important because they set the stage for many of the key events in the history of life over the last 500 million years. **2.** Following such a change, predators that were best able to kill or catch these well-defended prey might leave more offspring than would other (less capable) predators. As a result, evolution by natural selection in the predator population would likely improve the ability of the predators to eat these prey. If that took place, prey individuals with new defensive adaptations would be favored by natural selection, potentially leading to further changes in predator populations, and so on.

Concept Check 27.3

1. A body plan is a set of morphological and developmental traits, integrated into a functional whole (the living animal). One key feature is the type of symmetry (or absence of symmetry): Sponges lack symmetry, some animals exhibit radial symmetry, and others are bilaterally symmetric. Another key feature is the way tissues are organized. Sponges and a few other animal groups lack true tissues; the tissues of cnidarians and ctenophores originate from two embryonic germ layers, while the tissues of most animals (bilaterians) originate from three germ layers. A third feature found in most bilaterians is a body cavity, a fluid- or air-filled space located between the digestive tract and the outer body wall. **2.** The phylogeny in Figure 27.10 indicates that all animals share a common ancestor; that sponges are basal animals; that Eumetazoa is a clade of animals with true tissues; and that most phyla belong to the clade Bilateria. As for whether the Cambrian explosion consists of three explosions, note that the phylogeny in Figure 27.10 indicates that molluscs are members of Lophotrochozoa, one of the three main groups of bilaterians (the others being Deuterostomia and Ecdysozoa). As discussed in Concept 27.2, the fossil record shows that molluscs were present tens of millions of years before the Cambrian explosion. Thus, long before the Cambrian explosion, the lophotrochozoan clade had formed and was evolving independently of the evolutionary lineages leading to Deuterostomia and Ecdysozoa. Based on the phylogeny in Figure 27.10, we can also conclude that the lineages leading to Deuterostomia and Ecdysozoa were independent of one another before the Cambrian explosion. Since the lineages leading to the three main clades of bilaterians were evolving independently of one another prior to the Cambrian explosion, that explosion could be viewed as consisting of three "explosions," not one. **3.** During the time period covered by this question, a broad range of invertebrate phyla diversified in marine environments. Invertebrates in one of these phyla—Chordata—gave rise to early vertebrates, and those early vertebrates diversified further into two lineages of jawless vertebrates and three lineages of jawed vertebrates. One lineage of jawed vertebrates would ultimately give rise to the tetrapods, the vertebrate lineage that colonized land. But the other lineages of jawed vertebrates—along with the many lineages of invertebrates—continued to diversify in aquatic environments, making it hard to argue that the evolutionary changes that took place were directed toward the origin of terrestrial vertebrates.

Concept Check 27.4

1. The arthropod exoskeleton, which had already evolved in the ocean, allows terrestrial species to retain water and support their bodies on land. Wings allow insects to disperse quickly to new habitats and to find food and mates. The tracheal system allows for efficient gas exchange despite the presence of an exoskeleton. **2.** Descent with modification—the process by which organisms gradually accumulate differences from their ancestors—occurred in the colonization of land by plants as well as the colonization of land by animals. The modifications over time, however, were more extensive in plants than in animals. This was because land plants arose from a small alga with few features that were suitable for life on land. Animals, in contrast, colonized land repeatedly; in each of these events, the animals that colonized land already had a complete digestive tract and well-developed skeletal, muscle, and nerve systems. **3.** The egg came first. The amniotic egg, which all reptiles (including chickens) and all mammals have, arose more than 310 million years ago, long before the first chicken.

Concept Check 27.5

1. The oceans had cloudy waters and low oxygen levels for more than a billion years after the origin of eukaryotes; throughout this time, cyanobacteria were the dominant producers. By the early Cambrian period, the ocean waters were clearer and had higher oxygen levels; in addition, cyanobacteria were less abundant and algae had become the dominant producers. By removing large quantities of cyanobacteria, early filter-feeding animals would have made the waters less cloudy, a change that favored algae (which require more light for photosynthesis than do cyanobacteria). By about 530 million years ago, a variety of large animals were present, leading to dramatic changes in feeding relationships as formidable predators pursued well-defended prey. **2.** Before animals colonized land, terrestrial communities had a simple structure, the main elements of which consisted of producers (early land plants) and decomposers. The colonization of land by animals introduced new types of biotic interactions that involved herbivorous animals that ate plants, detritivores such as millipedes that consumed decaying organic matter, and predators. **3.** Gene flow occurs more readily between nearby than between distant populations; hence, we would predict that gene flow would be higher in the original population than in the remnant populations. And since genetic drift has more pronounced effects in small populations, we would predict that the role of genetic drift would be more pronounced in the remnant populations. Finally, since genetic drift can lead to the fixation of harmful alleles, we would predict that the risk of extinction would be higher in the remnant populations than in the original populations.

Summary of Key Concepts Questions

27.1 Sponge choanocyte cells are similar morphologically to the cells of choanoflagellates; DNA sequences of sponges and choanoflagellates are also very similar. These observations are consistent with the hypothesis that animals descended from a lineage of single-celled eukaryotes similar to present-day choanoflagellates. **27.2** Current hypotheses about the cause of the Cambrian explosion include new predator-prey relationships, an increase in atmospheric oxygen, and an increase in developmental flexibility provided by the origin of *Hox* genes and other genetic changes.

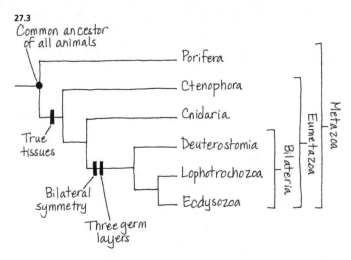

27.3

27.4 The major derived characteristic of the aminiotes is the amniotic egg, which contains four specialized membranes: the amnion, the chorion, the yolk sac, and the allantois. The amniotic egg provides protection to the embryo and allows the embryo to develop on land, eliminating the necessity of a watery environment for reproduction. As a result, the amniotes were able to expand into a wider range of terrestrial habitats than were earlier-diverging tetrapod groups (including the amphibians). **27.5** As organisms interact over time with other organisms and the physical environment, their populations can evolve. The activities of animals have altered the physical structure (for example, the water clarity) of the ocean and fundamentally changed biotic interactions in the sea and on land—thus potentially causing evolutionary change in a wide range of species. Examples include the effects animals have had on evolutionary radiations in parasites and plants, as well as the ongoing evolutionary changes that are taking place in populations that humans hunt for sport or food.

Test Your Understanding

1. b **2.** e **3.** d **4.** a **5.** c **6.** b

7. (a) Because brain size tends to increase consistently in such lineages, we can conclude that natural selection favored the evolution of larger brains and hence that the benefits outweighed the costs. (b) As long as the benefits of brains that are large relative to body size are greater than the costs, large brains can evolve. Natural selection might favor the evolution of brains that are large relative to body size because such brains confer an advantage in obtaining mates and/or an advantage in survival.

(c)

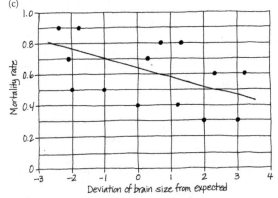

Adult mortality tends to be lower in birds with larger brains.

8. The circled clade should include birds, the two dinosaur lineages, and the common ancestor of the dinosaurs. The phylogeny shows that dinosaurs other than birds are nested between crocodilians and birds. Since crocodilians and birds differ with respect to whether they are endothermic, we cannot use phylogenetic bracketing to predict whether dinosaurs other than birds were endothermic (or not). However, we can conclude that the dinosaur that gave rise to birds was endothermic, as are all birds.

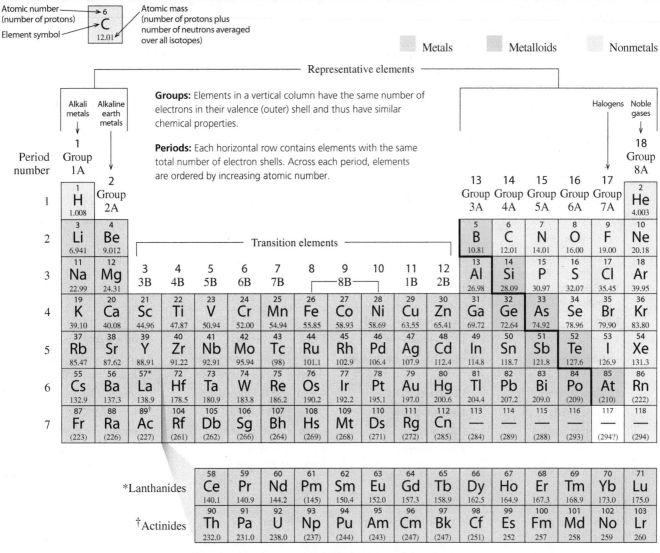

Atomic number (number of protons) — Element symbol — 6 C 12.01 — Atomic mass (number of protons plus number of neutrons averaged over all isotopes)

Metals · Metalloids · Nonmetals

Representative elements

Groups: Elements in a vertical column have the same number of electrons in their valence (outer) shell and thus have similar chemical properties.

Periods: Each horizontal row contains elements with the same total number of electron shells. Across each period, elements are ordered by increasing atomic number.

Transition elements

*Lanthanides

†Actinides

Name (Symbol)	Atomic Number	Name (Symbol)	Atomic Number	Name (Symbol)	Atomic Number	Name (Symbol)	Atomic Number	Name (Symbol)	Atomic Number
Actinium (Ac)	89	Copernicium (Cn)	112	Iridium (Ir)	77	Palladium (Pd)	46	Sodium (Na)	11
Aluminum (Al)	13	Copper (Cu)	29	Iron (Fe)	26	Phosphorus (P)	15	Strontium (Sr)	38
Americium (Am)	95	Curium (Cm)	96	Krypton (Kr)	36	Platinum (Pt)	78	Sulfur (S)	16
Antimony (Sb)	51	Darmstadtium (Ds)	110	Lanthanum (La)	57	Plutonium (Pu)	94	Tantalum (Ta)	73
Argon (Ar)	18	Dubnium (Db)	105	Lawrencium (Lr)	103	Polonium (Po)	84	Technetium (Tc)	43
Arsenic (As)	33	Dysprosium (Dy)	66	Lead (Pb)	82	Potassium (K)	19	Tellurium (Te)	52
Astatine (At)	85	Einsteinium (Es)	99	Lithium (Li)	3	Praseodymium (Pr)	59	Terbium (Tb)	65
Barium (Ba)	56	Erbium (Er)	68	Lutetium (Lu)	71	Promethium (Pm)	61	Thallium (Tl)	81
Berkelium (Bk)	97	Europium (Eu)	63	Magnesium (Mg)	12	Protactinium (Pa)	91	Thorium (Th)	90
Beryllium (Be)	4	Fermium (Fm)	100	Manganese (Mn)	25	Radium (Ra)	88	Thulium (Tm)	69
Bismuth (Bi)	83	Fluorine (F)	9	Meitnerium (Mt)	109	Radon (Rn)	86	Tin (Sn)	50
Bohrium (Bh)	107	Francium (Fr)	87	Mendelevium (Md)	101	Rhenium (Re)	75	Titanium (Ti)	22
Boron (B)	5	Gadolinium (Gd)	64	Mercury (Hg)	80	Rhodium (Rh)	45	Tungsten (W)	74
Bromine (Br)	35	Gallium (Ga)	31	Molybdenum (Mo)	42	Roentgenium (Rg)	111	Uranium (U)	92
Cadmium (Cd)	48	Germanium (Ge)	32	Neodymium (Nd)	60	Rubidium (Rb)	37	Vanadium (V)	23
Calcium (Ca)	20	Gold (Au)	79	Neon (Ne)	10	Ruthenium (Ru)	44	Xenon (Xe)	54
Californium (Cf)	98	Hafnium (Hf)	72	Neptunium (Np)	93	Rutherfordium (Rf)	104	Ytterbium (Yb)	70
Carbon (C)	6	Hassium (Hs)	108	Nickel (Ni)	28	Samarium (Sm)	62	Yttrium (Y)	39
Cerium (Ce)	58	Helium (He)	2	Niobium (Nb)	41	Scandium (Sc)	21	Zinc (Zn)	30
Cesium (Cs)	55	Holmium (Ho)	67	Nitrogen (N)	7	Seaborgium (Sg)	106	Zirconium (Zr)	40
Chlorine (Cl)	17	Hydrogen (H)	1	Nobelium (No)	102	Selenium (Se)	34		
Chromium (Cr)	24	Indium (In)	49	Osmium (Os)	76	Silicon (Si)	14		
Cobalt (Co)	27	Iodine (I)	53	Oxygen (O)	8	Silver (Ag)	47		

Metric Prefixes: 10^9 = giga (G) 10^{-2} = centi (c) 10^{-9} = nano (n)
10^6 = mega (M) 10^{-3} = milli (m) 10^{-12} = pico (p)
10^3 = kilo (k) 10^{-6} = micro (µ) 10^{-15} = femto (f)

Measurement	Unit and Abbreviation	Metric Equivalent	Metric-to-English Conversion Factor	English-to-Metric Conversion Factor
Length	1 kilometer (km)	= 1,000 (10^3) meters	1 km = 0.62 mile	1 mile = 1.61 km
	1 meter (m)	= 100 (10^2) centimeters = 1,000 millimeters	1 m = 1.09 yards 1 m = 3.28 feet 1 m = 39.37 inches	1 yard = 0.914 m 1 foot = 0.305 m
	1 centimeter (cm)	= 0.01 (10^{-2}) meter	1 cm = 0.394 inch	1 foot = 30.5 cm 1 inch = 2.54 cm
	1 millimeter (mm)	= 0.001 (10^{-3}) meter	1 mm = 0.039 inch	
	1 micrometer (µm) (formerly micron, µ)	= 10^{-6} meter (10^{-3} mm)		
	1 nanometer (nm) (formerly millimicron, mµ)	= 10^{-9} meter (10^{-3} µm)		
	1 angstrom (Å)	= 10^{-10} meter (10^{-4} µm)		
Area	1 hectare (ha)	= 10,000 square meters	1 ha = 2.47 acres	1 acre = 0.405 ha
	1 square meter (m^2)	= 10,000 square centimeters	1 m^2 = 1.196 square yards 1 m^2 = 10.764 square feet	1 square yard = 0.8361 m^2 1 square foot = 0.0929 m^2
	1 square centimeter (cm^2)	= 100 square millimeters	1 cm^2 = 0.155 square inch	1 square inch = 6.4516 cm^2
Mass	1 metric ton (t)	= 1,000 kilograms	1 t = 1.103 tons	1 ton = 0.907 t
	1 kilogram (kg)	= 1,000 grams	1 kg = 2.205 pounds	1 pound = 0.4536 kg
	1 gram (g)	= 1,000 milligrams	1 g = 0.0353 ounce 1 g = 15.432 grains	1 ounce = 28.35 g
	1 milligram (mg)	= 10^{-3} gram	1 mg = approx. 0.015 grain	
	1 microgram (µg)	= 10^{-6} gram		
Volume (solids)	1 cubic meter (m^3)	= 1,000,000 cubic centimeters	1 m^3 = 1.308 cubic yards 1 m^3 = 35.315 cubic feet	1 cubic yard = 0.7646 m^3 1 cubic foot = 0.0283 m^3
	1 cubic centimeter (cm^3 or cc)	= 10^{-6} cubic meter	1 cm^3 = 0.061 cubic inch	1 cubic inch = 16.387 cm^3
	1 cubic millimeter (mm^3)	= 10^{-9} cubic meter = 10^{-3} cubic centimeter		
Volume (liquids and gases)	1 kiloliter (kL or kl)	= 1,000 liters	1 kL = 264.17 gallons	
	1 liter (L or l)	= 1,000 milliliters	1 L = 0.264 gallon 1 L = 1.057 quarts	1 gallon = 3.785 L 1 quart = 0.946 L
	1 milliliter (mL or ml)	= 10^{-3} liter = 1 cubic centimeter	1 mL = 0.034 fluid ounce 1 mL = approx. ¼ teaspoon 1 mL = approx. 15–16 drops (gtt.)	1 quart = 946 mL 1 pint = 473 mL 1 fluid ounce = 29.57 mL 1 teaspoon = approx. 5 mL
	1 microliter (µL or µl)	= 10^{-6} liter (10^{-3} milliliter)		
Pressure	1 megapascal (MPa)	= 1,000 kilopascals	1 MPa = 10 bars	1 bar = 0.1 MPa
	1 kilopascal (kPa)	= 1,000 pascals	1 kPa = 0.01 bar	1 bar = 100 kPa
	1 pascal (Pa)	= 1 newton/m^2 (N/m^2)	1 Pa = 1.0×10^{-5} bar	1 bar = 1.0×10^5 Pa
Time	1 second (s or sec)	= ¹⁄₆₀ minute		
	1 millisecond (ms or msec)	= 10^{-3} second		
Temperature	Degrees Celsius (°C) (0 K [Kelvin] = −273.15°C)		°F = 9/5°C + 32	°C = 5/9 (°F − 32)

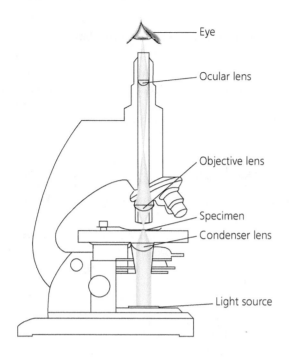

Eye
Ocular lens
Objective lens
Specimen
Condenser lens
Light source

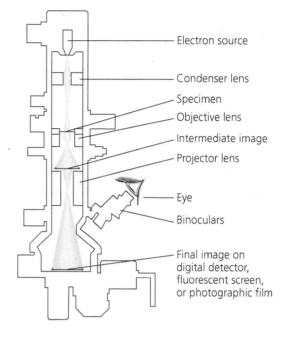

Electron source
Condenser lens
Specimen
Objective lens
Intermediate image
Projector lens
Eye
Binoculars
Final image on digital detector, fluorescent screen, or photographic film

Light Microscope

In light microscopy, light is focused on a specimen by a glass condenser lens; the image is then magnified by an objective lens and an ocular lens, for projection on the eye, digital camera, digital video camera, or photographic film.

Electron Microscope

In electron microscopy, a beam of electrons (top of the microscope) is used instead of light, and electromagnets are used instead of glass lenses. The electron beam is focused on the specimen by a condenser lens; the image is magnified by an objective lens and a projector lens for projection on a digital detector, fluorescent screen, or photographic film.

This appendix presents a taxonomic classification for the major extant groups of organisms discussed in this text; not all phyla are included. The classification presented here is based on the three-domain system, which assigns the two major groups of prokaryotes, bacteria and archaea, to separate domains (with eukaryotes making up the third domain).

Various alternative classification schemes are discussed in Unit Four of the text. The taxonomic turmoil includes debates about the number and boundaries of kingdoms and about the alignment of the Linnaean classification hierarchy with the findings of modern cladistic analysis. In this review, asterisks (*) indicate currently recognized phyla thought by some systematists to be paraphyletic.

DOMAIN BACTERIA

- **Proteobacteria**
- **Chlamydia**
- **Spirochetes**
- **Cyanobacteria**
- **Gram-positive bacteria**

DOMAIN ARCHAEA

- **Korarchaeota**
- **Euryarchaeota**
- **Crenarchaeota**
- **Nanoarchaeota**

DOMAIN EUKARYA

In the phylogenetic hypothesis we present in Chapter 25, major clades of eukaryotes are grouped together in the four "supergroups" listed in blue type. Formerly, all the eukaryotes generally called protists were assigned to a single kingdom, Protista. However, advances in systematics have made it clear that some protists are more closely related to plants, fungi, or animals than they are to other protists. As a result, the kingdom Protista has been abandoned.

Excavata
- Diplomonadida (diplomonads)
- Parabasala (parabasalids)
- Euglenozoa (euglenozoans)
  Kinetoplastida (kinetoplastids)
  Euglenophyta (euglenids)

The "SAR" clade
- Stramenopila (stramenopiles)
  Bacillariophyta (diatoms)
  Phaeophyta (brown algae)
- Alveolata (alveolates)
  Dinoflagellata (dinoflagellates)
  Apicomplexa (apicomplexans)
  Ciliophora (ciliates)

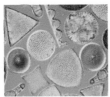

- Rhizaria
  Foraminifera (forams)
  Cercozoa (cercozoans)

Archaeplastida
- Rhodophyta (red algae)
- Chlorophyta (green algae: chlorophytes)
- Charophyta (green algae: charophytes)
- Plantae
  Phylum Hepatophyta (liverworts) ⎫ Nonvascular
  Phylum Bryophyta (mosses)   ⎬ plants (bryophytes)
  Phylum Anthocerophyta (hornworts)⎭
  Phylum Lycophyta (lycophytes)   ⎫ Seedless vascular
  Phylum Monilophyta (ferns, horsetails, ⎬ plants
    whisk ferns)   ⎭
  Phylum Ginkgophyta (ginkgo)   ⎫
  Phylum Cycadophyta (cycads)   ⎪
  Phylum Gnetophyta (gnetophytes) ⎬ Gymnosperms ⎫
  Phylum Coniferophyta (conifers) ⎪   ⎬ Seed
  Phylum Anthophyta (flowering   ⎫   ⎪ plants
    plants)   ⎬ Angiosperms ⎭

DOMAIN EUKARYA, continued

Unikonta
- Amoebozoa (amoebozoans)
  - Dictyostelida (cellular slime molds)
  - Entamoeba (entamoebas)
- Nucleariida (nucleariids)
- Fungi
  - *Phylum Chytridiomycota (chytrids)
  - *Phylum Zygomycota (zygomycetes)
  - Phylum Glomeromycota (glomeromycetes)
  - Phylum Ascomycota (sac fungi)
  - Phylum Basidiomycota (club fungi)

- Choanoflagellata (choanoflagellates)
- Animalia
  - Phylum Porifera (sponges)
  - Phylum Ctenophora (comb jellies)
  - Phylum Cnidaria (cnidarians)
  - Lophotrochozoa (lophotrochozoans)
  - Phylum Platyhelminthes (flatworms)
  - Phylum Ectoprocta (ectoprocts)
  - Phylum Brachiopoda (brachiopods)
  - Phylum Rotifera (rotifers)
  - Phylum Mollusca (molluscs)
  - Phylum Annelida (segmented worms)

Ecdysozoa (ecdysozoans)
  - Phylum Nematoda (roundworms)
  - Phylum Arthropoda (This survey groups arthropods into a single phylum, but some zoologists now split the arthropods into multiple phyla.)
    - Subphylum Chelicerata (horseshoe crabs, arachnids)
    - Subphylum Myriapoda (millipedes, centipedes)
    - Subphylum Hexapoda (insects, springtails)
    - Subphylum Crustacea (crustaceans)
  - Phylum Onychophora (velvet worms)
Deuterostomia (deuterostomes)
  - Phylum Hemichordata (hemichordates)
  - Phylum Echinodermata (echinoderms)
  - Phylum Chordata (chordates)
    - Subphylum Cephalochordata (lancelets)
    - Subphylum Urochordata (tunicates)
    - Subphylum Craniata (craniates)
      - Myxini (hagfishes)
      - Petromyzontida (lampreys)
      - Chondrichthyes (sharks, rays, chimaeras)
      - Actinopterygii (ray-finned fishes)
      - Actinistia (coelacanths)
      - Dipnoi (lungfishes)
      - Amphibia (amphibians)
      - Reptilia (tuataras, lizards, snakes, turtles, crocodilians, birds)
      - Mammalia (mammals)

Vertebrates

Graphs

Graphs provide a visual representation of numerical data. They may reveal patterns or trends in the data that are not easy to recognize in a table. A graph is a diagram that shows how one variable in a data set is related (or perhaps not related) to another variable. If one variable is dependent on the other, the dependent variable is typically plotted on the y-axis and the independent variable on the x-axis. Types of graphs that are frequently used in biology include scatter plots, line graphs, bar graphs, and histograms.

A **scatter plot** is used when the data for all variables are numerical and continuous. Each piece of data is represented by a point. In a **line graph**, each data point is connected to the next point in the data set with a straight line, as in the graph below.

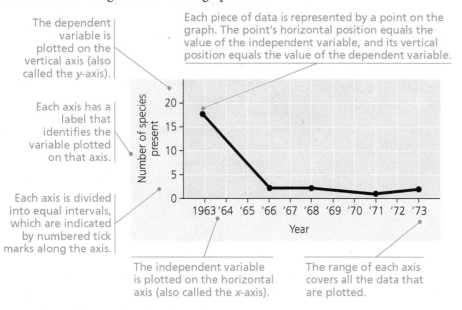

The dependent variable is plotted on the vertical axis (also called the y-axis).

Each axis has a label that identifies the variable plotted on that axis.

Each axis is divided into equal intervals, which are indicated by numbered tick marks along the axis.

Each piece of data is represented by a point on the graph. The point's horizontal position equals the value of the independent variable, and its vertical position equals the value of the dependent variable.

The independent variable is plotted on the horizontal axis (also called the x-axis).

The range of each axis covers all the data that are plotted.

Two or more data sets can be plotted on the same line graph to show how two dependent variables are related to the same independent variable.

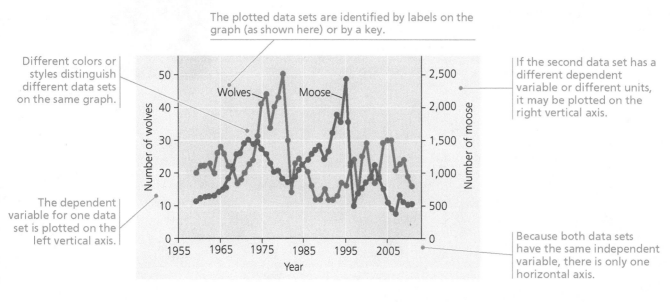

The plotted data sets are identified by labels on the graph (as shown here) or by a key.

Different colors or styles distinguish different data sets on the same graph.

The dependent variable for one data set is plotted on the left vertical axis.

If the second data set has a different dependent variable or different units, it may be plotted on the right vertical axis.

Because both data sets have the same independent variable, there is only one horizontal axis.

In some scatter-plot graphs, a straight or curved line is drawn through the entire data set to show the general trend in the data. A straight line that mathematically fits the data best is called a *regression line*. Alternatively, a mathematical function that best fits the data may describe a curved line, often termed a *best-fit curve*.

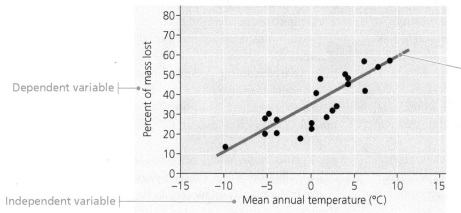

The regression line can be expressed as a mathematical equation. It allows you to predict the value of the dependent variable for any value of the independent variable within the range of the data set and, less commonly, beyond the range of the data.

A **bar graph** is a kind of graph in which the independent variable represents groups or nonnumerical categories and the values of the dependent variable(s) are shown by bars.

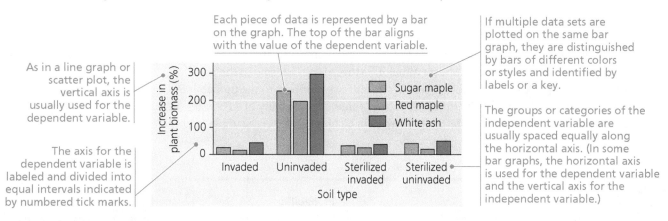

Each piece of data is represented by a bar on the graph. The top of the bar aligns with the value of the dependent variable.

If multiple data sets are plotted on the same bar graph, they are distinguished by bars of different colors or styles and identified by labels or a key.

As in a line graph or scatter plot, the vertical axis is usually used for the dependent variable.

The axis for the dependent variable is labeled and divided into equal intervals indicated by numbered tick marks.

The groups or categories of the independent variable are usually spaced equally along the horizontal axis. (In some bar graphs, the horizontal axis is used for the dependent variable and the vertical axis for the independent variable.)

A variant of a bar graph called a **histogram** can be made for numeric data by first grouping, or "binning," the variable plotted on the x-axis into intervals of equal width. The "bins" may be integers or ranges of numbers. In the histogram below, the intervals are 25 mg/dL wide. The height of each bar shows the percent (or alternatively, the number) of experimental subjects whose characteristics can be described by one of the intervals plotted on the x-axis.

The height of this bar shows the percent of individuals (about 4%) whose plasma LDL cholesterol levels are in the range indicated on the x-axis.

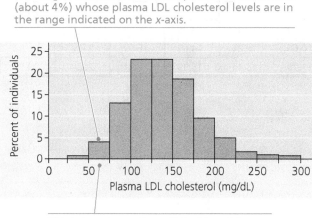

This interval runs from 50 to 74 mg/dL.

Glossary of Scientific Inquiry Terms

See Concept 1.3 for more discussion of the process of scientific inquiry.

control group In a controlled experiment, a set of subjects that lacks (or does not receive) the specific factor being tested. Ideally, the control group should be identical to the experimental group in other respects.

deductive reasoning A type of logic in which specific results are predicted from a general premise.

dependent variable In an experiment, a variable whose value is influenced by changes in another variable (the independent variable).

experimental group A set of subjects that has (or receives) the specific factor being tested in a controlled experiment.

hypothesis A testable explanation for a set of observations based on the available data and guided by inductive reasoning. A hypothesis is narrower in scope than a theory.

independent variable A variable whose value is manipulated or changed during an experiment to reveal possible effects on another variable (the dependent variable).

inductive reasoning A type of logic in which generalizations are based on a large number of specific observations.

model A physical or conceptual representation of a natural phenomenon.

prediction In deductive reasoning, a forecast that follows logically from a hypothesis. By testing predictions, experiments may allow certain hypotheses to be rejected.

theory An explanation that is broader in scope than a hypothesis, generates new hypotheses, and is supported by a large body of evidence.

Chi-Square (χ^2) Distribution Table

To use the table, find the row that corresponds to the degrees of freedom in your data set. (The degrees of freedom is the number of categories of data minus 1.) Move along that row to the pair of values that your calculated χ^2 value lies between. Move up from those numbers to the probabilities at the top of the columns to find the probability range for your χ^2 value. A probability of 0.05 or less is generally considered significant. See the Scientific Skills Exercise in Chapter 12 for an example of how to use the chi-square test.

Degrees of Freedom (df)	Probability										
	0.95	0.90	0.80	0.70	0.50	0.30	0.20	0.10	0.05	0.01	0.001
1	0.004	0.02	0.06	0.15	0.45	1.07	1.64	2.71	3.84	6.64	10.83
2	0.10	0.21	0.45	0.71	1.39	2.41	3.22	4.61	5.99	9.21	13.82
3	0.35	0.58	1.01	1.42	2.37	3.66	4.64	6.25	7.82	11.34	16.27
4	0.71	1.06	1.65	2.19	3.36	4.88	5.99	7.78	9.49	13.28	18.47
5	1.15	1.61	2.34	3.00	4.35	6.06	7.29	9.24	11.07	15.09	20.52
6	1.64	2.20	3.07	3.83	5.35	7.23	8.56	10.64	12.59	16.81	22.46
7	2.17	2.83	3.82	4.67	6.35	8.38	9.80	12.02	14.07	18.48	24.32
8	2.73	3.49	4.59	5.53	7.34	9.52	11.03	13.36	15.51	20.09	26.12
9	3.33	4.17	5.38	6.39	8.34	10.66	12.24	14.68	16.92	21.67	27.88
10	3.94	4.87	6.18	7.27	9.34	11.78	13.44	15.99	18.31	23.21	29.59

APPENDIX F SCIENTIFIC SKILLS REVIEW

Unit Openers **Unit 2 clockwise from top left** Christopher Futcher/iStockphoto.com; Mendel Museum; Peter Menzel/Photo Researchers, Inc.; National Institute of Health; S Meyers/AGE Fotostock America, Inc.; Andreas Werth, Aquatic Photography (andreaswerth.net); Bier Ethan; NIBSC/Photo Researchers, Inc.; Karen Huntt/Corbis; **Unit 3 clockwise from top left** ROBERT SISSON/National Geographic Stock; Pierson Hill; Rosemary B. Grant; Mark Jones/AGE Fotostock America Inc.; Gerhard Boeggemann; **Unit 4 clockwise from top left** B Christopher/Alamy; Biophoto Associates/Photo Researchers, Inc.; Martin Rugner/AGE Fotostock America Inc.; Stephen Dalton/Nature Picture Library.

Preface John Hawkins/FLPA

Detailed Contents p. xxv top Karen Huntt/Corbis; **p. xxvi** Wayne Lynch/AGE Fotostock America, Inc.; **page xxvii top** Gerhard Boeggemann; **p. xxvii top** Biophoto Associates/Photo Researchers, Inc.; **p. xxviii top left** Martin Rugner/AGE Fotostock America Inc.; **p. xxviii top right** Anup Shah/Image State/Alamy; **p. xxviii bottom right** Dan Cooper,

Pronunciation Key

Pronounce

ā	as in	ace
a/ah		ash
ch		chose
ē		meet
e/eh		bet
g		game
ī		ice
i		hit
ks		box
kw		quick
ng		song
ō		robe
o		ox
oy		boy
s		say
sh		shell
th		thin
ū		boot
u/uh		up
z		zoo

′ = primary accent
′ = secondary accent

5′ cap A modified form of guanine nucleotide added onto the end of a pre-mRNA molecule.

A site One of a ribosome's three binding sites for tRNA during translation. The A site holds the tRNA carrying the next amino acid to be added to the polypeptide chain. (A stands for aminoacyl tRNA.)

ABC hypothesis A model of flower formation identifying three classes of organ identity genes that direct formation of the four types of floral organs.

abiotic (ā′-bī-ot′-ik) Nonliving; referring to the physical and chemical properties of an environment.

abscisic acid (ABA) (ab-sis′-ik) A plant hormone that slows growth, often antagonizing the actions of growth hormones. Two of its many effects are to promote seed dormancy and facilitate drought tolerance.

absorption The third stage of food processing in animals: the uptake of small nutrient molecules by an organism's body.

absorption spectrum The range of a pigment's ability to absorb various wavelengths of light; also a graph of such a range.

accessory fruit A fruit, or assemblage of fruits, in which the fleshy parts are derived largely or entirely from tissues other than the ovary.

acetyl CoA Acetyl coenzyme A; the entry compound for the citric acid cycle in cellular respiration, formed from a two-carbon fragment of pyruvate attached to a coenzyme.

acetylcholine (as′-uh-til-kō′-lēn) One of the most common neurotransmitters; functions by binding to receptors and altering the permeability of the postsynaptic membrane to specific ions, either depolarizing or hyperpolarizing the membrane.

acid A substance that increases the hydrogen ion concentration of a solution.

acrosome (ak′-ruh-sōm) A vesicle in the tip of a sperm containing hydrolytic enzymes and other proteins that help the sperm reach the egg.

actin (ak′-tin) A globular protein that links into chains, two of which twist helically about each other, forming microfilaments (actin filaments) in muscle and other kinds of cells.

action potential An electrical signal that propagates (travels) along the membrane of a neuron or other excitable cell as a nongraded (all-or-none) depolarization.

action spectrum A graph that profiles the relative effectiveness of different wavelengths of radiation in driving a particular process.

activation energy The amount of energy that reactants must absorb before a chemical reaction will start; also called free energy of activation.

activator A protein that binds to DNA and stimulates gene transcription. In prokaryotes, activators bind in or near the promoter; in eukaryotes, activators generally bind to control elements in enhancers.

active immunity Long-lasting immunity conferred by the action of B cells and T cells and the resulting B and T memory cells specific for a pathogen. Active immunity can develop as a result of natural infection or immunization.

active site The specific region of an enzyme that binds the substrate and that forms the pocket in which catalysis occurs.

active transport The movement of a substance across a cell membrane against its concentration or electrochemical gradient, mediated by specific transport proteins and requiring an expenditure of energy.

adaptation Inherited characteristic of an organism that enhances its survival and reproduction in a specific environment.

adaptive evolution A process in which traits that enhance survival or reproduction tend to increase in frequency in a population over time.

adaptive immunity A vertebrate-specific defense that is mediated by B lymphocytes (B cells) and T lymphocytes (T cells) and that exhibits specificity, memory, and selfnonself recognition; also called acquired immunity.

adaptive radiation Period of evolutionary change in which groups of organisms form many new species whose adaptations allow them to fill different ecological roles in their communities.

addition rule A rule of probability stating that the probability of any one of two or more mutually exclusive events occurring can be determined by adding their individual probabilities.

adenosine triphosphate *See* ATP (adenosine triphosphate).

adhesion The clinging of one substance to another, such as water to plant cell walls, by means of hydrogen bonds.

aerobic respiration A catabolic pathway for organic molecules, using oxygen (O_2) as the final electron acceptor in an electron transport chain and ultimately producing ATP. This is the most efficient catabolic pathway and is carried out in most eukaryotic cells and many prokaryotic organisms.

aggregate fruit A fruit derived from a single flower that has more than one carpel.

AIDS (acquired immunodeficiency syndrome) The symptoms and signs present during the late stages of HIV infection, defined by a specified reduction in the number of T cells and the appearance of characteristic secondary infections.

alcohol fermentation Glycolysis followed by the reduction of pyruvate to ethyl alcohol, regenerating NAD^+ and releasing carbon dioxide.

aldosterone (al-dos′-tuh-rōn) A steroid hormone that acts on tubules of the kidney to regulate the transport of sodium ions (Na^+) and potassium ions (K^+).

alga (plural, **algae**) Member of a diverse collection of photosynthetic protists that includes unicellular and multicellular forms. Algal species are included in three eukaryote supergroups (Excavata, "SAR" clade, and Archaeplastida).

alimentary canal (al′-uh-men′-tuh-rē) A complete digestive tract, consisting of a tube running between a mouth and an anus.

allele (uh-lē′-ul) Any of the alternative versions of a gene that may produce distinguishable phenotypic effects.

allergen An antigen that triggers an exaggerated immune response.

allopatric speciation (al'-uh-pat'-rik) The formation of new species in populations that are geographically isolated from one another.

allopolyploid (al'-ō-pol'-ē-ployd) A fertile individual that has more than two chromosome sets as a result of two different species interbreeding and combining their chromosomes.

allosteric regulation The binding of a regulatory molecule to a protein at one site that affects the function of the protein at a different site.

alpha (α) helix (al'-fuh hē'-liks) A coiled region constituting one form of the secondary structure of proteins, arising from a specific pattern of hydrogen bonding between atoms of the polypeptide backbone (not the side chains).

alternation of generations A life cycle in which there is both a multicellular diploid form, the sporophyte, and a multicellular haploid form, the gametophyte; characteristic of plants and some algae.

alternative RNA splicing A type of eukaryotic gene regulation at the RNA-processing level in which different mRNA molecules are produced from the same primary transcript, depending on which RNA segments are treated as exons and which as introns.

altruism (al'-trū-iz-um) Selflessness; behavior that reduces an individual's fitness while increasing the fitness of another individual.

alveolates (al-vē'-uh-lets) One of the three major subgroups for which the "SAR" eukaryotic supergroup is named. Alveolate protists have membrane-enclosed sacs (alveoli) located just under the plasma membrane.

alveolus (al-vē'-uh-lus) (plural, **alveoli**) One of the dead-end air sacs where gas exchange occurs in a mammalian lung.

amino acid (uh-mēn'-ō) An organic molecule possessing both a carboxyl and an amino group. Amino acids serve as the monomers of polypeptides.

amino group A chemical group consisting of a nitrogen atom bonded to two hydrogen atoms; can act as a base in solution, accepting a hydrogen ion and acquiring a charge of 1+.

aminoacyl-tRNA synthetase An enzyme that joins each amino acid to the appropriate tRNA.

ammonia A small, toxic molecule (NH_3) produced by nitrogen fixation or as a metabolic waste product of protein and nucleic acid metabolism.

amniote (am'-nē-ōt) Member of a clade of tetrapods named for a key derived character, the amniotic egg, which contains specialized membranes, including the fluid-filled amnion, that protect the embryo. Amniotes include mammals as well as birds and other reptiles.

amniotic egg An egg that contains specialized membranes that function in protection, nourishment, and gas exchange. The amniotic egg was a major evolutionary innovation, allowing embryos to develop on land in a fluid-filled sac, thus reducing the dependence of tetrapods on water for reproduction.

amoeba (uh-mē'-buh) A member of one of several groups of unicellular eukaryotes that have pseudopodia.

amoebocyte (uh-mē'-buh-sīt') An amoeba-like cell that moves by pseudopodia and is found in most animals. Depending on the species, it may digest and distribute food, dispose of wastes, form skeletal fibers, fight infections, or change into other cell types.

amoebozoan (uh-mē'-buh-zō'-an) A protist in a clade that includes many species with lobe- or tube-shaped pseudopodia.

amphibian Member of the tetrapod class Amphibia, including salamanders, frogs, and caecilians.

amphipathic (am'-fē-path'-ik) Having both a hydrophilic region and a hydrophobic region.

amplification The strengthening of stimulus energy during transduction.

amylase (am'-uh-lās') An enzyme that hydrolyzes starch (a glucose polymer from plants) and glycogen (a glucose polymer from animals) into smaller polysaccharides and the disaccharide maltose.

anabolic pathway (an'-uh-bol'-ik) A metabolic pathway that consumes energy to synthesize a complex molecule from simpler molecules.

anaerobic respiration (an-er-ō'-bik) A catabolic pathway in which inorganic molecules other than oxygen accept electrons at the "downhill" end of electron transport chains.

analogous Having characteristics that are similar because of convergent evolution, not homology.

analogy (an-al'-uh-jē) Similarity between two species that is due to convergent evolution rather than to descent from a common ancestor with the same trait.

anaphase The fourth stage of mitosis, in which the chromatids of each chromosome have separated and the daughter chromosomes are moving to the poles of the cell.

anatomy The structure of an organism.

anchorage dependence The requirement that a cell must be attached to a substratum in order to initiate cell division.

aneuploidy (an'-yū-ploy'-dē) A chromosomal aberration in which one or more chromosomes are present in extra copies or are deficient in number.

angiosperm (an'-jē-ō-sperm) A flowering plant, which forms seeds inside a protective chamber called an ovary.

angiotensin II A peptide hormone that stimulates constriction of precapillary arterioles and increases reabsorption of NaCl and water by the proximal tubules of the kidney, increasing blood pressure and volume.

anion (an'-ī-on) A negatively charged ion.

anterior Pertaining to the front, or head, of a bilaterally symmetric animal.

anterior pituitary A portion of the pituitary that develops from non-neural tissue; consists of endocrine cells that synthesize and secrete several tropic and nontropic hormones.

anther In an angiosperm, the terminal pollen sac of a stamen, where pollen grains containing sperm-producing male gametophytes form.

antibody A protein secreted by plasma cells (differentiated B cells) that binds to a particular antigen; also called immunoglobulin. All antibodies have the same Y-shaped structure and in their monomer form consist of two identical heavy chains and two identical light chains.

anticodon (an'-tī-kō'-don) A nucleotide triplet at one end of a tRNA molecule that base-pairs with a particular complementary codon on an mRNA molecule.

antidiuretic hormone (ADH) (an'-tī-dī-yū-ret'-ik) A peptide hormone, also known as vasopressin, that promotes water retention by the kidneys. Produced in the hypothalamus and released from the posterior pituitary, ADH also functions in the brain.

antigen (an'-ti-jen) A substance that elicits an immune response by binding to receptors of B cells, antibodies, or T cells.

antigen presentation The process by which an MHC molecule binds to a fragment of an intracellular protein antigen and carries it to the cell surface, where it is displayed and can be recognized by a T cell.

antigen receptor The general term for a surface protein, located on B cells and T cells, that binds to antigens, initiating adaptive immune responses. The antigen receptors on B cells are called B cell receptors, and the antigen receptors on T cells are called T cell receptors.

antigen-presenting cell A cell that upon ingesting pathogens or internalizing pathogen proteins generates peptide fragments that are bound by class II MHC molecules and subsequently displayed on the cell surface to T cells. Macrophages, dendritic cells, and B cells are the primary antigen-presenting cells.

antiparallel Referring to the arrangement of the sugar-phosphate backbones in a DNA double helix (they run in opposite 5' → 3' directions).

aphotic zone (ā'-fō'-tik) The part of an ocean or lake beneath the photic zone, where light does not penetrate sufficiently for photosynthesis to occur.

apical bud (ā'-pik-ul) A bud at the tip of a plant stem; also called a terminal bud.

apical dominance (ā′-pik-ul) Tendency for growth to be concentrated at the tip of a plant shoot, because the apical bud partially inhibits axillary bud growth.

apical meristem (ā′-pik-ul mār′-uh-stem) Embryonic plant tissue in the tips of roots and buds of shoots. The dividing cells of an apical meristem enable the plant to grow in length.

apicomplexan (ap′-ē-kom-pleks′-un) A protist in a clade that includes many species that parasitize animals. Some apicomplexans cause human disease.

apomixis (ap′-uh-mik′-sis) The ability of some plant species to reproduce asexually through seeds without fertilization by a male gamete.

apoplast (ap′-ō-plast) Everything external to the plasma membrane of a plant cell, including cell walls, intercellular spaces, and the space within dead structures such as xylem vessels and tracheids.

apoptosis (ā-puh-tō′-sus) A type of programmed cell death that is brought about by activation of enzymes that break down many chemical components in the cell.

aposematic coloration (ap′-ō-si-mat′-ik) The bright warning coloration of many animals with effective physical or chemical defenses.

appendix A small, finger-like extension of the vertebrate cecum; contains a mass of white blood cells that contribute to immunity.

aquaporin A channel protein in the plasma membrane of a plant, animal, or microorganism cell that specifically facilitates osmosis, the diffusion of free water across the membrane.

aqueous solution (ā′-kwē-us) A solution in which water is the solvent.

arbuscular mycorrhizae (ar-bus′-kyū-lur mī′-kō-rī′-zē) Associations of a fungus with a plant root system in which the fungus causes the invagination of the host (plant) cells' plasma membranes.

arbuscular mycorrhizal fungus A symbiotic fungus whose hyphae grow through the cell wall of plant roots and extend into the root cell (enclosed in tubes formed by invagination of the root cell plasma membrane).

Archaea (ar′-kē′-uh) One of two prokaryotic domains, the other being Bacteria.

Archaeplastida (ar′-kē-plas′-tid-uh) One of four supergroups of eukaryotes proposed in a current hypothesis of the evolutionary history of eukaryotes. This monophyletic group, which includes red algae, green algae, and land plants, descended from an ancient protist ancestor that engulfed a cyanobacterium. *See also* Excavata, "SAR" clade, and Unikonta.

artery A vessel that carries blood away from the heart to organs throughout the body.

arthropod A segmented, molting bilaterian animal with a hard exoskeleton and jointed appendages. Familiar examples include insects, spiders, millipedes, and crabs.

artificial selection The selective breeding of domesticated plants and animals to encourage the occurrence of desirable traits.

asexual reproduction The generation of offspring from a single parent that occurs without the fusion of gametes (by budding, division of a single cell, or division of the entire organism into two or more parts). In most cases, the offspring are genetically identical to the parent.

associative learning The acquired ability to associate one environmental feature (such as a color) with another (such as danger).

aster A radial array of short microtubules that extends from each centrosome toward the plasma membrane in an animal cell undergoing mitosis.

astrocyte A glial cell with diverse functions, including providing structural support for neurons, regulating the interstitial environment, facilitating synaptic transmission, and assisting in regulating the blood supply to the brain.

atherosclerosis A cardiovascular disease in which fatty deposits called plaques develop in the inner walls of the arteries, obstructing the arteries and causing them to harden.

atom The smallest unit of matter that retains the properties of an element.

atomic mass The total mass of an atom, which is the mass in grams of 1 mole of the atom.

atomic nucleus An atom's dense central core, containing protons and neutrons.

atomic number The number of protons in the nucleus of an atom, unique for each element and designated by a subscript.

ATP (adenosine triphosphate) (a-den′-ō-sēn trī-fos′-fāt) An adenine-containing nucleoside triphosphate that releases free energy when its phosphate bonds are hydrolyzed. This energy is used to drive endergonic reactions in cells.

ATP synthase A complex of several membrane proteins that functions in chemiosmosis with adjacent electron transport chains, using the energy of a hydrogen ion (proton) concentration gradient to make ATP. ATP synthases are found in the inner mitochondrial membranes of eukaryotic cells and in the plasma membranes of prokaryotes.

atrioventricular (AV) node A region of specialized heart muscle tissue between the left and right atria where electrical impulses are delayed for about 0.1 second before spreading to both ventricles and causing them to contract.

atrioventricular (AV) valve A heart valve located between each atrium and ventricle that prevents a backflow of blood when the ventricle contracts.

atrium (ā′-trē-um) (plural, **atria**) A chamber of the vertebrate heart that receives blood from the veins and transfers blood to a ventricle.

autoimmune disease An immunological disorder in which the immune system turns against self.

autonomic nervous system (ot′-ō-nom′-ik) An efferent branch of the vertebrate peripheral nervous system that regulates the internal environment; consists of the sympathetic, parasympathetic, and enteric divisions.

autopolyploid (ot′-ō-pol′-ē-ployd) An individual that has more than two chromosome sets that are all derived from a single species.

autosome (ot′-ō-sōm) A chromosome that is not directly involved in determining sex; not a sex chromosome.

autotroph (ot′-ō-trōf) An organism that obtains organic food molecules without eating other organisms or substances derived from other organisms. Autotrophs use energy from the sun or from oxidation of inorganic substances to make organic molecules from inorganic ones.

auxin (ôk′-sin) A term that primarily refers to indoleacetic acid (IAA), a natural plant hormone that has a variety of effects, including cell elongation, root formation, secondary growth, and fruit growth.

avirulent Describing a pathogen that can mildly harm, but not kill, the host.

axillary bud (ak′-sil-ār-ē) A structure that has the potential to form a lateral shoot, or branch. The bud appears in the angle formed between a leaf and a stem.

axon (ak′-son) A typically long extension, or process, of a neuron that carries nerve impulses away from the cell body toward target cells.

B cells The lymphocytes that complete their development in the bone marrow and become effector cells for the humoral immune response.

Bacteria One of two prokaryotic domains, the other being Archaea.

bacteriophage (bak-tēr′-ē-ō-fāj) A virus that infects bacteria; also called a phage.

bacteroid A form of the bacterium *Rhizobium* contained within the vesicles formed by the root cells of a root nodule.

balancing selection Natural selection that maintains two or more phenotypic forms in a population.

bar graph A graph in which the independent variable represents groups or nonnumerical categories. Each piece of data is represented by a bar, whose height (or length) represents the value of the independent variable for the group or category indicated.

bark All tissues external to the vascular cambium, consisting mainly of the secondary phloem and layers of periderm.

Barr body A dense object lying along the inside of the nuclear envelope in cells of female mammals, representing a highly condensed, inactivated X chromosome.

basal body (bā′-sul) A eukaryotic cell structure consisting of a "9 + 0" arrangement of microtubule triplets. The basal body may organize the microtubule assembly of a cilium or flagellum and is structurally very similar to a centriole.

basal taxon In a specified group of organisms, a taxon whose evolutionary lineage diverged early in the history of the group.

base A substance that reduces the hydrogen ion concentration of a solution.

Batesian mimicry (bāt′-zē-un mim′-uh-krē) A type of mimicry in which a harmless species looks like a species that is poisonous or otherwise harmful to predators.

behavior Individually, an action carried out by muscles or glands under control of the nervous system in response to a stimulus; collectively, the sum of an animal's responses to external and internal stimuli.

behavioral ecology The study of the evolution of and ecological basis for animal behavior.

benign tumor A mass of abnormal cells with specific genetic and cellular changes such that the cells are not capable of surviving at a new site and generally remain at the site of the tumor's origin.

benthic zone The bottom surface of an aquatic environment.

benthos (ben′-thōz) The communities of organisms living in the benthic zone of an aquatic biome.

beta (β) pleated sheet One form of the secondary structure of proteins in which the polypeptide chain folds back and forth. Two regions of the chain lie parallel to each other and are held together by hydrogen bonds between atoms of the polypeptide backbone (not the side chains).

beta oxidation A metabolic sequence that breaks fatty acids down to two-carbon fragments that enter the citric acid cycle as acetyl CoA.

bicoid A maternal effect gene that codes for a protein responsible for specifying the anterior end in *Drosophila melanogaster.*

bilateral symmetry Body symmetry in which a central longitudinal plane divides the body into two equal but opposite halves.

bilaterian (bī′-luh-ter′-ē-uhn) Member of a clade of animals with bilateral symmetry and three germ layers.

bile A mixture of substances that is produced in the liver and stored in the gallbladder; enables formation of fat droplets in water as an aid in the digestion and absorption of fats.

binary fission A method of asexual reproduction by "division in half." In prokaryotes, binary fission does not involve mitosis, but in single-celled eukaryotes that undergo binary fission, mitosis is part of the process.

binomial A common term for the two-part, latinized format for naming a species, consisting of the genus and specific epithet; also called a binomen.

biodiversity hot spot A relatively small area with numerous endemic species and a large number of endangered and threatened species.

bioenergetics (1) The overall flow and transformation of energy in an organism. (2) The study of how energy flows through organisms.

biofilm A surface-coating colony of one or more species of prokaryotes that engage in metabolic cooperation.

biofuel A fuel produced from biomass.

biogenic amine A neurotransmitter derived from an amino acid.

biogeochemical cycle Any of the various chemical cycles that involve both biotic and abiotic components of ecosystems.

biogeography The scientific study of the past and present geographic distributions of species.

bioinformatics The use of computers, software, and mathematical models to process and integrate biological information from large data sets.

biological augmentation An approach to restoration ecology that uses organisms to add essential materials to a degraded ecosystem.

biological clock An internal timekeeper that controls an organism's biological rhythms. The biological clock marks time with or without environmental cues but often requires signals from the environment to remain tuned to an appropriate period. *See also* circadian rhythm.

biological magnification A process in which retained substances become more concentrated at each higher trophic level in a food chain.

biological species concept Definition of a species as a group of populations whose members have the potential to interbreed in nature and produce viable, fertile offspring, but do not produce viable, fertile offspring with members of other such groups.

biology The scientific study of life.

biomanipulation An approach that applies the top-down model of community organization to alter ecosystem characteristics. For example, ecologists can prevent algal blooms and eutrophication by altering the density of higher-level consumers in lakes instead of by using chemical treatments.

biomass The total mass of organic matter comprising a group of organisms in a particular habitat.

biome (bī′-ōm) Any of the world's major ecosystem types, often classified according to the predominant vegetation for terrestrial biomes and the physical environment for aquatic biomes and characterized by

adaptations of organisms to that particular environment.

bioremediation The use of organisms to detoxify and restore polluted and degraded ecosystems.

biosphere The entire portion of Earth inhabited by life; the sum of all the planet's ecosystems.

biotic (bī-ot′-ik) Pertaining to the living factors—the organisms—in an environment.

blade (1) A leaflike structure of a seaweed that provides most of the surface area for photosynthesis. (2) The flattened portion of a typical leaf.

blastocoel (blas′-tuh-sēl) The fluid-filled cavity that forms in the center of a blastula.

blastula (blas′-tyū-luh) A hollow ball of cells that marks the end of the cleavage stage during early embryonic development in animals.

blood A connective tissue with a fluid matrix called plasma in which red blood cells, white blood cells, and cell fragments called platelets are suspended.

blue-light photoreceptor A type of light receptor in plants that initiates a variety of responses, including phototropism and slowing of hypocotyl elongation.

body plan In multicellular eukaryotes, a set of morphological and developmental traits that are integrated into a functional whole—the living organism.

Bohr shift A lowering of the affinity of hemoglobin for oxygen, caused by a drop in pH. It facilitates the release of oxygen from hemoglobin in the vicinity of active tissues.

bolus A lubricated ball of chewed food.

bottleneck effect Genetic drift that occurs when the size of a population is reduced, as by a natural disaster or human actions. Typically, the surviving population is no longer genetically representative of the original population.

bottom-up model A model of community organization in which mineral nutrients influence community organization by controlling plant or phytoplankton numbers, which in turn control herbivore numbers, which in turn control predator numbers.

Bowman's capsule (bō′-munz) A cup-shaped receptacle in the vertebrate kidney that is the initial, expanded segment of the nephron where filtrate enters from the blood.

brain Organ of the central nervous system where information is processed and integrated.

brainstem A collection of structures in the vertebrate brain, including the midbrain, the pons, and the medulla oblongata; functions in homeostasis, coordination of movement, and conduction of information to higher brain centers.

branch point The representation on a phylogenetic tree of the divergence of two or more taxa from a common ancestor. A branch point is usually shown as a dichotomy in which a branch representing the ancestral lineage splits (at the branch point) into two branches, one for each of the two descendant lineages.

brassinosteroid A steroid hormone in plants that has a variety of effects, including inducing cell elongation, retarding leaf abscission, and promoting xylem differentiation.

breathing Ventilation of the lungs through alternating inhalation and exhalation.

bronchus (brong′-kus) (plural, **bronchi**) One of a pair of breathing tubes that branch from the trachea into the lungs.

brown alga A multicellular, photosynthetic protist with a characteristic brown or olive color that results from carotenoids in its plastids. Most brown algae are marine, and some have a plantlike body.

bryophyte (brī′-uh-fīt) An informal name for a moss, liverwort, or hornwort; a nonvascular plant that lives on land but lacks some of the terrestrial adaptations of vascular plants.

buffer A solution that contains a weak acid and its corresponding base. A buffer minimizes changes in pH when acids or bases are added to the solution.

bulk feeder An animal that eats relatively large pieces of food.

bulk flow The movement of a fluid due to a difference in pressure between two locations.

C_3 plant A plant that uses the Calvin cycle for the initial steps that incorporate CO_2 into organic material, forming a three-carbon compound as the first stable intermediate.

C_4 plant A plant in which the Calvin cycle is preceded by reactions that incorporate CO_2 into a four-carbon compound, the end product of which supplies CO_2 for the Calvin cycle.

callus A mass of dividing, undifferentiated cells growing in culture.

calorie (cal) The amount of heat energy required to raise the temperature of 1 g of water by 1°C; also the amount of heat energy that 1 g of water releases when it cools by 1°C. The Calorie (with a capital C), usually used to indicate the energy content of food, is a kilocalorie.

Calvin cycle The second of two major stages in photosynthesis (following the light reactions), involving fixation of atmospheric CO_2 and reduction of the fixed carbon into carbohydrate.

CAM plant A plant that uses crassulacean acid metabolism, an adaptation for photosynthesis in arid conditions. In this process, carbon dioxide entering open stomata during the night is converted to organic acids, which release CO_2 for the Calvin cycle during the day, when stomata are closed.

Cambrian explosion A relatively brief time in geologic history when many present-day phyla of animals first appeared in the fossil record. This burst of evolutionary change occurred about 535–525 million years ago and saw the emergence of the first large, hard-bodied animals.

canopy The uppermost layer of vegetation in a terrestrial biome.

capillary (kap′-il-ār′-ē) A microscopic blood vessel that penetrates the tissues and consists of a single layer of endothelial cells that allows exchange between the blood and interstitial fluid.

capillary bed A network of capillaries in a tissue or organ.

capsid The protein shell that encloses a viral genome. It may be rod-shaped, polyhedral, or more complex in shape.

capsule (1) In many prokaryotes, a dense and well-defined layer of polysaccharide or protein that surrounds the cell wall and is sticky, protecting the cell and enabling it to adhere to substrates or other cells. (2) The sporangium of a bryophyte (moss, liverwort, or hornwort).

carbohydrate (kar′-bō-hī′-drāt) A sugar (monosaccharide) or one of its dimers (disaccharides) or polymers (polysaccharides).

carbon fixation The initial incorporation of carbon from CO_2 into an organic compound by an autotrophic organism (a plant, another photosynthetic organism, or a chemoautotrophic prokaryote).

carbonyl group (kar-buh-nēl′) A chemical group present in aldehydes and ketones and consisting of a carbon atom double-bonded to an oxygen atom.

carboxyl group (kar-bok′-sil) A chemical group present in organic acids and consisting of a single carbon atom double-bonded to an oxygen atom and also bonded to a hydroxyl group.

cardiac cycle (kar′-dē-ak) The alternating contractions and relaxations of the heart.

cardiac muscle A type of striated muscle that forms the contractile wall of the heart. Its cells are joined by intercalated disks that relay the electrical signals underlying each heartbeat.

cardiovascular system A closed circulatory system with a heart and branching network of arteries, capillaries, and veins. The system is characteristic of vertebrates.

carnivore An animal that mainly eats other animals.

carotenoid (kuh-rot′-uh-noyd′) An accessory pigment, either yellow or orange, in the chloroplasts of plants and in some prokaryotes. By absorbing wavelengths of light that chlorophyll cannot, carotenoids broaden the spectrum of colors that can drive photosynthesis.

carpel (kar′-pul) The ovule-producing reproductive organ of a flower, consisting of the stigma, style, and ovary.

carrier In genetics, an individual who is heterozygous at a given genetic locus for a recessively inherited disorder. The heterozygote is generally phenotypically normal for the disorder but can pass on the recessive allele to offspring.

carrying capacity The maximum population size that can be supported by the available resources, symbolized as K.

Casparian strip (ka-spār′-ē-un) A water-impermeable ring of wax in the endodermal cells of plants that blocks the passive flow of water and solutes into the stele by way of cell walls.

catabolic pathway (kat′-uh-bol′-ik) A metabolic pathway that releases energy by breaking down complex molecules to simpler molecules.

catalyst (kat′-uh-list) A chemical agent that selectively increases the rate of a reaction without being consumed by the reaction.

cation (cat′-ī′-on) A positively charged ion.

cation exchange A process in which positively charged minerals are made available to a plant when hydrogen ions in the soil displace mineral ions from the clay particles.

cecum (sē′-kum) (plural, **ceca**) The blind pouch forming one branch of the large intestine.

cell body The part of a neuron that houses the nucleus and most other organelles.

cell cycle An ordered sequence of events in the life of a cell, from its origin in the division of a parent cell until its own division into two. The eukaryotic cell cycle is composed of interphase (including G_1, S, and G_2 subphases) and M phase (including mitosis and cytokinesis).

cell cycle control system A cyclically operating set of molecules in the eukaryotic cell that both triggers and coordinates key events in the cell cycle.

cell division The reproduction of cells.

cell fractionation The disruption of a cell and separation of its parts by centrifugation at successively higher speeds.

cell plate A membrane-bounded, flattened sac located at the midline of a dividing plant cell, inside which the new cell wall forms during cytokinesis.

cell wall A protective layer external to the plasma membrane in the cells of plants, prokaryotes, fungi, and some protists. Polysaccharides such as cellulose (in plants and some protists), chitin (in fungi), and peptidoglycan (in bacteria) are important structural components of cell walls.

cell-mediated immune response The branch of adaptive immunity that involves the activation of cytotoxic T cells, which defend against infected cells.

cellular respiration The catabolic pathways of aerobic and anaerobic respiration, which break down organic molecules and use an electron transport chain for the production of ATP.

cellulose (sel′-yū-lōs) A structural polysaccharide of plant cell walls, consisting of glucose monomers joined by β glycosidic linkages.

central nervous system (CNS) The portion of the nervous system where signal integration occurs; in vertebrate animals, the brain and spinal cord.

central vacuole In a mature plant cell, a large membranous sac with diverse roles in growth, storage, and sequestration of toxic substances.

centriole (sen′-trē-ōl) A structure in the centrosome of an animal cell composed of a cylinder of microtubule triplets arranged in a 9 + 0 pattern. A centrosome has a pair of centrioles.

centromere (sen′-trō-mēr) In a duplicated chromosome, the region on each sister chromatid where they are most closely attached to each other by proteins that bind to specific DNA sequences; this close attachment causes a constriction in the condensed chromosome. (An uncondensed, unduplicated chromosome has a single centromere, identified by its DNA sequence.)

centrosome (sen′-trō-sōm) A structure present in the cytoplasm of animal cells that functions as a microtubule-organizing center and is important during cell division. A centrosome has two centrioles.

cercozoan An amoeboid or flagellated protist that feeds with threadlike pseudopodia.

cerebellum (sār′-ruh-bel′-um) Part of the vertebrate hindbrain located dorsally; functions in unconscious coordination of movement and balance.

cerebral cortex (suh-rē′-brul) The surface of the cerebrum; the largest and most complex part of the mammalian brain, containing nerve cell bodies of the cerebrum; the part of the vertebrate brain most changed through evolution.

cerebral hemisphere The right or left side of the cerebrum.

cerebrum (suh-rē′-brum) The dorsal portion of the vertebrate forebrain, composed of right and left hemispheres; the integrating center for memory, learning, emotions, and other highly complex functions of the central nervous system.

cervix (ser′-viks) The neck of the uterus, which opens into the vagina.

chaparral A scrubland biome of dense, spiny evergreen shrubs found at midlatitudes along coasts where cold ocean currents circulate offshore; characterized by mild, rainy winters and long, hot, dry summers.

character An observable heritable feature that may vary among individuals.

character displacement The tendency for characteristics to be more divergent in sympatric populations of two species than in allopatric populations of the same two species.

checkpoint A control point in the cell cycle where stop and go-ahead signals can regulate the cycle.

chemical bond An attraction between two atoms, resulting from a sharing of outer-shell electrons or the presence of opposite charges on the atoms. The bonded atoms gain complete outer electron shells.

chemical energy Energy available in molecules for release in a chemical reaction; a form of potential energy.

chemical equilibrium In a chemical reaction, the state in which the rate of the forward reaction equals the rate of the reverse reaction, so that the relative concentrations of the reactants and products do not change with time.

chemical reaction The making and breaking of chemical bonds, leading to changes in the composition of matter.

chemiosmosis (kem′-ē-oz-mō′-sis) An energy-coupling mechanism that uses energy stored in the form of a hydrogen ion gradient across a membrane to drive cellular work, such as the synthesis of ATP. Under aerobic conditions, most ATP synthesis in cells occurs by chemiosmosis.

chemoreceptor A sensory receptor that responds to a chemical stimulus, such as a solute or an odorant.

chiasma (plural, **chiasmata**) (kī-az′-muh, kī-az′-muh-tuh) The X-shaped, microscopically visible region where crossing over has occurred earlier in prophase I between homologous nonsister chromatids. Chiasmata become visible after synapsis ends, with the two homologs remaining associated due to sister chromatid cohesion.

chitin (kī′-tin) A structural polysaccharide, consisting of amino sugar monomers, found in many fungal cell walls and in the exoskeletons of all arthropods.

chlorophyll (klōr′-ō-fil) A green pigment located in membranes within the chloroplasts of plants and algae and in the membranes of certain prokaryotes. Chlorophyll *a* participates directly in the light reactions, which convert solar energy to chemical energy.

chlorophyll *a* A photosynthetic pigment that participates directly in the light reactions, which convert solar energy to chemical energy.

chlorophyll *b* An accessory photosynthetic pigment that transfers energy to chlorophyll *a*.

chloroplast (klōr′-ō-plast) An organelle found in plants and photosynthetic protists that absorbs sunlight and uses it to drive the synthesis of organic compounds from carbon dioxide and water.

choanocyte (kō-an′-uh-sīt) A flagellated feeding cell found in sponges. Also called a collar cell, it has a collar-like ring that traps food particles around the base of its flagellum.

cholesterol (kō-les′-tuh-rol) A steroid that forms an essential component of animal cell membranes and acts as a precursor molecule for the synthesis of other biologically important steroids, such as many hormones.

chondrichthyan (kon-drik′-thē-an) Member of the class Chondrichthyes, vertebrates with skeletons made mostly of cartilage, such as sharks and rays.

chordate Member of the phylum Chordata, animals that at some point during their development have a notochord; a dorsal, hollow nerve cord; pharyngeal slits or clefts; and a muscular, post-anal tail.

chromatin (krō′-muh-tin) The complex of DNA and proteins that makes up eukaryotic chromosomes. When the cell is not dividing, chromatin exists in its dispersed form, as a mass of very long, thin fibers that are not visible with a light microscope.

chromosome (krō′-muh-sōm) A cellular structure consisting of one DNA molecule and associated protein molecules. (In some contexts, such as genome sequencing, the term may refer to the DNA alone.) A eukaryotic cell typically has multiple, linear chromosomes, which are located in the nucleus. A prokaryotic cell often has a single, circular chromosome, which is found in the nucleoid, a region that is not enclosed by a membrane. *See also* chromatin.

chromosome theory of inheritance A basic principle in biology stating that genes are located at specific positions (loci) on chromosomes and that the behavior of chromosomes during meiosis accounts for inheritance patterns.

chylomicron (kī′-lō-mī′-kron) A lipid transport globule composed of fats mixed with cholesterol and coated with proteins.

chyme (kīm) The mixture of partially digested food and digestive juices formed in the stomach.

ciliate (sil′-ē-it) A type of protist that moves by means of cilia.

cilium (sil′-ē-um) (plural, **cilia**) A short appendage containing microtubules in eukaryotic cells. A motile cilium is specialized for locomotion or moving fluid past the cell; it is formed from a core of nine outer doublet microtubules and two inner single microtubules (the "9 + 2" arrangement) ensheathed in an extension of the plasma membrane. A primary cilium is usually nonmotile and plays a sensory and signaling role; it lacks the two inner microtubules (the "9 + 0" arrangement).

circadian rhythm (ser-kā′-dē-un) A physiological cycle of about 24 hours that persists even in the absence of external cues.

citric acid cycle A chemical cycle involving eight steps that completes the metabolic breakdown of glucose molecules begun in glycolysis by oxidizing acetyl CoA (derived from pyruvate) to carbon dioxide; occurs within the mitochondrion in eukaryotic cells and in the cytosol of prokaryotes; together with pyruvate oxidation, the second major stage in cellular respiration.

clade (klayd) A group of species that includes an ancestral species and all of its descendants.

cladistics (kluh-dis′-tiks) An approach to systematics in which organisms are placed into groups called clades based primarily on common descent.

class In Linnaean classification, the taxonomic category above the level of order.

cleavage (1) The process of cytokinesis in animal cells, characterized by pinching of the plasma membrane. (2) The succession of rapid cell divisions without significant growth during early embryonic development that converts the zygote to a ball of cells.

cleavage furrow The first sign of cleavage in an animal cell; a shallow groove around the cell in the cell surface near the old metaphase plate.

climate The long-term prevailing weather conditions at a given place.

climograph A plot of the temperature and precipitation in a particular region.

clitoris (klit′-uh-ris) An organ at the upper intersection of the labia minora that engorges with blood and becomes erect during sexual arousal.

cloaca (klō-ā′-kuh) A common opening for the digestive, urinary, and reproductive tracts found in many nonmammalian vertebrates but in few mammals.

clonal selection The process by which an antigen selectively binds to and activates only those lymphocytes bearing receptors specific for the antigen. The selected lymphocytes proliferate and differentiate into a clone of effector cells and a clone of memory cells specific for the stimulating antigen.

clone (1) A lineage of genetically identical individuals or cells. (2) In popular usage, an individual that is genetically identical to another individual. (3) As a verb, to make one or more genetic replicas of an individual or cell. *See also* gene cloning.

cloning vector In genetic engineering, a DNA molecule that can carry foreign DNA into a host cell and replicate there. Cloning vectors include plasmids.

closed circulatory system A circulatory system in which blood is confined to vessels and is kept separate from the interstitial fluid.

cochlea (kok′-lē-uh) The complex, coiled organ of hearing that contains the organ of Corti.

codominance The situation in which the phenotypes of both alleles are exhibited in the heterozygote because both alleles affect the phenotype in separate, distinguishable ways.

codon (kō′-don) A three-nucleotide sequence of DNA or mRNA that specifies a particular amino acid or termination signal; the basic unit of the genetic code.

coefficient of relatedness The fraction of genes that, on average, are shared by two individuals.

coenzyme (kō-en′-zīm) An organic molecule serving as a cofactor. Most vitamins function as coenzymes in metabolic reactions.

cofactor Any nonprotein molecule or ion that is required for the proper functioning of an enzyme. Cofactors can be permanently bound to the active site or may bind loosely and reversibly, along with the substrate, during catalysis.

cognition The process of knowing that may include awareness, reasoning, recollection, and judgment.

cognitive map A neural representation of the abstract spatial relationships between objects in an animal's surroundings.

cohesion The linking together of like molecules, often by hydrogen bonds.

cohesion-tension hypothesis The leading explanation for the ascent of xylem sap. It states that transpiration exerts pull on xylem sap, putting the sap under negative pressure or tension, and that the cohesion of water molecules transmits this pull along the entire length of the xylem from shoots to roots.

cohort A group of individuals of the same age in a population.

coleoptile (kō′-lē-op′-tul) The covering of the young shoot of the embryo of a grass seed.

coleorhiza (kō′-lē-uh-rī′-zuh) The covering of the young root of the embryo of a grass seed.

collagen A glycoprotein in the extracellular matrix of animal cells that forms strong fibers, found extensively in connective tissue and bone; the most abundant protein in the animal kingdom.

collecting duct The location in the kidney where processed filtrate, called urine, is collected from the renal tubules.

collenchyma cell (kō-len′-kim-uh) A flexible plant cell type that occurs in strands or cylinders that support young parts of the plant without restraining growth.

colon (kō′-len) The largest section of the vertebrate large intestine; functions in water absorption and formation of feces.

commensalism (kuh-men′-suh-lizm) A symbiotic relationship in which one organism benefits but the other is neither helped nor harmed.

communication In animal behavior, a process involving transmission of, reception of, and response to signals. The term is also used in connection with other organisms, as well as individual cells of multicellular organisms.

community All the organisms that inhabit a particular area; an assemblage of populations of different species living close enough together for potential interaction.

community ecology The study of how interactions between species affect community structure and organization.

companion cell A type of plant cell that is connected to a sieve-tube element by many plasmodesmata and whose nucleus and ribosomes may serve one or more adjacent sieve-tube elements.

competitive exclusion The concept that when populations of two similar species compete for the same limited resources, one population will use the resources more efficiently and have a reproductive advantage that will eventually lead to the elimination of the other population.

competitive inhibitor A substance that reduces the activity of an enzyme by entering the active site in place of the substrate, whose structure it mimics.

complement system A group of about 30 blood proteins that may amplify the inflammatory response, enhance phagocytosis, or directly lyse extracellular pathogens.

complementary DNA (cDNA) A double-stranded DNA molecule made *in vitro* using mRNA as a template and the enzymes reverse transcriptase and DNA polymerase. A cDNA molecule corresponds to the exons of a gene.

complete dominance The situation in which the phenotypes of the heterozygote and dominant homozygote are indistinguishable.

complete flower A flower that has all four basic floral organs: sepals, petals, stamens, and carpels.

compound A substance consisting of two or more different elements combined in a fixed ratio.

compound eye A type of multifaceted eye in insects and crustaceans consisting of up to several thousand light-detecting, focusing ommatidia.

concentration gradient A region along which the density of a chemical substance increases or decreases.

conception The fertilization of an egg by a sperm in humans.

cone A cone-shaped cell in the retina of the vertebrate eye, sensitive to color.

conformer An animal for which an internal condition conforms to (changes in accordance with) changes in an environmental variable.

conifer Member of the largest gymnosperm phylum. Most conifers are cone-bearing trees, such as pines and firs.

conjugation (kon′-jū-gā′-shun) (1) In prokaryotes, the direct transfer of DNA between two cells that are temporarily joined. When the two cells are members of different species, conjugation results in horizontal gene transfer. (2) In ciliates, a sexual process in which two cells exchange haploid micronuclei but do not reproduce.

connective tissue Animal tissue that functions mainly to bind and support other tissues, having a sparse population of cells scattered through an extracellular matrix.

conservation biology The integrated study of ecology, evolutionary biology, physiology, molecular biology, and genetics to sustain biological diversity at all levels.

contraception The deliberate prevention of pregnancy.

contractile vacuole A membranous sac that helps move excess water out of certain freshwater protists.

control element A segment of noncoding DNA that helps regulate transcription of a gene by serving as a binding site for a transcription factor. Multiple control elements are present in a eukaryotic gene's enhancer.

control group In a controlled experiment, a set of subjects that lacks (or does not receive) the specific factor being tested. Ideally, the control group should be identical to the experimental group in other respects.

controlled experiment An experiment in which an experimental group is compared with a control group that varies only in the factor being tested.

convergent evolution The evolution of similar features in independent evolutionary lineages.

cooperativity A kind of allosteric regulation whereby a shape change in one subunit of a protein caused by substrate binding is transmitted to all the other subunits, facilitating binding of additional substrate molecules to those subunits.

coral reef Typically a warm-water, tropical ecosystem dominated by the hard skeletal structures secreted primarily by corals. Some coral reefs also exist in cold, deep waters.

corepressor A small molecule that binds to a bacterial repressor protein and changes the protein's shape, allowing it to bind to the operator and switch an operon off.

cork cambium (kam′-bē-um) A cylinder of meristematic tissue in woody plants that replaces the epidermis with thicker, tougher cork cells.

corpus callosum (kor′-pus kuh-lō′-sum) The thick band of nerve fibers that connects the right and left cerebral hemispheres in mammals, enabling the hemispheres to process information together.

corpus luteum (kor′-pus lū′-tē-um) A secreting tissue in the ovary that forms from the collapsed follicle after ovulation and produces progesterone.

cortex (1) The outer region of cytoplasm in a eukaryotic cell, lying just under the plasma membrane, that has a more gel-like consistency than the inner regions due to the

presence of multiple microfilaments. (2) In plants, ground tissue that is between the vascular tissue and dermal tissue in a root or eudicot stem.

cortical nephron In mammals and birds, a nephron with a loop of Henle located almost entirely in the renal cortex.

cotransport The coupling of the "downhill" diffusion of one substance to the "uphill" transport of another against its own concentration gradient.

countercurrent exchange The exchange of a substance or heat between two fluids flowing in opposite directions. For example, blood in a fish gill flows in the opposite direction of water passing over the gill, maximizing diffusion of oxygen into and carbon dioxide out of the blood.

countercurrent multiplier system A countercurrent system in which energy is expended in active transport to facilitate exchange of materials and generate concentration gradients.

covalent bond (kō-vā′-lent) A type of strong chemical bond in which two atoms share one or more pairs of valence electrons.

crassulacean acid metabolism (CAM) An adaptation for photosynthesis in arid conditions, first discovered in the family Crassulaceae. In this process, a plant takes up CO_2 at night when stomata are open and incorporates it into a variety of organic acids; during the day, when stomata are closed, CO_2 is released from the organic acids for use in the Calvin cycle.

crista (plural, **cristae**) (kris′-tuh, kris′-tē) An infolding of the inner membrane of a mitochondrion. The inner membrane houses electron transport chains and molecules of the enzyme catalyzing the synthesis of ATP (ATP synthase).

critical load The amount of added nutrient, usually nitrogen or phosphorus, that can be absorbed by plants without damaging ecosystem integrity.

cross-fostering study A behavioral study in which the young of one species are placed in the care of adults from another species.

crossing over The reciprocal exchange of genetic material between nonsister chromatids during prophase I of meiosis.

cryptic coloration Camouflage that makes a potential prey difficult to spot against its background.

culture A system of information transfer through social learning or teaching that influences the behavior of individuals in a population.

cuticle (kyū′-tuh-kul) (1) A waxy covering on the surface of stems and leaves that prevents desiccation in terrestrial plants. (2) The exoskeleton of an arthropod, consisting of layers of protein and chitin that are variously modified for different functions. (3) A tough coat that covers the body of a nematode.

cyclic AMP (cAMP) Cyclic adenosine monophosphate, a ring-shaped molecule made from ATP that is a common intracellular signaling molecule (second messenger) in eukaryotic cells. It is also a regulator of some bacterial operons.

cystic fibrosis (sis′-tik fī-brō′-sis) A human genetic disorder caused by a recessive allele for a chloride channel protein; characterized by an excessive secretion of mucus and consequent vulnerability to infection; fatal if untreated.

cytochrome (sī′-tō-krōm) An iron-containing protein that is a component of electron transport chains in the mitochondria and chloroplasts of eukaryotic cells and the plasma membranes of prokaryotic cells.

cytogenetic map A map of a chromosome that locates genes with respect to chromosomal features distinguishable in a microscope.

cytokine (sī′-tō-kīn′) Any of a group of small proteins secreted by a number of cell types, including macrophages and helper T cells, that regulate the function of other cells.

cytokinesis (sī′-tō-kuh-nē′-sis) The division of the cytoplasm to form two separate daughter cells immediately after mitosis, meiosis I, or meiosis II.

cytokinin (sī′-tō-kī′-nin) Any of a class of related plant hormones that retard aging and act in concert with auxin to stimulate cell division, influence the pathway of differentiation, and control apical dominance.

cytoplasm (sī′-tō-plaz′-um) The contents of the cell enclosed by the plasma membrane; in eukaryotes, the portion exclusive of the nucleus.

cytoplasmic determinant A maternal substance, such as a protein or RNA, that when placed into an egg influences the course of early development by regulating the expression of genes that affect the developmental fate of cells.

cytoskeleton A network of microtubules, microfilaments, and intermediate filaments that extends throughout the cytoplasm and serves a variety of mechanical, transport, and signaling functions.

cytosol (sī′-tō-sol) The semifluid portion of the cytoplasm.

cytotoxic T cell A type of lymphocyte that, when activated, kills infected cells as well as certain cancer cells and transplanted cells.

dalton A measure of mass for atoms and subatomic particles; the same as the atomic mass unit, or amu.

data Recorded observations.

day-neutral plant A plant in which flower formation is not controlled by photoperiod or day length.

decomposer An organism that absorbs nutrients from nonliving organic material such as corpses, fallen plant material, and the wastes of living organisms and converts them to inorganic forms; a detritivore.

deductive reasoning A type of logic in which specific results are predicted from a general premise.

deep-sea hydrothermal vent A dark, hot, oxygen-deficient environment associated with volcanic activity on or near the seafloor. The producers in a vent community are chemoautotrophic prokaryotes.

de-etiolation The changes a plant shoot undergoes in response to sunlight; also known informally as greening.

dehydration reaction A chemical reaction in which two molecules become covalently bonded to each other with the removal of a water molecule.

deletion (1) A deficiency in a chromosome resulting from the loss of a fragment through breakage. (2) A mutational loss of one or more nucleotide pairs from a gene.

demography The study of changes over time in the vital statistics of populations, especially birth rates and death rates.

denaturation (dē-nā'-chur-ā'-shun) In proteins, a process in which a protein loses its native shape due to the disruption of weak chemical bonds and interactions, thereby becoming biologically inactive; in DNA, the separation of the two strands of the double helix. Denaturation occurs under extreme (noncellular) conditions of pH, salt concentration, or temperature.

dendrite (den'-drīt) One of usually numerous, short, highly branched extensions of a neuron that receive signals from other neurons.

density The number of individuals per unit area or volume.

density dependent Referring to any characteristic that varies with population density.

density independent Referring to any characteristic that is not affected by population density.

density-dependent inhibition The phenomenon observed in normal animal cells that causes them to stop dividing when they come into contact with one another.

deoxyribonucleic acid (DNA) (dē-ok'-sē-rī'-bō-nū-klā'-ik) A nucleic acid molecule, usually a double-stranded helix, in which each polynucleotide strand consists of nucleotide monomers with a deoxyribose sugar and the nitrogenous bases adenine (A), cytosine (C), guanine (G), and thymine (T); capable of being replicated and determining the inherited structure of a cell's proteins.

deoxyribose (dē-ok'-si-rī'-bōs) The sugar component of DNA nucleotides, having one fewer hydroxyl group than ribose, the sugar component of RNA nucleotides.

dependent variable In an experiment, a variable whose value is influenced by changes in another variable (the independent variable).

depolarization A change in a cell's membrane potential such that the inside of the membrane is made less negative relative to the outside. For example, a neuron membrane is depolarized if a stimulus decreases its voltage from the resting potential of −70 mV in the direction of zero voltage.

dermal tissue system The outer protective covering of plants.

desert A terrestrial biome characterized by very low precipitation.

desmosome A type of intercellular junction in animal cells that functions as a rivet, fastening cells together.

determinate growth A type of growth characteristic of most animals and some plant organs, in which growth stops after a certain size is reached.

determination The progressive restriction of developmental potential whereby the possible fate of each cell becomes more limited as an embryo develops. At the end of determination, a cell is committed to its fate.

detritivore (deh-trī'-tuh-vōr) A consumer that derives its energy and nutrients from nonliving organic material such as corpses, fallen plant material, and the wastes of living organisms; a decomposer.

detritus (di-trī'-tus) Dead organic matter.

diabetes mellitus (dī'-uh-bē'-tis mel'-uh-tus) An endocrine disorder marked by an inability to maintain glucose homeostasis. The type 1 form results from autoimmune destruction of insulin-secreting cells; treatment usually requires daily insulin injections. The type 2 form most commonly results from reduced responsiveness of target cells to insulin; obesity and lack of exercise are risk factors.

diaphragm (dī'-uh-fram') (1) A sheet of muscle that forms the bottom wall of the thoracic cavity in mammals. Contraction of the diaphragm pulls air into the lungs. (2) A dome-shaped rubber cup fitted into the upper portion of the vagina before sexual intercourse. It serves as a physical barrier to the passage of sperm into the uterus.

diastole (dī-as'-tō-lē) The stage of the cardiac cycle in which a heart chamber is relaxed and fills with blood.

diatom A photosynthetic protist in the stramenopile clade; diatoms have a unique glass-like wall made of silicon dioxide embedded in an organic matrix.

differential gene expression The expression of different sets of genes by cells with the same genome.

differentiation The process by which a cell or group of cells becomes specialized in structure and function.

diffusion The random thermal motion of particles of liquids, gases, or solids. In the presence of a concentration or electrochemical gradient, diffusion results in the net movement of a substance from a region where it

is more concentrated to a region where it is less concentrated.

digestion The second stage of food processing in animals: the breaking down of food into molecules small enough for the body to absorb.

dihybrid (dī'-hī'-brid) An organism that is heterozygous with respect to two genes of interest. All the offspring from a cross between parents doubly homozygous for different alleles are dihybrids. For example, parents of genotypes $AABB$ and $aabb$ produce a dihybrid of genotype $AaBb$.

dihybrid cross A cross between two organisms that are each heterozygous for both of the characters being followed (or the self-pollination of a plant that is heterozygous for both characters).

dinoflagellate (dī'-nō-flaj'-uh-let) Member of a group of mostly unicellular photosynthetic algae with two flagella situated in perpendicular grooves in cellulose plates covering the cell.

dioecious (dī-ē'-shus) In plant biology, having the male and female reproductive parts on different individuals of the same species.

diploid cell (dip'-loyd) A cell containing two sets of chromosomes ($2n$), one set inherited from each parent.

diplomonad A protist that has modified mitochondria and multiple flagella.

directional selection Natural selection in which individuals at one end of the phenotypic range survive or reproduce more successfully than do other individuals.

disaccharide (dī-sak'-uh-rīd) A double sugar, consisting of two monosaccharides joined by a glycosidic linkage formed by a dehydration reaction.

dispersal The movement of individuals or gametes away from their parent location. This movement sometimes expands the geographic range of a population or species.

dispersion The pattern of spacing among individuals within the boundaries of a population.

disruptive selection Natural selection in which individuals on both extremes of a phenotypic range survive or reproduce more successfully than do individuals with intermediate phenotypes.

distal tubule In the vertebrate kidney, the portion of a nephron that helps refine filtrate and empties it into a collecting duct.

disturbance A natural or human-caused event that changes a biological community and usually removes organisms from it. Disturbances, such as fires and storms, play a pivotal role in structuring many communities.

disulfide bridge A strong covalent bond formed when the sulfur of one cysteine monomer bonds to the sulfur of another cysteine monomer.

DNA (deoxyribonucleic acid) (dē-ok′-sē-rī′-bō-nū-klā′-ik) A nucleic acid molecule, usually a double-stranded helix, in which each polynucleotide strand consists of nucleotide monomers with a deoxyribose sugar and the nitrogenous bases adenine (A), cytosine (C), guanine (G), and thymine (T); capable of being replicated and determining the inherited structure of a cell's proteins.

DNA ligase (lī′-gās) A linking enzyme essential for DNA replication; catalyzes the covalent bonding of the 3′ end of one DNA fragment (such as an Okazaki fragment) to the 5′ end of another DNA fragment (such as a growing DNA chain).

DNA methylation The presence of methyl groups on the DNA bases (usually cytosine) of plants, animals, and fungi. (The term also refers to the process of adding methyl groups to DNA bases.)

DNA microarray assay A method to detect and measure the expression of thousands of genes at one time. Tiny amounts of a large number of single-stranded DNA fragments representing different genes are fixed to a glass slide and tested for hybridization with samples of labeled cDNA.

DNA polymerase (puh-lim′-er-ās) An enzyme that catalyzes the elongation of new DNA (for example, at a replication fork) by the addition of nucleotides to the 3′ end of an existing chain. There are several different DNA polymerases; DNA polymerase III and DNA polymerase I play major roles in DNA replication in *E. coli*.

DNA replication The process by which a DNA molecule is copied; also called DNA synthesis.

DNA sequencing Determining the order of nucleotide bases in a gene or DNA fragment.

domain (1) A taxonomic category above the kingdom level. The three domains are Archaea, Bacteria, and Eukarya. (2) A discrete structural and functional region of a protein.

dominant allele An allele that is fully expressed in the phenotype of a heterozygote.

dominant species A species with substantially higher abundance or biomass than other species in a community. Dominant species exert a powerful control over the occurrence and distribution of other species.

dopamine A neurotransmitter that is a catecholamine, like epinephrine and norepinephrine.

dormancy A condition typified by extremely low metabolic rate and a suspension of growth and development.

dorsal Pertaining to the top of an animal with radial or bilateral symmetry.

double bond A double covalent bond; the sharing of two pairs of valence electrons by two atoms.

double circulation A circulatory system consisting of separate pulmonary and systemic circuits, in which blood passes through the heart after completing each circuit.

double fertilization A mechanism of fertilization in angiosperms in which two sperm cells unite with two cells in the female gametophyte (embryo sac) to form the zygote and endosperm.

double helix The form of native DNA, referring to its two adjacent antiparallel polynucleotide strands wound around an imaginary axis into a spiral shape.

Down syndrome A human genetic disease usually caused by the presence of an extra chromosome 21; characterized by developmental delays and heart and other defects that are generally treatable or non-life-threatening.

Duchenne muscular dystrophy (duh-shen′) A human genetic disease caused by a sex-linked recessive allele; characterized by progressive weakening and a loss of muscle tissue.

duodenum (dū′-uh-dēn′-um) The first section of the small intestine, where chyme from the stomach mixes with digestive juices from the pancreas, liver, and gallbladder as well as from gland cells of the intestinal wall.

duplication An aberration in chromosome structure due to fusion with a fragment from a homologous chromosome, such that a portion of a chromosome is duplicated.

dynein (dī′-nē-un) In cilia and flagella, a large motor protein extending from one microtubule doublet to the adjacent doublet. ATP hydrolysis drives changes in dynein shape that lead to bending of cilia and flagella.

E site One of a ribosome's three binding sites for tRNA during translation. The E site is the place where discharged tRNAs leave the ribosome. (E stands for exit.)

ecological footprint The aggregate land and water area required by a person, city, or nation to produce all of the resources it consumes and to absorb all of the wastes it generates.

ecological niche (nich) The sum of a species' use of the biotic and abiotic resources in its environment.

ecological species concept Definition of a species in terms of ecological niche, the sum of how members of the species interact with the nonliving and living parts of their environment.

ecological succession Transition in the species composition of a community following a disturbance; establishment of a community in an area virtually barren of life.

ecology The study of how organisms interact with each other and their environment.

ecosystem All the organisms in a given area as well as the abiotic factors with which they interact; one or more communities and the physical environment around them.

ecosystem ecology The study of energy flow and the cycling of chemicals among the various biotic and abiotic components in an ecosystem.

ecosystem engineer An organism that influences community structure by causing physical changes in the environment.

ecosystem service A function performed by an ecosystem that directly or indirectly benefits humans.

ecotone The transition from one type of habitat or ecosystem to another, such as the transition from a forest to a grassland.

ectoderm (ek′-tō-durm) The outermost of the three primary germ layers in animal embryos; gives rise to the outer covering and, in some phyla, the nervous system, inner ear, and lens of the eye.

ectomycorrhizae (ek′-tō-mī′-kō-rī′-zē) Associations of a fungus with a plant root system in which the fungus surrounds the roots but does not cause invagination of the host (plant) cell's plasma membrane.

ectomycorrhizal fungus A symbiotic fungus that forms sheaths of hyphae over the surface of plant roots and also grows into extracellular spaces of the root cortex.

ectoparasite A parasite that feeds on the external surface of a host.

ectothermic Referring to organisms for which external sources provide most of the heat for temperature regulation.

Ediacaran biota (ē′-dē-uh-keh′-run bī-ō′-tuh) An early group of macroscopic, soft-bodied, multicellular eukaryotes known from fossils that range in age from 635 million to 535 million years old.

effective population size An estimate of the size of a population based on the numbers of females and males that successfully breed; generally smaller than the total population.

effector cell (1) A muscle cell or gland cell that performs the body's response to stimuli as directed by signals from the brain or other processing center of the nervous system. (2) A lymphocyte that has undergone clonal selection and is capable of mediating an adaptive immune response.

egg The female gamete.

egg-polarity gene A gene that helps control the orientation (polarity) of the egg; also called a maternal effect gene.

ejaculation The propulsion of sperm from the epididymis through the muscular vas deferens, ejaculatory duct, and urethra.

ejaculatory duct In mammals, the short section of the ejaculatory route formed by the convergence of the vas deferens and a duct from the seminal vesicle. The ejaculatory duct transports sperm from the vas deferens to the urethra.

electrocardiogram (ECG or EKG) A record of the electrical impulses that travel through heart muscle during the cardiac cycle.

electrochemical gradient The diffusion gradient of an ion, which is affected by both the concentration difference of an ion across a membrane (a chemical force) and the ion's tendency to move relative to the membrane potential (an electrical force).

electrogenic pump An active transport protein that generates voltage across a membrane while pumping ions.

electromagnetic receptor A receptor of electromagnetic energy, such as visible light, electricity, or magnetism.

electromagnetic spectrum The entire spectrum of electromagnetic radiation, ranging in wavelength from less than a nanometer to more than a kilometer.

electron A subatomic particle with a single negative electrical charge and a mass about 1/2,000 that of a neutron or proton. One or more electrons move around the nucleus of an atom.

electron microscope (EM) A microscope that uses magnets to focus an electron beam on or through a specimen, resulting in a practical resolution a hundredfold greater than that of a light microscope using standard techniques. A transmission electron microscope (TEM) is used to study the internal structure of thin sections of cells. A scanning electron microscope (SEM) is used to study the fine details of cell surfaces.

electron shell An energy level of electrons at a characteristic average distance from the nucleus of an atom.

electron transport chain A sequence of electron carrier molecules (membrane proteins) that shuttle electrons down a series of redox reactions that release energy used to make ATP.

electronegativity The attraction of a given atom for the electrons of a covalent bond.

element Any substance that cannot be broken down to any other substance by chemical reactions.

elimination The fourth and final stage of food processing in animals: the passing of undigested material out of the body.

embryo sac (em'-brē-ō) The female gametophyte of angiosperms, formed from the growth and division of the megaspore into a multicellular structure that typically has eight haploid nuclei.

embryonic lethal A mutation with a phenotype leading to death of an embryo or larva.

embryophyte Alternate name for land plants that refers to their shared derived trait of multicellular, dependent embryos.

emergent properties New properties that arise with each step upward in the hierarchy of life, owing to the arrangement and interactions of parts as complexity increases.

emigration The movement of individuals out of a population.

endangered species A species that is in danger of extinction throughout all or a significant portion of its range.

endemic (en-dem'-ik) Referring to a species that is confined to a specific geographic area.

endergonic reaction (en'-der-gon'-ik) A nonspontaneous chemical reaction, in which free energy is absorbed from the surroundings.

endocrine gland (en'-dō-krin) A gland that secretes hormones directly into the interstitial fluid, from which they diffuse into the bloodstream.

endocrine system The internal system of communication involving hormones, the ductless glands that secrete hormones, and the molecular receptors on or in target cells that respond to hormones; functions in concert with the nervous system to effect internal regulation and maintain homeostasis.

endocytosis (en'-dō-sī-tō'-sis) Cellular uptake of biological molecules and particulate matter via formation of vesicles from the plasma membrane.

endoderm (en'-dō-durm) The innermost of the three primary germ layers in animal embryos; lines the archenteron and gives rise to the liver, pancreas, lungs, and the lining of the digestive tract in species that have these structures.

endodermis In plant roots, the innermost layer of the cortex that surrounds the vascular cylinder.

endomembrane system The collection of membranes inside and surrounding a eukaryotic cell, related either through direct physical contact or by the transfer of membranous vesicles; includes the plasma membrane, the nuclear envelope, the smooth and rough endoplasmic reticulum, the Golgi apparatus, lysosomes, vesicles, and vacuoles.

endometrium (en'-dō-mē'-trē-um) The inner lining of the uterus, which is richly supplied with blood vessels.

endoparasite A parasite that lives within a host.

endophyte A fungus that lives inside a leaf or other plant part without causing harm to the plant.

endoplasmic reticulum (ER) (en'-dō-plaz'-mik ruh-tik'-yū-lum) An extensive membranous network in eukaryotic cells, continuous with the outer nuclear membrane and composed of ribosome-studded (rough) and ribosome-free (smooth) regions.

endorphin (en-dōr'-fin) Any of several hormones produced in the brain and anterior pituitary that inhibit pain perception.

endoskeleton A hard skeleton buried within the soft tissues of an animal.

endosperm In angiosperms, a nutrient-rich tissue formed by the union of a sperm with two polar nuclei during double fertilization.

The endosperm provides nourishment to the developing embryo in angiosperm seeds.

endospore A thick-coated, resistant cell produced by some bacterial cells when they are exposed to harsh conditions.

endosymbiont theory The theory that mitochondria and plastids, including chloroplasts, originated as prokaryotic cells engulfed by host cells. The engulfed cell and its host cell then evolved into a single organism. *See also* endosymbiosis.

endosymbiosis A mutually beneficial relationship between two species in which one organism lives inside the cell or cells of another organism.

endothelium (en'-dō-thē'-lē-um) The simple squamous layer of cells lining the lumen of blood vessels.

endothermic Referring to organisms that are warmed by heat generated by their own metabolism. This heat usually maintains a relatively stable body temperature higher than that of the external environment.

endotoxin A toxic component of the outer membrane of certain gram-negative bacteria that is released only when the bacteria die.

energy The capacity to cause change, especially to do work (to move matter against an opposing force).

energy coupling In cellular metabolism, the use of energy released from an exergonic reaction to drive an endergonic reaction.

enhancer A segment of eukaryotic DNA containing multiple control elements, usually located far from the gene whose transcription it regulates.

enteric division One of three divisions of the autonomic nervous system; consists of networks of neurons in the digestive tract, pancreas, and gallbladder; normally regulated by the sympathetic and parasympathetic divisions of the autonomic nervous system.

entropy A measure of disorder, or randomness.

enzyme (en'-zīm) A macromolecule serving as a catalyst, a chemical agent that increases the rate of a reaction without being consumed by the reaction. Most enzymes are proteins.

enzyme-substrate complex A temporary complex formed when an enzyme binds to its substrate molecule(s).

epicotyl (ep'-uh-kot'-ul) In an angiosperm embryo, the embryonic axis above the point of attachment of the cotyledon(s) and below the first pair of miniature leaves.

epidemic A general outbreak of a disease.

epidermis (1) The dermal tissue system of nonwoody plants, usually consisting of a single layer of tightly packed cells. (2) The outermost layer of cells in an animal.

epididymis (ep'-uh-did'-uh-mus) A coiled tubule located adjacent to the mammalian testis where sperm are stored.

epigenetic inheritance Inheritance of traits transmitted by mechanisms not directly involving the nucleotide sequence of a genome.

epinephrine (ep′-i-nef′-rin) A catecholamine that, when secreted as a hormone by the adrenal medulla, mediates "fight-or-flight" responses to short-term stresses; also released by some neurons as a neurotransmitter; also known as adrenaline.

epiphyte (ep′-uh-fīt) A plant that nourishes itself but grows on the surface of another plant for support, usually on the branches or trunks of trees.

epistasis (ep′-i-stā′-sis) A type of gene interaction in which the phenotypic expression of one gene alters that of another independently inherited gene.

epithelial tissue (ep′-uh-thē′-lē-ul) Sheets of tightly packed cells that line organs and body cavities as well as external surfaces; also called epithelium.

epithelium An epithelial tissue.

epitope A small, accessible region of an antigen to which an antigen receptor or antibody binds; also called an antigenic determinant.

equilibrium potential (E_{ion}) The magnitude of a cell's membrane voltage at equilibrium, calculated using the Nernst equation.

erythrocyte (eh-rith′-ruh-sīt) A blood cell that contains hemoglobin, which transports oxygen; also called a red blood cell.

esophagus (eh-sof′-uh-gus) A muscular tube that conducts food, by peristalsis, from the pharynx to the stomach.

essential amino acid An amino acid that an animal cannot synthesize itself and must be obtained from food in prefabricated form.

essential element A chemical element required for an organism to survive, grow, and reproduce.

essential fatty acid An unsaturated fatty acid that an animal needs but cannot make.

essential nutrient A substance that an organism cannot synthesize from any other material and therefore must absorb in preassembled form.

estradiol (es′-truh-dī′-ol) A steroid hormone that stimulates the development and maintenance of the female reproductive system and secondary sex characteristics; the major estrogen in mammals.

estrous cycle (es′-trus) A reproductive cycle characteristic of female mammals except humans and certain other primates, in which the nonpregnant endometrium is reabsorbed rather than shed, and sexual response occurs only during mid-cycle at estrus.

estuary The area where a freshwater stream or river merges with the ocean.

ethylene (eth′-uh-lēn) A gaseous plant hormone involved in responses to mechanical stress, programmed cell death, leaf abscission, and fruit ripening.

etiolation Plant morphological adaptations for growing in darkness.

euchromatin (yū-krō′-muh-tin) The less condensed form of eukaryotic chromatin that is available for transcription.

euglenozoan Member of a diverse clade of flagellated protists that includes predatory heterotrophs, photosynthetic autotrophs, and pathogenic parasites.

Eukarya (yū-kar′-ē-uh) The domain that includes all eukaryotic organisms.

eukaryotic cell (yū′-ker-ē-ot′-ik) A type of cell with a membrane-enclosed nucleus and membrane-enclosed organelles. Organisms with eukaryotic cells (protists, plants, fungi, and animals) are called eukaryotes.

eumetazoan (yū′-met-uh-zō′-un) Member of a clade of animals with true tissues. All animals except sponges and a few other groups are eumetazoans.

Eustachian tube (yū-stā′-shun) The tube that connects the middle ear to the pharynx.

eutherian (yū-thēr′-ē-un) Placental mammal; mammal whose young complete their embryonic development within the uterus, joined to the mother by the placenta.

eutrophic lake (yū-trōf′-ik) A lake that has a high rate of biological productivity supported by a high rate of nutrient cycling.

eutrophication A process by which nutrients, particularly phosphorus and nitrogen, become highly concentrated in a body of water, leading to increased growth of organisms such as algae or cyanobacteria.

evaporative cooling The process in which the surface of an object becomes cooler during evaporation, a result of the molecules with the greatest kinetic energy changing from the liquid to the gaseous state.

evapotranspiration The total evaporation of water from an ecosystem, including water transpired by plants and evaporated from a landscape, usually measured in millimeters and estimated for a year.

evo-devo Evolutionary developmental biology; a field of biology that compares developmental processes of different multicellular organisms to understand how these processes have evolved and how changes can modify existing organismal features or lead to new ones.

evolution Descent with modification; the idea that living species are descendants of ancestral species that were different from the present-day ones; also defined more narrowly as the change in the genetic composition of a population from generation to generation.

Excavata One of four supergroups of eukaryotes proposed in a current hypothesis of the evolutionary history of eukaryotes. Excavates have unique cytoskeletal features, and some species have an "excavated" feeding groove on one side of the cell body. *See also* "SAR" clade, Archaeplastida, and Unikonta.

excitatory postsynaptic potential (EPSP) An electrical change (depolarization) in the membrane of a postsynaptic cell caused by the binding of an excitatory neurotransmitter from a presynaptic cell to a postsynaptic receptor; makes it more likely for a postsynaptic cell to generate an action potential.

excretion The disposal of nitrogen-containing metabolites and other waste products.

exergonic reaction (ek′-ser-gon′-ik) A spontaneous chemical reaction, in which there is a net release of free energy.

exocrine gland (ek′-sō-krin) A gland that secretes substances through a duct onto a body surface or into a body cavity.

exocytosis (ek′-sō-sī-tō′-sis) The cellular secretion of biological molecules by the fusion of vesicles containing them with the plasma membrane.

exon A sequence within a primary transcript that remains in the RNA after RNA processing; also refers to the region of DNA from which this sequence was transcribed.

exoskeleton A hard encasement on the surface of an animal, such as the shell of a mollusc or the cuticle of an arthropod, that provides protection and points of attachment for muscles.

exotoxin (ek′-sō-tok′-sin) A toxic protein that is secreted by a prokaryote or other pathogen and that produces specific symptoms, even if the pathogen is no longer present.

expansin Plant enzyme that breaks the cross-links (hydrogen bonds) between cellulose microfibrils and other cell wall constituents, loosening the wall's fabric.

experimental group A set of subjects that has (or receives) the specific factor being tested in a controlled experiment.

exponential population growth Growth of a population in an ideal, unlimited environment, represented by a J-shaped curve when population size is plotted over time.

external fertilization The fusion of gametes that parents have discharged into the environment.

extinction vortex A downward population spiral in which inbreeding and genetic drift combine to cause a small population to shrink and, unless the spiral is reversed, become extinct.

extracellular matrix (ECM) The meshwork surrounding animal cells, consisting of glycoproteins, polysaccharides, and proteoglycans synthesized and secreted by the cells.

extreme halophile An organism that lives in a highly saline environment, such as the Great Salt Lake or the Dead Sea.

extreme thermophile An organism that thrives in hot environments (often 60–80°C or hotter).

extremophile An organism that lives in environmental conditions so extreme that few other species can survive there. Extremophiles include extreme halophiles ("salt lovers") and extreme thermophiles ("heat lovers").

F factor In bacteria, the DNA segment that confers the ability to form pili for conjugation and associated functions required for the transfer of DNA from donor to recipient. The F factor may exist as a plasmid or be integrated into the bacterial chromosome.

F plasmid The plasmid form of the F factor.

F_1 generation The first filial, hybrid (heterozygous) offspring arising from a parental (P generation) cross.

F_2 generation The offspring resulting from interbreeding (or self-pollination) of the hybrid F_1 generation.

facilitated diffusion The passage of molecules or ions down their electrochemical gradient across a biological membrane with the assistance of specific transmembrane transport proteins, requiring no energy expenditure.

facilitation An interaction in which one species has a positive effect on the survival and reproduction of another species without the intimate association of a symbiosis.

facultative anaerobe (fak′-ul-tā′-tiv an′-uh-rōb) An organism that makes ATP by aerobic respiration if oxygen is present but that switches to anaerobic respiration or fermentation if oxygen is not present.

family In Linnaean classification, the taxonomic category above genus.

fast-twitch fiber A muscle fiber used for rapid, powerful contractions.

fat A lipid consisting of three fatty acids linked to one glycerol molecule; also called a triacylglycerol or triglyceride.

fatty acid A carboxylic acid with a long carbon chain. Fatty acids vary in length and in the number and location of double bonds; three fatty acids linked to a glycerol molecule form a fat molecule, also known as a triacylglycerol or triglyceride.

feces (fē′-sēz) The wastes of the digestive tract.

feedback inhibition A method of metabolic control in which the end product of a metabolic pathway acts as an inhibitor of an enzyme within that pathway.

fermentation A catabolic process that makes a limited amount of ATP from glucose (or other organic molecules) without an electron transport chain and that produces a characteristic end product, such as ethyl alcohol or lactic acid.

fertilization (1) The union of haploid gametes to produce a diploid zygote. (2) The addition of mineral nutrients to the soil.

fetus (fē′-tus) A developing mammal that has all the major structures of an adult. In humans, the fetal stage lasts from the 9th week of gestation until birth.

fiber A lignified cell type that reinforces the xylem of angiosperms and functions in mechanical support; a slender, tapered sclerenchyma cell that usually occurs in bundles.

fibronectin An extracellular glycoprotein secreted by animal cells that helps them attach to the extracellular matrix.

filtrate Cell-free fluid extracted from the body fluid by the excretory system.

filtration In excretory systems, the extraction of water and small solutes, including metabolic wastes, from the body fluid.

fimbria (plural, **fimbriae**) A short, hairlike appendage of a prokaryotic cell that helps it adhere to the substrate or to other cells.

first law of thermodynamics The principle of conservation of energy: Energy can be transferred and transformed, but it cannot be created or destroyed.

fixed action pattern In animal behavior, a sequence of unlearned acts that is essentially unchangeable and, once initiated, usually carried to completion.

flaccid (flas′-id) Limp. Lacking turgor (stiffness or firmness), as in a plant cell in surroundings where there is a tendency for water to leave the cell. (A walled cell becomes flaccid if it has a higher water potential than its surroundings, resulting in the loss of water.)

flagellum (fluh-jel′-um) (plural, **flagella**) A long cellular appendage specialized for locomotion. Like motile cilia, eukaryotic flagella have a core with nine outer doublet microtubules and two inner single microtubules (the "9 + 2" arrangement) ensheathed in an extension of the plasma membrane. Prokaryotic flagella have a different structure.

florigen A flowering signal, probably a protein, that is made in leaves under certain conditions and that travels to the shoot apical meristems, inducing them to switch from vegetative to reproductive growth.

flower In an angiosperm, a specialized shoot with up to four sets of modified leaves, bearing structures that function in sexual reproduction.

fluid feeder An animal that lives by sucking nutrient-rich fluids from another living organism.

fluid mosaic model The currently accepted model of cell membrane structure, which envisions the membrane as a mosaic of protein molecules drifting laterally in a fluid bilayer of phospholipids.

follicle (fol′-uh-kul) A microscopic structure in the ovary that contains the developing oocyte and secretes estrogens.

follicle-stimulating hormone (FSH) A tropic hormone that is produced and secreted by the anterior pituitary and that stimulates the production of eggs by the ovaries and sperm by the testes.

follicular phase That part of the ovarian cycle during which follicles are growing and oocytes maturing.

food chain The pathway along which food energy is transferred from trophic level to trophic level, beginning with producers.

food vacuole A membranous sac formed by phagocytosis of microorganisms or particles to be used as food by the cell.

food web The interconnected feeding relationships in an ecosystem.

foraging The seeking and obtaining of food.

foram (foraminiferan) An aquatic protist that secretes a hardened shell containing calcium carbonate and extends pseudopodia through pores in the shell.

forebrain One of three ancestral and embryonic regions of the vertebrate brain; develops into the thalamus, hypothalamus, and cerebrum.

fossil A preserved remnant or impression of an organism that lived in the past.

founder effect Genetic drift that occurs when a few individuals become isolated from a larger population and form a new population whose gene pool composition is not reflective of that of the original population.

fovea (fō′-vē-uh) The place on the retina at the eye's center of focus, where cones are highly concentrated.

fragmentation A means of asexual reproduction whereby a single parent breaks into parts that regenerate into whole new individuals.

frameshift mutation A mutation occurring when nucleotides are inserted in or deleted from a gene and the number inserted or deleted is not a multiple of three, resulting in the improper grouping of the subsequent nucleotides into codons.

free energy The portion of a biological system's energy that can perform work when temperature and pressure are uniform throughout the system. The change in free energy of a system (ΔG) is $G_{\text{final state}} - G_{\text{initial state}}$. It can be calculated by the equation $\Delta G = \Delta H - T\Delta S$, where ΔH is the change in enthalpy (in biological systems, equivalent to total energy), T is the absolute temperature, and ΔS is the change in entropy.

frequency-dependent selection Selection in which the fitness of a phenotype depends on how common the phenotype is in a population.

fruit A mature ovary of a flower. The fruit protects dormant seeds and often aids in their dispersal.

functional group A specific configuration of atoms commonly attached to the carbon skeletons of organic molecules and involved in chemical reactions.

G protein A GTP-binding protein that relays signals from a plasma membrane signal receptor, known as a G protein-coupled receptor, to other signal transduction proteins inside the cell.

G protein-coupled receptor (GPCR) A signal receptor protein in the plasma membrane that responds to the binding of a signaling molecule by activating a G protein. Also called a G protein-linked receptor.

G_0 phase A nondividing state occupied by cells that have left the cell cycle, sometimes reversibly.

G_1 phase The first gap, or growth phase, of the cell cycle, consisting of the portion of interphase before DNA synthesis begins.

G_2 phase The second gap, or growth phase, of the cell cycle, consisting of the portion of interphase after DNA synthesis occurs.

gallbladder An organ that stores bile and releases it as needed into the small intestine.

gamete (gam′-ēt) A haploid reproductive cell, such as an egg or sperm. Gametes unite during sexual reproduction to produce a diploid zygote.

gametogenesis The process by which gametes are produced.

gametophyte (guh-mē′-tō-fīt) In organisms (plants and some algae) that have alternation of generations, the multicellular haploid form that produces haploid gametes by mitosis. The haploid gametes unite and develop into sporophytes.

gamma-aminobutyric acid (GABA) An amino acid that functions as a neurotransmitter in the central nervous system of vertebrates.

ganglion (gang′-glē-uhn) (plural, **ganglia**) A cluster (functional group) of nerve cell bodies in a centralized nervous system.

gap junction A type of intercellular junction in animal cells, consisting of proteins surrounding a pore that allows the passage of materials between cells.

gas exchange The uptake of molecular oxygen from the environment and the discharge of carbon dioxide to the environment.

gas exchange circuit The branch of the circulatory system that supplies the organs where gases are exchanged with the environment; in many amphibians, it supplies the lungs and skin and is called a *pulmocutaneous circuit*, whereas in birds and mammals, it supplies only the lungs and is called a *pulmonary circuit*.

gastric juice A digestive fluid secreted by the stomach.

gastrovascular cavity A central cavity with a single opening in the body of certain animals, including cnidarians and flatworms, that functions in both the digestion and distribution of nutrients.

gastrula (gas′-trū-luh) An embryonic stage in animal development encompassing the formation of three layers: ectoderm, mesoderm, and endoderm.

gastrulation (gas′-trū-lā′-shun) In animal development, a series of cell and tissue movements in which the blastula-stage embryo folds inward, producing a three-layered embryo, the gastrula.

gated channel A transmembrane protein channel that opens or closes in response to a particular stimulus.

gated ion channel A gated channel for a specific ion. The opening or closing of such channels may alter a cell's membrane potential.

gel electrophoresis (ē-lek′-trō-fōr-ē′-sis) A technique for separating nucleic acids or proteins on the basis of their size and electrical charge, both of which affect their rate of movement through an electric field in a gel made of agarose or another polymer.

gene A discrete unit of hereditary information consisting of a specific nucleotide sequence in DNA (or RNA, in some viruses).

gene cloning The production of multiple copies of a gene.

gene expression The process by which information encoded in DNA directs the synthesis of proteins or, in some cases, RNAs that are not translated into proteins and instead function as RNAs.

gene flow The transfer of alleles from one population to another, resulting from the movement of fertile individuals or their gametes.

gene pool The aggregate of all copies of every type of allele at all loci in every individual in a population. The term is also used in a more restricted sense as the aggregate of alleles for just one or a few loci in a population.

gene-for-gene recognition A widespread form of plant disease resistance involving recognition of pathogen-derived molecules by the protein products of specific plant disease resistance genes.

genetic drift A process in which chance events cause unpredictable fluctuations in allele frequencies from one generation to the next. Effects of genetic drift are most pronounced in small populations.

genetic engineering The direct manipulation of genes for practical purposes.

genetic map An ordered list of genetic loci (genes or other genetic markers) along a chromosome.

genetic profile An individual's unique set of genetic markers, detected most often today by PCR.

genetic recombination General term for the production of offspring with combinations of traits that differ from those found in either parent.

genetic variation Differences among individuals in the composition of their genes or other DNA segments.

genetics The scientific study of heredity and hereditary variation.

genome (jē′-nōm) The genetic material of an organism or virus; the complete complement of an organism's or virus's genes along with its noncoding nucleic acid sequences.

genomics (juh-nō′-miks) The study of whole sets of genes and their interactions within a species, as well as genome comparisons between species.

genotype (jē′-nō-tīp) The genetic makeup, or set of alleles, of an organism.

genus (jē′-nus) (plural, **genera**) A taxonomic category above the species level, designated by the first word of a species' two-part scientific name.

geologic record A standard time scale dividing Earth's history into time periods grouped into four eons—Hadean, Archaean, Proterozoic, and Phanerozoic—and further subdivided into eras, periods, and epochs.

gestation (jes-tā′-shun) Pregnancy; the state of carrying developing young within the female reproductive tract.

gibberellin (jib′-uh-rel′-in) Any of a class of related plant hormones that stimulate growth in the stem and leaves, trigger the germination of seeds and breaking of bud dormancy, and (with auxin) stimulate fruit development.

glans The rounded structure at the tip of the clitoris or penis that is involved in sexual arousal.

glia (glial cells) Cells of the nervous system that support, regulate, and augment the functions of neurons.

global ecology The study of the functioning and distribution of organisms across the biosphere and how the regional exchange of energy and materials affects them.

glomerulus (glō-mār′-yū-lus) A ball of capillaries surrounded by Bowman's capsule in the nephron and serving as the site of filtration in the vertebrate kidney.

glutamate An amino acid that functions as a neurotransmitter in the central nervous system.

glyceraldehyde 3-phosphate (G3P) (glis′-er-al′-de-hīd) A three-carbon carbohydrate that is the direct product of the Calvin cycle; it is also an intermediate in glycolysis.

glycogen (glī′-kō-jen) An extensively branched glucose storage polysaccharide found in the liver and muscle of animals; the animal equivalent of starch.

glycolipid A lipid with one or more covalently attached carbohydrates.

glycolysis (glī-kol′-uh-sis) A series of reactions that ultimately splits glucose into pyruvate. Glycolysis occurs in almost all living cells, serving as the starting point for fermentation or cellular respiration.

glycoprotein A protein with one or more covalently attached carbohydrates.

glycosidic linkage A covalent bond formed between two monosaccharides by a dehydration reaction.

gnathostome (na′-thu-stōm) Member of the vertebrate subgroup possessing jaws.

Golgi apparatus (gol′-jē) An organelle in eukaryotic cells consisting of stacks of flat membranous sacs that modify, store, and route products of the endoplasmic reticulum and synthesize some products, notably noncellulose carbohydrates.

gonad (gō′-nad) A male or female gamete-producing organ.

graded potential In a neuron, a shift in the membrane potential that has an amplitude proportional to signal strength and that decays as it spreads.

gram-negative Describing the group of bacteria that have a cell wall that is structurally more complex and contains less peptidoglycan than the cell wall of gram-positive bacteria. Gram-negative bacteria are often more toxic than gram-positive bacteria.

gram-positive Describing the group of bacteria that have a cell wall that is structurally less complex and contains more peptidoglycan than the cell wall of gram-negative bacteria. Gram-positive bacteria are usually less toxic than gram-negative bacteria.

granum (gran′-um) (plural, **grana**) A stack of membrane-bounded thylakoids in the chloroplast. Grana function in the light reactions of photosynthesis.

gravitropism (grav′-uh-trō′-pizm) A response of a plant or animal to gravity.

gray matter Regions of dendrites and clustered neuron cell bodies within the CNS.

green alga A photosynthetic protist, named for green chloroplasts that are similar in structure and pigment composition to the chloroplasts of land plants. Green algae are a paraphyletic group; some members are more closely related to land plants than they are to other green algae.

greenhouse effect The warming of Earth due to the atmospheric accumulation of carbon dioxide and certain other gases, which absorb reflected infrared radiation and reradiate some of it back toward Earth.

gross primary production (GPP) The total primary production of an ecosystem.

ground tissue system Plant tissues that are neither vascular nor dermal, fulfilling a variety of functions, such as storage, photosynthesis, and support.

growth factor (1) A protein that must be present in the extracellular environment (culture medium or animal body) for the growth and normal development of certain types of cells. (2) A local regulator that acts on nearby cells to stimulate cell proliferation and differentiation.

guard cells The two cells that flank the stomatal pore and regulate the opening and closing of the pore.

gustation The sense of taste.

gymnosperm (jim′-nō-sperm) A vascular plant that bears naked seeds—seeds not enclosed in protective chambers.

hair cell A mechanosensory cell that alters output to the nervous system when hairlike projections on the cell surface are displaced.

half-life The amount of time it takes for 50% of a sample of a radioactive isotope to decay.

Hamilton's rule The principle that for natural selection to favor an altruistic act, the benefit to the recipient, devalued by the coefficient of relatedness, must exceed the cost to the altruist.

haploid cell (hap′-loyd) A cell containing only one set of chromosomes (*n*).

Hardy-Weinberg principle The principle that frequencies of alleles and genotypes in a population remain constant from generation to generation, provided that only Mendelian segregation and recombination of alleles are at work.

haustorium (plural, **haustoria**) (ho-stōr′-ē-um, ho-stōr′-ē-uh) In certain symbiotic fungi, a specialized hypha that can penetrate the tissues of host organisms.

heart A muscular pump that uses metabolic energy to elevate the hydrostatic pressure of the circulatory fluid (blood or hemolymph). The fluid then flows down a pressure gradient through the body and eventually returns to the heart.

heart attack The damage or death of cardiac muscle tissue resulting from prolonged blockage of one or more coronary arteries.

heart murmur A hissing sound that most often results from blood squirting backward through a leaky valve in the heart.

heat Thermal energy in transfer from one body of matter to another.

heat of vaporization The quantity of heat a liquid must absorb for 1 g of it to be converted from the liquid to the gaseous state.

heat-shock protein A protein that helps protect other proteins during heat stress. Heat-shock proteins are found in plants, animals, and microorganisms.

heavy chain One of the two types of polypeptide chains that make up an antibody molecule and B cell receptor; consists of a variable region, which contributes to the antigen-binding site, and a constant region.

helicase An enzyme that untwists the double helix of DNA at replication forks, separating the two strands and making them available as template strands.

helper T cell A type of T cell that, when activated, secretes cytokines that promote the response of B cells (humoral response) and cytotoxic T cells (cell-mediated response) to antigens.

hemoglobin (hē′-mō-glō′-bin) An iron-containing protein in red blood cells that reversibly binds oxygen.

hemolymph (hē′-mō-limf′) In invertebrates with an open circulatory system, the body fluid that bathes tissues.

hemophilia (hē′-muh-fil′-ē-uh) A human genetic disease caused by a sex-linked recessive allele, resulting in the absence of one or more blood-clotting proteins; characterized by excessive bleeding following injury.

hepatic portal vein A large vessel that conveys nutrient-laden blood from the small intestine to the liver, which regulates the blood's nutrient content.

herbivore (hur′-bi-vōr′) An animal that mainly eats plants or algae.

herbivory An interaction in which an organism eats parts of a plant or alga.

heredity The transmission of traits from one generation to the next.

hermaphroditism (hur-maf′-rō-dī-tizm) A condition in which an individual has both female and male gonads and functions as both a male and female in sexual reproduction by producing both sperm and eggs.

heterochromatin (het′-er-ō-krō′-muh-tin) Eukaryotic chromatin that remains highly compacted during interphase and is generally not transcribed.

heterochrony (het′-uh-rok′-ruh-nē) Evolutionary change in the timing or rate of an organism's development.

heterocyst (het′-er-ō-sist) A specialized cell that engages in nitrogen fixation in some filamentous cyanobacteria; also called a heterocyte.

heterotroph (het′-er-ō-trōf) An organism that obtains organic food molecules by eating other organisms or substances derived from them.

heterozygote advantage Greater reproductive success of heterozygous individuals compared with homozygotes; tends to preserve variation in a gene pool.

heterozygous (het′-er-ō-zī′-gus) Having two different alleles for a given gene.

high-density lipoprotein (HDL) A particle in the blood made up of thousands of cholesterol molecules and other lipids bound to a protein. HDL scavenges excess cholesterol.

hindbrain One of three ancestral and embryonic regions of the vertebrate brain; develops into the medulla oblongata, pons, and cerebellum.

histamine (his′-tuh-mēn) A substance released by mast cells that causes blood vessels to dilate and become more permeable in inflammatory and allergic responses.

histogram A variant of a bar graph in which a numerical independent variable is divided into equal intervals (or groups called "bins"). The height (or length) of each bar represents the value of the dependent variable for a particular interval.

histone (his′-tōn) A small protein with a high proportion of positively charged amino acids that binds to the negatively charged DNA and plays a key role in chromatin structure.

histone acetylation The attachment of acetyl groups to certain amino acids of histone proteins.

HIV (human immunodeficiency virus) The infectious agent that causes AIDS. HIV is a retrovirus.

holdfast A rootlike structure that anchors a seaweed.

homeobox (hō′-mē-ō-boks′) A 180-nucleotide sequence within homeotic genes and some other developmental genes that is widely conserved in animals. Related sequences occur in plants and yeasts.

homeostasis (hō′-mē-ō-stā′-sis) The steady-state physiological condition of the body.

homeotic gene (hō-mē-o′-tik) Any of the master regulatory genes that control placement and spatial organization of body parts in animals, plants, and fungi by controlling the developmental fate of groups of cells.

homologous chromosomes (hō-mol′-uh-gus) A pair of chromosomes of the same length, centromere position, and staining pattern that possess genes for the same characters at corresponding loci. One homologous chromosome is inherited from the organism's father, the other from the mother. Also called homologs, or a homologous pair.

homologous structures Structures in different species that are similar because of common ancestry.

homology (hō-mol′-ō-jē) Similarity in characteristics resulting from a shared ancestry.

homoplasy (hō′-muh-play′-zē) A similar (analogous) structure or molecular sequence that has evolved independently in two species.

homozygous (hō′-mō-zī′-gus) Having two identical alleles for a given gene.

horizontal gene transfer The transfer of genes from one genome to another through mechanisms such as transposable elements, plasmid exchange, viral activity, and perhaps fusions of different organisms.

hormone In multicellular organisms, one of many types of secreted chemicals that are formed in specialized cells, travel in body fluids, and act on specific target cells in other parts of the body, changing the target cells' functioning. Hormones are thus important in long-distance signaling.

host The larger participant in a symbiotic relationship, often providing a home and food source for the smaller symbiont.

host range The limited number of species whose cells can be infected by a particular virus.

Human Genome Project An international collaborative effort to map and sequence the DNA of the entire human genome.

human immunodeficiency virus (HIV) The pathogen that causes AIDS (acquired immune deficiency syndrome).

humoral immune response (hyū′-mer-ul) The branch of adaptive immunity that involves the activation of B cells and that leads to the production of antibodies, which defend against bacteria and viruses in body fluids.

humus (hyū′-mus) Decomposing organic material that is a component of topsoil.

Huntington's disease A human genetic disease caused by a dominant allele; characterized by uncontrollable body movements and degeneration of the nervous system; usually fatal 10 to 20 years after the onset of symptoms.

hybrid Offspring that results from the mating of individuals from two different species or from two true-breeding varieties of the same species.

hybrid zone A geographic region in which members of different species meet and mate, producing at least some offspring of mixed ancestry.

hybridization In genetics, the mating, or crossing, of two true-breeding varieties.

hydration shell The sphere of water molecules around a dissolved ion.

hydrocarbon An organic molecule consisting of only carbon and hydrogen.

hydrogen bond A type of weak chemical bond that is formed when the slightly positive hydrogen atom of a polar covalent bond in one molecule is attracted to the slightly negative atom of a polar covalent bond in another molecule or in another region of the same molecule.

hydrogen ion A single proton with a charge of $1+$. The dissociation of a water molecule (H_2O) leads to the generation of a hydroxide ion (OH^-) and a hydrogen ion (H^+); in water, H^+ is not found alone but associates with a water molecule to form a hydronium ion.

hydrolysis (hī-drol′-uh-sis) A chemical reaction that breaks bonds between two molecules by the addition of water; functions in disassembly of polymers to monomers.

hydronium ion A water molecule that has an extra proton bound to it; H_3O^+, commonly represented as H^+.

hydrophilic (hī′-drō-fil′-ik) Having an affinity for water.

hydrophobic (hī′-drō-fō′-bik) Having no affinity for water; tending to coalesce and form droplets in water.

hydrophobic interaction A type of weak chemical interaction caused when molecules that do not mix with water coalesce to exclude water.

hydroponic culture A method in which plants are grown in mineral solutions rather than in soil.

hydrostatic skeleton A skeletal system composed of fluid held under pressure in a closed body compartment; the main skeleton of most cnidarians, flatworms, nematodes, and annelids.

hydroxide ion A water molecule that has lost a proton; OH^-.

hydroxyl group (hī-drok′-sil) A chemical group consisting of an oxygen atom joined to a hydrogen atom. Molecules possessing this group are soluble in water and are called alcohols.

hymen A thin membrane that partly covers the vaginal opening in the human female. The hymen is ruptured by sexual intercourse or other vigorous activity.

hyperpolarization A change in a cell's membrane potential such that the inside of the membrane becomes more negative relative to the outside. Hyperpolarization reduces the chance that a neuron will transmit a nerve impulse.

hypersensitive response A plant's localized defense response to a pathogen, involving the death of cells around the site of infection.

hypertension A disorder in which blood pressure remains abnormally high.

hypertonic Referring to a solution that, when surrounding a cell, will cause the cell to lose water.

hypha (plural, **hyphae**) (hī′-fuh, hī′-fē) One of many connected filaments that collectively make up the mycelium of a fungus.

hypocotyl (hī′-puh-cot′-ul) In an angiosperm embryo, the embryonic axis below the point of attachment of the cotyledon(s) and above the radicle.

hypothalamus (hī′-pō-thal′-uh-mus) The ventral part of the vertebrate forebrain; functions in maintaining homeostasis, especially in coordinating the endocrine and nervous systems; secretes hormones of the posterior pituitary and releasing factors that regulate the anterior pituitary.

hypothesis (hī-poth′-uh-sis) A testable explanation for a set of observations based on the available data and guided by inductive reasoning. A hypothesis is narrower in scope than a theory.

hypotonic Referring to a solution that, when surrounding a cell, will cause the cell to take up water.

imbibition The physical adsorption of water onto the internal surfaces of structures.

immigration The influx of new individuals into a population from other areas.

immune system An animal body's system of defenses against agents that cause disease.

immunization The process of generating a state of immunity by artificial means. In active immunization, also called vaccination, an inactive or weakened form of a pathogen is administered, inducing B and T cell responses and immunological memory. In passive immunization, antibodies specific for a particular microbe are administered, conferring immediate but temporary protection.

immunoglobulin (Ig) (im′-yū-nō-glob′-yū-lin) *See* antibody.

imprinting In animal behavior, the formation at a specific stage in life of a long-lasting behavioral response to a specific individual or object.

in situ **hybridization** A technique using nucleic acid hybridization with a labeled probe to detect the location of a specific mRNA in an intact organism.

in vitro **fertilization (IVF)** (vē′-trō) Fertilization of oocytes in laboratory containers followed by artificial implantation of the early embryo in the mother's uterus.

inclusive fitness The total effect an individual has on proliferating its genes by producing its own offspring and by providing aid that enables other close relatives to increase production of their offspring.

incomplete dominance The situation in which the phenotype of heterozygotes is intermediate between the phenotypes of individuals homozygous for either allele.

incomplete flower A flower in which one or more of the four basic floral organs (sepals, petals, stamens, or carpels) are either absent or nonfunctional.

independent variable A variable whose value is manipulated or changed during an experiment to reveal possible effects on another variable (the dependent variable).

indeterminate growth A type of growth characteristic of plants, in which the organism continues to grow as long as it lives.

induced fit Caused by entry of the substrate, the change in shape of the active site of an enzyme so that it binds more snugly to the substrate.

inducer A specific small molecule that binds to a bacterial repressor protein and changes the repressor's shape so that it cannot bind to an operator, thus switching an operon on.

induction The process in which one group of embryonic cells influences the development of another, usually by causing changes in gene expression.

inductive reasoning A type of logic in which generalizations are based on a large number of specific observations.

inflammatory response An innate immune defense triggered by physical injury or infection of tissue involving the release of substances that promote swelling, enhance the infiltration of white blood cells, and aid in tissue repair and destruction of invading pathogens.

inflorescence A group of flowers tightly clustered together.

ingestion The first stage of food processing in animals: the act of eating.

ingroup A species or group of species whose evolutionary relationships are being examined in a given analysis.

inhibitory postsynaptic potential (IPSP) An electrical change (usually hyperpolarization) in the membrane of a postsynaptic neuron caused by the binding of an inhibitory neurotransmitter from a presynaptic cell to a postsynaptic receptor; makes it more difficult for a postsynaptic neuron to generate an action potential.

innate behavior Animal behavior that is developmentally fixed and under strong genetic control. Innate behavior is exhibited in virtually the same form by all individuals in a population despite internal and external environmental differences during development and throughout their lifetimes.

innate immunity A form of defense common to all animals that is active immediately upon exposure to pathogens and that is the same whether or not the pathogen has been encountered previously.

inner ear One of three main regions of the vertebrate ear; includes the cochlea (which in turn contains the organ of Corti) and the semicircular canals.

inquiry The search for information and explanation, often focusing on specific questions.

insertion A mutation involving the addition of one or more nucleotide pairs to a gene.

integral protein A transmembrane protein with hydrophobic regions that extend into and often completely span the hydrophobic interior of the membrane and with hydrophilic regions in contact with the aqueous solution on one or both sides of the membrane (or lining the channel in the case of a channel protein).

integrin In animal cells, a transmembrane receptor protein with two subunits that interconnects the extracellular matrix and the cytoskeleton.

integument (in-teg′-yū-ment) Layer of sporophyte tissue that contributes to the structure of an ovule of a seed plant.

intercalated disk (in-ter′-kuh-lā′-ted) A specialized junction between cardiac muscle cells that provides direct electrical coupling between the cells.

interferon (in′-ter-fēr′-on) A protein that has antiviral or immune regulatory functions. Interferon-α and interferon-β, secreted by virus-infected cells, help nearby cells resist viral infection; interferon-γ, secreted by T cells, helps activate macrophages.

intermediate disturbance hypothesis The concept that moderate levels of disturbance can foster greater species diversity than low or high levels of disturbance.

intermediate filament A component of the cytoskeleton that includes filaments intermediate in size between microtubules and microfilaments.

internal fertilization The fusion of eggs and sperm within the female reproductive tract. The sperm are typically deposited in or near the tract.

interneuron An association neuron; a nerve cell within the central nervous system that forms synapses with sensory and/or motor neurons and integrates sensory input and motor output.

internode A segment of a plant stem between the points where leaves are attached.

interphase The period in the cell cycle when the cell is not dividing. During interphase, cellular metabolic activity is high, chromosomes and organelles are duplicated, and cell size may increase. Interphase often accounts for about 90% of the cell cycle.

interspecific competition Competition for resources between individuals of two or more species when resources are in short supply.

interspecific interaction A relationship between individuals of two or more species in a community.

interstitial fluid The fluid filling the spaces between cells in most animals.

intertidal zone The shallow zone of the ocean adjacent to land and between the high- and low-tide lines.

introduced species A species moved by humans, either intentionally or accidentally, from its native location to a new geographic region; also called a non-native or exotic species.

intron (in′-tron) A noncoding, intervening sequence within a primary transcript that is removed from the transcript during RNA processing; also refers to the region of DNA from which this sequence was transcribed.

invasive species A species, often introduced by humans, that takes hold outside its native range.

inversion An aberration in chromosome structure resulting from reattachment of a chromosomal fragment in a reverse orientation to the chromosome from which it originated.

invertebrate An animal without a backbone. Invertebrates make up 95% of animal species.

ion (ī′-on) An atom or group of atoms that has gained or lost one or more electrons, thus acquiring a charge.

ion channel A transmembrane protein channel that allows a specific ion to diffuse across the membrane down its concentration or electrochemical gradient.

ionic bond (ī-on′-ik) A chemical bond resulting from the attraction between oppositely charged ions.

ionic compound A compound resulting from the formation of an ionic bond; also called a salt.

iris The colored part of the vertebrate eye, formed by the anterior portion of the choroid.

isotonic (ī′-sō-ton′-ik) Referring to a solution that, when surrounding a cell, causes no net movement of water into or out of the cell.

isotope (ī′-sō-tōp′) One of several atomic forms of an element, each with the same number of protons but a different number of neutrons, thus differing in atomic mass.

iteroparity Reproduction in which adults produce offspring over many years; also known as repeated reproduction.

joule (J) A unit of energy: 1 J = 0.239 cal; 1 cal = 4.184 J.

juxtaglomerular apparatus (JGA) (juks'-tuh-gluh-mār'-yū-ler) A specialized tissue in nephrons that releases the enzyme renin in response to a drop in blood pressure or volume.

juxtamedullary nephron In mammals and birds, a nephron with a loop of Henle that extends far into the renal medulla.

karyogamy (kār'-ē-og'-uh-mē) In fungi, the fusion of haploid nuclei contributed by the two parents; occurs as one stage of sexual reproduction, preceded by plasmogamy.

karyotype (kār'-ē-ō-tīp) A display of the chromosome pairs of a cell arranged by size and shape.

keystone species A species that is not necessarily abundant in a community yet exerts strong control on community structure by the nature of its ecological role or niche.

kidney In vertebrates, one of a pair of excretory organs where blood filtrate is formed and processed into urine.

kilocalorie (kcal) A thousand calories; the amount of heat energy required to raise the temperature of 1 kg of water by 1°C.

kin selection Natural selection that favors altruistic behavior by enhancing the reproductive success of relatives.

kinetic energy (kuh-net'-ik) The energy associated with the relative motion of objects. Moving matter can perform work by imparting motion to other matter.

kinetochore (kuh-net'-uh-kōr) A structure of proteins attached to the centromere that links each sister chromatid to the mitotic spindle.

kingdom A taxonomic category, the second broadest after domain.

K-selection Selection for life history traits that are sensitive to population density; also called density-dependent selection.

labia majora A pair of thick, fatty ridges that encloses and protects the rest of the vulva.

labia minora A pair of slender skin folds that surrounds the openings of the vagina and urethra.

lacteal (lak'-tē-ul) A tiny lymph vessel extending into the core of an intestinal villus and serving as the destination for absorbed chylomicrons.

lactic acid fermentation Glycolysis followed by the reduction of pyruvate to lactate, regenerating NAD^+ with no release of carbon dioxide.

lagging strand A discontinuously synthesized DNA strand that elongates by means of Okazaki fragments, each synthesized in a $5' \rightarrow 3'$ direction away from the replication fork.

landscape An area containing several different ecosystems linked by exchanges of energy, materials, and organisms.

landscape ecology The study of how the spatial arrangement of habitat types affects the distribution and abundance of organisms and ecosystem processes.

large intestine The portion of the vertebrate alimentary canal between the small intestine and the anus; functions mainly in water absorption and the formation of feces.

larynx (lār'-inks) The portion of the respiratory tract containing the vocal cords; also called the voice box.

lateral meristem (mār'-uh-stem) A meristem that thickens the roots and shoots of woody plants. The vascular cambium and cork cambium are lateral meristems.

lateral root A root that arises from the pericycle of an established root.

lateralization Segregation of functions in the cortex of the left and right cerebral hemispheres.

law of conservation of mass A physical law stating that matter can change form but cannot be created or destroyed. In a closed system, the mass of the system is constant.

law of independent assortment Mendel's second law, stating that each pair of alleles segregates, or assorts, independently of each other pair during gamete formation; applies when genes for two characters are located on different pairs of homologous chromosomes or when they are far enough apart on the same chromosome to behave as though they are on different chromosomes.

law of segregation Mendel's first law, stating that the two alleles in a pair segregate (separate from each other) into different gametes during gamete formation.

leading strand The new complementary DNA strand synthesized continuously along the template strand toward the replication fork in the mandatory $5' \rightarrow 3'$ direction.

leaf The main photosynthetic organ of vascular plants.

leaf primordium A finger-like projection along the flank of a shoot apical meristem, from which a leaf arises.

learning The modification of behavior based on specific experiences.

lens The structure in an eye that focuses light rays onto the photoreceptors.

lenticel (len'-ti-sel) A small raised area in the bark of stems and roots that enables gas exchange between living cells and the outside air.

leukocyte (lū'-kō-sīt') A blood cell that functions in fighting infections; also called a white blood cell.

Leydig cell (lī'-dig) A cell that produces testosterone and other androgens and is located between the seminiferous tubules of the testes.

lichen A mutualistic association between a fungus and a photosynthetic alga or cyanobacterium.

life cycle The generation-to-generation sequence of stages in the reproductive history of an organism.

life history The traits that affect an organism's schedule of reproduction and survival.

life table An age-specific summary of the survival pattern of a population.

ligand (lig'-und) A molecule that binds specifically to another molecule, usually a larger one.

ligand-gated ion channel A transmembrane protein containing a pore that opens or closes as it changes shape in response to a signaling molecule (ligand), allowing or blocking the flow of specific ions; also called an ionotropic receptor.

light chain One of the two types of polypeptide chains that make up an antibody molecule and B cell receptor; consists of a variable region, which contributes to the antigen-binding site, and a constant region.

light microscope (LM) An optical instrument with lenses that refract (bend) visible light to magnify images of specimens.

light reactions The first of two major stages in photosynthesis (preceding the Calvin cycle). These reactions, which occur on the thylakoid membranes of the chloroplast or on membranes of certain prokaryotes, convert solar energy to the chemical energy of ATP and NADPH, releasing oxygen in the process.

light-harvesting complex A complex of proteins associated with pigment molecules (including chlorophyll *a*, chlorophyll *b*, and carotenoids) that captures light energy and transfers it to reaction-center pigments in a photosystem.

lignin (lig'-nin) A strong polymer embedded in the cellulose matrix of the secondary cell walls of vascular plants that provides structural support in terrestrial species.

limiting nutrient An element that must be added for production to increase in a particular area.

limnetic zone In a lake, the well-lit, open surface waters far from shore.

linear electron flow A route of electron flow during the light reactions of photosynthesis that involves both photosystems (I and II) and produces ATP, NADPH, and O_2. The net electron flow is from H_2O to $NADP^+$.

line graph A two-dimensional graph in which each data point is connected to the next point in the data set with a straight line.

linkage map A genetic map based on the frequencies of recombination between markers during crossing over of homologous chromosomes.

linked genes Genes located close enough together on a chromosome that they tend to be inherited together.

lipid (lip'-id) Any of a group of large biological molecules, including fats, phospholipids, and steroids, that mix poorly, if at all, with water.

littoral zone In a lake, the shallow, well-lit waters close to shore.

liver A large internal organ in vertebrates that performs diverse functions, such as producing bile, maintaining blood glucose level, and detoxifying poisonous chemicals in the blood.

loam The most fertile soil type, made up of roughly equal amounts of sand, silt, and clay.

lobe-fin Member of a clade of osteichthyans having rod-shaped muscular fins. The group includes coelacanths, lungfishes, and tetrapods.

local regulator A secreted molecule that influences cells near where it is secreted.

locomotion Active motion from place to place.

locus (plural, **loci**) (lō′-kus, lō′-sī) A specific place along the length of a chromosome where a given gene is located.

logistic population growth Population growth that levels off as population size approaches carrying capacity.

long-day plant A plant that flowers (usually in late spring or early summer) only when the light period is longer than a critical length.

long-term memory The ability to hold, associate, and recall information over one's lifetime.

loop of Henle The hairpin turn, with a descending and ascending limb, between the proximal and distal tubules of the vertebrate kidney; functions in water and salt reabsorption.

low-density lipoprotein (LDL) A particle in the blood made up of thousands of cholesterol molecules and other lipids bound to a protein. LDL transports cholesterol from the liver for incorporation into cell membranes.

lung An infolded respiratory surface of a terrestrial vertebrate, land snail, or spider that connects to the atmosphere by narrow tubes.

luteinizing hormone (LH) (lū′-tē-uh-nī′-zing) A tropic hormone that is produced and secreted by the anterior pituitary and that stimulates ovulation in females and androgen production in males.

lycophyte (lī′-kuh-fīt) An informal name for a member of the phylum Lycophyta, a group of seedless vascular plants that includes club mosses and their relatives.

lymph The colorless fluid, derived from interstitial fluid, in the lymphatic system of vertebrates

lymph node An organ located along a lymph vessel. Lymph nodes filter lymph and contain cells that attack viruses and bacteria.

lymphatic system A system of vessels and nodes, separate from the circulatory system, that returns fluid, proteins, and cells to the blood.

lymphocyte A type of white blood cell that mediates immune responses. The two main classes are B cells and T cells.

lysogenic cycle (lī′-sō-jen′-ik) A type of phage replicative cycle in which the viral genome becomes incorporated into the bacterial host chromosome as a prophage, is replicated along with the chromosome, and does not kill the host.

lysosome (lī′-suh-sōm) A membrane-enclosed sac of hydrolytic enzymes found in the cytoplasm of animal cells and some protists.

lysozyme (lī′-sō-zīm) An enzyme that destroys bacterial cell walls; in mammals, found in sweat, tears, and saliva.

lytic cycle (lit′-ik) A type of phage replicative cycle resulting in the release of new phages by lysis (and death) of the host cell.

macroclimate Large-scale patterns in climate; the climate of an entire region.

macroevolution Evolutionary change above the species level. Examples of macroevolutionary change include the origin of a new group of organisms through a series of speciation events and the impact of mass extinctions on the diversity of life and its subsequent recovery.

macromolecule A giant molecule formed by the joining of smaller molecules, usually by a dehydration reaction. Polysaccharides, proteins, and nucleic acids are macromolecules.

macronutrient An essential element that an organism must obtain in relatively large amounts. *See also* micronutrient.

macrophage (mak′-rō-fāj) A phagocytic cell present in many tissues that functions in innate immunity by destroying microbes and in acquired immunity as an antigen-presenting cell.

major histocompatibility complex (MHC) molecule A host protein that functions in antigen presentation. Foreign MHC molecules on transplanted tissue can trigger T cell responses that may lead to rejection of the transplant.

malignant tumor A cancerous tumor containing cells that have significant genetic and cellular changes and are capable of invading and surviving in new sites. Malignant tumors can impair the functions of one or more organs.

mammal Member of the class Mammalia, amniotes that have hair and mammary glands (glands that produce milk).

mammary gland An exocrine gland that secretes milk to nourish the young. Mammary glands are characteristic of mammals.

map unit A unit of measurement of the distance between genes. One map unit is equivalent to a 1% recombination frequency.

marine benthic zone The ocean floor.

marsupial (mar-sū′-pē-ul) A mammal, such as a koala, kangaroo, or opossum, whose young complete their embryonic development inside a maternal pouch.

mass extinction The elimination of a large number of species throughout Earth, the result of global environmental changes.

mass number The sum of the number of protons and neutrons in an atom's nucleus.

mast cell A vertebrate body cell that produces histamine and other molecules that trigger inflammation in response to infection and in allergic reactions.

maternal effect gene A gene that, when mutant in the mother, results in a mutant phenotype in the offspring, regardless of the offspring's genotype. Maternal effect genes, also called egg-polarity genes, were first identified in *Drosophila melanogaster*.

matter Anything that takes up space and has mass.

maximum parsimony A principle that states that when considering multiple explanations for an observation, one should first investigate the simplest explanation that is consistent with the facts.

mechanoreceptor A sensory receptor that detects physical deformation in the body's environment associated with pressure, touch, stretch, motion, or sound.

medulla oblongata (meh-dul′-uh ōb′-long-go′-tuh) The lowest part of the vertebrate brain, commonly called the medulla; a swelling of the hindbrain anterior to the spinal cord that controls autonomic, homeostatic functions, including breathing, heart and blood vessel activity, swallowing, digestion, and vomiting.

megapascal (MPa) (meg′-uh-pas-kal′) A unit of pressure equivalent to about 10 atmospheres of pressure.

megaspore A spore from a heterosporous plant species that develops into a female gametophyte.

meiosis (mī-ō′-sis) A modified type of cell division in sexually reproducing organisms consisting of two rounds of cell division but only one round of DNA replication. It results in cells with half the number of chromosome sets as the original cell.

meiosis I The first division of a two-stage process of cell division in sexually reproducing organisms that results in cells with half the number of chromosome sets as the original cell.

meiosis II The second division of a two-stage process of cell division in sexually reproducing organisms that results in cells with half the number of chromosome sets as the original cell.

membrane potential The difference in electrical charge (voltage) across a cell's plasma membrane due to the differential distribution of ions. Membrane potential affects the activity of excitable cells and the transmembrane movement of all charged substances.

memory cell One of a clone of long-lived lymphocytes, formed during the primary immune response, that remains in a lymphoid organ until activated by exposure to the same antigen that triggered its formation. Activated memory cells mount the secondary immune response.

menopause The cessation of ovulation and menstruation, marking the end of a human female's reproductive years.

menstrual cycle (men′-strŭ-ul) In humans and certain other primates, a type of reproductive cycle in which the nonpregnant endometrium is shed through the cervix into the vagina; also called the uterine cycle.

menstruation The shedding of portions of the endometrium during a uterine (menstrual) cycle.

meristem (mãr′-uh-stem) Plant tissue that remains embryonic as long as the plant lives, allowing for indeterminate growth.

mesoderm (mez′-ō-derm) The middle primary germ layer in a triploblastic animal embryo; develops into the notochord, the lining of the coelom, muscles, skeleton, gonads, kidneys, and most of the circulatory system in species that have these structures.

mesophyll (mez′-ō-fil) Leaf cells specialized for photosynthesis. In C_3 and CAM plants, mesophyll cells are located between the upper and lower epidermis; in C_4 plants, they are located between the bundle-sheath cells and the epidermis.

messenger RNA (mRNA) A type of RNA, synthesized using a DNA template, that attaches to ribosomes in the cytoplasm and specifies the primary structure of a protein. (In eukaryotes, the primary RNA transcript must undergo RNA processing to become mRNA.)

metabolic pathway A series of chemical reactions that either builds a complex molecule (anabolic pathway) or breaks down a complex molecule to simpler molecules (catabolic pathway).

metabolic rate The total amount of energy an animal uses in a unit of time.

metabolism (muh-tab′-uh-lizm) The totality of an organism's chemical reactions, consisting of catabolic and anabolic pathways, which manage the material and energy resources of the organism.

metagenomics The collection and sequencing of DNA from a group of species, usually an environmental sample of microorganisms. Computer software sorts partial sequences and assembles them into genome sequences of individual species making up the sample.

metaphase The third stage of mitosis, in which the spindle is complete and the chromosomes, attached to microtubules at their kinetochores, are all aligned at the metaphase plate.

metaphase plate An imaginary structure located at a plane midway between the two poles of a cell in metaphase on which the centromeres of all the duplicated chromosomes are located.

metapopulation A group of spatially separated populations of one species that interact through immigration and emigration.

metastasis (muh-tas′-tuh-sis) The spread of cancer cells to locations distant from their original site.

methanogen (meth-an′-ō-jen) An organism that produces methane as a waste product of the way it obtains energy. All known methanogens are in domain Archaea.

methyl group A chemical group consisting of a carbon bonded to three hydrogen atoms. The methyl group may be attached to a carbon or to a different atom.

microevolution Evolutionary change below the species level; change in the allele frequencies in a population over generations.

microfilament A cable composed of actin proteins in the cytoplasm of almost every eukaryotic cell, making up part of the cytoskeleton and acting alone or with myosin to cause cell contraction; also known as an actin filament.

micronutrient An essential element that an organism needs in very small amounts. *See also* macronutrient.

microRNA (miRNA) A small, single-stranded RNA molecule, generated from a hairpin structure on a precursor RNA transcribed from a particular gene. The miRNA associates with one or more proteins in a complex that can degrade or prevent translation of an mRNA with a complementary sequence.

microspore A spore from a heterosporous plant species that develops into a male gametophyte.

microtubule A hollow rod composed of tubulin proteins that makes up part of the cytoskeleton in all eukaryotic cells and is found in cilia and flagella.

microvillus (plural, **microvilli**) One of many fine, finger-like projections of the epithelial cells in the lumen of the small intestine that increase its surface area.

midbrain One of three ancestral and embryonic regions of the vertebrate brain; develops into sensory integrating and relay centers that send sensory information to the cerebrum.

middle ear One of three main regions of the vertebrate ear; in mammals, a chamber containing three small bones (the malleus, incus, and stapes) that convey vibrations from the eardrum to the oval window.

middle lamella (luh-mel′-uh) In plants, a thin layer of adhesive extracellular material, primarily pectins, found between the primary walls of adjacent young cells.

migration A regular, long-distance change in location.

mineral In nutrition, a simple nutrient that is inorganic and therefore cannot be synthesized in the body.

minimum viable population (MVP) The smallest population size at which a species is able to sustain its numbers and survive.

mismatch repair The cellular process that uses specific enzymes to remove and replace incorrectly paired nucleotides.

missense mutation A nucleotide-pair substitution that results in a codon that codes for a different amino acid.

mitochondrial matrix The compartment of the mitochondrion enclosed by the inner membrane and containing enzymes and substrates for the citric acid cycle, as well as ribosomes and DNA.

mitochondrion (mī′-tō-kon′-drē-un) (plural, **mitochondria**) An organelle in eukaryotic cells that serves as the site of cellular respiration; uses oxygen to break down organic molecules and synthesize ATP.

mitosis (mī-tō′-sis) A process of nuclear division in eukaryotic cells conventionally divided into five stages: prophase, prometaphase, metaphase, anaphase, and telophase. Mitosis conserves chromosome number by allocating replicated chromosomes equally to each of the daughter nuclei.

mitotic (M) phase The phase of the cell cycle that includes mitosis and cytokinesis.

mitotic spindle An assemblage of microtubules and associated proteins that is involved in the movement of chromosomes during mitosis.

mixotroph An organism that is capable of both photosynthesis and heterotrophy.

model A physical or conceptual representation of a natural phenomenon.

model organism A particular species chosen for research into broad biological principles because it is representative of a larger group and usually easy to grow in a lab.

molarity A common measure of solute concentration, referring to the number of moles of solute per liter of solution.

mole (mol) The number of grams of a substance that equals its molecular weight in daltons and contains Avogadro's number of molecules.

molecular clock A method for estimating the time required for a given amount of evolutionary change, based on the observation that some regions of genomes evolve at constant rates.

molecular mass The sum of the masses of all the atoms in a molecule; sometimes called molecular weight.

molecule Two or more atoms held together by covalent bonds.

monilophyte An informal name for a member of the phylum Monilophyta, a group of seedless vascular plants that includes ferns and their relatives.

monoclonal antibody (mon'-ō-klōn'-ul) Any of a preparation of antibodies that have been produced by a single clone of cultured cells and thus are all specific for the same epitope.

monogamous (muh-nog'-uh-mus) Referring to a type of relationship in which one male mates with just one female.

monohybrid An organism that is heterozygous with respect to a single gene of interest. All the offspring from a cross between parents homozygous for different alleles are monohybrids. For example, parents of genotypes *AA* and *aa* produce a monohybrid of genotype *Aa*.

monohybrid cross A cross between two organisms that are heterozygous for the character being followed (or the self-pollination of a heterozygous plant).

monomer (mon'-uh-mer) The subunit that serves as the building block of a polymer.

monophyletic (mon'-ō-fī-let'-ik) Pertaining to a group of taxa that consists of a common ancestor and all of its descendants. A monophyletic taxon is equivalent to a clade.

monosaccharide (mon'-ō-sak'-uh-rīd) The simplest carbohydrate, active alone or serving as a monomer for disaccharides and polysaccharides. Also known as simple sugars, monosaccharides have molecular formulas that are generally some multiple of CH_2O.

monosomic Referring to a diploid cell that has only one copy of a particular chromosome instead of the normal two.

monotreme An egg-laying mammal, such as a platypus or echidna. Like all mammals, monotremes have hair and produce milk, but they lack nipples.

morphogen A substance, such as Bicoid protein in *Drosophila*, that provides positional information in the form of a concentration gradient along an embryonic axis.

morphogenesis (mōr'-fō-jen'-uh-sis) The development of the form of an organism and its structures.

morphological species concept Definition of a species in terms of measurable anatomical criteria.

motor neuron A nerve cell that transmits signals from the brain or spinal cord to muscles or glands.

motor protein A protein that interacts with cytoskeletal elements and other cell components, producing movement of the whole cell or parts of the cell.

motor system An efferent branch of the vertebrate peripheral nervous system composed of motor neurons that carry signals to skeletal muscles in response to external stimuli.

motor unit A single motor neuron and all the muscle fibers it controls.

movement corridor A series of small clumps or a narrow strip of quality habitat (usable by organisms) that connects otherwise isolated patches of quality habitat.

mucus A viscous and slippery mixture of glycoproteins, cells, salts, and water that moistens and protects the membranes lining body cavities that open to the exterior.

Müllerian mimicry (myū-lār'-ē-un) Reciprocal mimicry by two unpalatable species.

multifactorial Referring to a phenotypic character that is influenced by multiple genes and environmental factors.

multigene family A collection of genes with similar or identical sequences, presumably of common origin.

multiple fruit A fruit derived from an entire inflorescence.

multiplication rule A rule of probability stating that the probability of two or more independent events occurring together can be determined by multiplying their individual probabilities.

muscle tissue Tissue consisting of long muscle cells that can contract, either on its own or when stimulated by nerve impulses.

mutagen (myū'-tuh-jen) A chemical or physical agent that interacts with DNA and can cause a mutation.

mutation (myū-tā'-shun) A change in the nucleotide sequence of an organism's DNA or in the DNA or RNA of a virus.

mutualism (myū'-chū-ul-izm) A symbiotic relationship in which both participants benefit.

mycelium (mī-sē'-lē-um) The densely branched network of hyphae in a fungus.

mycorrhiza (plural, **mycorrhizae**) (mī'-kō-rī'-zuh, mī'-kō-rī'-zē) A mutualistic association of plant roots and fungus.

myelin sheath (mī'-uh-lin) Wrapped around the axon of a neuron, an insulating coat of cell membranes from Schwann cells or oligodendrocytes. It is interrupted by nodes of Ranvier, where action potentials are generated.

myofibril (mī'-ō-fī'-bril) A longitudinal bundle in a muscle cell (fiber) that contains thin filaments of actin and regulatory proteins and thick filaments of myosin.

myoglobin (mī'-uh-glō'-bin) An oxygen-storing, pigmented protein in muscle cells.

myosin (mī'-uh-sin) A type of motor protein that associates into filaments that interact with actin filaments, causing cell contraction.

NAD^+ Nicotinamide adenine dinucleotide, a coenzyme that cycles easily between oxidized (NAD^+) and reduced (NADH) states, thus acting as an electron carrier.

$NADP^+$ Nicotinamide adenine dinucleotide phosphate, an electron acceptor that, as NADPH, temporarily stores energized electrons produced during the light reactions.

natural killer cell A type of white blood cell that can kill tumor cells and virus-infected cells as part of innate immunity.

natural selection A process in which individuals that have certain inherited traits tend to survive and reproduce at higher rates than other individuals *because of* those traits.

negative feedback A form of regulation in which accumulation of an end product of a process slows the process; in physiology, a primary mechanism of homeostasis, whereby a change in a variable triggers a response that counteracts the initial change.

negative pressure breathing A breathing system in which air is pulled into the lungs.

nephron (nef'-ron) The tubular excretory unit of the vertebrate kidney.

nerve A fiber composed primarily of the bundled axons of neurons.

nerve net A weblike system of neurons, characteristic of radially symmetric animals, such as hydras.

nervous system The fast-acting internal system of communication involving sensory receptors, networks of nerve cells, and connections to muscles and glands that respond to nerve signals; functions in concert with the endocrine system to effect internal regulation and maintain homeostasis.

nervous tissue Tissue made up of neurons and supportive cells.

net ecosystem production (NEP) The gross primary production of an ecosystem minus the energy used by all autotrophs and heterotrophs for respiration.

net primary production (NPP) The gross primary production of an ecosystem minus the energy used by the producers for respiration.

neural plasticity The capacity of a nervous system to change with experience.

neuron (nyūr'-on) A nerve cell; the fundamental unit of the nervous system, having structure and properties that allow it to conduct signals by taking advantage of the electrical charge across its plasma membrane.

neuropeptide A relatively short chain of amino acids that serves as a neurotransmitter.

neurotransmitter A molecule that is released from the synaptic terminal of a neuron at a chemical synapse, diffuses across the synaptic cleft, and binds to the postsynaptic cell, triggering a response.

neutral variation Genetic variation that does not provide a selective advantage or disadvantage.

neutron A subatomic particle having no electrical charge (electrically neutral), with a mass of about 1.7×10^{-24} g, found in the nucleus of an atom.

neutrophil The most abundant type of white blood cell. Neutrophils are phagocytic and tend to self-destruct as they destroy foreign invaders, limiting their life span to a few days.

nitrogen cycle The natural process by which nitrogen, either from the atmosphere or from decomposed organic material, is converted by soil bacteria to compounds assimilated by plants. This incorporated nitrogen is then taken in by other organisms and subsequently released, acted on by bacteria, and made available again to the nonliving environment.

nitrogen fixation The conversion of atmospheric nitrogen (N_2) to ammonia (NH_3). Biological nitrogen fixation is carried out by certain prokaryotes, some of which have mutualistic relationships with plants.

nociceptor (nō′-si-sep′-tur) A sensory receptor that responds to noxious or painful stimuli; also called a pain receptor.

node A point along the stem of a plant at which leaves are attached.

node of Ranvier (ron′-vē-ā′) Gap in the myelin sheath of certain axons where an action potential may be generated. In saltatory conduction, an action potential is regenerated at each node, appearing to "jump" along the axon from node to node.

nodule A swelling on the root of a legume. Nodules are composed of plant cells that contain nitrogen-fixing bacteria of the genus *Rhizobium*.

noncompetitive inhibitor A substance that reduces the activity of an enzyme by binding to a location remote from the active site, changing the enzyme's shape so that the active site no longer effectively catalyzes the conversion of substrate to product.

nondisjunction An error in meiosis or mitosis in which members of a pair of homologous chromosomes or sister chromatids fail to separate properly from each other.

nonequilibrium model A model that maintains that communities change constantly after being buffeted by disturbances.

nonpolar covalent bond A type of covalent bond in which electrons are shared equally between two atoms of similar electronegativity.

nonsense mutation A mutation that changes an amino acid codon to one of the three stop codons, resulting in a shorter and usually nonfunctional protein.

norepinephrine A catecholamine that is chemically and functionally similar to epinephrine and that acts as a hormone or neurotransmitter; also known as noradrenaline.

northern coniferous forest A terrestrial biome characterized by long, cold winters and dominated by cone-bearing trees.

notochord (nō′-tuh-kord′) A longitudinal, flexible rod that runs along the anterior-posterior axis of a chordate in the dorsal part of the body.

nuclear envelope In a eukaryotic cell, the double membrane that surrounds the

nucleus, perforated with pores that regulate traffic with the cytoplasm. The outer membrane is continuous with the endoplasmic reticulum.

nuclear lamina A netlike array of protein filaments that lines the inner surface of the nuclear envelope and helps maintain the shape of the nucleus.

nucleariid Member of a group of unicellular, amoeboid protists that are more closely related to fungi than they are to other protists.

nuclease An enzyme that cuts DNA or RNA, either removing one or a few bases or hydrolyzing the DNA or RNA completely into its component nucleotides.

nucleic acid (nū-klā′-ik) A polymer (polynucleotide) consisting of many nucleotide monomers; serves as a blueprint for proteins and, through the actions of proteins, for all cellular activities. The two types are DNA and RNA.

nucleic acid hybridization The process of base pairing between a gene and a complementary sequence on another nucleic acid molecule.

nucleic acid probe In DNA technology, a labeled single-stranded nucleic acid molecule used to locate a specific nucleotide sequence in a nucleic acid sample. Molecules of the probe hydrogen-bond to the complementary sequence wherever it occurs; radioactive, fluorescent, or other labeling of the probe allows its location to be detected.

nucleoid (nū′-klē-oyd) A non-membrane-enclosed region in a prokaryotic cell where its chromosome is located.

nucleolus (nū-klē′-ō-lus) (plural, **nucleoli**) A specialized structure in the nucleus consisting of chromosomal regions containing ribosomal RNA (rRNA) genes along with ribosomal proteins imported from the cytoplasm; site of rRNA synthesis and ribosomal subunit assembly. *See also* ribosome.

nucleosome (nū′-klē-ō-sōm′) The basic, bead-like unit of DNA packing in eukaryotes, consisting of a segment of DNA wound around a protein core composed of two copies of each of four types of histone.

nucleotide (nū′-klē-ō-tīd′) The building block of a nucleic acid, consisting of a five-carbon sugar covalently bonded to a nitrogenous base and one or more phosphate groups.

nucleotide excision repair A repair system that removes and then correctly replaces a damaged segment of DNA using the undamaged strand as a guide.

nucleotide-pair substitution A type of point mutation in which one nucleotide in a DNA strand and its partner in the complementary strand are replaced by another pair of nucleotides.

nucleus (1) An atom's central core, containing protons and neutrons. (2) The organelle of a eukaryotic cell that contains the genetic ma-

terial in the form of chromosomes, made up of chromatin. (3) A cluster of neurons.

nutrition The process by which an organism takes in and makes use of food substances.

obligate anaerobe (ob′-lig-et an′-uh-rōb) An organism that only carries out fermentation or anaerobic respiration. Such organisms cannot use oxygen and in fact may be poisoned by it.

oceanic pelagic zone Most of the ocean's waters far from shore, constantly mixed by ocean currents.

odorant A molecule that can be detected by sensory receptors of the olfactory system.

Okazaki fragment (ō′-kah-zah′-kē) A short segment of DNA synthesized away from the replication fork on a template strand during DNA replication. Many such segments are joined together to make up the lagging strand of newly synthesized DNA.

olfaction The sense of smell.

oligodendrocyte A type of glial cell that forms insulating myelin sheaths around the axons of neurons in the central nervous system.

oligotrophic lake A nutrient-poor, clear lake with few phytoplankton.

ommatidium (ōm′-uh-tid′-ē-um) (plural, **ommatidia**) One of the facets of the compound eye of arthropods and some polychaete worms.

omnivore An animal that regularly eats animals as well as plants or algae.

oncogene (on′-kō-jēn) A gene found in viral or cellular genomes that is involved in triggering molecular events that can lead to cancer.

oocyte A cell in the female reproductive system that differentiates to form an egg.

oogenesis (ō′-uh-jen′-uh-sis) The process in the ovary that results in the production of female gametes.

oogonium (ō′-uh- gō′-nē-em) (plural, **oogonia**) A cell that divides mitotically to form oocytes.

open circulatory system A circulatory system in which fluid called hemolymph bathes the tissues and organs directly and there is no distinction between the circulating fluid and the interstitial fluid.

operator In bacterial and phage DNA, a sequence of nucleotides near the start of an operon to which an active repressor can attach. The binding of the repressor prevents RNA polymerase from attaching to the promoter and transcribing the genes of the operon.

operon (op′-er-on) A unit of genetic function found in bacteria and phages, consisting of a promoter, an operator, and a coordinately regulated cluster of genes whose products function in a common pathway.

opisthokont (uh-pis′-thuh-kont′) Member of an extremely diverse clade of eukaryotes that includes fungi, animals, and several closely-related groups of protists.

opsin A membrane protein bound to a light-absorbing pigment molecule.

oral cavity The mouth of an animal.

order In Linnaean classification, the taxonomic category above the level of family.

organ A specialized center of body function composed of several different types of tissues.

organ of Corti The actual hearing organ of the vertebrate ear, located in the floor of the cochlear duct in the inner ear; contains the receptor cells (hair cells) of the ear.

organ system A group of organs that work together in performing vital body functions.

organelle (ōr-guh-nel′) Any of several kinds of membrane-enclosed structures with specialized functions, suspended in the cytosol of eukaryotic cells.

organic compound A chemical compound containing carbon.

organismal ecology The branch of ecology concerned with the morphological, physiological, and behavioral ways in which individual organisms meet the challenges posed by their biotic and abiotic environments.

organogenesis (ōr-gan′-ō-jen′-uh-sis) The process in which organ rudiments develop from the three germ layers after gastrulation.

origin of replication Site where the replication of a DNA molecule begins, consisting of a specific sequence of nucleotides.

osmoconformer An animal that is isoosmotic with its environment.

osmolarity (oz′-mō-lār′-uh-tē) Solute concentration expressed as molarity.

osmoregulation Regulation of solute concentrations and water balance by a cell or organism.

osmoregulator An animal that controls its internal osmolarity independent of the external environment.

osmosis (oz-mō′-sis) The diffusion of free water molecules across a selectively permeable membrane.

osteichthyan (os′-tē-ik′-thē-an) Member of a vertebrate clade with jaws and mostly bony skeletons.

outer ear One of three main regions of the ear in reptiles (including birds) and mammals; made up of the auditory canal and, in many birds and mammals, the pinna.

outgroup A species or group of species from an evolutionary lineage that is known to have diverged before the lineage that contains the group of species being studied. An outgroup is selected so that its members are closely related to the group of species being studied, but not as closely related as any study-group members are to each other.

oval window In the vertebrate ear, a membrane-covered gap in the skull bone,

through which sound waves pass from the middle ear to the inner ear.

ovarian cycle (ō-vār′-ē-un) The cyclic recurrence of the follicular phase, ovulation, and the luteal phase in the mammalian ovary, regulated by hormones.

ovary (ō′-vuh-rē) (1) In flowers, the portion of a carpel in which the egg-containing ovules develop. (2) In animals, the structure that produces female gametes and reproductive hormones.

oviduct (ō′-vuh-duct) A tube passing from the ovary to the vagina in invertebrates or to the uterus in vertebrates, where it is also known as a fallopian tube.

ovulation The release of an egg from an ovary. In humans, an ovarian follicle releases an egg during each uterine (menstrual) cycle.

ovule (o′-vyūl) A structure that develops within the ovary of a seed plant and contains the female gametophyte.

oxidation The complete or partial loss of electrons from a substance involved in a redox reaction.

oxidative phosphorylation (fos′-fōr-uh-lā′-shun) The production of ATP using energy derived from the redox reactions of an electron transport chain; the third major stage of cellular respiration.

oxidizing agent The electron acceptor in a redox reaction.

oxytocin (ok′-si-tō′-sen) A hormone produced by the hypothalamus and released from the posterior pituitary. It induces contractions of the uterine muscles during labor and causes the mammary glands to eject milk during nursing.

P generation The true-breeding (homozygous) parent individuals from which F_1 hybrid offspring are derived in studies of inheritance; P stands for "parental."

P site One of a ribosome's three binding sites for tRNA during translation. The P site holds the tRNA carrying the growing polypeptide chain. (P stands for peptidyl tRNA.)

p53 **gene** A tumor-suppressor gene that codes for a specific transcription factor that promotes the synthesis of proteins that inhibit the cell cycle.

paedomorphosis (pē′-duh-mōr′-fuh-sis) The retention in an adult organism of the juvenile features of its evolutionary ancestors.

pain receptor A sensory receptor that responds to noxious or painful stimuli; also called a nociceptor.

paleontology (pā′-lē-un-tol′-ō-jē) The scientific study of fossils.

pancreas (pan′-krē-us) A gland with exocrine and endocrine tissues. The exocrine portion functions in digestion, secreting enzymes and an alkaline solution into the small intestine via a duct; the ductless endocrine portion functions in homeostasis, secreting the hormones insulin and glucagon into the blood.

pandemic A global epidemic.

Pangaea (pan-jē′-uh) The supercontinent that formed near the end of the Paleozoic era, when plate movements brought all the landmasses of Earth together.

parabasalid A protist, such as a trichomonad, with modified mitochondria.

paraphyletic (pār′-uh-fī-let′-ik) Pertaining to a group of taxa that consists of a common ancestor and some, but not all, of its descendants.

parasite (pār′-uh-sīt) An organism that feeds on the cell contents, tissues, or body fluids of another species (the host) while in or on the host organism. Parasites harm but usually do not kill their host.

parasitism (pār′-uh-sit-izm) A symbiotic relationship in which one organism, the parasite, benefits at the expense of another, the host, by living either within or on the host.

parasympathetic division One of three divisions of the autonomic nervous system; generally enhances body activities that gain and conserve energy, such as digestion and reduced heart rate.

parenchyma cell (puh-ren′-ki-muh) A relatively unspecialized plant cell type that carries out most of the metabolism, synthesizes and stores organic products, and develops into a more differentiated cell type.

parental type An offspring with a phenotype that matches one of the true-breeding parental (P generation) phenotypes; also refers to the phenotype itself.

parthenogenesis (par′-thuh-nō′-jen′-uh-sis) A form of asexual reproduction in which females produce offspring from unfertilized eggs.

partial pressure The pressure exerted by a particular gas in a mixture of gases (for instance, the pressure exerted by oxygen in air).

passive immunity Short-term immunity conferred by the transfer of antibodies, as occurs in the transfer of maternal antibodies to a fetus or nursing infant.

passive transport The diffusion of a substance across a biological membrane with no expenditure of energy.

pathogen An organism or virus that causes disease.

pattern formation The development of a multicellular organism's spatial organization, the arrangement of organs and tissues in their characteristic places in three-dimensional space.

PCR *See* polymerase chain reaction.

pedigree A diagram of a family tree with conventional symbols, showing the occurrence of heritable characters in parents and offspring over multiple generations.

pelagic zone The open-water component of aquatic biomes.

penis The copulatory structure of male mammals.

pepsin An enzyme present in gastric juice that begins the hydrolysis of proteins. Pepsin is synthesized as an inactive precursor form, pepsinogen.

peptide bond The covalent bond between the carboxyl group on one amino acid and the amino group on another, formed by a dehydration reaction.

peptidoglycan (pep′-tid-ō-glī′-kan) A type of polymer in bacterial cell walls consisting of modified sugars cross-linked by short polypeptides.

perception The interpretation of sensory system input by the brain.

pericycle The outermost layer in the vascular cylinder, from which lateral roots arise.

periderm (pār′-uh-derm′) The protective coat that replaces the epidermis in woody plants during secondary growth, formed of the cork and cork cambium.

peripheral nervous system (PNS) The sensory and motor neurons that connect to the central nervous system.

peripheral protein A protein loosely bound to the surface of a membrane or to part of an integral protein and not embedded in the lipid bilayer.

peristalsis (pār′-uh-stal′-sis) (1) Alternating waves of contraction and relaxation in the smooth muscles lining the alimentary canal that push food along the canal. (2) A type of movement on land produced by rhythmic waves of muscle contractions passing from front to back, as in many annelids.

peritubular capillary One of the tiny blood vessels that form a network surrounding the proximal and distal tubules in the kidney.

peroxisome (puh-rok′-suh-sōm′) An organelle containing enzymes that transfer hydrogen atoms from various substrates to oxygen (O_2), producing and then degrading hydrogen peroxide (H_2O_2).

petal A modified leaf of a flowering plant. Petals are the often colorful parts of a flower that advertise it to insects and other pollinators.

petiole (pet′-ē-ōl) The stalk of a leaf, which joins the leaf to a node of the stem.

pH A measure of hydrogen ion concentration equal to $-\log[H^+]$ and ranging in value from 0 to 14.

phage (fāj) A virus that infects bacteria; also called a bacteriophage.

phagocytosis (fag′-ō-sī-tō′-sis) A type of endocytosis in which large particulate substances or small organisms are taken up by a cell. It is carried out by some protists and by certain immune cells of animals (in mammals, mainly macrophages, neutrophils, and dendritic cells).

pharyngeal cleft (fuh-rin′-jē-ul) In chordate embryos, one of the grooves that separate a series of pouches along the sides of the pharynx and may develop into a pharyngeal slit.

pharyngeal slit (fuh-rin′-jē-ul) In chordate embryos, one of the slits that form from the pharyngeal clefts and communicate to the outside, later developing into gill slits in many vertebrates.

pharynx (fār′-inks) (1) An area in the vertebrate throat where air and food passages cross. (2) In flatworms, the muscular tube that protrudes from the ventral side of the worm and ends in the mouth.

phenotype (fē′-nō-tīp) The observable physical and physiological traits of an organism, which are determined by its genetic makeup.

pheromone (fār′-uh-mōn) In animals and fungi, a small molecule released into the environment that functions in communication between members of the same species. In animals, it acts much like a hormone in influencing physiology and behavior.

phloem (flō′-em) Vascular plant tissue consisting of living cells arranged into elongated tubes that transport sugar and other organic nutrients throughout the plant.

phloem sap The sugar-rich solution carried through a plant's sieve tubes.

phosphate group A chemical group consisting of a phosphorus atom bonded to four oxygen atoms; important in energy transfer.

phospholipid (fos′-fō-lip′-id) A lipid made up of glycerol joined to two fatty acids and a phosphate group. The hydrocarbon chains of the fatty acids act as nonpolar, hydrophobic tails, while the rest of the molecule acts as a polar, hydrophilic head. Phospholipids form bilayers that function as biological membranes.

phosphorylated intermediate A molecule (often a reactant) with a phosphate group covalently bound to it, making it more reactive (less stable) than the unphosphorylated molecule.

photic zone (fō′-tic) The narrow top layer of an ocean or lake, where light penetrates sufficiently for photosynthesis to occur.

photomorphogenesis Effects of light on plant morphology.

photon (fō′-ton) A quantum, or discrete quantity, of light energy that behaves as if it were a particle.

photoperiodism (fō′-tō-pēr′-ē-ō-dizm) A physiological response to photoperiod, the relative lengths of night and day. An example of photoperiodism is flowering.

photophosphorylation (fō′-tō-fos′-fōr-uh-lā′-shun) The process of generating ATP from ADP and phosphate by means of chemiosmosis, using a proton-motive force generated across the thylakoid membrane of the chloroplast or the membrane of certain prokaryotes during the light reactions of photosynthesis.

photoreceptor An electromagnetic receptor that detects the radiation known as visible light.

photorespiration A metabolic pathway that consumes oxygen and ATP, releases carbon dioxide, and decreases photosynthetic output. Photorespiration generally occurs on hot, dry, bright days, when stomata close and the O_2/CO_2 ratio in the leaf increases, favoring the binding of O_2 rather than CO_2 by rubisco.

photosynthesis (fō′-tō-sin′-thi-sis) The conversion of light energy to chemical energy that is stored in sugars or other organic compounds; occurs in plants, algae, and certain prokaryotes.

photosystem A light-capturing unit located in the thylakoid membrane of the chloroplast or in the membrane of some prokaryotes, consisting of a reaction-center complex surrounded by numerous light-harvesting complexes. There are two types of photosystems, I and II; they absorb light best at different wavelengths.

photosystem I (PS I) One of two light-capturing units in a chloroplast's thylakoid membrane or in the membrane of some prokaryotes; it has two molecules of P700 chlorophyll *a* at its reaction center.

photosystem II (PS II) One of two light-capturing units in a chloroplast's thylakoid membrane or in the membrane of some prokaryotes; it has two molecules of P680 chlorophyll *a* at its reaction center.

phototropism (fō′-tō-trō′-pizm) Growth of a plant shoot toward or away from light.

phyllotaxy (fil′-uh-tak′-sē) The pattern of leaf attachment to the stem of a plant.

phylogenetic species concept Definition of a species as the smallest group of individuals that share a common ancestor, forming one branch on the tree of life.

phylogenetic tree A branching diagram that represents a hypothesis about the evolutionary history of a group of organisms.

phylogeny (fī-loj′-uh-nē) The evolutionary history of a species or group of related species.

phylum (fī′-lum) (plural, **phyla**) In Linnaean classification, the taxonomic category above class.

physiology The processes and functions of an organism.

phytochrome (fī′-tuh-krōm) A type of light receptor in plants that mostly absorbs red light and regulates many plant responses, such as seed germination and shade avoidance.

pilus (plural, **pili**) (pī′-lus, pī′-lī) In bacteria, a structure that links one cell to another at the start of conjugation; also known as a sex pilus or conjugation pilus.

pinocytosis (pī′-nō-sī-tō′-sis) A type of endocytosis in which the cell ingests extracellular fluid and its dissolved solutes.

pistil A single carpel or a group of fused carpels.

pith Ground tissue that is internal to the vascular tissue in a stem; in many monocot roots, parenchyma cells that form the central core of the vascular cylinder.

pituitary gland (puh-tū′-uh-tār′-ē) An endocrine gland at the base of the hypothalamus; consists of a posterior lobe, which stores and releases two hormones produced by the hypothalamus, and an anterior lobe, which produces and secretes many hormones that regulate diverse body functions.

placenta (pluh-sen′-tuh) A structure in the pregnant uterus for nourishing a viviparous fetus with the mother's blood supply; formed from the uterine lining and embryonic membranes.

plasma (plaz′-muh) The liquid matrix of blood in which the blood cells are suspended.

plasma cell The antibody-secreting effector cell of humoral immunity. Plasma cells arise from antigen-stimulated B cells.

plasma membrane The membrane at the boundary of every cell that acts as a selective barrier, regulating the cell's chemical composition.

plasmid (plaz′-mid) A small, circular, double-stranded DNA molecule that carries accessory genes separate from those of a bacterial chromosome; in DNA cloning, can be used as a vector carrying up to about 10,000 base pairs (10 kb) of DNA.

plasmodesma (plaz′-mō-dez′-muh) (plural, **plasmodesmata**) An open channel through the cell wall that connects the cytoplasm of adjacent plant cells, allowing water, small solutes, and some larger molecules to pass between the cells.

plasmogamy (plaz-moh′-guh-mē) In fungi, the fusion of the cytoplasm of cells from two individuals; occurs as one stage of sexual reproduction, followed later by karyogamy.

plasmolysis (plaz-mol′-uh-sis) A phenomenon in walled cells in which the cytoplasm shrivels and the plasma membrane pulls away from the cell wall; occurs when the cell loses water to a hypertonic environment.

plastid One of a family of closely related organelles that includes chloroplasts, chromoplasts, and amyloplasts. Plastids are found in the cells of photosynthetic eukaryotes.

plate tectonics The theory that the continents are part of great plates of Earth's crust that float on the hot, underlying portion of the mantle. Movements in the mantle cause the continents to move slowly over time.

platelet A pinched-off cytoplasmic fragment of a specialized bone marrow cell. Platelets circulate in the blood and are important in blood clotting.

pleiotropy (pli′-o-truh-pē) The ability of a single gene to have multiple effects.

pluripotent Describing a cell that can give rise to many, but not all, parts of an organism.

point mutation A change in a single nucleotide pair of a gene.

polar covalent bond A covalent bond between atoms that differ in electronegativity. The shared electrons are pulled closer to the more electronegative atom, making it slightly negative and the other atom slightly positive.

polar molecule A molecule (such as water) with an uneven distribution of charges in different regions of the molecule.

pollen grain In seed plants, a structure consisting of the male gametophyte enclosed within a pollen wall.

pollen tube A tube that forms after germination of the pollen grain and that functions in the delivery of sperm to the ovule.

pollination (pol′-uh-nā′-shun) The transfer of pollen to the part of a seed plant containing the ovules, a process required for fertilization.

poly-A tail A sequence of 50–250 adenine nucleotides added onto the 3′ end of a premRNA molecule.

polygamous Referring to a type of relationship in which an individual of one sex mates with several of the other.

polygenic inheritance (pol′-ē-jen′-ik) An additive effect of two or more genes on a single phenotypic character.

polymer (pol′-uh-mer) A long molecule consisting of many similar or identical monomers linked together by covalent bonds.

polymerase chain reaction (PCR) (puh-lim′-uh-rās) A technique for amplifying DNA *in vitro* by incubating it with specific primers, a heat-resistant DNA polymerase, and nucleotides.

polynucleotide (pol′-ē-nū′-klē-ō-tīd) A polymer consisting of many nucleotide monomers in a chain. The nucleotides can be those of DNA or RNA.

polypeptide (pol′-ē-pep′-tīd) A polymer of many amino acids linked together by peptide bonds.

polyphyletic (pol′-ē-fī-let′-ik) Pertaining to a group of taxa derived from two or more different ancestors.

polyploidy (pol′-ē-ploy′-dē) A chromosomal alteration in which the organism possesses more than two complete chromosome sets. It is the result of an accident of cell division.

polyribosome (pol′-ē-rī′-buh-sōm′) A group of several ribosomes attached to, and translating, the same messenger RNA molecule; also called a polysome.

polysaccharide (pol′-ē-sak′-uh-rīd) A polymer of many monosaccharides, formed by dehydration reactions.

polyspermy Fusion of the egg with more than one sperm.

polytomy (puh-lit′-uh-mē) In a phylogenetic tree, a branch point from which more than two descendant taxa emerge. A polytomy indicates that the evolutionary relationships between the descendant taxa are not yet clear.

pons A portion of the brain that participates in certain automatic, homeostatic functions, such as regulating the breathing centers in the medulla.

population A group of individuals of the same species that live in the same area and interbreed, producing fertile offspring.

population dynamics The study of how complex interactions between biotic and abiotic factors influence variations in population size.

population ecology The study of populations in relation to their environment, including environmental influences on population density and distribution, age structure, and variations in population size.

positional information Molecular cues that control pattern formation in an animal or plant embryonic structure by indicating a cell's location relative to the organism's body axes. These cues elicit a response by genes that regulate development.

positive feedback A form of regulation in which an end product of a process speeds up that process; in physiology, a control mechanism in which a change in a variable triggers a response that reinforces or amplifies the change.

positive pressure breathing A breathing system in which air is forced into the lungs.

posterior Pertaining to the rear, or tail end, of a bilaterally symmetric animal.

posterior pituitary An extension of the hypothalamus composed of nervous tissue that secretes oxytocin and antidiuretic hormone made in the hypothalamus; a temporary storage site for these hormones.

postzygotic barrier (pōst′-zī-got′-ik) A reproductive barrier that prevents hybrid zygotes produced by two different species from developing into viable, fertile adults.

potential energy The energy that matter possesses as a result of its location or spatial arrangement (structure).

predation An interaction between species in which one species, the predator, eats the other, the prey.

prediction In deductive reasoning, a forecast that follows logically from a hypothesis. By testing predictions, experiments may allow certain hypotheses to be rejected.

prepuce (prē′-pyūs) A fold of skin covering the head of the clitoris or penis.

pressure potential (Ψ_p) A component of water potential that consists of the physical pressure on a solution, which can be positive, zero, or negative.

prezygotic barrier (prē′-zī-got′-ik) A reproductive barrier that impedes mating between species or hinders fertilization if interspecific mating is attempted.

primary cell wall In plants, a relatively thin and flexible layer that surrounds the plasma membrane of a young cell.

primary consumer An herbivore; an organism that eats plants or other autotrophs.

primary electron acceptor In the thylakoid membrane of a chloroplast or in the membrane of some prokaryotes, a specialized molecule that shares the reaction-center complex with a pair of chlorophyll *a* molecules and that accepts an electron from them.

primary growth Growth produced by apical meristems, lengthening stems and roots.

primary immune response The initial adaptive immune response to an antigen, which appears after a lag of about 10–17 days.

primary oocyte (ō'-uh-sīt) An oocyte prior to completion of meiosis I.

primary producer An autotroph, usually a photosynthetic organism. Collectively, autotrophs make up the trophic level of an ecosystem that ultimately supports all other levels.

primary production The amount of light energy converted to chemical energy (organic compounds) by the autotrophs in an ecosystem during a given time period.

primary structure The level of protein structure referring to the specific linear sequence of amino acids.

primary succession A type of ecological succession that occurs in an area where there were originally no organisms present and where soil has not yet formed.

primary transcript An initial RNA transcript from any gene; also called pre-mRNA when transcribed from a protein-coding gene.

primase An enzyme that joins RNA nucleotides to make a primer during DNA replication, using the parental DNA strand as a template.

primer A short stretch of RNA with a free 3' end, bound by complementary base pairing to the template strand and elongated with DNA nucleotides during DNA replication.

problem solving The cognitive activity of devising a method to proceed from one state to another in the face of real or apparent obstacles.

producer An organism that produces organic compounds from CO_2 by harnessing light energy (in photosynthesis) or by oxidizing inorganic chemicals (in chemosynthetic reactions carried out by some prokaryotes).

product A material resulting from a chemical reaction.

production efficiency The percentage of energy stored in assimilated food that is not used for respiration or eliminated as waste.

progesterone A steroid hormone that prepares the uterus for pregnancy; the major progestin in mammals.

prokaryote An organism that has a prokaryotic cell; an informal term for an organism in either domain Bacteria or domain Archaea.

prokaryotic cell (prō'-kār'-ē-ot'-ik) A type of cell lacking a membrane-enclosed nucleus and membrane-enclosed organelles. Organisms with prokaryotic cells (bacteria and archaea) are called prokaryotes.

prometaphase The second stage of mitosis, in which the nuclear envelope fragments and the spindle microtubules attach to the kinetochores of the chromosomes.

promoter A specific nucleotide sequence in the DNA of a gene that binds RNA polymerase, positioning it to start transcribing RNA at the appropriate place.

prophage (prō'-fāj) A phage genome that has been inserted into a specific site on a bacterial chromosome.

prophase The first stage of mitosis, in which the chromatin condenses into discrete chromosomes visible with a light microscope, the mitotic spindle begins to form, and the nucleolus disappears but the nucleus remains intact.

prostate gland (pros'-tāt) A gland in human males that secretes an acid-neutralizing component of semen.

protease An enzyme that digests proteins by hydrolysis.

protein (prō'-tēn) A biologically functional molecule consisting of one or more polypeptides folded and coiled into a specific three-dimensional structure.

protein kinase An enzyme that transfers phosphate groups from ATP to a protein, thus phosphorylating the protein.

protein phosphatase An enzyme that removes phosphate groups from (dephosphorylates) proteins, often functioning to reverse the effect of a protein kinase.

proteoglycan (prō'-tē-ō-glī'-kan) A large molecule consisting of a small core protein with many carbohydrate chains attached, found in the extracellular matrix of animal cells. A proteoglycan may consist of up to 95% carbohydrate.

proteomics (prō'-tē-ō'-miks) The systematic study of the full protein sets (proteomes) encoded by genomes.

protist An informal term applied to any eukaryote that is not a plant, animal, or fungus. Most protists are unicellular, though some are colonial or multicellular.

protocell An abiotic precursor of a living cell that had a membrane-like structure and that maintained an internal chemistry different from that of its surroundings.

proton (prō'-ton) A subatomic particle with a single positive electrical charge, with a mass of about 1.7×10^{-24} g, found in the nucleus of an atom.

proton pump An active transport protein in a cell membrane that uses ATP to transport hydrogen ions out of a cell against their concentration gradient, generating a membrane potential in the process.

proton-motive force The potential energy stored in the form of a proton electrochemical gradient, generated by the pumping of hydrogen ions (H^+) across a biological membrane during chemiosmosis.

proto-oncogene (prō'-tō-on'-kō-jēn) A normal cellular gene that has the potential to become an oncogene.

protoplast The living part of a plant cell, which also includes the plasma membrane.

provirus A viral genome that is permanently inserted into a host genome.

proximal tubule In the vertebrate kidney, the portion of a nephron immediately downstream from Bowman's capsule that conveys and helps refine filtrate.

pseudogene (sū'-dō-jēn) A DNA segment that is very similar to a real gene but does not yield a functional product; a DNA segment that formerly functioned as a gene but has become inactivated in a particular species because of mutation.

pseudopodium (sū'-dō-pō'-dē-um) (plural, **pseudopodia**) A cellular extension of amoeboid cells used in moving and feeding.

pulse The rhythmic bulging of the artery walls with each heartbeat.

punctuated equilibria In the fossil record, long periods of apparent stasis, in which a species undergoes little or no morphological change, interrupted by relatively brief periods of sudden change.

Punnett square A diagram used in the study of inheritance to show the predicted genotypic results of random fertilization in genetic crosses between individuals of known genotype.

pupil The opening in the iris, which admits light into the interior of the vertebrate eye. Muscles in the iris regulate its size.

purine (pyū'-rēn) One of two types of nitrogenous bases found in nucleotides, characterized by a six-membered ring fused to a five-membered ring. Adenine (A) and guanine (G) are purines.

pyrimidine (puh-rim'-uh-dēn) One of two types of nitrogenous bases found in nucleotides, characterized by a six-membered ring. Cytosine (C), thymine (T), and uracil (U) are pyrimidines.

quantitative character A heritable feature that varies continuously over a range rather than in an either-or fashion.

quaternary structure (kwot'-er-nār'-ē) The particular shape of a complex, aggregate protein, defined by the characteristic three-dimensional arrangement of its constituent subunits, each a polypeptide.

R plasmid A bacterial plasmid carrying genes that confer resistance to certain antibiotics.

radial symmetry Symmetry in which the body is shaped like a pie or barrel (lacking a left side and a right side) and can be divided into mirror-imaged halves by any plane through its central axis.

radicle An embryonic root of a plant.

radioactive isotope An isotope (an atomic form of a chemical element) that is unstable;

the nucleus decays spontaneously, giving off detectable particles and energy.

radiometric dating A method for determining the absolute age of rocks and fossils, based on the half-life of radioactive isotopes.

ras **gene** A gene that codes for Ras, a G protein that relays a growth signal from a growth factor receptor on the plasma membrane to a cascade of protein kinases, ultimately resulting in stimulation of the cell cycle.

ray-finned fish Member of the class Actinopterygii, aquatic osteichthyans with fins supported by long, flexible rays, including tuna, bass, and herring.

reabsorption In excretory systems, the recovery of solutes and water from filtrate.

reactant A starting material in a chemical reaction.

reaction-center complex A complex of proteins associated with a special pair of chlorophyll *a* molecules and a primary electron acceptor. Located centrally in a photosystem, this complex triggers the light reactions of photosynthesis. Excited by light energy, the pair of chlorophylls donates an electron to the primary electron acceptor, which passes an electron to an electron transport chain.

reading frame On an mRNA, the triplet grouping of ribonucleotides used by the translation machinery during polypeptide synthesis.

receptacle The base of a flower; the part of the stem that is the site of attachment of the floral organs.

reception The binding of a signaling molecule to a receptor protein, activating the receptor by causing it to change shape. *See also* sensory reception.

receptor potential An initial response of a receptor cell to a stimulus, consisting of a change in voltage across the receptor membrane proportional to the stimulus strength.

receptor-mediated endocytosis (en′-dō-sī-tō′-sis) The movement of specific molecules into a cell by the inward budding of vesicles containing proteins with receptor sites specific to the molecules being taken in; enables a cell to acquire bulk quantities of specific substances.

recessive allele An allele whose phenotypic effect is not observed in a heterozygote.

recombinant chromosome A chromosome created when crossing over combines DNA from two parents into a single chromosome.

recombinant DNA A DNA molecule made *in vitro* with segments from different sources.

recombinant type (recombinant) An offspring whose phenotype differs from that of the true-breeding P generation parents; also refers to the phenotype itself.

rectum The terminal portion of the large intestine, where the feces are stored prior to elimination.

red alga A photosynthetic protist, named for its color, which results from a red pigment that masks the green of chlorophyll. Most red algae are multicellular and marine.

redox reaction (rē′-doks) A chemical reaction involving the complete or partial transfer of one or more electrons from one reactant to another; short for **red**uction-**ox**idation reaction.

reducing agent The electron donor in a redox reaction.

reduction The complete or partial addition of electrons to a substance involved in a redox reaction.

reflex An automatic reaction to a stimulus, mediated by the spinal cord or lower brain.

refractory period (rē-frakt′-ōr-ē) The short time immediately after an action potential in which the neuron cannot respond to another stimulus, owing to the inactivation of voltage-gated sodium channels.

regression line A line drawn through a scatter plot that shows the general trend of the data. It represents an equation that is calculated mathematically to best fit the data and can be used to predict the value of the dependent variable for any value of the independent variable.

regulator An animal for which mechanisms of homeostasis moderate internal changes in a particular variable in the face of external fluctuation of that variable.

regulatory gene A gene that codes for a protein, such as a repressor, that controls the transcription of another gene or group of genes.

reinforcement In evolutionary biology, a process in which natural selection strengthens prezygotic barriers to reproduction, thus reducing the chances of hybrid formation. Such a process is likely to occur only if hybrid offspring are less fit than members of the parent species.

relative abundance The proportional abundance of different species in a community.

relative fitness The contribution an individual makes to the gene pool of the next generation, relative to the contributions of other individuals in the population.

renal cortex The outer portion of the vertebrate kidney.

renal medulla The inner portion of the vertebrate kidney, beneath the renal cortex.

renal pelvis The funnel-shaped chamber that receives processed filtrate from the vertebrate kidney's collecting ducts and is drained by the ureter.

renin-angiotensin-aldosterone system (RAAS) A hormone cascade pathway that helps regulate blood pressure and blood volume.

repetitive DNA Nucleotide sequences, usually noncoding, that are present in many copies in a eukaryotic genome. The repeated units may be short and arranged tandemly

(in series) or long and dispersed in the genome.

replication fork A Y-shaped region on a replicating DNA molecule where the parental strands are being unwound and new strands are being synthesized.

repressor A protein that inhibits gene transcription. In prokaryotes, repressors bind to the DNA in or near the promoter. In eukaryotes, repressors may bind to control elements within enhancers, to activators, or to other proteins in a way that blocks activators from binding to DNA.

reproductive isolation The existence of biological factors (barriers) that impede members of two species from producing viable, fertile offspring.

reproductive table An age-specific summary of the reproductive rates in a population.

reptile Member of the clade of amniotes that includes tuataras, lizards, snakes, turtles, crocodilians, and birds.

residual volume The amount of air that remains in the lungs after forceful exhalation.

resource partitioning The division of environmental resources by coexisting species such that the niche of each species differs by one or more significant factors from the niches of all coexisting species.

respiratory pigment A protein that transports oxygen in blood or hemolymph.

response (1) In cellular communication, the change in a specific cellular activity brought about by a transduced signal from outside the cell. (2) In feedback regulation, a physiological activity triggered by a change in a variable.

resting potential The membrane potential characteristic of a nonconducting excitable cell, with the inside of the cell more negative than the outside.

restriction enzyme An endonuclease (type of enzyme) that recognizes and cuts DNA molecules foreign to a bacterium (such as phage genomes). The enzyme cuts at specific nucleotide sequences (restriction sites).

restriction fragment A DNA segment that results from the cutting of DNA by a restriction enzyme.

restriction site A specific sequence on a DNA strand that is recognized and cut by a restriction enzyme.

retina (ret′-i-nuh) The innermost layer of the vertebrate eye, containing photoreceptor cells (rods and cones) and neurons; transmits images formed by the lens to the brain via the optic nerve.

retinal The light-absorbing pigment in rods and cones of the vertebrate eye.

retrotransposon (re′-trō-trans-pō′-zon) A transposable element that moves within a genome by means of an RNA intermediate, a transcript of the retrotransposon DNA.

retrovirus (re′-trō-vī′-rus) An RNA virus that replicates by transcribing its RNA into

DNA and then inserting the DNA into a cellular chromosome; an important class of cancer-causing viruses.

reverse transcriptase (tran-skrip′-tās) An enzyme encoded by certain viruses (retroviruses) that uses RNA as a template for DNA synthesis.

reverse transcriptase–polymerase chain reaction (RT-PCR) A technique for determining expression of a particular gene. It uses reverse transcriptase and DNA polymerase to synthesize cDNA from all the mRNA in a sample and then subjects the cDNA to PCR amplification using primers specific for the gene of interest.

rhizarians (rī-za′-rē-uhns) One of the three major subgroups for which the "SAR" eukaryotic supergroup is named. Many species in this clade are amoebas characterized by threadlike pseudopodia.

rhizobacterium A soil bacterium whose population size is much enhanced in the rhizosphere, the soil region close to a plant's roots.

rhizoid (rī′-zoyd) A long, tubular single cell or filament of cells that anchors bryophytes to the ground. Unlike roots, rhizoids are not composed of tissues, lack specialized conducting cells, and do not play a primary role in water and mineral absorption.

rhizosphere The soil region close to plant roots and characterized by a high level of microbiological activity.

rhodopsin (rō-dop′-sin) A visual pigment consisting of retinal and opsin. Upon absorbing light, the retinal changes shape and dissociates from the opsin.

ribonucleic acid (RNA) (rī′-bō-nū-klā′-ik) A type of nucleic acid consisting of a polynucleotide made up of nucleotide monomers with a ribose sugar and the nitrogenous bases adenine (A), cytosine (C), guanine (G), and uracil (U); usually single-stranded; functions in protein synthesis, gene regulation, and as the genome of some viruses.

ribose The sugar component of RNA nucleotides.

ribosomal RNA (rRNA) (rī′-buh-sō′-mul) RNA molecules that, together with proteins, make up ribosomes; the most abundant type of RNA.

ribosome (rī′-buh-sōm′) A complex of rRNA and protein molecules that functions as a site of protein synthesis in the cytoplasm; consists of a large subunit and a small subunit. In eukaryotic cells, each subunit is assembled in the nucleolus. *See also* nucleolus.

ribozyme (rī′-buh-zīm) An RNA molecule that functions as an enzyme, such as an intron that catalyzes its own removal during RNA splicing.

RNA interference (RNAi) A technique used to silence the expression of selected genes. RNAi uses synthetic double-stranded

RNA molecules that match the sequence of a particular gene to trigger the breakdown of the gene's messenger RNA.

RNA polymerase An enzyme that links ribonucleotides into a growing RNA chain during transcription, based on complementary binding to nucleotides on a DNA template strand.

RNA processing Modification of RNA primary transcripts, including splicing out of introns, joining together of exons, and alteration of the 5′ and 3′ ends.

RNA splicing After synthesis of a eukaryotic primary RNA transcript, the removal of portions of the transcript (introns) that will not be included in the mRNA and the joining together of the remaining portions (exons).

rod A rodlike cell in the retina of the vertebrate eye, sensitive to low light intensity.

root An organ in vascular plants that anchors the plant and enables it to absorb water and minerals from the soil.

root cap A cone of cells at the tip of a plant root that protects the apical meristem.

root hair A tiny extension of a root epidermal cell, growing just behind the root tip and increasing surface area for absorption of water and minerals.

root system All of a plant's roots, which anchor it in the soil, absorb and transport minerals and water, and store food.

rooted Describing a phylogenetic tree that contains a branch point (often, the one farthest to the left) representing the most recent common ancestor of all taxa in the tree.

rough ER That portion of the endoplasmic reticulum with ribosomes attached.

round window In the mammalian ear, the point of contact where vibrations of the stapes create a traveling series of pressure waves in the fluid of the cochlea.

***r*-selection** Selection for life history traits that maximize reproductive success in uncrowded environments; also called density-independent selection.

rubisco (rū-bis′-kō) Ribulose bisphosphate (RuBP) carboxylase, the enzyme that catalyzes the first step of the Calvin cycle (the addition of CO_2 to RuBP).

ruminant (rū′-muh-nent) An animal, such as a cow or a sheep, with multiple stomach compartments specialized for an herbivorous diet.

S phase The synthesis phase of the cell cycle; the portion of interphase during which DNA is replicated.

saccule In the vertebrate ear, a chamber in the vestibule behind the oval window that participates in the sense of balance.

salicylic acid (sal′-i-sil′-ik) A signaling molecule in plants that may be partially responsible for activating systemic acquired resistance to pathogens.

salivary gland A gland associated with the oral cavity that secretes substances that lubricate food and begin the process of chemical digestion.

salt A compound resulting from the formation of an ionic bond; also called an ionic compound.

saltatory conduction (sol′-tuh-tōr′-ē) Rapid transmission of a nerve impulse along an axon, resulting from the action potential jumping from one node of Ranvier to another, skipping the myelin-sheathed regions of membrane.

"SAR" clade One of four supergroups of eukaryotes proposed in a current hypothesis of the evolutionary history of eukaryotes. This supergroup contains a large, extremely diverse collection of protists from three major subgroups: stramenopiles, alveolates, and rhizarians. *See also* Excavata, Archaeplastida, and Unikonta.

sarcomere (sar′-kō-mēr) The fundamental, repeating unit of striated muscle, delimited by the Z lines.

sarcoplasmic reticulum (SR) (sar′-kō-plaz′-mik ruh-tik′-yū-lum) A specialized endoplasmic reticulum that regulates the calcium concentration in the cytosol of muscle cells.

saturated fatty acid A fatty acid in which all carbons in the hydrocarbon tail are connected by single bonds, thus maximizing the number of hydrogen atoms attached to the carbon skeleton.

savanna A tropical grassland biome with scattered trees and large herbivores and maintained by occasional fires and drought.

scanning electron microscope (SEM) A microscope that uses an electron beam to scan the surface of a sample, coated with metal atoms, to study details of its topography.

scatter plot A graph in which each piece of data is represented by a point, but individual points are not connected by lines.

Schwann cell A type of glial cell that forms insulating myelin sheaths around the axons of neurons in the peripheral nervous system.

science An approach to understanding the natural world.

scion (sī′-un) The twig grafted onto the stock when making a graft.

sclereid (sklār′-ē-id) A short, irregular sclerenchyma cell in nutshells and seed coats. Sclereids are scattered throughout the parenchyma of some plants.

sclerenchyma cell (skluh-ren′-kim-uh) A rigid, supportive plant cell type usually lacking a protoplast and possessing thick secondary walls strengthened by lignin at maturity.

scrotum A pouch of skin outside the abdomen that houses the testes; functions in maintaining the testes at the lower temperature required for spermatogenesis.

second law of thermodynamics The principle stating that every energy transfer or transformation increases the entropy of the universe. Usable forms of energy are at least partly converted to heat.

second messenger A small, nonprotein, water-soluble molecule or ion, such as a calcium ion (Ca^{2+}) or cyclic AMP, that relays a signal to a cell's interior in response to a signaling molecule bound by a signal receptor protein.

secondary cell wall In plant cells, a strong and durable matrix that is often deposited in several laminated layers around the plasma membrane and that provides protection and support.

secondary consumer A carnivore that eats herbivores.

secondary endosymbiosis A process in eukaryotic evolution in which a heterotrophic eukaryotic cell engulfed a photosynthetic eukaryotic cell, which survived in a symbiotic relationship inside the heterotrophic cell.

secondary growth Growth produced by lateral meristems, thickening the roots and shoots of woody plants.

secondary immune response The adaptive immune response elicited on second or subsequent exposures to a particular antigen. The secondary immune response is more rapid, of greater magnitude, and of longer duration than the primary immune response.

secondary oocyte (ō'-uh-sīt) An oocyte that has completed the first of the two meiotic divisions.

secondary production The amount of chemical energy in consumers' food that is converted to their own new biomass during a given time period.

secondary structure Regions of repetitive coiling or folding of the polypeptide backbone of a protein due to hydrogen bonding between constituents of the backbone (not the side chains).

secondary succession A type of succession that occurs where an existing community has been cleared by some disturbance that leaves the soil or substrate intact.

secretion (1) The discharge of molecules synthesized by a cell. (2) The discharge of wastes from the body fluid into the filtrate.

seed An adaptation of some terrestrial plants consisting of an embryo packaged along with a store of food within a protective coat.

seed coat A tough outer covering of a seed, formed from the outer coat of an ovule. In a flowering plant, the seed coat encloses and protects the embryo and endosperm.

seedless vascular plant An informal name for a plant that has vascular tissue but lacks seeds. Seedless vascular plants form a paraphyletic group that includes the phyla Lycophyta (club mosses and their relatives) and Monilophyta (ferns and their relatives).

selective permeability A property of biological membranes that allows them to regulate the passage of substances across them.

self-incompatibility The ability of a seed plant to reject its own pollen and sometimes the pollen of closely related individuals.

semelparity Reproduction in which an organism produces all of its offspring in a single event; also known as big-bang reproduction.

semen (sē'-mun) The fluid that is ejaculated by the male during orgasm; contains sperm and secretions from several glands of the male reproductive tract.

semicircular canals A three-part chamber of the inner ear that functions in maintaining equilibrium.

semiconservative model Type of DNA replication in which the replicated double helix consists of one old strand, derived from the parental molecule, and one newly made strand.

semilunar valve A valve located at each exit of the heart, where the aorta leaves the left ventricle and the pulmonary artery leaves the right ventricle.

seminal vesicle (sem'-i-nul ves'-i-kul) A gland in males that secretes a fluid component of semen that lubricates and nourishes sperm.

seminiferous tubule (sem'-i-nif'-er-us) A highly coiled tube in the testis in which sperm are produced.

senescence (se-nes'-ens) The growth phase in a plant or plant part (as a leaf) from full maturity to death.

sensitive period A limited phase in an animal's development when learning of particular behaviors can take place; also called a critical period.

sensor In homeostasis, a receptor that detects a stimulus.

sensory adaptation The tendency of sensory neurons to become less sensitive when they are stimulated repeatedly.

sensory neuron A nerve cell that receives information from the internal or external environment and transmits signals to the central nervous system.

sensory reception The detection of a stimulus by sensory cells.

sensory receptor An organ, cell, or structure within a cell that responds to specific stimuli from an organism's external or internal environment.

sensory transduction The conversion of stimulus energy to a change in the membrane potential of a sensory receptor cell.

sepal (sē'-pul) A modified leaf in angiosperms that helps enclose and protect a flower bud before it opens.

serial endosymbiosis A hypothesis for the origin of eukaryotes consisting of a sequence of endosymbiotic events in which mitochondria, chloroplasts, and perhaps other cellular structures were derived from small prokaryotes that had been engulfed by larger cells.

serotonin (ser'-uh-tō'-nin) A neurotransmitter, synthesized from the amino acid tryptophan, that functions in the central nervous system.

Sertoli cell A support cell of the seminiferous tubule that surrounds and nourishes developing sperm.

set point In homeostasis in animals, a value maintained for a particular variable, such as body temperature or solute concentration.

sex chromosome A chromosome responsible for determining the sex of an individual.

sex-linked gene A gene located on either sex chromosome. Most sex-linked genes are on the X chromosome and show distinctive patterns of inheritance; there are very few genes on the Y chromosome.

sexual dimorphism (dī-mōr'-fizm) Differences between the secondary sex characteristics of males and females of the same species.

sexual reproduction A type of reproduction in which two parents give rise to offspring that have unique combinations of genes inherited from both parents via the gametes.

sexual selection A form of natural selection in which individuals with certain inherited characteristics are more likely than other individuals to obtain mates.

Shannon diversity index An index of community diversity symbolized by H and represented by the equation $H = -(p_A \ln p_A + p_B \ln p_B + p_C \ln p_C + \ldots)$, where A, B, C . . . are species, p is the relative abundance of each species, and ln is the natural logarithm.

shared ancestral character A character that is shared by members of a particular clade but that originated in an ancestor that is not a member of that clade.

shared derived character An evolutionary novelty that is unique to a particular clade.

shoot system The aerial portion of a plant body, consisting of stems, leaves, and (in angiosperms) flowers.

short tandem repeat (STR) Simple sequence DNA containing multiple tandemly repeated units of two to five nucleotides. Variations in STRs act as genetic markers in STR analysis, used to prepare genetic profiles.

short-day plant A plant that flowers (usually in late summer, fall, or winter) only when the light period is shorter than a critical length.

short-term memory The ability to hold information, anticipations, or goals for a time and then release them if they become irrelevant.

sickle-cell disease A recessively inherited human blood disorder in which a single nucleotide change in the β-globin gene causes hemoglobin to aggregate, changing red blood cell shape and causing multiple symptoms in afflicted individuals.

sieve plate An end wall in a sieve-tube element, which facilitates the flow of phloem sap in angiosperm sieve tubes.

sieve-tube element A living cell that conducts sugars and other organic nutrients in the phloem of angiosperms; also called a sieve-tube member. Connected end to end, they form sieve tubes.

sign stimulus An external sensory cue that triggers a fixed action pattern by an animal.

signal In animal behavior, transmission of a stimulus from one animal to another. The term is also used in the context of communication in other kinds of organisms and in cell-to-cell communication in all multicellular organisms.

signal peptide A sequence of about 20 amino acids at or near the leading (amino) end of a polypeptide that targets it to the endoplasmic reticulum or other organelles in a eukaryotic cell.

signal transduction pathway A series of steps linking a mechanical, chemical, or electrical stimulus to a specific cellular response.

signal-recognition particle (SRP) A protein-RNA complex that recognizes a signal peptide as it emerges from a ribosome and helps direct the ribosome to the endoplasmic reticulum (ER) by binding to a receptor protein on the ER.

silent mutation A nucleotide-pair substitution that has no observable effect on the phenotype; for example, within a gene, a mutation that results in a codon that codes for the same amino acid.

simple fruit A fruit derived from a single carpel or several fused carpels.

simple sequence DNA A DNA sequence that contains many copies of tandemly repeated short sequences.

single bond A single covalent bond; the sharing of a pair of valence electrons by two atoms.

single circulation A circulatory system consisting of a single pump and circuit, in which blood passes from the sites of gas exchange to the rest of the body before returning to the heart.

single nucleotide polymorphism (SNP) A single base-pair site in a genome where nucleotide variation is found in at least 1% of the population.

single-lens eye The camera-like eye found in some jellies, polychaete worms, spiders, and many molluscs.

single-strand binding protein A protein that binds to the unpaired DNA strands during DNA replication, stabilizing them and holding them apart while they serve as templates for the synthesis of complementary strands of DNA.

sinoatrial (SA) node A region in the right atrium of the heart that sets the rate and timing at which all cardiac muscle cells contract; the pacemaker.

sister chromatids Two copies of a duplicated chromosome attached to each other by proteins at the centromere and, sometimes, along the arms. While joined, two sister chromatids make up one chromosome. Chromatids are eventually separated during mitosis or meiosis II.

sister taxa Groups of organisms that share an immediate common ancestor and hence are each other's closest relatives.

skeletal muscle A type of striated muscle that is generally responsible for the voluntary movements of the body.

sliding-filament model The idea that muscle contraction is based on the movement of thin (actin) filaments along thick (myosin) filaments, shortening the sarcomere, the basic unit of muscle organization.

slow-twitch fiber A muscle fiber that can sustain long contractions.

small interfering RNA (siRNA) One of multiple small, single-stranded RNA molecules generated by cellular machinery from a long, linear, double-stranded RNA molecule. The siRNA associates with one or more proteins in a complex that can degrade or prevent translation of an mRNA with a complementary sequence. In some cases, siRNA can also block transcription by promoting chromatin modification.

small intestine The longest section of the alimentary canal, so named because of its small diameter compared with that of the large intestine; the principal site of the enzymatic hydrolysis of food macromolecules and the absorption of nutrients.

smooth ER That portion of the endoplasmic reticulum that is free of ribosomes.

smooth muscle A type of muscle lacking the striations of skeletal and cardiac muscle because of the uniform distribution of myosin filaments in the cells; responsible for involuntary body activities.

social learning Modification of behavior through the observation of other individuals.

sodium-potassium pump A transport protein in the plasma membrane of animal cells that actively transports sodium out of the cell and potassium into the cell.

solute (sol'-yūt) A substance that is dissolved in a solution.

solute potential (Ψ_S) A component of water potential that is proportional to the molarity of a solution and that measures the effect of solutes on the direction of water movement; also called osmotic potential, it can be either zero or negative.

solution A liquid that is a homogeneous mixture of two or more substances.

solvent The dissolving agent of a solution. Water is the most versatile solvent known.

somatic cell (sō-mat'-ik) Any cell in a multicellular organism except a sperm or egg or their precursors.

spatial learning The establishment of a memory that reflects the environment's spatial structure.

spatial summation A phenomenon of neural integration in which the membrane potential of the postsynaptic cell is determined by the combined effect of EPSPs or IPSPs produced nearly simultaneously by different synapses.

speciation (spē'-sē-ā'-shun) An evolutionary process in which one species splits into two or more species.

species (spē'-sēz) A population or group of populations whose members have the potential to interbreed in nature and produce viable, fertile offspring, but do not produce viable, fertile offspring with members of other such groups.

species diversity The number and relative abundance of species in a biological community.

species richness The number of species in a biological community.

species-area curve The biodiversity pattern that shows that the larger the geographic area of a community is, the more species it has.

specific heat The amount of heat that must be absorbed or lost for 1 g of a substance to change its temperature by 1°C.

spectrophotometer An instrument that measures the proportions of light of different wavelengths absorbed and transmitted by a pigment solution.

sperm The male gamete.

spermatogenesis The continuous and prolific production of mature sperm cells in the testis.

spermatogonium (plural, **spermatogonia**) A cell that divides mitotically to form spermatocytes.

sphincter (sfink'-ter) A ringlike band of muscle fibers that controls the size of an opening in the body, such as the passage between the esophagus and the stomach.

spliceosome (splī'-sō-sōm) A large complex made up of proteins and RNA molecules that splices RNA by interacting with the ends of an RNA intron, releasing the intron and joining the two adjacent exons.

spontaneous process A process that occurs without an overall input of energy; a process that is energetically favorable.

sporangium (spôr-an'-jē-um) (plural, **sporangia**) A multicellular organ in fungi and plants in which meiosis occurs and haploid cells develop.

spore (1) In the life cycle of a plant or alga undergoing alternation of generations, a haploid cell produced in the sporophyte by meiosis. A spore can divide by mitosis to develop into a multicellular haploid individual, the gametophyte, without fusing with another cell. (2) In fungi, a haploid cell, produced either sexually or asexually, that produces a mycelium after germination.

sporophyte (spō-ruh-fīt′) In organisms (plants and some algae) that have alternation of generations, the multicellular diploid form that results from the union of gametes. The sporophyte produces haploid spores by meiosis that develop into gametophytes.

sporopollenin (spōr-uh-pol′-eh-nin) A durable polymer that covers exposed zygotes of charophyte algae and forms the walls of plant spores, preventing them from drying out.

stabilizing selection Natural selection in which intermediate phenotypes survive or reproduce more successfully than do extreme phenotypes.

stamen (stā′-men) The pollen-producing reproductive organ of a flower, consisting of an anther and a filament.

starch A storage polysaccharide in plants, consisting entirely of glucose monomers joined by α glycosidic linkages.

start point In transcription, the nucleotide position on the promoter where RNA polymerase begins synthesis of RNA.

statocyst (stat′-uh-sist′) A type of mechanoreceptor that functions in equilibrium in invertebrates by use of statoliths, which stimulate hair cells in relation to gravity.

statolith (stat′-uh-lith′) (1) In plants, a specialized plastid that contains dense starch grains and may play a role in detecting gravity. (2) In invertebrates, a dense particle that settles in response to gravity and is found in sensory organs that function in equilibrium.

stele (stēl) The vascular tissue of a stem or root.

stem A vascular plant organ consisting of an alternating system of nodes and internodes that support the leaves and reproductive structures.

stem cell Any relatively unspecialized cell that can produce, during a single division, one identical daughter cell and one more specialized daughter cell that can undergo further differentiation.

steroid A type of lipid characterized by a carbon skeleton consisting of four fused rings with various chemical groups attached.

sticky end A single-stranded end of a double-stranded restriction fragment.

stigma (plural, **stigmata**) The sticky part of a flower's carpel, which receives pollen grains.

stimulus In feedback regulation, a fluctuation in a variable that triggers a response.

stipe A stemlike structure of a seaweed.

stock The plant that provides the root system when making a graft.

stoma (stō′-muh) (plural, **stomata**) A microscopic pore surrounded by guard cells in the epidermis of leaves and stems that allows gas exchange between the environment and the interior of the plant.

stomach An organ of the digestive system that stores food and performs preliminary steps of digestion.

stramenopiles One of the three major subgroups for which the "SAR" eukaryotic supergroup is named. This clade arose by secondary endosymbiosis and includes diatoms and brown algae.

stratum (strah′-tum) (plural, **strata**) A rock layer formed when new layers of sediment cover older ones and compress them.

stroke The death of nervous tissue in the brain, usually resulting from rupture or blockage of arteries in the head.

stroma (strō′-muh) The dense fluid within the chloroplast surrounding the thylakoid membrane and containing ribosomes and DNA; involved in the synthesis of organic molecules from carbon dioxide and water.

stromatolite Layered rock that results from the activities of prokaryotes that bind thin films of sediment together.

style The stalk of a flower's carpel, with the ovary at the base and the stigma at the top.

substrate The reactant on which an enzyme works.

substrate feeder An animal that lives in or on its food source, eating its way through the food.

substrate-level phosphorylation The enzyme-catalyzed formation of ATP by direct transfer of a phosphate group to ADP from an intermediate substrate in catabolism.

sugar sink A plant organ that is a net consumer or storer of sugar. Growing roots, shoot tips, stems, and fruits are examples of sugar sinks supplied by phloem.

sugar source A plant organ in which sugar is being produced by either photosynthesis or the breakdown of starch. Mature leaves are the primary sugar sources of plants.

sulfhydryl group A chemical group consisting of a sulfur atom bonded to a hydrogen atom.

suprachiasmatic nucleus (SCN) A group of neurons in the hypothalamus of mammals that functions as a biological clock.

surface tension A measure of how difficult it is to stretch or break the surface of a liquid.

surfactant A substance secreted by alveoli that decreases surface tension in the fluid that coats the alveoli.

survivorship curve A plot of the number of members of a cohort that are still alive at each age; one way to represent age-specific mortality.

suspension feeder An animal that feeds by capturing small organisms or food particles suspended in the surrounding medium.

sustainable development Development that meets the needs of people today without limiting the ability of future generations to meet their needs.

symbiont (sim′-bē-ont) The smaller participant in a symbiotic relationship, living in or on the host.

symbiosis An ecological relationship between organisms of two different species that live together in direct and intimate contact.

sympathetic division One of three divisions of the autonomic nervous system; generally increases energy expenditure and prepares the body for action.

sympatric speciation (sim-pat′-rik) The formation of new species in populations that live in the same geographic area.

symplast In plants, the continuum of cytoplasm connected by plasmodesmata between cells.

synapse (sin′-aps) The junction where a neuron communicates with another cell across a narrow gap via a neurotransmitter or an electrical coupling.

synapsid Member of an amniote clade distinguished by a single hole on each side of the skull. Synapsids include the mammals.

synapsis (si-nap′-sis) The pairing and physical connection of duplicated homologous chromosomes during prophase I of meiosis.

systematics A scientific discipline focused on classifying organisms and determining their evolutionary relationships.

systemic acquired resistance A defensive response in infected plants that helps protect healthy tissue from pathogenic invasion.

systemic circuit The branch of the circulatory system that supplies oxygenated blood to and carries deoxygenated blood away from organs and tissues throughout the body.

systems biology An approach to studying biology that aims to model the dynamic behavior of whole biological systems based on a study of the interactions among the system's parts.

systole (sis′-tō-lē) The stage of the cardiac cycle in which a heart chamber contracts and pumps blood.

T cells The class of lymphocytes that mature in the thymus; they include both effector cells for the cell-mediated immune response and helper cells required for both branches of adaptive immunity.

taproot A main vertical root that develops from an embryonic root and gives rise to lateral (branch) roots.

tastant Any chemical that stimulates the sensory receptors in a taste bud.

taste bud A collection of modified epithelial cells on the tongue or in the mouth that are receptors for taste in mammals.

TATA box A DNA sequence in eukaryotic promoters crucial in forming the transcription initiation complex.

taxis (tak′-sis) An oriented movement toward or away from a stimulus.

taxon (plural, **taxa**) A named taxonomic unit at any given level of classification.

taxonomy (tak-son′-uh-mē) A scientific discipline concerned with naming and classifying the diverse forms of life.

Tay-Sachs disease A human genetic disease caused by a recessive allele for a dysfunctional enzyme, leading to accumulation of certain lipids in the brain. Seizures, blindness, and degeneration of motor and mental performance usually become manifest a few months after birth, followed by death within a few years.

technology The application of scientific knowledge for a specific purpose, often involving industry or commerce but also including uses in basic research.

telophase The fifth and final stage of mitosis, in which daughter nuclei are forming and cytokinesis has typically begun.

temperate broadleaf forest A biome located throughout midlatitude regions where there is sufficient moisture to support the growth of large, broadleaf deciduous trees.

temperate grassland A terrestrial biome that exists at midlatitude regions and is dominated by grasses and forbs.

temperate phage A phage that is capable of replicating by either a lytic or lysogenic cycle.

temperature A measure in degrees of the average kinetic energy (thermal energy) of the atoms and molecules in a body of matter.

template strand The DNA strand that provides the pattern, or template, for ordering, by complementary base pairing, the sequence of nucleotides in an RNA transcript.

temporal summation A phenomenon of neural integration in which the membrane potential of the postsynaptic cell in a chemical synapse is determined by the combined effect of EPSPs or IPSPs produced in rapid succession.

terminator In bacteria, a sequence of nucleotides in DNA that marks the end of a gene and signals RNA polymerase to release the newly made RNA molecule and detach from the DNA.

territoriality A behavior in which an animal defends a bounded physical space against encroachment by other individuals, usually of its own species.

tertiary consumer (ter'-shē-ār'-ē) A carnivore that eats other carnivores.

tertiary structure The overall shape of a protein molecule due to interactions of amino acid side chains, including hydrophobic interactions, ionic bonds, hydrogen bonds, and disulfide bridges.

test In foram protists, a porous shell that consists of a single piece of organic material hardened with calcium carbonate.

testcross Breeding an organism of unknown genotype with a homozygous recessive individual to determine the unknown genotype. The ratio of phenotypes in the offspring reveals the unknown genotype.

testis (plural, **testes**) The male reproductive organ, or gonad, in which sperm and reproductive hormones are produced.

testosterone A steroid hormone required for development of the male reproductive system, spermatogenesis, and male secondary sex characteristics; the major androgen in mammals.

tetanus (tet'-uh-nus) The maximal, sustained contraction of a skeletal muscle, caused by a very high frequency of action potentials elicited by continual stimulation.

tetrapod Member of a vertebrate clade characterized by limbs with digits. Tetrapods include mammals, amphibians, and birds and other reptiles.

thalamus (thal'-uh-mus) An integrating center of the vertebrate forebrain. Neurons with cell bodies in the thalamus relay neural input to specific areas in the cerebral cortex and regulate what information goes to the cerebral cortex.

theory An explanation that is broader in scope than a hypothesis, generates new hypotheses, and is supported by a large body of evidence.

thermal energy Kinetic energy due to the random motion of atoms and molecules; energy in its most random form. *See also* heat.

thermocline A narrow stratum of abrupt temperature change in the ocean and in many temperate-zone lakes.

thermodynamics (ther'-mō-dī-nam'-iks) The study of energy transformations that occur in a collection of matter. *See* first law of thermodynamics; second law of thermodynamics.

thermoreceptor A receptor stimulated by either heat or cold.

thermoregulation The maintenance of internal body temperature within a tolerable range.

thick filament A filament composed of staggered arrays of myosin molecules; a component of myofibrils in muscle fibers.

thigmomorphogenesis A response in plants to chronic mechanical stimulation, resulting from increased ethylene production. An example is thickening stems in response to strong winds.

thigmotropism (thig-mo'-truh-pizm) A directional growth of a plant in response to touch.

thin filament A filament consisting of two strands of actin and two strands of regulatory protein coiled around one another; a component of myofibrils in muscle fibers.

threatened species A species that is considered likely to become endangered in the foreseeable future.

threshold The potential that an excitable cell membrane must reach for an action potential to be initiated.

thrombus A fibrin-containing clot that forms in a blood vessel and blocks the flow of blood.

thylakoid (thī'-luh-koyd) A flattened, membranous sac inside a chloroplast. Thylakoids often exist in stacks called grana that are interconnected; their membranes contain molecular "machinery" used to convert light energy to chemical energy.

thymus (thī'-mus) A small organ in the thoracic cavity of vertebrates where maturation of T cells is completed.

tidal volume The volume of air a mammal inhales and exhales with each breath.

tight junction A type of intercellular junction between animal cells that prevents the leakage of material through the space between cells.

tissue An integrated group of cells with a common structure, function, or both.

Toll-like receptor (TLR) A membrane receptor on a phagocytic white blood cell that recognizes fragments of molecules common to a set of pathogens.

tonicity The ability of a solution surrounding a cell to cause that cell to gain or lose water.

top-down model A model of community organization in which predation influences community organization by controlling herbivore numbers, which in turn control plant or phytoplankton numbers, which in turn control nutrient levels; also called the trophic cascade model.

topoisomerase A protein that breaks, swivels, and rejoins DNA strands. During DNA replication, topoisomerase helps to relieve strain in the double helix ahead of the replication fork.

totipotent (tō'-tuh-pōt'-ent) Describing a cell that can give rise to all parts of the embryo and adult, as well as extraembryonic membranes in species that have them.

trace element An element indispensable for life but required in extremely minute amounts.

trachea (trā'-kē-uh) The portion of the respiratory tract that passes from the larynx to the bronchi; also called the windpipe.

tracheal system In insects, a system of branched, air-filled tubes that extends throughout the body and carries oxygen directly to cells.

tracheid (trā'-kē-id) A long, tapered water-conducting cell found in the xylem of nearly all vascular plants. Functioning tracheids are no longer living.

trait One of two or more detectable variants in a genetic character.

transcription The synthesis of RNA using a DNA template.

transcription factor A regulatory protein that binds to DNA and affects transcription of specific genes.

transcription initiation complex The completed assembly of transcription factors and RNA polymerase bound to a promoter.

transcription unit A region of DNA that is transcribed into an RNA molecule.

transduction (1) A process in which phages (viruses) carry bacterial DNA from one bacterial cell to another. When these two cells are members of different species, transduction results in horizontal gene transfer. (2) In cellular communication, the conversion of a signal from outside the cell to a form that can bring about a specific cellular response; also called signal transduction.

transfer RNA (tRNA) An RNA molecule that functions as a translator between nucleic acid and protein languages by carrying specific amino acids to the ribosome, where they recognize the appropriate codons in the mRNA.

transformation (1) The conversion of a normal animal cell to a cancerous cell. (2) A change in genotype and phenotype due to the assimilation of external DNA by a cell. When the external DNA is from a member of a different species, transformation results in horizontal gene transfer.

transgenic Pertaining to an organism whose genome contains a gene introduced from another organism of the same or a different species.

translation The synthesis of a polypeptide using the genetic information encoded in an mRNA molecule. There is a change of "language" from nucleotides to amino acids.

translocation (1) An aberration in chromosome structure resulting from attachment of a chromosomal fragment to a nonhomologous chromosome. (2) During protein synthesis, the third stage in the elongation cycle, when the RNA carrying the growing polypeptide moves from the A site to the P site on the ribosome. (3) The transport of organic nutrients in the phloem of vascular plants.

transmission electron microscope (TEM) A microscope that passes an electron beam through very thin sections stained with metal atoms and is primarily used to study the internal ultrastructure of cells.

transpiration The evaporative loss of water from a plant.

transport epithelium One or more layers of specialized epithelial cells that carry out and regulate solute movement.

transport protein A transmembrane protein that helps a certain substance or class of closely related substances to cross the membrane.

transport vesicle A small membranous sac in a eukaryotic cell's cytoplasm carrying molecules produced by the cell.

transposable element A segment of DNA that can move within the genome of a cell by means of a DNA or RNA intermediate; also called a transposable genetic element.

transposon A transposable element that moves within a genome by means of a DNA intermediate.

transverse (T) tubule An infolding of the plasma membrane of skeletal muscle cells.

triacylglycerol (trī-as′-ul-glis′-uh-rol) A lipid consisting of three fatty acids linked to one glycerol molecule; also called a fat or triglyceride.

triple response A plant growth maneuver in response to mechanical stress, involving slowing of stem elongation, thickening of the stem, and a curvature that causes the stem to start growing horizontally.

triplet code A genetic information system in which a set of three-nucleotide-long words specifies the amino acids for polypeptide chains.

trisomic Referring to a diploid cell that has three copies of a particular chromosome instead of the normal two.

trophic efficiency The percentage of production transferred from one trophic level to the next.

trophic structure The different feeding relationships in an ecosystem, which determine the route of energy flow and the pattern of chemical cycling.

trophoblast The outer epithelium of a mammalian blastocyst. It forms the fetal part of the placenta, supporting embryonic development but not forming part of the embryo proper.

tropic hormone A hormone that has an endocrine gland or endocrine cells as a target.

tropical dry forest A terrestrial biome characterized by relatively high temperatures and precipitation overall but with a pronounced dry season.

tropical rain forest A terrestrial biome characterized by relatively high precipitation and temperatures year-round.

tropics Latitudes between 23.5° north and south.

tropism A growth response that results in the curvature of whole plant organs toward or away from stimuli due to differential rates of cell elongation.

tropomyosin The regulatory protein that blocks the myosin-binding sites on actin molecules.

troponin complex The regulatory proteins that control the position of tropomyosin on the thin filament.

true-breeding Referring to organisms that produce offspring of the same variety over many generations of self-pollination.

tumor-suppressor gene A gene whose protein product inhibits cell division, thereby preventing the uncontrolled cell growth that contributes to cancer.

tundra A terrestrial biome at the extreme limits of plant growth. At the northernmost limits, it is called arctic tundra, and at high altitudes, where plant forms are limited to low shrubby or matlike vegetation, it is called alpine tundra.

turgid (ter′-jid) Swollen or distended, as in plant cells. (A walled cell becomes turgid if

it has a lower water potential than its surroundings, resulting in entry of water.)

turgor pressure The force directed against a plant cell wall after the influx of water and swelling of the cell due to osmosis.

turnover time The time required to replace the standing crop of a population or group of populations (for example, of phytoplankton), calculated as the ratio of standing crop to production.

twin study A behavioral study in which researchers compare the behavior of identical twins raised apart with that of identical twins raised in the same household.

tympanic membrane Another name for the eardrum, the membrane between the outer and middle ear.

Unikonta (yū′-ni-kon′-tuh) One of four supergroups of eukaryotes proposed in a current hypothesis of the evolutionary history of eukaryotes. This clade, which is supported by studies of myosin proteins and DNA, consists of amoebozoans and opisthokonts. *See also* Excavata, "SAR" clade, and Archaeplastida.

unsaturated fatty acid A fatty acid that has one or more double bonds between carbons in the hydrocarbon tail. Such bonding reduces the number of hydrogen atoms attached to the carbon skeleton.

urea A soluble nitrogenous waste produced in the liver by a metabolic cycle that combines ammonia with carbon dioxide.

ureter (yū-rē′-ter) A duct leading from the kidney to the urinary bladder.

urethra (yū-rē′-thruh) A tube that releases urine from the mammalian body near the vagina in females and through the penis in males; also serves in males as the exit tube for the reproductive system.

uric acid A product of protein and purine metabolism and the major nitrogenous waste product of insects, land snails, and many reptiles. Uric acid is relatively nontoxic and largely insoluble.

urinary bladder The pouch where urine is stored prior to elimination.

uterine cycle The changes that occur in the uterus during the reproductive cycle of the human female; also called the menstrual cycle.

uterus A female organ where eggs are fertilized and/or development of the young occurs.

utricle In the vertebrate ear, a chamber in the vestibule behind the oval window that opens into the three semicircular canals.

vaccine A harmless variant or derivative of a pathogen that stimulates a host's immune system to mount defenses against the pathogen.

vacuole (vak′-yū-ōl′) A membrane-bounded vesicle whose specialized function varies in different kinds of cells.

vagina Part of the female reproductive system between the uterus and the outside opening;

the birth canal in mammals. During copulation, the vagina accommodates the male's penis and receives sperm.

valence The bonding capacity of a given atom; the number of covalent bonds an atom can form usually equals the number of unpaired electrons in its outermost (valence) shell.

valence electron An electron in the outermost electron shell.

valence shell The outermost energy shell of an atom, containing the valence electrons involved in the chemical reactions of that atom.

van der Waals interactions Weak attractions between molecules or parts of molecules that results from transient local partial charges.

variation Differences between members of the same species.

vas deferens In mammals, the tube in the male reproductive system in which sperm travel from the epididymis to the urethra.

vasa recta The capillary system in the kidney that serves the loop of Henle.

vascular cambium A cylinder of meristematic tissue in woody plants that adds layers of secondary vascular tissue called secondary xylem (wood) and secondary phloem.

vascular plant A plant with vascular tissue. Vascular plants include all living plant species except liverworts, mosses, and hornworts.

vascular tissue Plant tissue consisting of cells joined into tubes that transport water and nutrients throughout the plant body.

vascular tissue system A transport system formed by xylem and phloem throughout a vascular plant. Xylem transports water and minerals; phloem transports sugars, the products of photosynthesis.

vasoconstriction A decrease in the diameter of blood vessels caused by contraction of smooth muscles in the vessel walls.

vasodilation An increase in the diameter of blood vessels caused by relaxation of smooth muscles in the vessel walls.

vector An organism that transmits pathogens from one host to another.

vegetative propagation Cloning of plants by humans.

vegetative reproduction Cloning of plants in nature.

vein (1) In animals, a vessel that carries blood toward the heart. (2) In plants, a vascular bundle in a leaf.

ventilation The flow of air or water over a respiratory surface.

ventral Pertaining to the underside, or bottom, of an animal with radial or bilateral symmetry.

ventricle (ven′-tri-kul) (1) A heart chamber that pumps blood out of the heart. (2) A

space in the vertebrate brain, filled with cerebrospinal fluid.

vernalization The use of cold treatment to induce a plant to flower.

vertebrate A chordate animal with a backbone. Vertebrates include sharks and rays, ray-finned fishes, coelacanths, lungfishes, amphibians, reptiles, and mammals.

vesicle (ves′-i-kul) A membranous sac in the cytoplasm of a eukaryotic cell.

vessel A nonliving, water-conducting tube found in most angiosperms and a few nonflowering vascular plants that is formed by the end-to-end connection of vessel elements.

vessel element A short, wide, water-conducting cell found in the xylem of most angiosperms and a few nonflowering vascular plants. Dead at maturity, vessel elements are aligned end to end to form vessels.

vestigial structure A feature of an organism that is a historical remnant of a structure that served a function in the organism's ancestors.

villus (plural, **villi**) (1) A finger-like projection of the inner surface of the small intestine. (2) A finger-like projection of the chorion of the mammalian placenta. Large numbers of villi increase the surface areas of these organs.

viral envelope A membrane, derived from membranes of the host cell, that cloaks the capsid, which in turn encloses a viral genome.

virulent Describing a pathogen against which an organism has little specific defense.

virulent phage A phage that replicates only by a lytic cycle.

virus An infectious particle incapable of replicating outside of a cell, consisting of an RNA or DNA genome surrounded by a protein coat (capsid) and, for some viruses, a membranous envelope.

visible light That portion of the electromagnetic spectrum that can be detected as various colors by the human eye, ranging in wavelength from about 380 nm to about 750 nm.

vital capacity The maximum volume of air that a mammal can inhale and exhale with each breath.

vitamin An organic molecule required in the diet in very small amounts. Many vitamins serve as coenzymes or parts of coenzymes.

voltage-gated ion channel A specialized ion channel that opens or closes in response to changes in membrane potential.

vulva Collective term for the female external genitalia.

water potential (Ψ) The physical property predicting the direction in which water will flow, governed by solute concentration and applied pressure.

wavelength The distance between crests of waves, such as those of the electromagnetic spectrum.

wetland A habitat that is inundated by water at least some of the time and that supports plants adapted to water-saturated soil.

white matter Tracts of axons within the CNS.

whole-genome shotgun approach Procedure for genome sequencing in which the genome is randomly cut into many overlapping short segments that are sequenced; computer software then assembles the complete sequence.

wild type The phenotype most commonly observed in natural populations; also refers to the individual with that phenotype.

wilting The drooping of leaves and stems that occurs when plant cells become flaccid.

wobble Flexibility in the base-pairing rules in which the nucleotide at the 5′ end of a tRNA anticodon can form hydrogen bonds with more than one kind of base in the third position (3′ end) of a codon.

xerophyte A plant adapted to an arid climate.

X-linked gene A gene located on the X chromosome; such genes show a distinctive pattern of inheritance.

X-ray crystallography A technique used to study the three-dimensional structure of molecules. It depends on the diffraction of an X-ray beam by the individual atoms of a crystallized molecule.

xylem (zī′-lum) Vascular plant tissue consisting mainly of tubular dead cells that conduct most of the water and minerals upward from the roots to the rest of the plant.

xylem sap The dilute solution of water and dissolved minerals carried through vessels and tracheids.

yeast Single-celled fungus. Yeasts reproduce asexually by binary fission or by the pinching of small buds off a parent cell. Many fungal species can grow both as yeasts and as a network of filaments; relatively few species grow only as yeasts.

zero population growth (ZPG) A period of stability in population size, when additions to the population through births and immigration are balanced by subtractions through deaths and emigration.

zoned reserve An extensive region that includes areas relatively undisturbed by humans surrounded by areas that have been changed by human activity and are used for economic gain.

zoonotic pathogen A disease-causing agent that is transmitted to humans from other animals.

zygote (zī′-gōt) The diploid cell produced by the union of haploid gametes during fertilization; a fertilized egg.

NOTE: A page number in regular type indicates where a topic is discussed in the text (the topic may also be in a figure or table on that page); a **bold** page number indicates where a term is bold and defined; an *f* following a page number indicates a figure (the topic may also be discussed in the text on that page); a *t* following a page number indicates a table (the topic may also be discussed in the text on that page).

A

abdominal-A (*abd-A*) gene, 536*f*
Abiotic synthesis, organic compound, 459–460
Absolute dating, 438
Absorption
    fungal feeding by, 508–509
Acorn worm, 535*f*
Acquired immunity. *See* Adaptive immunity
Acquired immunodeficiency syndrome (AIDS). *See* AIDS (acquired immunodeficiency syndrome)
Acquired traits, inheritance of, 367
Actin. *See also* Thick filaments (actin)
Actinistia, 538*f*
Actinomycetes, 473*f*
Actinopterygii, 538*f*
Active transport. *See also* Passive transport; Sodium-potassium pump
Adaptations, **369**. *See also* Evolution; Natural selection
    adaptive evolution and, 410–415
    artificial selection, natural selection, and, 371–372
    fungal, for feeding by absorption, 508–509
    prokaryotic, 458–459*f*, 462–467
    research by Charles Darwin on, 369
    terrestrial, of fungi and plants, 505–508, 511–513, 516–517
Adaptive evolution, **410**–415. *See also* Adaptations
    biodiversity from, 450
    directional, disruptive, and stabilizing selection in, 411–412
    natural selection in, 407, 412, 414–415
    preservation of genetic variation in, 413–414
    relative fitness and, 411
    sexual selection in, 412–413
Adaptive radiations, **447**–449. *See also* Radiations
Adenomatous polyposis coli (*APC*) gene, 327
Adenosine diphosphate. *See* ADP (adenosine diphosphate)
Adenosine triphosphate. *See* ATP (adenosine triphosphate)
Adult stem cells, 323–324
Aerobic prokaryotes, 464*f*
Aerobic respiration. *See also* Cellular respiration
African elephants, 370–371
Africans
    genomes of, 360
    malaria and sickle-cell alleles in, 414*f*
Aglaophyton major, 508*f*, 511*f*
Agriculture. *See also* Crop plants
    polyploidy in, 426
    prokaryotes in disease-suppressive soil and, 477

Agrobacterium, 472*f*, 477, 485
AIDS (acquired immunodeficiency syndrome), 402. *See also* HIV (human immunodeficiency virus)
Ailuropoda melanoleuca, 348*t*
Aleuria aurantia, 512*f*
Algae, **482***f*
    in eukaryotic phylogeny, 491*f*
    evolution of land plants from green, 505, 507–508
    in fossil record, 482*f*–483*f*
    land animals vs., 540*f*
    lichens as symbioses of fungi and, 522*f*
    in marine ecosystems, 547
    origins of photosynthetic, 486–487
Allantois, **544***f*
Alleles
    alteration in frequencies of, in populations, 400, 406–410
    frequencies of, in populations, 402–406
    genetic variation and, 413–414
    microevolution as alteration in frequencies of, in populations, 400
    mutations as sources of new, 401–402
Alligators, 545*f*
Allopatric speciation, **423**
    continental drift and, 444
    evidence of, 424–425
    identifying dependent and independent variables, making scatter plots, and interpreting data on, 427
    process of, 423
    sympatric speciation vs., 423*f*
Allopolyploids, **425**–426
α-globin genes, 352–353
α-lactalbumin, 355
Alpha proteobacteria, 472*f*, 485–486
Alpheus genus, 424–425
Alternation of generations, **506***f*–507
Alternative RNA splicing, 348
Alu elements, 351, 359
Alveolates, 491*f*, **494**, 501–502
Alveoli, 494
Amanita muscaria, 512*f*
Amborella trichopoda, 520*f*–521
Amino acids
    abiotic synthesis of, 459–460
    evolution of human globin gene sequences of, 356
Amino acid sequence identity tables, 356
Amitochondrate protists, 489
Amnion, 543–**544***f*
Amniotes, **543**–547
Amniotic eggs, **543**–544
Amoebas, 491*f*, **494**, 497
Amoebocytes, 529*f*–**530**
Amoebozoans, **497**–498
Amphibians, **543**
    as terrestrial vertebrates, 543
Amplification, cancer gene, 324–325
Amplification, PCR. *See* Polymerase chain reaction (PCR)
Anabaena, 466
Anabrus simplex, 348
Anacystis nidulans, 485
Anaerobic respiration, **465**–466
Analogies, **385**–386
Analogous structures, **376**

Anatomical homologies, 375–376
Ancestry, common, 375–376, 384, 387–388
Angiosperms, **516**. *See also* Crop plants; Plant(s)
    evolution of, 519–521
    flowers, seeds, and fruits of, 518–519 (*see also* Flowers; Fruits; Seeds)
    gametophyte-sporophyte relationship in, 515*f*
    insect radiations and radiation of, 541–542
    phylogeny of, 513*f*, 520–521
    as seed plants, 516
Angraecum sesquipedale, 548*f*
Animal(s), 528–551. *See also* Birds; Eukaryotes; Fishes; Human(s); Insects; Invertebrates; Mammals; Vertebrates
    aquatic vs. terrestrial, 540*f* (*see also* Aquatic animals; Land animals)
    body plans of, 532–533
    Cambrian explosion and bilaterian radiation of, 530–532
    cloning of, 320–322
    colonization of land by, 539–547
    comparing genomes of, 358–360 (*see also* Genome(s))
    development processes of, 360–361 (*see also* Embryonic development)
    ecological and evolutionary effects of, 547–550
    evolution of, 488–489
    in fossil record, 436–440, 441*f*, 531*f*
    herbivore adaptations in, 373–374
    land plant interactions with, 524
    origination of, in sponges and cnidarians, 528–530
    phylogeny of, 533–534
    radiations of aquatic, 532–539 (*see also* Aquatic animals)
    Unikonta supergroup and, 496–497
Animal cells. *See also* Eukaryotic cells
    apoptosis of, 315
    nuclear transplantation of differentiated, in cloning, 320–322
    reproductive cloning of mammalian, 321–322
    of sponges, 529*f*–530
    stem cells, 322–324
Animalia, kingdom, 395
Animal reproduction. *See also* Human reproduction
Ankle bones, 376*f*
Annelids, 535*f*
Anomalocaris, 531*f*
Anopheles mosquitoes, 501–502
Antarctica, 436
Anterior ends, **533**
Anthers, 519
Anthoceros, 514*f*
Anthozoa, **530***f*
Anthrax, 473*f*
Antibiotic drugs
    bacterial resistance to, 374–375, 469–470, 476, 548
    gram-positive bacteria and, 473*f*
    peptidoglycan and, 463
    prokaryotic ribosomes and, 465
Ants, 541*f*
Apes, 546
Apical meristems, **507**
Apicomplexans, **501**–502
Apicoplast, 501–502

Domains, taxonomy, 348*t*, 358*f*, **382**, 395–396, 470*f*, 471*t*. *See also* Archaea domain; Bacteria domain; Eukarya domain
Donkeys, 421*f*
Dormancy, 463
Dorsal, hollow nerve cords, 537
Dorsal sides, **532**–533
Double circulation. *See also* Cardiovascular systems
Douglas fir tree, 518*f*
Drift, genetic, 407–409
Drosophila melanogaster (fruit fly)
 changes in developmental genes of, 451
 complete genome sequence for, 343, 346
 genetic variability of, 400–401*f*
 genome size of, 348
 homeotic genes in, 360–361
 as model organism for study of development, 311
 natural selection and insecticide resistance in, 407
 pattern formation and body plan of, 317–320
 phylogenetic tree of, 388, 389*f*
Drosophila pseudoobscura (fruit fly), 424*f*, 433
Drugs
 cocktails of, in AIDS treatment, 402
 evolution of resistance to, 374–375
Duoshantuophyton, 483*f*
Duplications, chromosome, 353–355
Duplications, gene, 402
Dusky salamanders, 427
Dysentery, 469

E
Ears
 bones of mammalian, 440, 441*f*
Earth
 conditions on early, and development of life, 459–462
 mass extinctions of life on, 444–447
 plate tectonics of, 442–444
 prokaryotic cells as first cells of life on, 458
Earthworms. *See also Caenorhabditis elegans*
Eastern glass lizard, 381–382
Ecdysozoa, 534–535*f*
Echinoderms, 535*f*
Ecological interactions. *See* Interactions, ecological
Ecological niches, 422
Ecological species concept, **422**
Ecology
 ecological effects of animals, 547
 mass extinctions and, 447
 prokaryotic roles in, 474–475
Ecosystems
 effects of animals on, 547
 effects of mass extinctions on, 445*f*, 446–447
 genome sequencing of metagenomes in, 345–346
 prokaryotic roles in, 474–475
Ectoderm, **533**
Ectomycorrhizae, **509**, 512*f*
Ectoprocts, 535*f*
Ectothermic organisms, **544**
Ediacaran biota, 437*f*, 450, **483***f*, **529**, 531–532
Egg-polarity genes, **318**–320
Eggs
 of birds and dinosaurs, 391–392
Electrical signaling, neurons and. *See also* Neurons
Elephants, 370–371
Embryo(s)
 anatomical similarities in vertebrate, 375
 land plant, 506*f*
Embryonic development, 311–320

analyzing quantitative and spatial data on *Hox* genes in, 316
 cytoplasmic determinants and inductive signals in, 312–313
 genetic program for, 312
 model organisms in study of development and, 311
 pattern formation and body plans in, 317–320
 sequential gene regulation in, 313–315
Embryonic lethals, **318**
Embryonic stem (ES) cells, 323–324
Embryophytes, **506***f*
ENCODE (Encyclopedia of DNA Elements), 346
Endangered species
 molluscs as, 549
Endemic species, **378**
Endoderm, **533**
Endophytes, **523**–524
Endospores, **463**
Endosymbionts, 484
Endosymbiont theory, **484**–486
Endosymbiosis, **484**–487
Endothermic organisms, **544**
Endotoxins, **476**
Energy. *See also* Energy flow
Engineering, genetic. *See* Genetic engineering
Ensatina genus, 421*f*
Entamoebas, 497
Environment
 adaptive evolution as fitness to, 407, 411
 bottleneck effect and changes in, 408–409
 Cambrian explosion and changes in, 531
 cancer development and, 327–328
 Earth's early, and origin of life, 459–462
 genome sequencing of metagenomes in, 345–346
 impacts of evolution of land plants and fungi on, 521–524
 induction from, in cellular differentiation, 313
 interaction of chance, natural selection, and, 415
 as surroundings and organisms, 365
Enzymatic hydrolysis. *See also* Chemical digestion
Enzymes
 fungal, 508
Eons, geologic, 439*t*
Epochs, geologic, 439*t*
Epsilon proteobacteria, 472*f*
Epstein-Barr virus, 328
Equilibrium
 Hardy-Weinberg, 403–405
Equus, 454–455
Eras, geologic, 439*t*
Ergot fungus, 523*f*
Erythrocytes. *See also* Red blood cells
Escherichia coli (E. coli) bacteria
 complete genome sequence for, 343
 genetic recombination and conjugation in, 468–470
 genome size of, 348
 pathogenic strains of, 476
 as proteobacteria, 472*f*
 rapid reproduction and mutation of, 467–468
 in research on origin of mitochondria, 485
Ethanol (ethyl alcohol), 477
Eudicots
 in angiosperm phylogenies, 520*f*–521*f*
Euglenids, 492
Euglenozoans, **492**–493*f*
Euhadra, 432–433
Eukarya, domain. *See also* Eukaryotes
 compared with Bacteria and Archaea, 471*t*
 evolutionary relationships of, 358*f*
 genome size and number of genes for, 348*t*
 horizontal gene transfer and, 395–396

Eukaryotes, 481–503. *See also* Animal(s); Eukarya domain; Plant(s)
 Cambrian explosion and evolution of, 530–532
 cell structure of, 481–482 (*see also* Eukaryotic cells)
 early evolution of, 482*f*–483*f*
 endosymbiosis in evolution of, 484–487
 fossil record of, 482–484
 four supergroups in phylogeny of, 489–498
 in geologic record, 440
 origination of animals in, 528–530
 origination of multicellularity in, 483*f*, 487–489
 origins of key features of, 484*t*
 phylogenetic tree of, 490*f*–491*f*
 protists as unicellular, 481, 499–502 (*see also* Protists)
 taxonomy of, 395–397
 Unikonta as root of phylogenetic tree of, 497
Eukaryotic cells. *See also* Cell(s)
 characteristics of, 481–482
Eukaryotic gene regulation. *See also* Gene regulation
Eukaryotic genomes, 348–357. *See also* Genome(s)
 evolution of, from DNA duplication, rearrangement, and mutation, 353–357
 genes and multigene families in, 352–353
 pseudogenes and repetitive DNA in, 349–350
 simple sequence DNA and short tandem repeats in, 351–352
 size, number of genes, and gene density of, 348–349
 transposable elements and related sequences in, 350–351
Eumetazoans, 530, **534**
European green crab, 548
European Molecular Biology Laboratory, 345
Euryarchaeota clade, 474
Eutherians, 447*f*, **546**
Even-toed ungulates, 376–377
Evo-devo (evolutionary developmental biology), **360**–361, 449
Evolution, **365**–380. *See also* Adaptations; Natural selection
 of animals from sponges and cnidarians, 528–530
 comparing genome sequences to study, 357–361
 convergent, 376, 381*f*, 385–386
 as descent with modification by natural selection, 365–366, 370–372
 divergent, 423–425, 432
 early, of eukaryotes, 481–487
 effects of animals on, 548, 549
 effects of humans on, 548–550
 evidence for, in biogeography and geographical distribution of species, 377–378
 evidence for, in direct observations of evolutionary change, 373–375
 evidence for, in fossil record, 376–377
 evidence for, in homologies, 375–376
 field research on, by Charles Darwin, 368–370
 of fungi, 510–513
 of genomes from DNA duplication, rearrangement, and mutation, 353–357
 of gymnosperms, 518
 historical context of Darwinian revolution in, 366–367
 of human globin gene amino acid sequences, 356
 J.-B. de Lamarck's theory of, 367
 of land plants, 513*f*
 of land plants and fungi, 505–508
 molecular clocks and rates of, 392–394
 phylogenies as evolutionary histories, 381–382 (*see also* Phylogenies)